ENVIRONMENTAL ECONOMICS AND MANAGEMENT

Theory, Policy, and Applications

THE IRWIN SERIES IN ECONOMICS

Appleyard and Field
INTERNATIONAL ECONOMICS
Second Edition

Appleyard and Field
**INTERNATIONAL ECONOMICS:
TRADE THEORY AND POLICY**
Second Edition

Appleyard and Field
**INTERNATIONAL ECONOMICS:
PAYMENTS, EXCHANGE RATES,
AND MACRO POLICY**
Second Edition

Aslanbeigui and Naples
**RETHINKING ECONOMIC
PRINCIPLES: CRITICAL ESSAYS
ON INTRODUCTORY
TEXTBOOKS**

Baily and Friedman
**MACROECONOMICS,
FINANCIAL MARKETS, AND
THE INTERNATIONAL SECTOR**
Second Edition

Barron and Lynch
ECONOMICS
Third Edition

Baye and Beil
**MANAGERIAL ECONOMICS
AND BUSINESS STRATEGY**

Bornstein
**COMPARATIVE ECONOMICS
SYSTEMS: MODELS AND CASES**
Seventh Edition

Brickley, Smith, and Zimmerman
**ORGANIZATIONAL
ARCHITECTURE: A
MANAGERIAL ECONOMICS
APPROACH**

Brown and Moore
**READINGS, ISSUES AND
PROBLEMS IN PUBLIC FINANCE**
Fourth Edition

Callan and Thomas
**ENVIRONMENTAL ECONOMICS
AND MANAGEMENT: THEORY,
POLICY, AND APPLICATIONS**

Colander
ECONOMICS
Second Edition

Colander
MICROECONOMICS
Second Edition

Colander
Macroeconomics
Second Edition

Fisher
**STATE AND LOCAL PUBLIC
FINANCE**
Second Edition

Hadjimichalakis and Hadjimichalakis
**CONTEMPORARY MONEY,
BANKING, AND THE FINANCIAL
MARKETS**

Hyman
ECONOMICS
Third Edition

Hyman
MICROECONOMICS
Third Edition

Hyman
MACROECONOMICS
Third Edition

Hyman
**MODERN MICROECONOMICS
ANALYSIS AND APPLICATIONS**
Third Edition

Katz and Rosen
MICROECONOMICS
Second Edition

Lehmann
**REAL WORLD ECONOMIC
APPLICATIONS: THE WALL
STREET JOURNAL WORKBOOK**
Fourth Edition

Lindert
INTERNATIONAL ECONOMICS
Tenth Edition

Maurice and Phillips
**ECONOMIC ANALYSIS:
THEORY AND APPLICATION**
Sixth Edition

Maurice and Thomas
**MANAGERIAL ECONOMICS:
APPLIED MICROECONOMICS
FOR DECISION MAKING**
Fifth Edition

Nadler and Hansen
**MICROCOMPUTER MACRO-
ECONOMICS WITH IBM DISK**

O'Sullivan
URBAN ECONOMICS
Third Edition

O'Sullivan
**ESSENTIALS OF URBAN
ECONOMICS**

Rima
**DEVELOPMENT OF ECONOMIC
ANALYSIS**
Fifth Edition

Roger and Daniel
**PRINCIPLES OF ECONOMICS
SOFTWARE SIMULATION**

Rosen
PUBLIC FINANCE
Fourth Edition

Schwarz and Van Dyken
**MANAGER: MANAGERIAL
ECONOMICS SOFTWARE**

Rosser and Rosser
**COMPARATIVE ECONOMICS IN
A TRANSFORMING WORLD
ECONOMY**

Santerre and Neun
**HEALTH ECONOMICS:
THEORIES, APPLICATIONS AND
INDUSTRY STUDIES**

Sharp, Register, and Grimes
ECONOMICS OF SOCIAL ISSUES
Twelfth Edition

Slavin
ECONOMICS
Fourth Edition

Slavin
MICROECONOMICS
Fourth Edition

Slavin
MACROECONOMICS
Fourth Edition

Streifford
ECONOMIC PERSPECTIVE

Walton and Wykoff
**UNDERSTANDING ECONOMICS
TODAY**
Fifth Edition

ENVIRONMENTAL ECONOMICS AND MANAGEMENT

Theory, Policy, and Applications

Scott J. Callan
Janet M. Thomas
Both of Bentley College

IRWIN

Chicago · Bogotá · Boston · Buenos Aires · Caracas
London · Madrid · Mexico City · Sydney · Toronto

© Richard D. Irwin, a Times Mirror Higher Education Group, Inc., company, 1996

Irwin Book Team

Senior sponsoring editor: *Gary Nelson*
Editorial assistant: *Tia Schultz*
Marketing manager: *Michael Douglas*
Project editor: *Karen M. Smith*
Production supervisor: *Bob Lange*
Manager, graphics and desktop services: *Kim Meriwether*
Designer: *Crispin Prebys*
Compositor: *Wm. C. Brown Publishers*
Typeface: *10/12 Times Roman*
Printer: *R. R. Donnelley & Sons Company*

Times Mirror
Higher Education Group

Library of Congress Cagaloging-in-Publication Data

Callan. Scott.
    Environmental economics and management : theory, policy, and applications / Scott J. Callan, Janet M. Thomas.
        p.   cm.
    Includes index.
    ISBN 0-256-13254-2 0 07 114 128 6
    1. Environmental economics. 2. Industrial management-
-Environmental aspects. 3. Environmental economics—Case studies.
I. Thomas. Janet M. II. Title.
HC79.E5C355   1996
333.7—dc20   95–33128

Printed in the United States of America
1 2 3 4 5 6 7 8 9 0 DO 2 1 0 9 8 7 6 5

To Karen
S. J. C.

To David
J. M. T.

PREFACE

Few contemporary issues have influenced consumer behavior, corporate strategy, and public policy as much as have environmental concerns. In the last two decades, we have witnessed changes in product design, capital investment practices, tax policies, product packaging, and technology—all because environmental issues have been integrated into private and public decision-making. New industries are emerging in environmental products and services. National and international policies are being developed to preserve natural resources and ecosystems. Firms are redefining their business strategies in response to new regulations and the changing demands of more environmentally conscious consumers. As a society, we have come to recognize that economic activity and the natural environment are inexorably linked, and this profound relationship is at the core of environmental economics and management.

When we began our academic careers in a business school setting, the environment was not among the topics typically covered in traditional core courses. Along with some of our colleagues, we became involved in developing curricula that would prepare both our business and our liberal arts students for the more complex decision-making that integrates environmental concerns with privately motivated interests. One of the greatest challenges of this collaborative effort has been to find ways to educate a diverse audience of students about an enormous field that is evolving at a rapid pace. To further our own contribution to environmental education, we began the research for and writing of this text.

We wrote *Environmental Economics and Management* to give undergraduate and MBA students a clear perspective of the relationship between market activity and the environment. Our general approach is to illustrate how economic analytical tools such as market models and benefit-cost analysis can be used to assess environmental problems and to evaluate policy solutions. Along with more traditional discussions, we have incorporated the business perspective in our development of environmental decision-making—a vantage point often overlooked in more conventional treatments. Our presentation does not compromise theoretical economic concepts, but it does complement them with timely, real-world applications. In so doing, seemingly abstract concepts are given relevance through actual cases about consumers, industry, and public policy.

Content: A Modular Approach

Organizing the vast amount of material that an environmental economics course attempts to cover is a challenge at best. Mindful of the usual time constraint in a one-semester course and the fact that the student audience can be highly varied, we devised a modular structure for the text. This approach not only organizes the presentation by major topic but also provides a format that facilitates customizing the material to suit a variety of course objectives. At the instructor's discretion, certain chapters within a given module can be omitted or covered less thoroughly without loss of continuity in the overall presentation.

The first three modules are the foundation for the course:

Part I. Modeling Environmental Problems: a three-chapter module illustrating how environmental problems are modeled from an economic perspective. Primary topics are the materials balance model, a review of market theory and price determination in an environmental context, and the market failure of pollution using both a public goods model and externality theory.

Part II. Modeling Solutions to Environmental Problems: a two-chapter module on environmental regulatory approaches—one on command-and-control and one on the market approach. Allocative efficiency and cost-effectiveness are used to analyze these, and models are developed to study various control instruments such as technology-based standards, pollution charges, deposit/refund systems, and tradeable pollution permits.

Part III. Analytical Tools for Environmental Planning: a four-chapter module introduced by a general model of environmental policy development followed by an in-depth investigation of risk assessment, risk management, and benefit-cost analysis. Included is a thorough presentation of benefit estimation procedures such as the contingent valuation method and the averting expenditure approach.

We also have planned three media-specific modules that are actually comprehensive case studies of major environmental problems and policy solutions.

Using economic modeling and analytical tools, each module assesses the associated environmental risk, evaluates the policy response, and presents a benefit-cost analysis of major U.S. legislation. These three modules can be covered in any sequence following the foundational material covered in the first half of the text.

Part IV. The Case of Air: a three-chapter module assessing major air pollution problems and the policy initiatives aimed at controlling them. Integrated in the analysis of the Clean Air Act and its amendments are discussions of urban smog, acidic deposition, ozone depletion, and global warming. Economic modeling and benefit-cost analysis are used to facilitate the investigation throughout.

Part V. The Case of Water: a three-chapter module covering the problems of ground and surface water contamination and specific policies aimed at point and nonpoint polluting sources. Two chapters are devoted to an economic analysis of the Clean Water Act, and a third conducts the same type of investigation of the Safe Drinking Water Act.

Part VI. The Case of Solid Wastes and Toxic Substances: a three-chapter module analyzing the solid waste cycle and the use of pesticides and other toxic substances. Among the primary topics discussed are risk management of the hazardous waste stream, the Superfund controversy, market solutions to controlling municipal solid waste, and risk-benefit analysis in pesticide control.

The final module ties together the materials balance model, economic objectives, and the media-specific policy analyses to discuss the direction of future environmental policy.

Part VII. Environmental Management in Transition: a one-chapter module examining evolving trends in environmental policy and the objective of sustainable development. Key topics include environmental literacy, the shift toward pollution prevention, and cooperative partnerships among nations and among economic sectors to achieve environmental quality and economic prosperity.

Pedagogical Features

In planning this text, we included a number of features to make the material interesting and accessible to students without compromising the integrity of the subject matter. Perhaps the most important of these is our extensive use of real-world **Applications** throughout the text.

Applications: Over 75 applications are used to complement the presentation by illustrating the relevance of economic theory, environmental risk, and public policy. The content of these has been drawn from a variety of sources, including the business press, government reports, and the economic and environmental science literature. Topics range from corporate strategies to international policy. These real-world cases or examples motivate learning because they illustrate fundamental concepts in relevant, contemporary settings. They also may stimulate more in-depth study in a term paper or course project. Application titles include:

> *Design for Disassembly: Materials Management at BMW*
> *Market Incentives to Phase Out Lead Emissions*
> *Abatement Costs: The Promise of Remediation Technology*
> *Searching for Alternatives to CFCs: The Corporate Response*
> *Who Regulates the Quality of Bottled Water?*
> *Taxing Gasoline Consumption: An International Comparison*
> *Germany's Effluent Charge System*

Margin Definitions, Key Concepts, and Acronyms: In each chapter, **Margin Definitions** of terms and relationships are placed adjacent to the relevant text presentation. A list of **Key Concepts** is also provided at the end of each chapter. These features call attention to important points in the text, help familiarize students with new terminology, and assist them in reviewing and self-testing their comprehension. We also have added chapter appendixes of commonly used **Acronyms** throughout the media-specific modules. These serve as a quick reference for students as they are reading chapters in which acronyms are frequently used.

End-of-Chapter Learning Tools: Each chapter concludes with a **Summary** to help students review and assimilate what they have read. Instructors also may find these summaries valuable in organizing the course and in preparing lectures. We also provide a list of **Review Questions** that can be used for regular assignments, in-class discussions, or sample test questions. Finally, we offer a selection of **Additional Readings** (beyond those cited in the chapter) that are useful for supplementing course reading assignments. A list of **References** at the end of the text gives complete information on all sources cited in short form throughout the book. Both instructors and students should find this collection of resources helpful in conducting independent investigations of selected topics.

Scott J. Callan
Janet M. Thomas

ACKNOWLEDGMENTS

No text is ever produced without the help and support of many individuals. In our case, we owe a debt of gratitude to Bentley College, particularly the administration, for its support of this project and our related work in environmental economics. Without the approval of sabbatical leave, course release time, and research grants, this text likely would still be among our works-in-progress. We also thank our colleagues who offered valuable commentary and remembered to ask how the book was coming along. We are particularly indebted to our library director, Sherman Hayes, who guided us through a maze of computerized resources, provided us with additional graduate assistance, and enhanced the library's resources in support of environmental issues on campus. To our students as well, we are grateful for their input in reading early drafts of our chapters and their patience in working with preliminary sketches of graphs and tables in rough form. Special thanks go to our graduate assistant, Sergei Akopov, who commented on preliminary drafts and helped us with the tedious task of verifying and updating material for the finished manuscript.

Many economists contributed to this text at various stages of the review process. These include: Bill Ballard, College of Charleston; Laurie Bates, Bryant College; John Braden, University of Illinois (Urbana); Michelle Correia, Florida Atlantic University; Warren Fisher, Susquehanna University; Joyce Gleason, Nebraska Wesleyan College; Sue Eileen Hayes, Sonoma State University; Charles Howe, University of Colorado; Donn Johnson, University of Northern Iowa; Supriya Lahiri, University of Massachusetts; Donald Marron, University of Chicago; Arden Pope, Brigham Young University; H. David Robison, La Salle University; Richard Rosenberg, Penn. State University; Jeffrey Sundberg, Lake Forest College; David Terkla, University of Massachusetts; John Whitehead, East Carolina University; and Keith Willett,

Oklahoma State University. To these teachers and scholars, we offer our thanks for their constructive criticism and many insightful comments. By incorporating most of their suggestions, which led in part to a major revision of the media modules, we believe the finished text is much improved. Of all the reviewers, two deserve special mention. Jeffrey Sundberg of Lake Forest College carefully read the entire second draft and found many ways to improve the final product. His knowledge of the discipline, fair-mindedness, and objectivity were extremely valuable. We also are indebted to Donn Johnson of the University of Northern Iowa for his continued support of this project. His interest in the field and his enthusiasm for our approach to the subject matter were important sources of encouragement.

There are also many people to thank at Richard D. Irwin. First among these is Nancy Reilly Webster, who initiated our professional relationship with Irwin and who remained dedicated to this project throughout its many phases. We are grateful for her support, insight, and invaluable perspective on the process of textbook writing and publishing. Thanks also go to Gary Nelson for his encouragement during the early stages of the project, to Tia Schultz for guiding the review process, and to Karen Smith for her invaluable direction and expertise throughout the production stage.

Finally and most importantly, we thank our spouses, Karen and David, for their patience and their continued support of our professional work. Throughout our respective careers, they have endured with us the long hours of graduate school, the anxiety of the tenure process, and now the years of textbook writing. While we often have wondered why they have tolerated the sometimes trying aspects of academic life, we are nonetheless eternally grateful that they have.

S.J.C.

J.M.T.

CONTENTS IN BRIEF

CONTENTS

PART VII

ENVIRONMENTAL MANAGEMENT IN TRANSITION

19   Strategic Planning for Sustainable Development   641

MODELING ENVIRONMENTAL PROBLEMS

Environmental problems, while not new, have taken on a far more significant role in business decisions and corporate planning in the last two decades. The world has become more aware of the natural environment and more sensitive to the implications of ecological damage. Individuals are altering their consumption patterns to incorporate environmental responsibility into their market decisions. Many are reordering their preferences in favor of biodegradable household detergents, non-ozone-depleting personal products, recyclable packaging, and the like. Similarly, governments are responding on both a local and national level by passing environmental laws and establishing pollution monitoring networks to protect the ecology. Firms are adding environmental concerns to their list of business priorities. This corporate response is necessary, not only to comply with the growing number of regulations on production and product design, but also to remain competitive in a marketplace where many consumers are seeking environmentally responsible producers.

To comprehend this changing marketplace and to participate in it as an informed member of society, it is necessary to understand the fundamentals of how markets work and the relationship between market activity and nature. Economic analysis uses models or prototypes of markets to explain the strategic decision-making and underlying economic conditions that define the marketplace. By abstracting from unnecessary detail, models allow economists to test hypotheses about economic relationships and to make predictions about behavioral and institutional reactions to changes in market conditions. As such, modeling is a fundamental tool in the study of environmental economics.

In this first module of the text, three chapters are devoted to basic market models that are of direct use in understanding environmental issues. Chapter 1 develops what is called the materials balance model, which illustrates the linkages between the circular flow of economic activity and nature. In so doing, the model shows precisely how environmental damage and resource depletion occur as a result of market decision-making. This provides a forum through which the basic concepts of environmental economics are discussed. Working from this broad overview, Chapter 2 focuses in on the fundamentals of the market process, reviewing key concepts like supply and demand, measures of welfare, and economic criteria. All of this lays the foundation for Chapter 3, which explains how environmental problems occur when the market fails. Here too, models are used to illustrate the sources of market failure and the conditions under which such an outcome arises.

THE ROLE OF ECONOMICS IN ENVIRONMENTAL MANAGEMENT

1

As society moves into the 21st century, it faces one of its greatest challenges—to protect and preserve the earth's resources as its continues to develop economically. That such an objective is ambitious is evidenced by even a casual retrospective of the last hundred years. The rapid growth and advancing technology that began in earnest with the Industrial Revolution took a tremendous toll on the natural environment. Mass transport, manufacturing processes, telecommunications, and synthetic chemicals are responsible both for the highly advanced lifestyle that society enjoys *and* for much of the environmental degradation it now faces. With 20/20 hindsight, we now recognize that there was a significant trade-off between economic growth and environmental quality. But it is not one that we can carry forward into the future.

The resolution is to recognize the critical relationship between economic activity and nature and use that information to make better and wiser decisions. Of course, there will always be some amount of trade-off—precisely what is conveyed by economic theory. We cannot expect to have perfectly clean air or completely pure water, nor can we continue to grow economically with no regard for the future. But there *is* a solution, though it is a compromise of sorts. We first have to decide what level of environmental quality is acceptable, and then make appropriate adjustments in our market behavior to sustain that quality as we continue to develop as a society.

The adjustment process is not an easy one, and it takes time. As a society, we are still learning—about nature, about market behavior, and about the important relationships that link the two together. What economics contributes to this learning process are analytical tools that help to explain the interaction of markets and the environment, the implications of that relationship, and the opportunities for effective solutions.

In this chapter, we begin to support these assertions with a simple but powerful model that illustrates the link between economic activity and nature.

The accompanying analysis illustrates how fundamental market decisions affect the earth's natural resource stock. As we will discover, the underlying relationships motivate economic analysis of environmental issues, which is formally defined through two disciplines—natural resource economics and environmental economics, the latter being our focus in this text. With this model as a foundation, we then begin to lay the groundwork for our course of study, starting with an introduction of basic concepts. From there, primary objectives in environmental economics are identified and discussed, followed by an overview of policy development and the role of economics in that process.

Economics and the Environment

One of the most powerful and pervasive applications of economic theory is that it logically explains what we observe in reality. For example, through microeconomic analysis, we can understand the behavior of consumers and firms and the decision-making that defines what we abstractly refer to as the marketplace. This same application of economic theory can be used to analyze environmental problems—why they occur and what can be done about them. Stop to consider how pollution or resource depletion comes about—not from a sophisticated scientific level, just a fundamental perspective. The answer? Both arise from decisions made by households and firms. Consumption and production draw upon the earth's supply of natural resources. Furthermore, both activities generate by-products that can contaminate the environment. Thus, the fundamental decisions that comprise economic activity are directly connected to environmental problems. To illustrate this relationship, we begin by presenting a basic model of economic activity. Then, we expand it to show exactly how the linkages arise.

The Fundamental Model of Economic Activity: The Circular Flow Model

circular flow model
Illustrates the real and monetary flows of economic activity through the factor market and the output market.

The basis for modeling the relationship between economic activity and the environment is precisely the same one that underlies all of economic theory—the **circular flow model.** Typically, this is the first model students learn about in introductory economics, and it is without question one of the more powerful explanatory tools in the field. Figure 1.1 illustrates a simple circular flow model, which we use as a starting point for discussion.

First, consider how the flows operate, holding all else constant. Notice how the so-called **real flow** (i.e., the nonmonetary flow), runs counter-clockwise between the two market sectors, households (or consumers), and firms (or producers). Households supply resources or factors of production to the **factor market,** where they are demanded by firms to produce goods and services. These commodities are then supplied to the **output market,** where

FIGURE 1.1

*The circular flow
model of economic
activity*

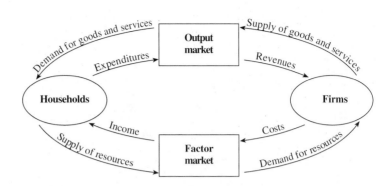

they are demanded by households. Running clockwise is the **money flow.** The exchange of inputs in the factor market generates a flow of income to households, and that flow represents costs incurred by firms. Analogously, the money flow through the output market shows how households' expenditures on goods and services are revenues to firms.

Now, think about how the volume of economic activity and hence the *size* of the flow are influenced by such factors as population growth, technological change, labor productivity, capital accumulation, and natural phenomena such as drought or floods. For example, holding all else constant, technological advance would increase the productive capacity of the economy, which in turn would increase the size of the flow. Similarly, a population increase would give rise to a greater demand for goods and services, which would call forth more production and lead to a larger circular flow.

Notice that by analyzing how the flows operate and how the size of an economy can change, we can understand the basic functioning of an economic system and the market relationships between households and firms. However, the model does not *explicitly* show the linkage between economic activity and the environment, though it is implied. To illustrate this interdependence, the circular flow model must be expanded to depict market activity as part of a broader paradigm called the **materials balance model.**

**materials balance
model**
Positions the circular
flow within a larger
schematic to show
the connections
between economic
decision-making and
the natural
environment.

The Materials Balance Model

The explicit relationship between economic activity and the natural environment is illustrated by the **materials balance model** shown in Figure 1.2.[1] Notice how the real flow of the circular flow model is positioned within a larger schematic to clearly show the various connections between economic decision-making and nature. The result is an important analytical tool for understanding and managing environmental problems.

---

[1]Kneese, Ayres, and D'Arge (1970). See Chart 1, p. 9, in this source for a more detailed depiction of this model.

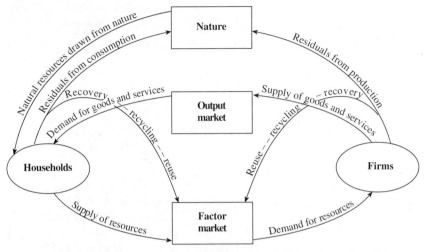

Source: Adapted from Allen V. Kneese, Robert U. Ayres, and Ralph C. D'Arge, *Economics and the
Environment: A Materials Balance Approach* (Washington, D.C.: Resources for the Future, 1970).

**natural resource
economics**
A field of study
concerned with the
flow of resources
from nature to
economic activity.

**renewable natural
resources**
Those resources that
are replenished
naturally at a
measurable rate.

**nonrenewable
natural resources**
Those resources that
are present in a finite
quantity with a
negligible rate of
natural
replenishment; also
known as depletable
natural resources.

The Flow of Resources: Natural Resource Economics.   Start by focusing
on' the linkages between the upper block representing nature and the two
market sectors, households and firms, paying particular attention to the direction of the arrows. Notice that one way an economic system is linked to nature
is through a flow of *materials* or natural resources that runs *from,*the environment *to* the economy, specifically through the household sector. (Recall that,
by assumption, households are the owners of *all* factors of production, including natural resources.) This flow describes how economic activity draws
upon the earth's stock of natural resources, such as soil, minerals, and water.
It is the primary focus of the discipline called **natural resource economics,**
which is a field of study concerned with the flows of resources *from* nature *to*
economic activity.

   A key issue in natural resource economics is to identify which resources
are **renewable** and which are **nonrenewable.**

- **Renewable natural resources** are those that are replenished naturally at
  a measurable rate. Examples include animal populations and timber.
- **Nonrenewable natural resources**, also known as **depletable natural
  resources,** are those that are present in a finite quantity with a negligible
  rate of natural replenishment. Examples include metal deposits, such as
  tin and copper, and oil.

   Although these concepts appear to be straightforward, there are a couple
of caveats. For example, even though some resources are renewable, they
nonetheless can be overutilized to the point where the supply is exterminated.
This is the case for certain animal species with long gestation periods or the

great forests that take decades to mature. On the other side of the coin, some depletable resources are also **recyclable resources,** meaning that it is possible to recover them from a given use and subsequently use them in another function. An example would be steel salvaged from a used automobile that is melted down for another industrial use.

The Flow of Residuals: Environmental Economics.   A second set of linkages runs in the opposite direction, that is, *from* the economy *to* the environment. This flow illustrates how the raw materials entering the system eventually are released back to nature as by-products or **residuals.** A **residual** is the amount of a pollutant that remains in the environment after a natural or technological process has occurred.

residual
The amount of a pollutant remaining in the environment after a natural or technological process has occurred.

Most residuals are in the form of gases released into the atmosphere. In the short run, most are not harmful, and in fact some are absorbed naturally through what is called the **assimilative capacity** of the environment. A case in point is carbon dioxide emissions from the combustion of fossil fuels (i.e., oil, coal, and natural gas), which can be partially absorbed by the earth's oceans and forests. Other released gases are not easily assimilated and may cause harm even in the short term. There are also liquid residuals, such as industrial wastewaters, and solid residuals like municipal trash and hazardous waste materials—all of which are potential threats to health and ecological systems.[2]

Notice on the diagram that there are two residual outflows, one leading from each of the two market sectors, meaning that residuals arise from both consumption and production activity. This set of flows is the chief concern of **environmental economics.**

environmental economics
A field of study concerned with the flow of residuals from economic activity back to nature.

It is possible that the flow of residuals back to nature can be delayed—though not prevented—through **recovery, recycling,** and **reuse.** Notice in the model that there are inner flows running from the two residual outflows back to the factor market. These inner flows show that some residuals can be recovered from the stream and either recycled into another usable form or reused in their existing form. For example, Germany's Bavarian Motor Works (BMW) has made some important advances in designing automobiles specifically so that the materials used in production are more easily recycled once the vehicle has reached the end of its economic life. Read Application 1.1 for more on BMW's innovative and environmentally conscious approach to automobile manufacturing.

Although recycling efforts are important, keep in mind that they are only short-term measures, since even recycled and reused products eventually become residuals that are returned to nature. Indeed, what the materials balance model shows is that *all* resources drawn from the environment ultimately are returned there in the form of residuals. The two flows are balanced—a profound fact that is supported by science.

---

[2]Kneese, Ayres, and D'Arge (1970), pp. 11–12.

Application 1.1

Design for Disassembly:
Materials Management at BMW

Known for its well-engineered automobiles, BMW is seeking another type of distinction. The German carmaker has set its sights on building an automobile from 100 percent reusable or recyclable parts by the year 2000. To achieve its goal, the company is researching an approach called "Design for Disassembly (DFD)"—a manufacturing method aimed at building a product specifically to facilitate recycling at the end of its useful life. Along with other major corporations like Volkswagen, 3M, and General Electric, BMW is researching ways to manufacture a DFD product that is economically competitive and that stands up to the company's high standards for quality engineering.

Orchestrating a Design for Disassembly program in automobile production depends upon a coordinated effort among the manufacturer, the automobile dismantler, and the materials supplier. Manufacturers must design cars to facilitate dismantling, educate dismantlers about parts removal, and encourage suppliers to accept recovered materials from dismantlers. They also need to stipulate to suppliers that they will purchase only parts made from recovered materials.

Although virtually all firms in the industry are attempting to increase the recyclability of automobiles, Germany's producers currently have the strongest incentive to act. In 1993 the German cabinet approved unprecedented legislation that will require manufacturers to accept and recycle their products at the end of their useful lives. If approved by the German parliament, the law will apply to *all* products sold in Germany, even if produced in other countries.

This aggressive proposal has strengthened BMW's commitment to environmentally conscious production decisions. The company has been recycling its catalytic converters since 1987. A year later, it introduced its limited-production Z1 roadster. The two-seater is totally recyclable and

considered to be the first DFD product ever made. Since then, BMW has constructed a pilot plant in Bavaria dedicated solely to researching the DFD approach to manufacturing. Teams of workers at the facility systematically dismantle cars, beginning with all its fluids and oils and ending with the removal and sorting of interior materials. Currently, the plant disassembles 25 cars per day with nearly 80 percent of the company's 3-series being recovered for reuse.

A major objective is to build an automobile that can be dismantled at a relatively low cost. Long hours for the disassembly process elevates costs, which ultimately forces up car prices and reduces competitiveness—an outcome no carmaker can afford. Another key goal is to assure that parts can be readily sorted. This is particularly critical for plastics, which are more complex to recycle. Hence, producers need to find ways to reduce both the amount and the variety of materials used in production and to facilitate the sorting of recovered parts. BMW currently uses about 20 types of plastics in its automobiles, and it is looking to reduce this by a wide margin. The company also is establishing a network of recycling centers in Germany and the United States to make it more convenient for BMW owners to dispose of their cars. As a further incentive, the company offers a $500 voucher toward a new BMW to anyone turning in a vehicle at one of its dismantling centers.

BMW's efforts to advance the "Design for Disassembly" approach are well ahead of the rest of the industry, though other manufacturers are beginning to follow suit. Japan's Nissan Motor Company has launched a variety of new research programs—some aimed directly at the DFD approach, others at using more recycled materials and fewer plastics in production. In the United States, manufacturers have announced plans to label plastic parts to facilitate sorting for recycling, and they have

Application 1.1 (concluded)

established a consortium with suppliers and recyclers. Hence, there appears to be a consensus that increasing the recyclability of automobiles is a worthwhile pursuit. But, there are many technological and financial problems to overcome before anything like the DFD approach becomes an industry standard.

Sources: Ferdinand Protzman, ''Germany's Push to Expand The Scope of Recycling,'' *New York Times*, July 4, 1992; Bruce Nussbaum and John Templeman, ''Built to Last—Until It's Time to Take It Apart,'' *Business Week*, September 17, 1990; U.S. Congress, Office of Technology Assessment (OTA), *Green Products by Design: Choices for a Cleaner Environment* (Washington, D.C.: U.S. Government Printing Office, October 1992), p. 11; Mike Knepper, ''Recycling: Investment in the Future,'' *BMW Magazine*, January 1993, pp. 66–69. Michael Marley, ''Germany Eyes Recycling Law,'' *American Metal Market*, April 2, 1993, p. 9.

Using Science to Understand the Materials Balance.   According to the well-known **first law of thermodynamics,** matter and energy can neither be created nor destroyed. Applying this fundamental law to the materials balance model means that in the long run, the flow of materials and energy drawn from nature into consumption and production must be equivalent to the flow of residuals that run from these activities back into the environment. Thus, when raw materials are used in economic activity, they are converted into other forms of matter and energy, but nothing is lost in the process. And, over time, all of these materials become residuals that are returned to nature. Some arise in the short run, such as waste materials during production. Other resources are first transformed into commodities and do not enter the residual flow until the goods are used up. At this point, the residuals can take a variety of forms, like carbon monoxide emissions associated with gasoline usage to fuel an automobile, trash disposed in a municipal landfill, or sewage sent to a municipal facility for treatment and subsequent disposal in a nearby water body. Even if recovery takes place, the conversion of residuals into recycled or reused goods is only temporary. In the long run, these too end up as wastes.

first law of thermodynamics
Matter and energy can neither be created nor destroyed.

There is one further point. Accepting that matter and energy cannot be destroyed, it may seem as if the materials flow can go on forever. But, the **second law of thermodynamics** states that nature's capacity to convert matter and energy is not without bound. During energy conversion, some of the energy becomes unusable. It still exists, but it is no longer available to use in another process. Hence, the fundamental process upon which economic activity depends is finite. In fact, based on existing and projected growth trends, there is some evidence that the earth may be approaching its limit. According to the *Global 2000 Report of the President,* the population of the world should reach 10 billion by the year 2030 and will be approaching 30 billion by the end of the 21st century. The U.S. Natural Academy of Sciences reports that these population projections are markedly close to estimates of the earth's maximum carrying capacity.[3]

second law of thermodynamics
Nature's capacity to convert matter and energy is not without bound.

---

[3]Council on Environmental Quality (1980a) as cited in Daly (1992).

These scientific laws that support the materials balance model communicate important, practical information to society. First, we must recognize that every resource drawn into economic activity ends up as a residual, which has the potential to damage the environment. The process can be delayed through recovery but not stopped. Second, nature's ability to convert resources to other forms of matter and energy is limited. Taken together, these assertions provide a comprehensive perspective of environmental problems and the important connections between economic activity and nature.

It is the existence of these connections that motivates the discipline of environmental economics, a field of study that uses economic theory to analyze environmental damage and the policy initiatives designed to control it. In the context of the materials balance model, the emphasis is on the damage associated with the flow of residuals from economic activity back to nature. Although it is not necessary to master the rigors of environmental science, it is important to become familiar with the basic concepts scientists use to identify environmental damage and to communicate their findings to policymakers.

Fundamental Concepts in Environmental Economics

pollution
The presence of matter or energy whose nature, location, or quantity has undesired effects on the environment.

Environmental economics is concerned with identifying and solving the problem of environmental damage, or **pollution,** associated with the flow of residuals. Although pollution is defined differently in different contexts, such as within various legislative acts, a general definition provides a good basis for present purposes. **Pollution** refers to the presence of matter or energy whose nature, location, or quantity has undesired effects on the environment.

Notice the comprehensive reference to both matter and energy, suggesting that pollution can take any possible form. Virtually any substance can become pollution solely on the basis of a single characteristic, such as its fundamental constituents, its geographical location, or its quantity. What this implies is that finding appropriate solutions to environmental damage depends critically upon an identification of the causes, sources, and scope of the damage.

Identifying the Causes of Environmental Damage: Types of Pollutants

One way to identify which substances are causing environmental damage is to distinguish them by their general origin—whether they arise from nature, that is, **natural pollutants,** or whether they result from some human activity, that is, **anthropogenic pollutants.**

natural pollutants
Those contaminants that come about through nonartificial processes in nature.

anthropogenic pollutants
Contaminants associated with human activity; includes polluting residuals from consumption and production.

- **Natural pollutants** are those contaminants that come about through nonartificial processes in nature, such as gases associated with the decay of animals and plants, particles from such events as volcanic eruptions, pollen, and salt spray from the oceans.
- **Anthropogenic pollutants** are those that are human induced, including all the residuals associated with the processes of consumption and production. Examples include gases and particles from combustion and chemical wastes from certain manufacturing processes.

Of the two, anthropogenic pollutants are of primary concern to environmental economists, particularly those for which nature has little or no assimilative capacity.[4] Such nondegradable substances pose a greater and longer-term risk to society and to the ecology. Hence, policy initiatives aimed at these more harmful pollutants are typically stringent and may even call for their complete elimination.

Identifying the Sources of Pollution: Classifying Polluting Sources

Once pollutants have been identified, the next step is to determine the sources responsible for their release. Polluting sources are many and varied, ranging from automobiles to waste disposal sites. Even seemingly pristine settings like cropland in the Midwest can be a polluting source. For example, rainwater can transport chemical pesticides and fertilizers from farmland to nearby lakes and streams, contaminating fish and other aquatic life and tainting drinking water supplies. Because polluting sources are so diverse, they are generally classified into broadly defined categories that are meaningful to policy development. Depending on the environmental media (i.e., air, water, or land), sources of pollution are generally grouped either by: (1) their mobility; or (2) how readily they can be identified.

Sources Grouped by Mobility.   Whether or not a polluting source remains in a single location affects how the resulting pollution can be controlled. The categories are straightforward and logical, simply designated as **stationary sources** or **mobile sources.**

stationary source
A fixed-site producer of pollution, such as a building or manufacturing plant.

mobile source
Any nonstationary polluting source; includes all transport vehicles.

- A **stationary source** is a fixed-site producer of pollution, such as a building or manufacturing plant that releases residuals into the environment. Examples include coal-burning power plants and sewage treatment facilities.
- A **mobile source** refers to any nonstationary polluting source including all transport vehicles such as automobiles, airplanes, and ships.

---

[4]As we will discover in upcoming chapters, some pollutants actually increase in concentration as they are consumed by living organisms and move up the food chain. These are referred to as bioaccumulants, and the process itself is known as bioaccumulation or biological magnification.

point source
Any single identifiable source from which pollutants are released, such as a factory smokestack, a pipe, or a ship.

nonpoint source
A source that cannot be identified accurately and degrades the environment in a diffuse, indirect way over a relatively broad area.

The most common policy application of these two groups of sources is in the context of air pollution, where both types of sources are major contributors to air quality damage yet each requires specific forms of control.

Sources Grouped by Identifiability.   Similarly, the identifiability of a polluting source is critical to understanding environmental damage and to finding ways to control it. Hence, a distinction is made between **point sources** and **nonpoint sources.**

- A **point source** refers to any single identifiable polluting source from which pollutants are released, such as a factory smokestack, a pipe, or a ship.
- A **nonpoint source** is one that cannot be identified accurately and degrades the environment in a diffuse, indirect way over a relatively broad area.

This set of classifications is most commonly used in the context of water pollution control policy because nonpoint sources are so significant to this particular problem. As these definitions suggest, pollutants released from nonpoint sources are much more difficult to control than those released from point sources. Hence, it should not be surprising that even after many years of studying environmental damage and developing policy initiatives, governments everywhere continue to struggle with the problem of nonpoint source pollution.

Identifying the Scope of Environmental Damage: Local, Regional, and Global Pollution

Although environmental damage is a universal concern, some pollution problems cause detrimental effects that are limited to a single city or town, while others pose a risk over a large geographical region. The point is, the extent of the damage associated with pollution can vary considerably—an observation vitally important to policy formulation. Consequently, environmental pollution is often classified according to the relative size of its geographical impact, that is, local, regional, and global pollution.

local pollution
Environmental damage that does not extend very far from the polluting source and typically is confined to a single community, such as urban smog.

Local Pollution.   **Local pollution** refers to environmental damage that does not extend very far from the polluting source and typically is confined to a single community. Although the negative effects are limited in scope, they nonetheless pose a risk to society and can be difficult to control. A common local pollution problem is urban air pollution, particularly the presence of **urban smog.** Visible as a thick yellowish haze, smog is caused by a number of pollutants that chemically react in sunlight. Some cities have experienced particularly severe air quality problems, among them, Los Angeles and Mexico City, as the graphic in Figure 1.3 suggests. As we will learn in upcoming chapters, improving urban air quality is a long-term undertaking involving both the private and public sectors.

FIGURE 1.3

*Comparison of
pollutants
contributing to urban
air pollution in major
cities*

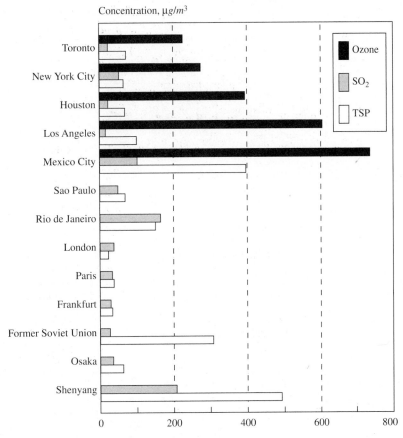

Notes:
1. Ozone refers to ground level ozone; SO_2 is sulfur dioxide, the condensation of which contributes
   significantly to particulate matter in the air; and TSP refers to total suspended particles such as dust,
   soot, smoke and other contaminants.
2. Concentrations are given in $\mu g/m^3$ = Micrograms per cubic meter.

Source: U.S. Environmental Protection Agency, Office of Air Quality Planning and Standards, *National Air
Quality and Emissions Trends Report, 1991.* Research Triangle Park, N.C.: October 1992, Figure 6–5,
p. 6-7, which is drawn from numerous sources.

Another local pollution problem that is receiving increasing attention is
solid waste pollution. Poor waste management practices can allow leaching
of contaminants such as lead and mercury into soil and nearby water supplies—a health problem for local residents. Beyond corrective measures
aimed at improving waste management are efforts directed toward reducing
the *amount* of waste being generated in the first place. Examine the estimates
on municipal waste generation for selected countries given in Table 1.1.
Notice how citizens in industrialized nations such as the United States
and France generate much larger amounts of trash than residents of less developed countries.

TABLE 1.1   **Municipal Solid Waste (top 50)**
Per Capita Generation in Selected Countries

Country	Waste (lbs. per capita per day)	Rank	Country	Waste (lbs. per capita per day)	Rank
Australia	4.2	1	Spain	1.9	26
New Zealand	4.0	2	Germany	1.8	27
France	4.0	3	Iceland	1.8	28
Canada	3.7	4	Hungary	1.6	29
United States	3.3	5	Greece	1.5	30
Norway	2.9	6	Italy	1.5	31
Netherlands	2.6	7	Portugal	1.5	32
Denmark	2.6	8	Soviet Union		
Finland	2.4	9	(former)	1.3	33
Bahrain	2.4	10	Czechoslovakia	1.3	34
United Arab			Albania	1.3	35
Emirates	2.4	11	Bulgaria	1.3	36
Saudi Arabia	2.4	12	Austria	1.3	37
Kuwait	2.4	13	Poland	1.3	38
Oman	2.4	14	Romania	1.3	39
Israel	2.4	15	Indonesia	1.3	40
Qatar	2.4	16	Colombia	1.2	41
Iraq	2.4	17	Guatemala	1.1	42
Luxembourg	2.2	18	Liberia	1.1	43
Switzerland	2.2	19	Cote d'Ivoire	1.1	44
United Kingdom	2.2	20	Malta	1.1	45
Belgium	2.0	21	Gabon	1.1	46
Sweden	2.0	22	Kenya	1.1	47
Japan	2.0	23	Trinidad and Tobago	1.1	48
Ireland	2.0	24	Cape Verde	1.1	49
Singapore	1.9	25	Mozambique	1.1	50

Regional Pollution.   Other types of environmental pollution pose a risk that extends well beyond the polluting source. These are typically referred to as **regional pollution.** An important example is **acidic deposition.** Acidic deposition arises from acidic compounds that mix with other particles in the air and fall to the earth either as dry deposits or in fog, snow, or rain—thus the common reference, "acid rain." These compounds are produced by chemical reactions involving sulfur dioxide and nitrogen oxide, both of which are emitted when fossil fuels are burned. Acid rain is characterized as regional pollution because the harmful emissions can travel hundreds of miles from their source. Among the associated effects are health problems such as respiratory illness, the loss of aquatic life due to acidification of water bodies, forest damage, and erosion of buildings.

regional pollution
Degradation that extends well beyond the polluting source, such as acidic deposition.

global pollution
Environmental effects that are widespread with global implications, such as global warming and ozone depletion.

Global Pollution.   Finally, there are some environmental problems whose effects are so extensive that they are referred to as **global pollution.** Global pollution is difficult to control, both because the associated effects are so widespread and because international cooperation is needed to implement effective solutions. Consider, for example, the problem of **global warming.** Also known as the "greenhouse effect," global warming occurs as sunlight passes through the atmosphere to the earth's surface and is radiated back into the air, where it is absorbed by so-called greenhouse gases such as carbon dioxide. Although this warming process is quite natural, certain human activities such as fossil-fuel combustion add to the normal level of greenhouse gases, which in turn can increase the earth's natural temperature. According to scientific models, such disruptions to normal climate patterns could change the productivity of agricultural regions, weather conditions, and the level of the earth's oceans—all effects that are worldwide in scope.

Similarly widespread are the risks associated with **ozone depletion,** a thinning of the earth's ozone layer caused by the release of various pollutants. The ozone layer protects the earth from harmful ultraviolet radiation, which can weaken human immune systems, increase the risk of skin cancer, and adversely affect ecosystems. In 1985, scientists discovered that a previously observed thinning of the ozone layer over the Antarctic region had become an "ozone hole" the size of North America. There is a consensus that ozone depletion is caused mainly by a group of chemicals known as chlorofluorocarbons, or CFCs. CFCs had been commonly used in refrigeration, air-conditioning, product packaging, insulation, and aerosol propellants. Although national governments have instituted laws to control CFC usage, the main policy thrust has arisen through international agreements because of the global nature of the problem.

As society has learned more about environmental degradation and the associated risks, it has recognized the need to establish goals that would in turn identify what had to be done. Although the task of setting objectives is an ongoing process, there are certain worldwide environmental goals that have been endorsed through a variety of international forums. Because they are global in scope, these objectives are necessarily general, but nonetheless significant in intent. They are meant to give direction to private and public initiatives and to set the overall agenda for national and international policy. A discussion of some of these important goals follows.

Identifying Environmental Objectives

In some sense, just as fundamental environmental problems are universal, so too are the overall objectives. But, articulating the specifics of these objectives *and* accepting the trade-offs that such goals imply is a process that is not without debate. Indeed, such is the substance of environmental summits, where national leaders, industry officials, and environmentalists gather to exchange ideas about appropriate objectives and to garner cooperation from one another. A case in point was the United Nations Conference on Environment and Development (UNCED) held in Rio de Janeiro, Brazil (known as the Earth Summit) in 1992. Held on the 20th anniversary of the first worldwide environmental conference in Stockholm, this event was attended by 6,000 delegates representing over 170 countries—a true landmark in global negotiations aimed at a better environment.[5]

Although the objective-setting process has been arduous at times and often immersed in political debate, it *is* nonetheless moving forward—no small triumph given that these universal goals set the course of both public and private environmental initiatives for every region of the world and at every level of government. Today, virtually every environmental decision is guided by what have become worldwide goals. Among the more critical are **environmental quality, sustainable development,** and **biodiversity.**

Environmental Quality

Given the pervasive problems of local, regional, and global pollution, few would debate including environmental quality among the world's objectives. However, there *is* a lack of consensus about how to define this seemingly straightforward concept in practice. In common parlance, most of us consider environmental quality to mean clean air, water, and land. But when this objective is being defined to guide policy, the dilemma becomes one of deciding just how clean is clean.

environmental quality
A reduction in anthropogenic contamination to a level that is "acceptable" to society.

The debate usually begins with asking why **environmental quality** should not mean the *absence* of all pollution. But such an objective is impossible, at least in a pure sense. Recall that some pollution is natural and therefore not controllable. Furthermore, the absence of all anthropogenic pollutants could be achieved only if there were a total prohibition on virtually all the goods and services that characterize modern living. Hence, a more rational perception of environmental quality is that it represents a reduction in anthropogenic contamination to a level that is "acceptable" to society.

This "acceptable" level of pollution will, of course, be different for different contaminants. But in each case, certain factors are considered in making the determination. Among them are the associated gains to human health and ecosystems, the expenditures needed to achieve the reduction, the availability of technology, and the relative risk of a given environmental hazard. Which of these determinants are used and to what degree each is considered are difficult decisions. Later, we will explore some of the strategies that have been developed to guide this important and complex process.

Although there is ongoing debate about how environmental quality ought to be defined, there is agreement that the world has begun to make progress toward reducing pollutant discharges. But there is still much work to be done.

---

[5]Council on Environmental Quality (January 1993), p. 140.

Application 1.2

Conflict between Economic Development and the Environment: China's View

As China attempts to develop its economy into an industrialized power, the quality of its air, water, and land resources is deteriorating. Although officials are beginning to draft pollution control plans, much of the ecological damage is going virtually unchecked. As is sometimes the case in developing economies, environmentalism is perceived as an obstacle to economic advance. Pollution controls are viewed as financial burdens that will serve only to frustrate China's progress toward industrial development. Many observers believe that unless officials change their perspective toward environmental issues, the official response to China's pollution problems will be insufficient, yielding little or no measurable improvement in environmental quality.

China's air pollution problems can be traced primarily to the country's heavy reliance on coal as an energy source. In fact, during the 1980s, coal consumption increased from 620 million tons to more than 1 billion tons. As economic development continues, this dependence is expected to increase with dire consequences for China's air quality. Industrial centers, like Chongqing, are already facing severe acid rain problems because of the use of high-sulfur coal. Documented damages range from soiling and erosion of buildings to the destruction of agricultural crops and vegetation. Reportedly, trees along city streets have had to be replaced three times in the last 30 years. China's water resources are also at risk. Sewage treatment is often inadequate, even nonexistent in some locations, and industrial wastes are contaminating many of the

country's rivers and streams. Clearly, these are nontrivial problems, but they are particularly serious for a nation with hundreds of cities facing water shortages.

According to China's environmental protection committee, economic losses from environmental pollution are estimated at about 3 percent of China's GNP, or approximately $11.5 billion per year. The country now spends about 0.7 percent of its GNP on environmental protection, which apparently is not nearly enough to address the extent and seriousness of China's pollution problems. Nonetheless, Chinese officials are reluctant to allocate resources away from economic development and toward environmental cleanup and protection, accepting the pollution as a necessary sacrifice to achieve industrial growth. Instead, China is relying on financial support from other countries and international organizations. Denmark is helping Chongqing build a modern sewage treatment plant, and the World Bank is providing loans to fund major environmental efforts, including a multi-million-dollar project to clean up Beijing. Notwithstanding the significance of these international endeavors, the most important effort has to come from China itself. And that can follow only if this vast nation learns to balance growth with resource preservation and the needs of future generations with those of the present.

Sources: Dan Biers, ''China Creates Environmental Nightmare in Industrial Rush,'' *The Brockton Enterprise,* June 16, 1994; Charles A. Radin, ''With China's 'Miracle,' Pollution Surges,'' *Boston Globe,* January 2, 1995, pp. 47, 50.

In some parts of the world, such as in eastern Europe and the developing nations, environmental pollution is extreme, and progress toward mitigating the negative effects is slow. Application 1.2 discusses some of the environmental problems China is dealing with as it strives to advance economically. Even in wealthier, industrialized countries, there continue to be localized problems, such as in urban centers where air quality is often poor, and in some rural areas where water supplies are threatened by pesticide contamination. Hence, achieving environmental quality continues to be a strong motivation for public and private initiatives the world over.

Recognizing environmental quality as a worldwide objective has triggered an awareness of its importance over a longer time horizon. Society has begun to realize that the pursuit of economic growth could so adversely affect the natural resource stock that the productive capacity and overall welfare of future generations would be threatened. The potential of such an *intertemporal* trade-off has prompted a sense of obligation to the future that has materialized into two related objectives, **sustainable development** and **biodiversity.**

Sustainable Development

Economists define economic growth as an increase in the real gross domestic product (GDP) of an economic system. While growth is a favorable outcome, there are nonetheless long-term environmental considerations that must be addressed, as the materials balance model clearly suggests. Among these is the intensified use or misuse of resources associated with servicing a larger economy. One of the greatest challenges society faces is achieving a healthy rate of economic growth without so damaging or depleting the supply of natural resources that the productive needs of future generations are jeopardized. Finding an appropriate balance between economic growth and the preservation of natural resources is the essence of the objective known as **sustainable development,** which is the management of the earth's resources such that their long-term quality and abundance are ensured.[6]

sustainable development
The management of the earth's resources such that their long-term quality and abundance are ensured.

What this reminds us of is that the circular flow of economic activity cannot be properly understood without recognizing *how* it fits into the larger scheme of the natural environment. Yet, only in the past decade or so have economists and society at large begun to come to grips with this broader and more realistic view. For example, as Application 1.3 explains, new methods are being proposed to capture the ecological effects of growth in macroeconomic performance measures.

On a broader scale, sustainable development was an important agenda item at the 1992 Earth Summit. In fact, one of the summit's primary documents, the *Rio Declaration,* outlines 27 principles to act as guidelines for global environmental protection and economic development. Similar commitments are given in the summit's 40-chapter document, *Agenda 21,* a voluntary, international agenda of comprehensive environmental goals. Its text is dedicated in large part to sustainable development, with special emphasis on regions where achieving this objective is particularly critical such as developing nations.[7]

---

[6]Council on Environmental Quality (January 1993), p. 135.
[7]Parson, Haas, and Levy (1992).

Application 1.3

National Income Accounting and the Bias against Environmental Assets

Assessing a nation's macroeconomic performance is an important and complex undertaking. The objective is to monetize total production and use the result as a means to assess and monitor a nation's growth. Measures of economic activity are also useful in making international comparisons, provided the accounting methods used are standardized. Currently, the accepted methodology follows the so-called System of National Accounts (SNA) endorsed by the United Nations, a universal accounting framework for calculating such performance measures as gross domestic product (GDP) and national income.

As defined in most introductory economics texts, GDP is a monetized value of all final goods and services produced in a country each year. Although designed to be a fully comprehensive measure of productive activity, GDP is admittedly flawed. Difficulties in attempting to capture the value of nonmarketed goods, such as the value of "do-it-yourself" projects and the so-called underground economy, necessarily bias the measure. Beyond these well-known flaws, there are other inherent biases that have caused some economists and government officials to question the validity of GDP as a measure of economic welfare. Among these is the absence of consideration for the ecological damage and natural resource depletion associated with productive activity.

Recognizing this shortcoming, some economists and statistical analysts have argued in favor of an environmentally adjusted national income measure that explicitly values natural resources as economic assets. The justifications for this proposal are based on the following considerations. Just as the SNA allows for the depreciation of physical capital such as plant and equipment, so too should it recognize the devaluation of natural resources associated with economic activity. If pesticides leach into underground springs, the damage to drinking water supplies should be monetized and explicitly recognized by the GDP measure. Likewise, if a forest is destroyed to make way for urban development, that loss should be recorded. In both

cases, important assets would be depreciating, and that depreciation should be captured in the SNA income and product accounts to avoid a serious bias. Furthermore, this practice is inconsistent with other SNA rules. Specifically, land, minerals, and timber *are* recognized as economic assets in the model balance sheet, which is rarely prepared in practice. But the same treatment is not allowed in the official preparation of product accounts.

Proponents of environmentally adjusted performance measures also make a broader-based argument. They claim that ignoring the economic value of natural resources perpetuates society's failure to acknowledge the effect of economic growth on future generations. In fact, in some cases, current accounting practices falsely record environmental deterioration as a contribution to economic welfare. A case in point is increased medical expenditures associated with the effects of a toxic chemical leak or government spending for cleaning up toxic waste sites, both of which ironically *elevate* a nation's GDP measure. An explicit accounting of resource depletion and environmental damage would correct this perverse outcome and restore some accuracy to national product and income accounts.

Officials in many nations are aware of the environmental bias in national income accounts, and some are compiling internal accounts that explicitly value natural resources and the negative effects of environmental pollution. But to date, authorities at the UN are refusing to acknowledge the need to correct the bias against environmental assets in the SNA. The official response has been limited to developing guidelines on how individual nations should prepare their own natural resource accounts. Proponents of environmentally adjusted performance measures view this response as grossly inadequate as long as the SNA continues to be the universally accepted approach to measuring economic well-being.

Sources: Robert Repetto, "Earth in the Balance Sheet: Incorporating Natural Resources in National Income Accounts," *Environment* 34 no. 7 (September 1992), pp. 12–20, 43–45; Robert Repetto, "Accounting for Environmental Assets," *Scientific American,* June 1992, pp. 94–100.

Third-world countries are particularly vulnerable to the strains that economic development and rapid population growth place upon their resource stock. Many of these poorer nations are already facing serious shortages of water, food, land, and energy, and rapid population growth threatens to exacerbate these extreme conditions. Kenya, for example, is a country whose population could reach almost 100 million over the next 35 years if its growth continues at its present rate. Similar conditions characterize Bangladesh, where nearly all the cultivable land is already being used, and population is projected to increase from 110 million to 220 million over the next 35 years. More advanced nations are working to help these countries break the cycle of poverty and resource overuse that threatens their future growth.[8]

Biodiversity

biodiversity
The variety of distinct species, their genetic variability, and the variety of ecosystems they inhabit; also called biological diversity.

Another environmental objective that addresses the environmental legacy left to future generations is the preservation of biodiversity. **Biodiversity, or biological diversity,** refers to the variety of distinct species, their genetic variability, and the variety of ecosystems they inhabit.[9]

There is still much that scientists do not know about the diversity of life on earth. Although approximately 2.5 million species have been identified by taxonomists, most estimates suggest that the actual number may be at least 5 to 10 million, and some biologists believe there may be as many as 100 million.[10] Although there are still many unknowns, there is consensus within the scientific community that the variety of species on earth is, in and of itself, important to the ecology. Beyond the preservation of a species for its own sake, it has also become apparent that all life on earth is inexorably connected. Hence, the loss of one species may have serious implications for others, including human life.

Although plant and animal life are replenishable, this natural ability does not assure the continuance of a species. The longevity of any biological species can be *directly* threatened by exposure to pollutants or by other human actions like commercial or sport hunting. But the major threat to biodiversity is the *destruction* of natural habitats, which affects entire ecosystems. Population growth, poverty, and economic development are primarily responsible for this destruction, which includes the harvesting of tropical forests and the engineered conversion of natural land masses into alternative uses.[11] For example, by the mid-1970s, literally half of the 200 million acres of wetlands within the contiguous United States had been lost to other uses, such as agriculture

---

[8]Ramphal (April–June 1993).
[9]Council on Environmental Quality (January 1993), p. 135.
[10]Raven, Berg, and Johnson (1993), p. 144.
[11]Raven, Berg, and Johnson (1993), pp. 262–63; 353–58.

TABLE 1.2   **Threatened and Endangered Species in the United States as of 1990**

	Endangered	*Threatened*	*Total*
Mammals	53	8	61
Birds	74	11	85
Herptiles (reptiles, amphibians)	22	22	44
Fishes	54	33	87
Invertebrates (snails, clams, crustaceans, insects, arachnids)	62	19	81
Plants	180	60	240
Total	445	153	598

Source: U.S. Department of the Interior, U.S. Fish and Wildlife Service, *Endangered Species Technical Bulletin* 15(11) (Washington, D.C., December 1990), p. 16, as cited in Council on Environmental Quality, *United Nations Conference on Environment and Development: United States of America National Report* (Washington, D.C., 1992), p. 295, Exhibit 6f.1.

and urban development.[12] Biodiversity can also be jeopardized by habitat *alteration,* which is often attributed to environmental pollution. For example, acid rain has been linked to changes in the chemical composition of rivers and lakes as well as to observed forest declines in Europe and North America. Such disturbances in the natural conditions to which biological life have become adapted can pose a threat to the longevity of these species.

The extent of biodiversity loss is not known. So complex are the relationships that give rise to ecosystems and biological communities that scientists may never fully understand them. There are, however, indications that concern about diversity loss is warranted. Declines in some species populations have been observed by scientists. As of 1990, nearly 600 U.S. species have been classified as endangered or threatened, as shown in Table 1.2. More recent statistics prepared by the U.S. Fish and Wildlife Service show that the total has risen to 755 as of 1992. Globally, 1,284 species fall into this category, with another 3,964 listed as candidates.[13]

That this issue is one of global concern is evidenced by the *Convention on Biodiversity* executed by 153 nations at the Rio Summit after more than two years of tough negotiations. Among its mandates are to find measures that identify which species are in decline and to discover reasons for any declines that are observed. Although the United States participated in the negotiations for this convention, it was not among the signatories. The United States did, however, promise that its efforts to preserve biodiversity would exceed the

[12]U.S. Environmental Protection Agency (August 1988), p. 57.
[13]Council on Environmental Quality (January 1993), p. 20.

treaty's requirements.[14] In fact, the United States has developed a number of programs to support both domestic and global biodiversity. As Table 1.3 indicates, some of these programs are research oriented, others promote education in biodiversity issues, while still others attempt to improve the scientific knowledge base.

Collectively, the goals of environmental quality, sustainable development, and biodiversity set an ambitious environmental agenda and one that requires commitment from both the private and public sectors. As such, all of society must work toward the development of strategic policy initiatives. Central to this effort is a planning process in which public officials, industry, and private citizens participate. In the context of environmental pollution problems, this process involves a series of decisions about assessing environmental risk and responding to it, as the following overview explains.

Environmental Policy Planning: An Overview

Devising policy solutions for environmental pollution relies on careful research and planning. Many disciplines play a role in the process—among them biology, chemistry, medicine, law, and economics. Input from these and other fields are used to evaluate data and to make decisions that ultimately lead to specific policy prescriptions. Although the details of this process vary according to the context, the underlying tool that guides policy planning is **risk analysis.** Fundamentally, risk analysis involves two decision-making procedures: **risk assessment** and **risk management.** We examine each of these in turn.

Risk Assessment

risk assessment
The qualitative and quantitative evaluation of the risk posed to health or the ecology by an actual or potential environmental hazard.

At any given point in time, there are many environmental objectives that need to be met with only a limited amount of economic resources. Hence, as problems are identified, they have to be prioritized in some way. Generally, this is done through a scientific assessment of the *relative* harm to human health and the ecology of a given environmental hazard—a procedure known as **risk assessment.** This refers to the qualitative and quantitative evaluation of the risk posed to health or the ecology by an actual or potential environmental hazard.

Various elements of the scientific community are responsible for conducting this assessment and communicating the findings clearly to policymakers. The evaluation must determine if there is a causal relationship between the identified hazard and any observed health or ecological effects.

---

[14]Explaining the nation's decision not to sign the treaty, President Bush announced that certain provisions unrelated to conservation were found to be unacceptable. Specifically, these deal with intellectual property rights, financial assistance, and the accessibility to genetic information in biotechnology by governments (Council on Environmental Quality, January 1993, pp. 18–28).

TABLE 1.3   Selected U.S. Policies and Programs to Support Domestic and Global Biodiversity

Program	Description
National Biodiversity Center	Proposed in 1992 as a center for information on biodiversity; its purpose is to improve access to information in private and public institutions, assess the scientific knowledge base, and provide standardization for data collection, reporting, and management.
Inventory and Research Proposal	Proposed at the Rio Summit to encourage global cooperation on surveys, inventories, and data management; the objective is to increase availability, comparability, and quality of information.
Gap Analysis	Implemented by the U.S. Fish and Wildlife Service, scientists use satellite imagery, habitat data, and geographic information systems to examine species distribution and biological communities relative to existing land use and land management patterns.
Ecosystem Management	Adopted in June 1992 jointly by the Bureau of Land Management in the U.S. Department of Interior and the U.S. Forest Service in the Department of Agriculture as a philosophy on ecosystem management; included are plans to manage land and water resources to restore and sustain biodiversity, to develop conservation partnerships, and to strengthen relationships between scientists and land managers.
Biodiversity Conference Series	Conducted by the Council on Environmental Quality with the support of the EPA and various executive departments, the conferences explored ways to incorporate biodiversity and ecosystem management into analyses currently prepared under the U.S. National Environmental Policy Act.
Initiative for Private Lands	Launched in 1992 by the President's Commission on Environmental Quality, the initiative was aimed at integrating biodiversity considerations into land management decisions in the private sector.
U.N./U.S. Man and the Biosphere Program	Instituted interdisciplinary research on the sustainability of ecosystems in biosphere reserves in New Jersey, Virginia, and Florida.
Forest Service Natural Resource Conservation Education Program	Supports lifelong education about natural resources and ecosystems, their interdependence, conservation, management, and value.
Biodiversity Symposium	Held in 1992 by the USDA Forest Service, this international forum was attended by 400 people from 12 nations; among its goals were to document applications of biodiversity theory and concepts, to study policies affecting conservation, and to promote cooperation and understanding through open exchange and dialogue.

Source: Council on Environmental Quality, *Environmental Quality: 23rd Annual Report* (Washington, D.C.: U.S. Government Printing Office, January 1993), pp. 18–28.

If such a relationship is believed to exist, scientists must attempt to quantify *how* the effects are likely to change with increased exposure to the hazard. These findings are critical, since they determine whether or not a policy response is necessary, and if so, how immediate and how stringent that policy should be.

Risk Management

risk management
The decision-making process of evaluating and choosing from alternative responses to environmental risk.

Assuming that the risk assessment findings warrant it, the planning process enters its next phase called **risk management.** This refers to the decision-making process of evaluating and choosing from alternative responses to environmental risk. In a public policy context, risk responses refer to alternative types of control instruments, such as a legal limit on pollution releases or an excise tax on pollution-generating products. The objective of risk management is clear—to choose a policy instrument that reduces the risk of harm to society. What is less obvious is how public officials determine the level of risk society can tolerate and on what basis they evaluate various policy options.

A number of risk-management strategies have been devised to guide these important decisions. These strategies use specific criteria to evaluate policy options. Generally, these criteria are based on measures of risk, costs, or benefits—either singularly or in comparison to one another. Two that are economic in motivation are **allocative efficiency** and **cost-effectiveness.** Allocative efficiency requires that resources be appropriated such that the additional benefits to society are equal to the incremental costs incurred. An alternative criterion is cost-effectiveness, which calls for the use of the least amount of resources to achieve a given objective.

In practice, the choice, the choice of criteria is mandated, or at least implied, by law. For example, some provisions in U.S. legislation specifically disallow cost considerations in policy formulation, implicitly blocking either an efficient or cost-effective outcome—a result that is frequently debated in the literature and one that we will analyze in later chapters. For now, it is important to recognize that the decisions made in the risk-management phase of the planning process have important implications for society and the overall direction of environmental policy. In fact, in the United States two important policy trends have begun to emerge from this policy planning process—one dealing with government's overall approach to policy and the other with the time horizon targeted by regulatory initiatives.

command-and-control approach
A policy that directly regulates polluters through the use of rules or standards.

Government's Overall Policy Approach.   An important issue in policy analysis is the regulatory approach selected by government. Policies calling for *direct regulation* of polluting sources by control authorities are reflective of what is known as a **command-and-control approach.** This form of regulation uses rules or *standards* to control the release of pollution by every regulated entity. In practice, standards either set a maximum on the amount of residuals each polluter may release or they designate a pollution abatement technology that all sources must use. In either case, this approach allows polluters little or no flexibility in how they comply with the law and requires every polluter to meet the same standard regardless of its location, its access to resources, its existing emission levels, or its technology. Command-and-control has been the predominant approach used in the United States over the past several decades. But in recent years, more economic incentives have been integrated into strategic policy plans, which is indicative of a shift toward a market approach to policy.

market approach
An incentive-based policy that attempts to encourage conservation practices or pollution reduction strategies.

The **market approach** to policy is an incentive-based method that attempts to *encourage* conservation practices or pollution reduction strategies rather than force polluters to follow a specific rule. There are many different policy instruments that can achieve this result, such as a fee charged on pollutant releases or a tax levied on pollution-generating commodities. What all such instruments have in common is that they tap into the natural forces of the market so that the optimizing decisions of polluters will benefit the environment. Think about how private firms are influenced by economic profit. What a market approach does is strategically use this information to design environmental policy. For example, if a profit-maximizing firm were discharging a dangerous chemical into a river, a market approach might be to charge that polluter a fee for every unit of chemical released. In so doing, the firm would be made to pay for the damage it caused, and that payment would erode its profits. This tactic is sometimes called the **"polluter pays principle."** The expected outcome is that a rational, profit-maximizing firm will take steps to reduce the amount of chemicals it releases, using the most cost-effective method available. The favorable outcome is that society enjoys the benefit of a cleaner environment, *and* the associated costs to achieve that gain are minimized.

That such market-based strategies can be effective is validated by recent experience all over the world. In the United States and other industrialized nations, more market incentives are being integrated within the conventional command-and-control policy approach. In fact, in a 1987 study of 14 nations, the Organisation of Economic Cooperation and Development (OECD), which supports the Polluter Pays Principle, found that approximately 150 economic instruments were in use across these countries.[15] Market forces are also at work in the formation of new environmental industries. Again, the motivating force is profit. Entrepreneurs observe the potential profitability of market opportunities that help polluters meet new environmental regulations. A case in point is a Massachusetts-based firm that has developed a new technology for dealing with hazardous wastes. For more on this innovative enterprise and a general discussion of new "envirotech" markets, see Application 1.4.

Setting the Time Horizon.   Another element of risk management decision-making is determining the most effective time plan for policy initiatives. One

---

[15]OECD (1989a).

Application 1.4

Breaking Ground in the Environmental Technology Industry

In the United States, the environmental technology (or "envirotech") industry is being touted as a high-growth market that encompasses a broad range of business activities, ranging from environmental consulting to abatement equipment manufacturing. Recent estimates place demand for envirotech goods and services at $200 billion—a market expected to reach $500 billion by the end of the century. By any measure, the numbers are impressive, given that the industry was virtually nonexistent only 20 years ago.

Beyond its characterization as a rapidly growing industry, this market has yet to be clearly defined. In its relatively short history, it has had to adjust to numerous legislative changes as well as shifts in private attitudes toward environmental issues. For example, the recent regulatory trend toward preventing pollution rather than controlling it after the fact is expected to have a strong influence on the future of envirotech markets. The need for new technologies to preempt ecological contamination and reduce toxic use is expected to stimulate the industry's growth and create new market opportunities. Likewise, more stringent regulations and tougher enforcement laws will likely increase the need for expert advice on achieving compliance in a cost-effective manner.

Massachusetts is one state that is already benefiting from this emerging marketplace. During 1993, there were approximately 1,500 envirotech firms doing business in the northeastern state. Nearly 50,000 workers were employed by these new ventures, which generated approximately $5.5 billion in revenues that year. The state is hoping that the new market can rally its economy, which is still recovering from the effects of an ailing computer industry.

Capturing considerable attention both locally and on Wall Street is one Massachusetts-based company, Molten Metal Technology, Inc. Headquartered in Waltham, a Boston suburb, the firm evolved from an idea that its founders believed would revolutionize hazardous waste management. Drawing from the disciplines of chemical engineering and metallurgical science, the aspiring entrepreneurs developed a technology that uses a bath of molten metal to treat toxic wastes. Immersed in molten iron at 3,000 degrees Fahrenheit, chemical wastes are broken down into their basic atomic elements, such as hydrogen and carbon. Special reactants in the mixture produce recoverable materials and gases that can be recycled into marketable products.

As with most start-ups, all has not been easy for Molten Metals. Faced with a conservative regulatory process, the firm suffered long delays in obtaining official approval to research and market its technology. Overall, the company waited 18 months to obtain permits to open and operate a $10 million pilot plant in Fall River, Massachusetts. In large part, the delay was blamed on hazardous waste regulations that did not allow for such unconventional technologies, however innovative and effective. Responding to the well-publicized event, analysts have pointed to the need for greater flexibility in regulatory processes and for more incentives to reward rather than stifle innovation.

Despite the delays and the inherent risks of any new venture, Molten Metals has managed to attract substantial capital from both private investors and public entities, including the U.S. Department of Energy. There is little question that the small company is setting its sights on a successful future. Following the signing of the North American Free Trade Agreement (NAFTA), Molten Metals bid for a $750 million contract to recycle over 450,000 tons of hazardous waste each year in Mexico City. While it is too soon to predict the long-term success of Molten Metal's technology, there are at least some Wall Street analysts who believe the firm's revenues could grow from $6 million in 1993 to more than $150 million by 1997.

Sources: John Campbell, "The Ecology Alchemists," *Federal Reserve Bank of Boston Regional Review,* Winter 1994, pp. 13–18; Susan Drummet, "Molten Metals Vies for Mexican Cleanup Work," *Boston Globe,* January 18, 1994; Ana Puga, "Envirotech Goes Global," *Boston Globe,* June 6, 1993; Ronald Rosenberg, "Taking a (Really) Hot Bath," *Boston Globe,* July 7, 1993.

management strategies
Methods that address existing environmental problems and attempt to reduce the damage from the residual flow.

approach is to target policy at more immediate or short-run problems. These types of initiatives are sometimes referred to as **management strategies,** since their purpose is to deal with or manage an *existing* problem. Here, the intent is *ameliorative.* In terms of the materials balance model, such management strategies attempt to *reduce the damage* from the flow of residuals back to the environment. Generally, this is accomplished through controls on the treatment or disposal of residuals.

An alternative approach deals with the potential of *future* deterioration and is therefore *preventive* in purpose. This *long-term* strategy is referred to as **pollution prevention** and is implemented by *reducing the amount* of residuals that flow back to nature and/or by minimizing the harmful components of residuals like toxic chemicals. Preventive strategies are becoming more prevalent in U.S. policy initiatives. In fact, the United States made a formal commitment to pollution prevention when Congress enacted the Pollution Prevention Act of 1990. The clear intent of this legislation is apparent in its policy statement:

pollution prevention
A long-term strategy aimed at reducing the amount or toxicity of residuals released to nature.

> The Congress hereby declares it to be the national policy of the United States that pollution should be prevented or reduced at the source whenever feasible . . .[16]

There have also been some important private initiatives that support preventive strategies. One such effort is exemplified in a corporate pledge, originally known as the ''Valdez Principles,'' which is discussed in Application 1.5. Using a longer time horizon for environmental initiatives is still fairly new, so it is too soon to judge its overall effectiveness. Nonetheless, there are many who believe that the use of preventive strategies is the only way to assure environmental quality for future generations.

Application 1.5

The Coalition for Environmentally Responsible Economies: Valdez Principles

In the fall of 1989, the Coalition for Environmentally Responsible Economies (CERES) was formed. Its purpose is simple and direct—to encourage the corporate sector to assume full responsibility for the environmental consequences of its actions. The coalition comprises 14 environmental organizations, including the Sierra Club and the National Wildlife Association, plus the 325-member Social Investment Forum (SIF)—a national trade association of investment professionals concerned with social issues. To

accomplish its goal, CERES embarked on a plan to draft a formal pledge document through which private firms would commit to environmental objectives.

The membership collaborated to define specific standards to which signatories of the compact would be held accountable. Biodiversity, sustainable development, and pollution prevention were among the issues considered for the final document. Ultimately, the group settled on a set of 10 guidelines originally called the ''Valdez Principles,''

---

[16]See Pollution Prevention Act of 1990, Sec.6602(b).

named after the infamous March 1989 Alaskan oil spill. The designation was purposefully chosen to serve as a reminder of the potential effects of corporate irresponsibility.

The next step was critical. The CERES membership invited thousands of corporations to sign the environmental pledge. With endorsements from groups that collectively control $150 billion in investment funds, CERES believed its financial clout would be effective in garnering and rewarding corporate participation. But, despite a strong effort, response has been less than enthusiastic. As of 1994, only about 75 companies have agreed to commit formally to what are now known as the ''CERES Principles.'' However, the recent endorsement of such major corporations as Sun Co. and General Motors may encourage other firms to follow suit. The ten guidelines that make up the CERES Principles are itemized below.

The CERES Principles

1. **Protection of the Biosphere:** We will minimize and strive to eliminate the release of any pollutant that may cause environmental damage to the air, water, or earth or its inhabitants. We will safeguard habitats in rivers, lakes, wetlands, coastal zones and oceans and will minimize contributing to the greenhouse effect, depletion of the ozone layer, acid rain, or smog.

2. **Sustainable Use of Natural Resources:** We will make sustainable use of renewable natural resources, such as water, soils and forests. We will conserve nonrenewable resources through efficient use and careful planning. We will protect wildlife habitat, open spaces and wilderness, while preserving biodiversity.

3. **Reduction and Disposal of Waste:** We will minimize the creation of waste, especially hazardous waste, and wherever

possible recycle materials. We will dispose of all wastes through safe and responsible methods.

4. **Wise Use of Energy:** We will make every effort to use environmentally safe and sustainable energy sources to meet our needs. We will invest in improved energy efficiency and conservation in our operations. We will maximize the energy efficiency of products we produce or sell.

5. **Risk Reduction:** We will minimize the environmental, health and safety risks to our employees and the communities in which we operate by employing safe technologies and operating procedures and by being constantly prepared for emergencies.

6. **Marketing of Safe Products and Services:** We will sell products or services that minimize adverse environmental impacts and that are safe as consumers commonly use them. We will inform consumers of the environmental impacts of our products.

7. **Damage Compensation:** We will take responsibility for any harm we cause to the environment by making every effort to fully restore the environment and to compensate those persons who are adversely affected.

8. **Disclosure:** We will disclose to our employees and to the public incidents relating to our operations that cause environmental harm or pose health or safety hazards. We will disclose potential environmental, health or safety hazards posed by our operations, and we will not take any action against employees who report any condition that creates a danger to the environment or poses health and safety hazards.

Application 1.5 (concluded)

9. **Environmental Directors and Managers:** We will commit management resources to implement the Principles, to monitor and to sustain a process to ensure that the Board of Directors and Chief Executive Officer are kept informed of and are fully responsible for all environmental matters. We will establish a Committee of the Board of Directors with responsibility for environmental affairs. At least one member of the Board of Directors will be a person qualified to represent environmental interests to come before the company.

10. **Assessment and Annual Audit:** We will conduct and make public an annual self-evaluation of our progress in implementing

the Principles and in complying with all applicable laws and regulations throughout our worldwide operations. We will work toward the timely creation of independent environmental audit procedures which we will complete annually and make available to the public.

Sources: Keiko Ohnuma, ''Missed Manners,'' *Sierra,* March/April 1990, pp. 24–26; Coalition for Environmentally Responsible Economies (CERES), ''The Valdez Principles,'' USA, 1989, as reported in The Canadian Institute of Chartered Accountants, *Environmental Auditing and the Role of the Accounting Profession* (Toronto, Ontario: The Canadian Institute of Chartered Accountants, 1992), Table 2.1, pp. 7–8; Michael Parrish, ''GM Signs on to Environmental Code of Conduct,'' *Los Angeles Times,* February 4, 1994; Matthew L. Wald, ''Sun Oil Takes Environmental Pledge,'' *New York Times,* February 11, 1993.

Conclusions

Concern about the risks of pollution and the threat of natural resource depletion is widespread. The surge of environmentalism witnessed over the last two decades has been felt by private citizens, the business community, and governments all over the globe. In large part, this change in perspective has come from a growing awareness of the delicate balance between nature and economic activity. The materials balance model illustrates the strength of this relationship and the inescapable consequences of naive decision-making that ignores it.

Recognizing the implications, the United States and many other nations have made measurable progress in identifying the problems and setting an agenda to address them. As that work continues, comparable efforts are under way to develop and implement solutions. To that end, policy reform, collaborative arrangements between government and industry, and international summits are being aimed at resolving environmental problems. Research scientists are working to learn more about the ecology, the diversity of species, and environmental risks. Laws are being amended to incorporate more preventive measures as well as incentive-based instruments that encourage pollution reduction and resource conservation. And as the process evolves, society is changing the way it thinks about the earth's resources, the long-term consequences of its decisions, and its obligation to the future.

Economics has much to contribute to this evolution—in large part because of the interdependence between market decisions and nature. The fundamental concepts of price and optimizing behavior can be used to analyze the effectiveness of environmental policy and to develop alternative solutions. As we explore the discipline of environmental economics, we will use these same applications of theory to study the effects of environmental pollution as well as the public policy and private responses to the associated risks.

As this chapter suggests, there is a lot of ground to cover. But, the importance and relevance of the issues justify the effort. This field of study, much like the problem it examines, presents both a challenge and an opportunity—a characterization drawn from the opening address to the Rio Summit:

> The Earth Summit is not an end in itself, but a new beginning. . . . The road beyond Rio will be a long and difficult one; but it will also be a journey of renewed hope, of excitement, challenge and opportunity, leading as we move into the 21st century to the dawning of a new world in which the hopes and aspirations of all the world's children for a more secure and hospitable future can be fulfilled.[17]

Summary

- The basis for modeling the link between economic activity and nature is the same paradigm that underlies all of economic theory—the circular flow model.
- The relationship between economic activity and the natural environment is illustrated by the materials balance model, which positions the real flow of the circular flow model within a larger schematic to show the connections between economic decision-making and nature.
- One way economic activity is linked to nature is through a flow *from* the environment *to* the economy through the household sector. This flow represents the use of all natural resources in consumption and production and is the subject of natural resource economics.
- An important element of natural resource analysis is to identify which resources are renewable, that is, those that are replenished naturally at a measurable rate, and which are nonrenewable, that is, those present in a finite quantity with a negligible rate of natural replenishment.
- A second set of linkages runs *from* the economy *to* the environment and shows how nature is affected by the release of residuals arising from consumption and production. This flow can be delayed through recovery, recycling, and reuse, but not prevented. This residual flow is the primary concern of environmental economics.

----

[17]Maurice F. Strong, UNCED secretary-general. Opening address to UNCED Conference on Environment and Development, Rio de Janeiro, Brazil, June 3, 1992, as cited in Haas, Levy, and Parson (1992), p. 7.

- The first law of thermodynamics asserts that matter and energy can be neither created nor destroyed. However, one can be transformed into the other. This means that all of the resources drawn from nature eventually become residuals or wastes that are returned to the environment. The second law of thermodynamics states that the conversion capacity of nature is limited.

- Pollution refers to the presence of matter or energy, whose nature, location, or quantity produces undesired environmental effects. Some pollutants are natural, arising from nonartificial processes in nature, and others are anthropogenic, or human induced.

- Sources of pollution are sometimes grouped into mobile and stationary sources. Another common classification is to distinguish point sources, that is, those readily identified, from nonpoint sources, that is, those that degrade the environment in a diffuse, indirect manner.

- Local pollution problems, such as urban smog and solid waste pollution, are those whose effects do not extend far from the polluting source. Regional pollution is so identified because its effects extend well beyond the source of the pollution. Acidic deposition is one important example. Global pollution problems, such as ozone depletion and global warming, are those whose effects are so extensive that the entire earth is affected.

- Among the most critical environmental objectives are environmental quality, sustainable development, and biodiversity.

- A rational perception of environmental quality is that it represents a reduction in contamination to a level that is ''acceptable'' to society.

- Sustainable development is concerned with managing natural resources such that their quality and abundance are preserved for future generations.

- Biodiversity refers to the variety of distinct species, their genetic variability, and the variety of ecosystems they inhabit.

- The underlying tool that guides policy planning is risk analysis. Fundamentally, risk analysis involves two decision-making procedures: risk assessment and risk management.

- Risk management strategies are distinguished by the use of specific criteria by which policy decisions are evaluated. Generally, these criteria use measures of risk, costs, or benefits—either singularly or in combination. Two economic criteria are allocative efficiency and cost-effectiveness.

- A command-and-control policy approach uses specific limits or standards to regulate environmental pollution. A market approach makes use of economic incentives to encourage pollution reduction or resource conservation.

- Management strategies deal with existing environmental problems and are ameliorative in intent. Pollution prevention strategies have a more long-term perspective and are aimed at precluding the potential for further environmental damage.

Key Concepts

circular flow model
factor market
output market
materials balance model
natural resource economics
renewable natural resources
nonrenewable natural resources
depletable natural resources
recyclable resources
residuals
assimilative capacity
environmental economics
recovery
recycling
reuse
first law of thermodynamics
second law of thermodynamics
pollution
natural pollutants
anthropogenic pollutants

stationary source
mobile source
point source
nonpoint source
local pollution
regional pollution
global pollution
environmental quality
sustainable development
biodiversity
risk analysis
risk assessment
risk management
allocative efficiency
cost-effectiveness
command-and-control approach
market approach
''polluter pays principle''
management strategies
pollution prevention

Review Questions

1. *a.* State how each of the following factors affect the materials balance model: (i) population growth; (ii) income growth; (iii) increased consumer recycling actions; (iv) increased industrial recycling; (v) increased use of pollution prevention technologies.

   b. Assume that stringent pollution controls are placed on the flow of residuals released into the atmosphere. According to the materials balance model, what does this imply about the residual flows to the other environmental media, and/or the flow of inputs into the economy?

2. Faced with the oil crisis of the mid 1970s, the U.S. Congress instituted Corporate Average-Fuel Economy (CAFE) standards, which were intended to increase the miles per gallon (MPG) of automobiles.

   a. Briefly describe the expected environmental effect of increasing the MPG of automobiles, holding all else constant.

   b. There has been serious criticism lodged against these standards because U.S. automakers responded by using more plastics in automobiles to make cars lighter in weight as a way to meet the more restrictive CAFE standards. Explain how the use of this particular technology affects your answer to part *(a).* Are there any other relevant issues associated with this manufacturing decision?

3. Use your basic knowledge of economic principles to discuss how the market premise operates under the ''polluter pays principle.''

4. Reconsider the problem of U.S. wetlands loss and the implications for biological diversity. Briefly contrast how a command-and-control policy approach to this problem would differ in intent and implementation from a market approach.

5. In your view, should employment in the forest industry be sacrificed to save the northern spotted owl? If so, by how much, and how should the extent of employment loss be determined? If not, why not?

Additional Readings

Blum, Elissa. "Making Biodiversity Conservation Profitable: A Case Study of the Merck/INBio Agreement." *Environment* 35, no. 4 (May 1993), pp. 16–20, 38–45.

Briscoe, John. "When the Cup Is Half Full: Improving Water and Sanitation Services in the Developing World." *Environment* 35, no. 4 (May 1993), pp. 7–15, 28–37.

Commoner, Barry. "Economic Growth and Environmental Quality: How to Have Both." *Social Policy,* Summer 1985, pp. 18–26.

DiLorenzo, Thomas J. "The Mirage of Sustainable Development." *The Futurist,* September/October 1993, pp. 14–19.

Haas, Peter M., Marc A. Levy, and Edward A. Parson. "Appraising the Earth Summit: How Should We Judge UNCED's Success?" *Environment* 34, no. 8 (October 1992), pp. 6–11, 26–33.

Kneese, Allen V. "Analysis of Environmental Pollution." *Swedish Journal of Economics,* March 1971, pp. 59–81.

National Wildlife Federation. "25th Environmental Quality Index: A Year of Crucial Decision." *National Wildlife,* February/March 1993, pp. 35–41.

Sessions, Kathy. "Building the Capacity for Change." *EPA Journal* 19, no. 2 (April–June 1993), pp. 15–19.

Smith, Emily T. "Growth vs. Environment: In Rio Next Month, A Push for Sustainable Development." *Business Week,* May 11, 1992, pp. 66–75.

Solow, Robert M. "Sustainability: An Economist's Perspective." In Robert Dorfman and Nancy S. Dorfman, eds. *Economics of the Environment: Selected Readings.* New York: W.W. Norton & Company, 1993, pp. 179–87.

2

MODELING THE MARKET PROCESS
A Review of the Basics

According to the materials balance model, environmental problems are directly linked to market activity. The basic decisions made by consumers and firms affect both the abundance and quality of the earth's natural resource stock. Since environmental economics is concerned with resource *damage,* we need to develop a thorough understanding of how market activity gives rise to polluting residuals and why the usual market forces cannot resolve the problem. From an economic perspective, environmental pollution is characterized as a type of market failure. Hence, environmental economics uses market failure models to analyze the problem and to identify solutions. But these models rely on a fairly solid understanding of the market process itself.

To that end, this chapter reviews the essential components of a market and the basic concepts that are used in microeconomic analysis. Essentially, we will be focusing in on the operation of the circular flow model, which is central to the materials balance paradigm. The fundamentals of supply and demand are reviewed to reestablish a good grasp of market behavior, the motivations for consumer and firm decision-making, and the determination of price.

The context for our review is a hypothetical market for bottled mineral water in which competitive conditions are assumed. Through an analysis of market equilibrium, we discuss the economic criterion of efficiency—a notion used throughout the study of environmental economics to evaluate public and private responses to pollution problems. From this point, we develop both an intuitive and a quantitative presentation of welfare measures, which can be useful in evaluating the effect of environmental policy on society. All of the analytical and modeling tools presented here will serve as the foundation for our study of market failure in the next chapter.

Market Models: The Fundamentals

Defining the Relevant Market

market
The interaction between consumers (or buyers) and producers (or sellers) to execute the exchange of a well-defined commodity.

In economic analysis, the concept of a **market** is given a broader definition than in everyday usage. Rather than identifying a physical location, the term is used to describe a set of economic conditions. A **market** refers to the interaction between consumers (or buyers) and producers (or sellers) for the purpose of executing the exchange of a well-defined commodity. This more theoretical definition is purposefully general and abstract, since an economic market per se is meant to refer to the process of exchange and the conditions underlying that exchange for a broad range of economic activities. For example, this definition is as relevant to the purchase and sale of labor services in the factor market as it is to the exchange of groceries at a supermarket. As we will discover in upcoming chapters, it can even be applied to an analysis of pollution control in the ''market for environmental quality.'' Hence, one of the more critical steps in economic analysis is defining the market context for the good or service under investigation.

Specifying the Market Model

Once the relevant market is determined and defined, a model of that market and its characteristics must be specified. The form of the model varies with the objective of the prospective study and its level of complexity. Simple qualitative relationships among economic variables can be modeled using a two-dimensional graph. To quantify these relationships, models are refined through the use of equations or functions. For the most part, when we do use equations, we will specify linear relationships for simplicity. Formal testing is accomplished through empirical analysis of these theorized relationships using real-world data.[1]

The Model of Supply and Demand: An Overview

By definition, a market exchange for any commodity comprises two sets of independent decision-makers—buyers and sellers. Each is motivated by different objectives, and each is influenced and even constrained by different economic factors. Thus, modeling the exchange of a product involves the specification of these two distinct market perspectives. The decisions of sellers or producers are modeled through a **supply** function, while consumers' decisions are modeled through a **demand** function. When considered simultaneously, the resulting market model of supply and demand determines equilibrium output and price.

---

[1]Throughout the text, we will examine the results of some important empirical studies in environmental economics.

The Purpose of the Model

The primary objective of the supply and demand model is to facilitate an analysis of market conditions and any observed changes in price. An investigation of price movements can discern the presence of shortages and surpluses, the existence of resource misallocations, and the economic implications of government policy initiatives. For example, environmental economists can use supply and demand models to investigate the effectiveness of a gasoline tax in reducing gas consumption as a way to help improve urban air quality. By studying the associated changes in relevant market conditions and movements in gasoline prices, economists can determine how consumption patterns are affected, how the burden of such a tax is shared between the consumer and the producer, and how income distribution is affected.

More complex analysis is necessary when the market system fails to operate properly. In such instances, the conventional model of supply and demand must be modified to account for those conditions that weaken the operation of market forces. Economic theory suggests that the persistence of environmental problems such as urban smog and water pollution are the result of failures or breakdowns in the market system as it is classically defined. Of course, in order to understand why this is so and to begin to formulate solutions, it is necessary to have a good command of the market process, the underlying supply and demand conditions, and the mechanisms of the price system.

Building a Basic Model: Competitive Markets for Private Goods

To develop a basic model of supply and demand absent the complexities of market imperfections, a number of assumptions must be made. First, a competitive *goods* market is assumed, which is characterized by a large number of independent buyers and sellers with no control over price; a homogeneous or standardized product; the absence of entry barriers; and perfect information and mobility of resources. Second, the market for *resources* also is assumed to be competitive. This implies that the individual firm has no control over input prices—a result that will keep the model simpler. Finally, the output being exchanged in the market is assumed to be a **private good.**

private good
A commodity that has two characteristics, rivalry in consumption and excludability.

A **private good** is a commodity that has two characteristics, rivalry in consumption and excludability. This means that consumption of the good by one person precludes that of another and the benefits of consumption are exclusive to that single consumer. This assumption of a private (as opposed to a public[2]) good is critical to a conventional analysis of exchange and price determination.

---

[2]Public goods are excluded from our analysis because they represent a type of market failure. These are commodities like national defense and clean air whose consumption is both nonrival and nonexclusive. That is, once a public good is provided to one consumer, it is difficult or very costly to prevent others from sharing in its consumption. A more formal development of the theory of public goods as it pertains to environmental issues will be presented in the next chapter.

Market Demand

demand
The quantities of a good the consumer is willing and able to purchase at a set of prices during some discrete time period, *c.p.*

Demand refers to the market response of consumers who adjust their purchasing decisions to maximize their satisfaction, or what economists term utility. There are many factors that influence consumers' decisions. However, since a key objective of market analysis is price determination, the demand function is specified as the relationship between the quantity demanded by consumers and price, holding constant all other variables that influence this decision. Economists use the latin phrase, *ceteris paribus,* abbreviated ''*c.p.,*'' to mean ''holding all else constant.'' Hence, **demand** is formally defined as the quantities of a good the consumer is willing and able to purchase at some set of prices during some discrete time period, *c.p.* The consumer's ''ability to pay'' refers to the income constraint that limits consumer choice. The ''willingness to pay'' is the value or benefit the consumer expects to receive from consumption of the commodity. In fact, this **willingness to pay, or demand price,** can be considered as a measure of the **marginal benefit (MB)** associated with consumption of another unit of the good.

The key economic variables held constant when specifying demand are the wealth and income of the consumer, prices of related goods (i.e., substitute products or complementary goods), preferences, and price expectations. A change in any of these variables alters the *entire* price-quantity relationship, which represents a *change in demand.* This is distinct from the effect on consumption of a change in price, which causes only a *change in quantity demanded.* For example, consumers typically buy more of a good when it goes on sale. This is simply a change in the quantity demanded of the product in response to a price change. On the other hand, if, for example, consumers' tastes change such that they desire more of a product at *all* possible prices, the result would be a change in *demand.* A case in point is the observed shift in consumer preferences toward ''environmentally friendly'' products at all possible prices. Application 2.1 discusses some recent survey data that speak to this phenomenon and its impact on market demand.

The Law of Demand

Law of Demand
There is an inverse relationship between the price of a good and the quantity demanded of that good by consumers, *c.p.*

Under conventional circumstances, the qualitative relationship between quantity demanded and price is an inverse one. Hence, a *rise* in price is associated with a *fall* in quantity demanded, and the converse is true as well. This relationship is referred to as the **Law of Demand,** which asserts that there is an inverse relationship between the price of a good and the quantity demanded of that good by consumers, *c.p.* This is a highly intuitive theory, since it is reasonable to expect consumers to view price as an obstacle that limits consumption, given their income constraints.[3]

---

[3]There are more advanced explanations for the Law of Demand, specifically the income effect and the substitution effect. The interested reader can refer to any microeconomics text for a discussion of these concepts.

Application 2.1

Consumer Demand and Environmental Issues: What Really Matters?

According to a recent survey of 410 New York adults, environmental safety has become an important influence on consumer decision-making. Approximately 93 percent of the respondents in the survey believe that protecting the environment is a "very important factor" in their purchasing decisions. While this new influence on consumer demand is a viable one, only 1 in 10 of the survey respondents place environmental safety as a top priority. Product price and quality continue to be the most significant determinants of consumers' buying decisions.

Notwithstanding the strong hold that price and quality have on American buyers, the survey *does* indicate that consumers will switch brands in favor of environmentally safer products. This change in preferences implies a shift in market demand toward these products and away from less safe substitutes. Some of the nondurable consumer product groups affected by this phenomenon are detergents, diapers, aerosol sprays, and cleaners. Overall, 44.6 percent of all survey participants say they have switched brands for environmental reasons, with a higher proportion reported for the 31- to 45-year-old age group. Gender differences also exist with respect to this switching phenomenon. Some 49.4 percent of females in the survey express a willingness to substitute toward more environmentally safe brands, while the comparable proportion for males is reported at 37.9 percent.

Recognizing the market opportunity, manufacturers are responding to this trend in consumers' buying habits by promoting their respective brand names as "environmentally safe." The survey results provide some information about the relative success of this effort across competitive commodities. Brand names such as Clorox, Arm & Hammer, Tide, L'Oreal, and Revlon are among those perceived by consumers as associated with environmentally superior products. This brand recognition suggests that the advertised commitment to environmental concerns of certain manufacturers is perceived as more credible than that of other firms.

Just as demand theory dictates, consumer decision-making depends on a variety of market conditions and product characteristics. According to this survey, price continues to be a major determinant of demand, particularly in an economic slowdown. Nonetheless, environmental concerns appear to be having some effect on consumers' buying habits—at least for some nondurable products. On the supply side, manufacturers are having to adjust their production and marketing strategies to respond to this change in consumer preferences or else miss out on a lucrative opportunity. Of course, the demand for some products is more sensitive to this influence than others. And as time progresses, firms will have to monitor the degree of market responsiveness to environmental safety to determine if the observed reaction is growing or if it is just a short-term phenomenon. In the interim, the market mechanism is performing its function to satisfy the changing preferences of society—in this case to provide the market with more environmentally responsible products.

Source: Lorne Manly, "It Doesn't Pay to Go Green When Consumers are Seeing Red," *Adweek,* March 23, 1992, pp. 32–33.

Modeling Individual Demand

To illustrate the **Law of Demand,** Table 2.1 presents hypothetical data for an individual's demand for one-liter bottles of mineral water. The values show the utility-maximizing quantity decisions in a one-month period for a set

TABLE 2.1   Single Consumer's Demand Data for Bottled Mineral Water

Price in Dollars P	Quantity Demanded (bottles/month) $q_d = -4P + 20$
$0.50	18
1.00	16
1.50	14
2.00	12
2.50	10
3.00	8
3.50	6
4.00	4
4.50	2
5.00	0

of prices ranging from $0.50 to $5.00 per bottle. Notice how the inverse relationship between quantity demanded and price holds throughout. While these data give only a limited sampling of price-quantity pairs, an equation of the same relationship models *all* possible price-quantity responses for the consumer. In this case, the demand function is the simple linear relationship: $q_d = -4P + 20$, where the lowercase "q_d" signifies the quantity demanded of a single individual and P represents the dollar price per one-liter bottle. Notice that if any of the P values from Table 2.1 are substituted into the right-hand side of the equation, the corresponding q_d values can be obtained algebraically. For example, if $P = \$3$, $q_d = -4(3) + 20 = 8$.

By convention, the graphical depiction of demand uses the *inverse* form of the function, that is, $P = f(q_d)$. Solving the equation for P in terms of q_d generates the following: $P = -0.25q_d + 5$. The graph of this single consumer's demand curve (*d*) is shown in Figure 2.1.

FIGURE 2.1

Graphical model of one consumer's demand (d) *for bottled mineral water*

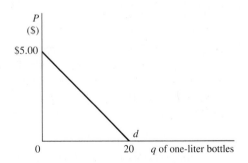

This graphical model of one consumer's demand (*d*) uses the *inverse* form of the function, $P = -0.25q_d + 5$, where -0.25 is the slope and $+5$ is the vertical intercept. The negative slope illustrates the Law of Demand.

TABLE 2.2   **Combined Demand Data for Bottled Mineral Water for Two Consumers, Consumer 1 and Consumer 2**

Price in Dollars P	Quantity Demanded by Consumer 1 (bottles/month) $q_{d1} = -4P + 20$	Quantity Demanded by Consumer 2 (bottles/month) $q_{d2} = -2P + 10$	Combined Quantity Demanded by Both Consumers (bottles/month) $q_{d(1+2)} = q_{d1} + q_{d2}$ $= -6P + 30$
$0.50	18	9	27
1.00	16	8	24
1.50	14	7	21
2.00	12	6	18
2.50	10	5	15
3.00	8	4	12
3.50	6	3	9
4.00	4	2	6
4.50	2	1	3
5.00	0	0	0

Deriving Market Demand from Individual Demand Data

market demand for a private good
The decisions of all consumers willing and able to purchase a good; derived by summing each individual demand *horizontally* to find the market quantity demanded ($Q_d = \Sigma q_d$) at each and every possible demand price (*P*), *c.p.*

For most applications in economics, the collective decision-making of *all* consumers in a given market is more relevant than that of a single consumer. Thus, the more appropriate concept is **market demand,** representing all consumers who are willing and able to purchase the commodity. This is derived by summing over the individual demand data. For private goods, this summing is done over the *quantity* levels at each demand price and is therefore referred to as "horizontal summing," since quantity is conventionally plotted on the *horizontal* axis.[4] Even though price is the same for all consumers, quantity decisions are variable because of differences in consumer income, wealth, tastes, expectations, and so forth.

For simplicity, we first illustrate this summing procedure by adding the demand of only one other consumer to the model specified previously. Individual demand data for two hypothetical consumers, Consumers 1 and 2, are given in Table 2.2. Notice that each makes unique decisions about quantity because each has a unique income level, stock of wealth, preference ordering, and so forth. The aggregate demand for these two individuals is found by summing the two quantity columns at each price level, the result of which is shown in the far right-hand column of the table. The same method can be

---

[4]Horizontal summing is characteristic of **private goods.** Because consumption of such goods is excludable, each individual is able to choose his or her own quantity. As we will discuss in the next chapter, this will *not* be true for public goods, an outcome with important environmental implications.

TABLE 2.3   Market Demand Data for Bottled Mineral Water

Price in Dollars P	Quantity Demanded by Consumers 1 and 2 (bottles/month) $q_{d(1+2)} = -6P + 30$	Quantity Demanded by Consumers 3 through 100 (bottles/month) $q_{d(3..100)} = -94P + 1{,}120$	Market Demand (bottles/month) $Q_d = -100P + 1{,}150$
$0.50	27	1,073	1,100
1.00	24	1,026	1,050
1.50	21	979	1,000
2.00	18	932	950
2.50	15	885	900
3.00	12	838	850
3.50	9	791	800
4.00	6	744	750
4.50	3	697	700
5.00	0	650	650

applied to an algebraic model by adding each pair of corresponding terms in the two demand equations. This is shown below:

Demand for Consumer 1:	q_{d1}	$= -4P + 20$
+ Demand for Consumer 2:	q_{d2}	$= -2P + 10$
Demand for Consumers 1 and 2:	$q_{d1} + q_{d2} = q_{d(1+2)}$	$= -6P + 30$

As an exercise, be sure to verify that the price-quantity pairs given in Table 2.2 satisfy each corresponding algebraic expression.

To derive the market demand, we use the same approach to aggregate across *all* consumers. Maintaining the characteristics of a competitive market, we assume there are 100 consumers in the market for bottled mineral water. The hypothetical data are shown in Table 2.3. For each price, we show the combined quantity values for Consumers 1 and 2 in the second column, the aggregated data for the remaining 98 consumers in the third, and the market quantity demanded, $Q_d = \Sigma q_d$, in the fourth. The corresponding equations are as follows:

Demand for Consumers 1 and 2:	$q_{d(1+2)}$	$= -6P + 30$
Demand for Consumers 3 through 100:	$q_{d(3..100)}$	$= -94P + 1{,}120$
Market demand:	Q_d	$= -100P + 1{,}150$

The graphical depiction of the *inverse* market demand curve (*D*) is shown in Figure 2.2.[5] At each price level, the horizontal distance between the vertical axis and *D* is exactly equal to the sum of the analogous horizontal intervals for each of the 100 individual demand (*d*) curves.

---

[5] The algebraic expression for the inverse market demand function is $P = -0.01Q_d + 11.5$.

FIGURE 2.2

Graphical model of the market demand (D) for bottled mineral water

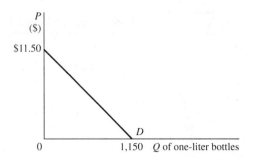

This graphical model of the market demand (*D*) for bottled mineral water uses the *inverse* market demand function, $P = -0.01Q_d + 11.5$, which represents the aggregate decisions of all consumers in the market. The market demand curve is derived using a horizontal summing procedure across all individual demand curves. Thus, at each price level, the horizontal distance between the vertical axis and *D* is exactly equal to the sum of the analogous horizontal intervals for each of the 100 individual demand (*d*) curves.

Market Supply

On the opposite side of the market, we derive a **supply** relationship based on the decisions of producers who are motivated by profit. Each firm's supply decision is modeled as a function of price, even though this decision is influenced by many other economic variables. A more formal definition captures the precise relationship. **Supply** refers to the quantities of a good the producer is willing and able to bring to market at a given set of prices during some discrete time period, *c.p.*

Among the variables that potentially affect the price-quantity response of a firm are production technology, input prices, taxes and subsidies, and price expectations. Analogous to the demand side of the market, changes in these determinants affect the entire price-quantity relationship, causing a *change in supply,* while a movement in price is associated with a *change in quantity supplied.*

supply
The quantities of a good the producer is willing and able to bring to market at a given set of prices during some discrete time period, *c.p.*

The Law of Supply

The qualitative relationship between quantity supplied and price is generally a positive one. That is, a *rise* in price is associated with a *rise* in quantity supplied, and the converse holds as well. This important relationship is referred to as the **Law of Supply,** which asserts that there is a direct relationship between the price of a good and the quantity of that good supplied by producers, *c.p.* The conventional assumption that firms are profit-maximizers suggests that a higher price should be an incentive for firms to bring more of the product to market. A contemporary example of how powerful the profit motive can be is in the context of ''green markets'' discussed in Application 2.2.

Law of Supply
There is a direct relationship between the price of a good and the quantity supplied of that good by producers, *c.p.*

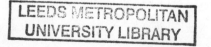

Application 2.2

Profit Opportunities in Green Markets:
Japan Takes the Lead

The lure of profit is one of the most powerful influences on firms' market decisions. A case in point is the entrepreneurial response to emerging industries in pollution abatement equipment and energy-saving technologies. Nowhere is the reaction more striking than in Japan. Promoting a technology-oriented solution to environmental problems, Japan's industrial sector has already taken the lead in these new high-growth "green markets."

Japan is pursuing opportunities proffered by environmental markets with a momentum virtually unmatched by any other nation. Patterned after their time-tested success in achieving dominance in other world markets, the Japanese are using a technology-based approach toward developing these new industries. For example, Toyota, Nissan, Honda, and Mazda are intensely focused on developing cleaner-running engines, superior catalytic converters, and lightweight car bodies. Fuji Electric's innovative efforts have won it world dominance in fuel-cell technology. And an ongoing research project directed by the Ministry of International Trade and Industry plans to use biotechnology to manufacture hydrogen, believed to be the energy source of the future.

Potential profit rather than environmentalism is the most likely motivation for Japan's tenacious efforts to cultivate environmental markets, despite the nation's own problems with air and water pollution. Densely populated and heavily reliant on manufacturing, this small eastern nation has witnessed measurable environmental damage associated with its steady advance toward industrial growth and development. Yet, Japan's leaders have been criticized for being shortsighted about environmental issues. In the international forum, the country has been a relative latecomer to efforts aimed at global warming and ozone depletion, responding only after being pressured by its global partners. After years of abuse to its natural resources associated with its post–World War II industrial buildup, Japan did embark on a tough cleanup plan, but only after many lives had been lost to industrial-poisoning accidents.

Indeed, Japan's approach to environmental concerns is rooted in a belief that economic growth need *not* be sacrificed to protect the ecology as long as production methods are properly adjusted through technological innovation. Some see this ideology as myopic, ignoring important issues such as the destruction of rain forests and the decline of endangered species, which cannot be corrected solely through high-tech invention. Others perceive Japan's national posture as an accurate long-term assessment of how to control environmental damage and one that will allow the Japanese to achieve dominance in still another group of important industries.

Why aren't other countries' industrial sectors pursuing these opportunities with the same energy? Often the question is pointed squarely at American industry. After all, the United States generates disproportionately higher amounts of pollutants like sulfur oxides than Japan. Reportedly, part of the reason is that incentives at the firm level have been weaker in the United States, where federal legislation is relatively lenient by Japanese standards. Another more deeply rooted issue may be that American industry tends to view environmental controls as an obstacle to growth and a negative influence on productivity.

In any case, Japanese corporations are confronting environmental problems and turning them into opportunities for growth and worldwide commercial success. While their high-tech approach may not be driven by social consciousness, there is little doubt that their head start in many environmental industries will likely win them market power that will be hard to surpass in the future. The message to industry in other nations is clear—"green markets" are offering lucrative profits, long-term opportunities for commercial success, and a chance to participate directly in solving the world's environmental problems.

Sources: Neil Gross, "The Green Giant? It May Be Japan," *Business Week,* February 24, 1992, p. 74; Jacob M. Schlesinger, "In Japan, Environment Means an Opportunity for New Technologies," *The Wall Street Journal,* November 5, 1990; Dianne Dumanoski, "Some See Profits; We See Obstacles," *Boston Globe,* November 5, 1990.

TABLE 2.4   Single Producer's Supply Data for Bottled Mineral Water

Price in Dollars P	Quantity Supplied (bottles/month) $q_s = 16P - 4$
$0.50	4
1.00	12
1.50	20
2.00	28
2.50	36
3.00	44
3.50	52
4.00	60
4.50	68
5.00	76

A more formal justification for the Law of Supply is based upon the nature of firms' costs as production is carried out. As the firm produces more and more output, its **total costs (TC)** rise faster than its output (Q), meaning the ratio of ΔTC to ΔQ is increasing. This ratio defines the firm's **marginal cost (MC)** of production, the additional cost of producing another unit of output. Since MC rises as Q rises, firms need to charge a higher price for each extra unit of output they produce. Hence, the existence of rising MC supports the positive price-quantity relationship given by the Law of Supply.

Modeling Individual Supply

The Law of Supply is illustrated using hypothetical data for a single producer of bottled mineral water given in Table 2.4. The quantity column shows a single firm's profit-maximizing output decisions associated with prices ranging from $0.50 to $5.00. Notice how the positive relationship between the **supply price** and quantity supplied holds throughout. The linear equation associated with these data is: $q_s = 16P - 4$, where the lowercase "q_s" is used to signify the quantity supplied by a *single* firm. Any of the price-quantity pairs given in Table 2.4 satisfies this equation.

The graphical model of the single firm's supply curve (s) is illustrated in Figure 2.3. Again, the convention is to plot price on the vertical axis and quantity on the horizontal, using the inverse form of the equation. In this case, the inverse supply function is $P = 0.0625q_s + 0.25$. Given the absence of extremes in the model, the supply curve has the expected positive slope in accordance with the Law of Supply and the underlying theory of rising MC. In fact, under the assumption of competitive output markets, the firm's short-run supply curve *is* its MC curve.

FIGURE 2.3

*Graphical model of
one producer's
supply (s) of bottled
mineral water*

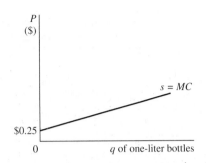

The model shown is the supply (*s*) of one representative producer in the bottled mineral water market. It is based on the inverse supply function, $P = 0.0625q_s + 0.25$. Notice that this function has a slope of $+0.0625$ and a vertical intercept of $+0.25$. The positive slope supports the relationship given in the Law of Supply and the theory of rising *MC*. Since the market for bottled mineral water is assumed to be competitive, this supply curve is the firm's *MC* curve.

Deriving Market Supply from Individual Supply Data

market supply of a private good
The combined decisions of all producers in a given industry; derived by horizontally summing each individual supply to determine market quantity supplied ($Q_s = \Sigma q_s$) at each and every possible price (*P*), *c.p.*

To analyze production at an aggregated level, **market supply of a private good** is derived using a *horizontal* summing procedure over all the individual quantity decisions of firms, analogous to what is done on the demand side. However, because the output market is assumed to be competitive, the adding-up process on the supply side is simpler, since all firms are identical under such market conditions.

Just as on the demand side, we begin by illustrating the aggregation procedure using only two firms. Hypothetical data for two representative producers of bottled mineral water and their combined supply decisions are given in Table 2.5. The algebraic counterpart is as follows:

Supply by Producer 1:	q_{s1}	$= +16P - 4$
Supply by Producer 2:	q_{s2}	$= +16P - 4$
Combined supply by Producers 1 and 2:	$q_{s1} + q_{s2} = q_{s(1+2)}$	$= +32P - 8$

To bring the supply relationship up to the market level, we follow the same summing procedure for *all* firms in the industry assumed to total 25 in number. The hypothetical **market supply** data are shown in Table 2.6. For each market price, the combined supply decisions for Producers 1 and 2 are given in the second column, the aggregated data for the remaining 23 producers in the third, and the market quantity supplied, $Q_s = \Sigma q_s$, in the last. The corresponding supply equations are as follows:

Supply by Producers 1 and 2:	$q_{s(1+2)}$	$= 32P - 8$
Supply by Producers 3 through 25:	$q_{s(3..25)}$	$= 368P - 92$
Market supply:	Q_s	$= 400P - 100$

TABLE 2.5   Combined Supply Data for Bottled Mineral Water for Two Producers, Producer 1 and Producer 2

Price in Dollars P	Quantity Supplied by Producer 1 (bottles/month) $q_{s1} = +16P - 4$	Quantity Supplied by Producer 2 (bottles/month) $q_{s(1+2)} = q_{s1} + q_{s2}$	Combined Quantity Supplied by Both Producers (bottles/month) $q_{s2} = +16P - 4$ $= +32P - 8$
$0.50	4	4	8
1.00	12	12	24
1.50	20	20	40
2.00	28	28	56
2.50	36	36	72
3.00	44	44	88
3.50	52	52	104
4.00	60	60	120
4.50	68	68	136
5.00	76	76	152

TABLE 2.6   Market Supply Data for Bottled Mineral Water

Price in Dollars P	Quantity Supplied by Producers 1 and 2 (bottles/month) $q_{s(1+2)} = 32P - 8$	Quantity Supplied by Producers 3 through 25 (bottles/month) $q_{s(3..25)} = 368P - 92$	Market Supply (bottles/month) $Q_s = 400P - 100$
$0.50	8	92	100
1.00	24	276	300
1.50	40	460	500
2.00	56	644	700
2.50	72	828	900
3.00	88	1,012	1,100
3.50	104	1,196	1,300
4.00	120	1,380	1,500
4.50	136	1,564	1,700
5.00	152	1,748	1,900

Figure 2.4 shows the graphical model of the market supply curve (S) in inverse form.[6] At each price level, the horizontal distance between the vertical axis and S is exactly equal to the sum of the analogous horizontal intervals for each of the 25 individual supply (s) curves. Furthermore, since the competitive firm's supply (s) curve is its MC curve, the market supply (S) curve is in turn the horizontal sum of each of the individual firm's MC curves.

---

[6]The corresponding equation for market supply in inverse form is: $P = 0.0025Q_s + 0.25$.

FIGURE 2.4

Graphical model of the market supply (S) of bottled mineral water

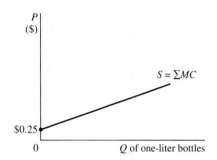

This depicts the graphical model of the market supply curve (*S*) for bottled mineral water based on the inverse form of the market supply function: $P = 0.0025Q_s + 0.25$. The market supply curve is derived by summing all the individual supply curves (*s*) horizontally. Hence, at each price level, the horizontal distance between the vertical axis and *S* is exactly equal to the sum of the analogous horizontal intervals for each of the 25 individual supply (*s*) curves. And, since each individual supply (*s*) curve is the single firm's *MC* curve, the market supply (*S*) represents the horizontal sum of all of these *MC* curves.

Market Equilibrium

Thus far, we have considered each side of the market separately to develop distinct models of economic decision-making. To advance the analysis to a model of price determination, we need to consider supply and demand *simultaneously* to allow for the interactions of consumers and producers in the marketplace. The formal theory that price is simultaneously determined by supply and demand is one of the most significant in all of economic analysis.[7]

Equilibrium Price and Quantity

equilibrium price and quantity
The "market-clearing" price (P_e) where quantity demanded by consumers equals quantity supplied by producers, or where $Q_d = Q_s$, which is equilibrium quantity (Q_e).

Together, the forces of supply and demand determine a unique **equilibrium price** (P_e) at which point the market system "comes to rest" or has no tendency for change. **Equilibrium or "market-clearing" price** (P_e) is the price at which quantity demanded by consumers, Q_d, is exactly equal to the quantity supplied by producers, Q_s, that is, where $Q_d = Q_s$. Only at P_e will the associated **equilibrium quantity** (Q_e) be both the profit-maximizing production level for firms and the utility-maximizing consumption level for consumers.

Market equilibrium for our hypothetical mineral water market is illustrated in Table 2.7 where market supply and demand data are presented together. Notice that the equilibrium price in this market is $2.50, the only price at which quantity supplied (Q_s) is exactly equal to the quantity demanded (Q_d)

---

[7]This theory is attributable to Alfred Marshall, who first published this hypothesis in his *Principles of Economics* in 1890.

TABLE 2.7   Market Supply and Demand Data for Bottled Mineral Water

Price in Dollars P	Market Quantity Supplied $Q_s = 400P - 100$	Market Quantity Demanded $Q_d = -100P + 1150$	Market Surplus/ Shortage
$0.50	100	1,100	Shortage = 1,000
1.00	300	1,050	Shortage = 750
1.50	500	1,000	Shortage = 500
2.00	700	950	Shortage = 250
2.50	900	900	Equilibrium
3.00	1,100	850	Surplus = 250
3.50	1,300	800	Surplus = 500
4.00	1,500	750	Surplus = 750
4.50	1,700	700	Surplus = 1,000
5.00	1,900	650	Surplus = 1,250

of 900 units. This result also can be determined algebraically by solving the market demand and market supply equations simultaneously.[8]

Graphically, market equilibrium is modeled by diagramming the market demand (D) and market supply (S) curves together on a single coordinate system. This is illustrated in Figure 2.5. In this graphical model, equilibrium is shown as the point where D and S intersect or where $Q_d = Q_s$.

FIGURE 2.5

Equilibrium in the market for bottled mineral water: market supply and market demand

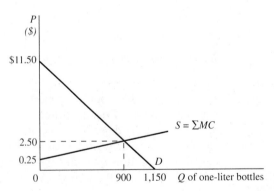

The model of market demand (D) and market supply (S) on a single coordinate system determines equilibrium price (P_e) and quantity (Q_e) at their point of intersection.

---

[8]Verify this assertion by substituting the market supply equation, $Q_s = 400P - 100$, and the market demand equation, $Q_d = -100P + 1,150$, into the equilibrium condition, $Q_s = Q_d$.

Market Adjustment to Disequilibrium

If the prevailing market price is at some level other than at its equilibrium level, it must be the case that $Q_d \neq Q_s$, and the market is said to be in **disequilibrium.** As a consequence, consumers and producers have an incentive to initiate some type of action that will restore equilibrium to the market. The motivation for the change and the process by which it is implemented depend upon whether there is an excess demand or an excess supply.

shortage
Excess demand of a commodity equal to $(Q_d - Q_s)$ that arises if actual price is *below* its equilibrium level.

Shortage.   If the actual price, *P,* is *below* the equilibrium price, P_e, there is **excess demand,** meaning Q_d exceeds Q_s at that prevailing price level. The result is a market **shortage** of the commodity equal to $(Q_d - Q_s)$. Refer back to Table 2.7 to see the shortages arising in the mineral water market at every price below $2.50. This means that consumers want more of the good at the existing price level than firms are willing and able to provide to the market. Responding to this, firms would be willing to increase quantity supplied, moving up the market supply curve and elevating price as they do so. This process would continue until the incentive to change quantity no longer exists, which occurs when price is increased to its equilibrium level.

surplus
Excess supply of a commodity equal to $(Q_s - Q_d)$ that arises if actual price is *above* its equilibrium level.

Surplus.   When the actual price is *above* its equilibrium level, firms are unable to sell all their output at the prevailing price level, and they begin to observe their inventories accumulating with unsold stock. In this case, there is **excess supply,** meaning that Q_s exceeds Q_d at the prevailing price level. The result is a market **surplus** equal to $(Q_s - Q_d)$. Look back at Table 2.7 to see the surpluses in the mineral water market at all prices above $2.50. Observing unsold supplies, firms will have an incentive to lower the price to eliminate the surplus. This price reduction will continue until all of the unsold supplies are purchased, which occurs at the equilibrium price.

Notice how price movements serve as an effective signal that either a shortage or surplus exists in the market, while the stability of price suggests the presence of equilibrium. The adjustments that occur when the market is in disequilibrium happen because of the market's internal forces. An example of how this adjustment process operates is discussed in Application 2.3 in the context of the recycled newspaper market. As long as the assumptions of the model hold (and this is an important caveat), there is no need for government intervention or any other third-party mediation to achieve equilibrium. This is a significant outcome, given that the participants in the market are not altruistic. Rather, as Adam Smith observed over 200 years ago in *The Wealth of Nations* (1776), although independent decision-making is governed by self-interest, the market outcome ultimately benefits all of society.[9]

Thus far, we have examined the fundamental elements of a competitive market and illustrated how the simultaneous effect of demand and supply

---

[9]Smith (1937), (originally published in 1776).

Application 2.3

Recycling Efforts Cause a Glut of Newsprint: Supply Doesn't Create Demand

The amount of garbage generated in the United States has risen from approximately 88 million tons in 1960 to over 195 million tons in 1990. Of this tonnage, nearly 41 percent is paper and paper products, with newspaper comprising a major proportion. In a logical move, many communities faced with declining landfill space began to establish recycling programs. Of course, the first step was to encourage individuals and firms to bring their wastes to appropriate collection centers. According to the EPA, this recovery stage has met with some success, as the data shown below will attest.

Although these statistics suggest that society is responding responsibly to the nation's waste disposal dilemma, nonetheless they belie a very real problem. While the actions of these communities and their residents were well intentioned, they were clearly misguided. In their haste to reduce waste disposal in landfills, many communities failed to recognize that the problem cannot be solved without the creation of a market for the collected materials. And, of course, both a demand and a supply are necessary to establish such a market. The recovery stage of the recycling process generates a supply of used materials, but if there is insufficient demand to move this supply into a secondary use, communities will face a glut of recovered waste products. All that will be accomplished is a transfer of the used materials from landfills to collection centers.

This potential problem became a reality for recovered newspapers, which grew by 34 percent over a five-year period in the late 1980s. Just as economic theory predicts, this excess supply sent the price of used newsprint plummeting—potentially a financial dilemma for many American towns and cities. According to a recent *Business Week* report, towns in New Jersey that used to *sell* the material for $20 per ton later had to *pay* as much as $10 a ton to get rid of it. Hence, the price actually fell to a negative value. Similar scenarios were reported by communities throughout the northeastern United States.

Who exactly are the demanders of used newsprint? The answer is a bit complex, since more than one market is involved. First, there is the market for old newspapers, in which the suppliers are the community collection centers, and the demanders are the used paper processors, firms that convert the old newsprint into a material that is reusable. For newsprint, an important and quite costly step in the processing is de-inking, a procedure that removes the ink and other contaminants from the newsprint so that the "cleaned" paper can be converted to

Type of Paper Waste	Percent Recovered		
	1970	*1980*	*1990*
Corrugated boxes	21.3%	37.1%	48.0%
Newspaper	24.2	27.3	42.5
Books and magazines	12.0	11.8	21.0
Office papers	25.9	25.0	26.5

Source: U.S. Environmental Protection Agency, Office of Solid Waste and Emergency Response, *Characterization of Municipal Solid Waste in the United States, 1992 Update* (Washington, D.C.: U.S. EPA, July 1992), Table 4, p. 2-5.

pulp. The pulp is then used by paper mills to produce new newsprint. This recycled newsprint defines the second market, in which the suppliers are the paper mills, and the primary demanders are firms in the newspaper industry.

So, at what stage of the process, or in what market, does the problem arise? Basically, there is not enough demand for recycled newsprint at the end of the cycle to stimulate the intermediate-level processing market to buy up the recovered newspapers collected by local municipalities. This in turn means that correcting the dilemma of excess supplies of recovered newspapers necessitates two important steps. The first is to stimulate existing demand or create new demand for recycled newsprint. The second is to assure sufficient capacity for de-inking and converting old newsprint into usable paper to meet that newly created demand.

Attempts to stimulate demand in this unusual market are coming from government. For example, in 1989 California passed new laws requiring state newspapers to use increasing amounts of recycled paper. There are similar laws as well as voluntary programs in at least 21 other states. At the federal level, President Bush signed Executive Order 12780 in 1991, which requires all federal agencies to sanction the use of recycled products in order to stimulate market demand. The EPA is also taking an active role by attempting to develop markets for recycled paper. Among the agency's efforts is the establishment of procurement guidelines for federal purchases of products containing recycled materials. In addition, the EPA is setting up clearinghouses, cooperatives, and hotlines to bring together suppliers and demanders of recyclable products.

As demand increases, it is imperative that the intermediary processing stage be well established. In the northwestern part of the United States and in western Canada, newsprint mills are adding capacity for processing old newspapers, and eight de-inking plants are currently operating in the region. Similar growth is expected to accommodate processing needs for the Midwest and Northeast. Seven new de-inking facilities are scheduled to be on line by 1996, bringing the total in eastern North America up to 20. Interestingly, many of these facilities are scrambling to buy up recovered newspapers, and some are setting up contracts with waste collection companies to assure future supplies. Some analysts are predicting an eventual shortage of old newsprint. As a result, prices of recovered newspapers are unstable, and there is a fair amount of price variability across different regions of the country. For example, by 1991 West Coast prices had tripled over the prior three-year period to $75 per ton as compared to a $15-per-ton price on the East Coast.

The lesson is clear. Recycling is a complex process, which depends on a series of steps involving a number of different markets. Collection is just one step in that process. For recycling to be successful, there have to be complete markets—both supply *and* demand—all along the way, or the market process will simply break down.

Sources: Michael Alexander, "The Challenge of Markets: The Supply of Recyclables Is Larger Than the Demand," *EPA Journal,* July/August 1992, pp. 29–33; Dori Jones Yang et al., "Recycling Is Rewriting the Rules of Papermaking," *Business Week,* April 22, 1991, pp. 100H–101H; Vicky Cahan, "Waste Not, Want Not? Not Necessarily," *Business Week,* July 17, 1989, pp. 116–17; U.S. Environmental Protection Agency, Office of Solid Waste and Emergency Response, "EPA's Role in Market Development," *Reusable News* (Washington, D.C., Fall 1991).

decisions determines equilibrium price and quantity. But we need to go beyond this point to understand the *implications* of a competitive equilibrium—first in terms of the allocation of economic resources and then in terms of the overall well-being of society.

The Economic Criteria of Efficiency

Economic analysis is guided by what theory tells us are important criteria. One of these deals with the proper allocation of resources among alternative productive uses, referred to as **allocative efficiency.** Another is concerned with economizing on resources allocated for a *given* production level, called **technical efficiency.** Each of these criteria is used frequently in all types of applied economic analyses, including environmental economics. We begin with a discussion of allocative efficiency.

Allocative Efficiency

Recalling the materials balance model, it should be apparent that the way in which a market system uses resources is critical, not only for production and consumption decisions, but also for the natural environment. But how is the resource allocation to be evaluated? The answer is through a procedure that involves two elements:

1. An assessment of benefits and costs.
2. The use of marginal analysis.

We have already introduced both of these elements in our prior discussion of demand and supply. Now, we use these together to draw some important conclusions about decision-making and equilibrium under competitive conditions—first at the *market* level and then at the *firm* level.

Evaluating Resource Allocation at the Market Level.   Competitive markets are considered to be an ideal, a standard by which other market conditions are evaluated. If we look carefully at what is conveyed by a competitive equilibrium, we can better appreciate this characterization. At equilibrium, we know that market demand intersects market supply. But what does this mean in terms of resource allocation? Recall that we argued that the set of prices along the demand curve are measures of marginal benefit (*MB*). Each demand price communicates the *value* consumers place on the *next,* or *marginal,* unit of the good based on the added benefit they expect to receive from consumption. On the supply side, there is also a marginal interpretation, but here the prices are measures of economic *cost.* Since the market supply in a competitive market is the horizontal sum of each firm's marginal cost (*MC*) curve, each supply price represents the additional cost of resources needed to produce another unit of the good. Economic costs include both the *explicit* or "out-of-pocket" costs associated with production and all *implicit* or opportunity costs based on the highest-valued alternative use of any economic resource.

Taking these two interpretations together, we arrive at an important result. At the competitive equilibrium, the value society places on the good is equivalent to the value of the resources given up to produce it, or *MB = MC.* By

allocative efficiency
The economic criterion that the value society places on an additional unit of the good be equivalent to the value of the resources given up to produce it.

definition, this result assures that there is an efficient allocation of scarce economic resources, or that **allocative efficiency** is achieved. **Allocative efficiency** requires that the additional value society places on another unit of the good is precisely equivalent to what society must give up in scarce resources to produce it. Recognizing this outcome as part of the competitive model is important, but it is just as critical to understand *why* it arises. For that, we need to focus in on the decision-making of individual producers under these market conditions.

Evaluating Resource Allocation at the Firm Level.   Starting from a general perspective, the assumed motivation governing firm decision-making is profit maximization. We further assume that the choice variable for producers is output. Hence, all firms, regardless of competitive conditions, choose the level of output that will maximize profit. **Total profit** (π) is defined as **Total revenue (TR) − Total costs (TC).** *TR* is simply the dollar value of the firm's sales, determined as the product of market price (*P*) and the number of units of output sold (*q*), that is, $TR = P \cdot q$. Total costs (*TC*) include all economic costs associated with producing the output.

total profit(π)
Total profit (π) = Total revenue (*TR*) − Total costs (*TC*).

To find the *q* that achieves the highest possible π, the firm makes its decisions *at the margin,* considering the relative benefits and costs of producing each additional unit of output. From the firm's perspective, the benefit is measured by *TR* and the cost by *TC*. Thus, it considers the profit implications of each successive unit of output by looking at the associated *changes* in *TR* and *TC*. If producing the *next* unit of output adds more to its *TR* than it does to its *TC*, the firm increases production. If production adds more to *TC* than to *TR*, production is decreased. The process goes on until there is no incentive to continue, or when the *change in TR* from increasing output is equal to the *change in TC*. At this point, the *change in* π from producing the last unit of output is zero, and any further increase in output would cause π to decline. Thus, at this precise point π is at its maximum.[10]

Notice that the entire decision-making process relies on *changes,* which is the definition of marginal analysis. In this context, the relevant marginal variables are as follows:

- **Marginal revenue (*MR*)** is the change in total revenue (*TR*) associated with a change in production level, that is, $MR = \Delta TR / \Delta q$.
- **Marginal cost (*MC*)** is the change in total costs (*TC*) associated with a change in production level, that is, $MC = \Delta TC / \Delta q$.
- **Marginal profit (*Mπ*)** is the change in total profit (π) associated with a change in production level, that is, $M\pi = \Delta\pi / \Delta q$.

---

[10]This, of course, assumes that in the short run the firm's revenues cover its variable costs. If not, it will shut down. In the long run, the firm produces as long as its total revenues cover all of its total costs. If not, it will exit from the market.

Thus, the firm implicitly makes its π-maximizing decisions according to the following rules:

The firm increases its production level as long as $MR > MC$ or as long as $M\pi > 0$.

The firm contracts its production level as long as $MR < MC$ or as long as $M\pi < 0$.

profit maximization
Achieved at the
output level where
$MR = MC$ or where
$M\pi = 0$.

The firm achieves **profit maximization** at the level of output where $MR = MC$, or where $M\pi = 0$.

Notice that the individual firm's optimal output level occurs at precisely the point where the marginal benefit *to the firm* of doing so, *MR,* is exactly offset by the marginal cost of the resources it uses, *MC*. Although this outcome validates the use of benefits and costs at the margin, it does not necessarily result in an allocatively efficient outcome. Why? Because *MR* is the marginal benefit *to the firm,* which is *not* necessarily equal to the marginal benefit *to society,* which is measured by price, *P*. In fact, the only way the firm's optimizing behavior achieves allocative efficiency is if *MR* is equal to *P,* and this equivalency occurs only under competitive conditions. To understand this, we need to reconsider how the firm's profit-maximizing decision is affected by a competitive market.

As a price taker, each firm in a competitive market must accept the market-determined price as a given. It is unable to charge a higher price, since by assumption its product is identical to that of all other firms in the market. Thus, if it were to *raise* price, consumers would demand none of its output and buy from any of the other suppliers. Moreover, the firm has no incentive to *lower* price, since it can sell all it wants at the market-determined price. (Recall that the single firm is small compared to the entire market, so "selling all it wants" means that its output adjustments are, in a relative sense, insignificant.)

Since the competitive firm has no control over prevailing market conditions, it faces a price that is constant. Consequently, each additional unit the firm sells raises its revenue by an amount exactly equal to the price of the good. This outcome translates to an important equality that is unique to competitive markets, namely $P = MR$. Thus, although competitive firms follow the basic profit-maximizing decision rules derived above, the equilibrium outcome is markedly different in that allocative efficiency is automatically assured. This is summarized in the following simple derivation:

π-maximization requires	$MR = MC$
Competitive markets imply:	$P = MR$
Thus, π-maximization for competitive firms requires:	$P = MC$

Now, it should be clear why the competitive *market* equilibrium achieves allocative efficiency—because every firm in that market independently produces where $P = MC$.

**TABLE 2.8   Revenue and Cost Data for a Representative Firm
in the Bottled Mineral Water Market**

Price in Dollars P_e	Quantity q	Total Revenue TR	Marginal Revenue MR	Marginal Cost MC
$2.50	4	$ 10.00	$2.50	$0.50
2.50	12	30.00	2.50	1.00
2.50	20	50.00	2.50	1.50
2.50	28	70.00	2.50	2.00
2.50	36	90.00	2.50	2.50
2.50	44	110.00	2.50	3.00
2.50	52	130.00	2.50	3.50
2.50	60	150.00	2.50	4.00
2.50	68	170.00	2.50	4.50
2.50	76	190.00	2.50	5.00

To illustrate this outcome, Table 2.8 presents selected revenue and cost data for a representative firm in our mineral water market. First, let's confirm that $P = MR$ at all output levels. In accordance with the competitive model, notice that the prices faced by the firm are constant at the market-determined equilibrium price (P_e) of $2.50. The MR values are found by calculating the change in TR divided by the change in q. So, for example, when output is increased from 28 units to 36 units, generating an increase in TR from $70 to $90, $MR = \Delta TR/\Delta q = (\$90 - \$70)/(36 - 28) = \$20/8 = \$2.50$. As this calculation is repeated for all changes in q shown in the table, $MR = \$2.50$ in every case—exactly equal to P_e.

Now, let's examine how the firm chooses a production level that maximizes profit. In accordance with competitive conditions, the MC values shown in the last column of the table are the same as the set of prices associated with the firm's supply schedule. To guide its production decisions, the firm considers the MC of production relative to the MR at each output level. In this case, the profit-maximizing equilibrium output occurs at $q_e = 36$, where $MR = MC = \$2.50$. And since $P = MR$ at all q levels, this decision also assures that $P = MC$, indicating that resources are being allocated to production in an efficient manner.

Two final observations are worth noting. First, be sure to recognize why alternative output decisions would not maximize profit. At any output level *below* q_e, the firm's MR exceeds MC, meaning that its $M\pi$ is greater than zero. Hence, the firm can *increase* π by expanding production. Conversely, at all output levels *above* q_e, its MR is less than MC, meaning its $M\pi$ is less than zero or its π is declining. So, the firm is better off by contracting production. Only at $q = 36$ is $MR = MC$ or $M\pi = 0$, meaning that further additions to π are not possible or that π is at its maximum level.

The second observation is to realize that each of the other 24 firms in the bottled mineral water market would follow this same decision-making process, and each would arrive at the same q_e of 36, since competitive firms are identical. Therefore, the market equilibrium quantity (Q_e) is equal to 900 units—the product of the number of firms in the market, 25, and the firm-level q_e of 36. Notice that this result confirms the equilibrium quantity determined from the market supply and demand model.

Technical Efficiency

technical efficiency
Production decisions that generate maximum output given some stock of resources or equivalently the production of some given output level using a minimum amount of resources.

Another important economic criterion used in market analysis is **technical efficiency.** This refers to production decisions that generate maximum output, given some stock of resources, or (saying the same thing from a slightly different perspective), the production of some given output level using a minimum amount of resources. In the context of the materials balance model, achieving technical efficiency is important to preserving the stock of natural resources and minimizing the subsequent generation of residuals arising from resource use. Furthermore, given the relationship between production and costs, we see that technical efficiency implies that economic costs are minimized when producing a given level of output. When viewed from this cost perspective, it becomes apparent that technical efficiency is an application of the more general cost-effectiveness criterion introduced in the last chapter.

The issue here is to understand that market forces exist to provide for the achievement of technical efficiency. When allowed to function freely, the profit motive acts as an incentive for firms to minimize production costs. But this natural incentive is dampened if something interferes with the price mechanism, such as government regulations or the presence of market power. Because of the potential influence of market imperfections, competitive conditions are used to illustrate technically efficient production. To remain viable, the competitive firm must minimize costs, since it cannot raise price to cover the added expense of inefficient production. Were it to attempt such a strategy, demand for its product would fall to zero, since there are many other firms bringing the same product to market at a lower price. Recognizing how technical efficiency is achieved under such ideal market conditions helps economists determine *why* it is not being met in some other market context. More importantly, the magnitude of a technically inefficient decision can be assessed by comparing the resulting costs to what they *would* be if the market were allowed to operate freely.

Hence, although the competitive model per se is not observed in reality, it is useful as a benchmark against which to evaluate actual market conditions. Indeed, the criteria of allocative efficiency and cost-effectiveness are used frequently in environmental economics to evaluate the extent of environmental damage and to assess policy decisions that attempt to correct the problem. If these criteria are not met, economists assert that society's welfare has been detrimentally affected—an outcome that can be illustrated using measures known as consumer and producer surplus.

Welfare Measures: Consumer Surplus and Producer Surplus

In economics, an important objective is to assess the gains and losses to society associated with any event that alters market price. It turns out that the basic supply and demand model provides the information necessary to perform these types of analyses, using concepts known as **consumer surplus** and **producer surplus.** By comparing these measures both before and after a market disturbance, it is possible to quantify how society has been affected. Both consumer and producer surplus are highly intuitive concepts that follow directly from the derivation of demand and supply. We begin by examining consumer surplus.

Consumer Surplus

consumer surplus
The net benefit accruing to buyers of a good estimated by the excess of what they are willing to pay, the marginal benefit (*MB*) of consumption, over what they must actually pay, the market price (*P*), aggregated over all units of the good purchased.

To gain a sense of the logic of consumer surplus, we start with a general working definition. **Consumer surplus** is a measure of net benefit accruing to buyers of a good, which is estimated by the excess of what they are willing to pay over what they must actually pay aggregated over all units of the good purchased in the market.[11]

Notice that consumer surplus depends on two distinct notions of price— one that measures a *willingness to pay,* and one that measures what *is actually paid.* The series of prices consumers are *willing to pay* for various quantities of a good are those that define the demand curve. And as discussed, each demand price is a measure of the marginal benefit (*MB*) associated with consuming another unit of the good. Conversely, the price that consumers must *actually pay* is the prevailing market price (*P*) determined by *both* demand and supply.

There are two major differences between these prices. First, they have different determinants. The demand price, or *MB,* is determined *solely* by demand, a sort of psychic price based on how consumers value a good. On the other hand, market price arises from the forces of supply and demand and is driven by *both* producer and consumer incentives. Secondly, while there is a whole series of demand prices, there is only one market price charged for *all* units sold. The result? Once the market price is determined, *all* units are sold for that single price—even those for which the demand price is much

---

[11]This definition and the subsequent discussion focus on consumer surplus at the market level of analysis, where it is suited to most applications. However, the concept also applies to a single consumer and the corresponding individual demand curve.

FIGURE 2.6

Consumer surplus in the competitive market for bottled mineral water

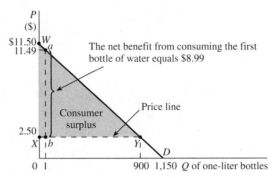

For the first bottle of mineral water, consumers' demand price is $11.49, but the market-determined price is only $2.50, so they receive a net benefit from this first bottle of water equal to $11.49 − $2.50 = $8.99, shown as the vertical distance *ab*. Aggregating this net benefit over all units of water consumed yields the measure of consumer surplus shown as the triangular area *WXY*. The dollar value of this area is $(1/2 \cdot 900 \cdot \$9.00) = \$4,050$.

higher. Hence, consumers receive a *surplus benefit* for every unit purchased whose demand price exceeds the market price.

To graphically illustrate consumer surplus, Figure 2.6 reproduces the market demand for mineral water derived previously. Added to the diagram is a reference price line drawn horizontally at the equilibrium price level of $2.50. Notice that for every output level up *to* the equilibrium quantity of 900, the demand price is higher than the market price. So, each unit purchased yields consumers a surplus benefit over and above what they had to pay for. For example, for the first bottle of mineral water, consumers are willing to pay a price of $11.49 based on the market inverse demand function.[12] But they actually have to pay only $2.50. Thus, they receive a net benefit from consuming the first unit of the good equal to the excess of $11.49 over $2.50, or $8.99. Geometrically, this amount is measured as the vertical distance from the demand curve to the price line at $Q = 1$, shown in Figure 2.6 as distance *ab*.

Since consumers receive a net benefit for every unit purchased up to the equilibrium point, this value must be aggregated over all units of the good consumed to derive the measure of **consumer surplus.** Graphically, this is represented as the series of vertical distances bounded by the demand curve and the price line, which is simply the triangular area above the price line and below the demand curve, up to the equilibrium point. In Figure 2.6, the consumer surplus for mineral water is the area labeled *WXY*. This makes sense, since the entire area under the demand curve is a measure of total benefit from consumption, (i.e., the aggregation of the marginal benefit from each unit of the good), and the rectangular area under the price line is the total expenditure

---

[12]The price of $11.49 is found by substituting $Q_d = 1$ into the inverse demand function, $P = -0.01Q_d + 11.5$.

on the commodity. Thus, the difference between the two is the net benefit to the consumer.

The dollar value of consumer surplus can be found by calculating the area of the triangle that represents it in the graphical model, using the familiar formula, Area = ½ · Base · Height. Returning to Figure 2.6, the base of the *WXY* triangle is the horizontal distance from the vertical axis to the equilibrium quantity, or 900. The height is $9.00, which is the difference between the vertical intercept of the demand curve, $11.50, and the price line, $2.50. Thus, the dollar value of consumer surplus in this market is ½ · 900 · $9.00 = $4,050.

It is important to recognize that the applicability of consumer surplus stems from the fact that its magnitude is related to equilibrium price and quantity. So, any disturbance to market equilibrium will change the size of consumer surplus. Since this surplus is a measure of consumer benefit, the change can be used to assess the associated gain or loss to consumer welfare.

Producer Surplus

producer surplus
The gain accruing to sellers of a good estimated by the excess of the market price (*P*) of a product over the marginal cost (*MC*) to produce it, aggregated over all units sold.

On the supply side of the market, the comparable measure of welfare is **producer surplus.** It is a measure of gain accruing to sellers that is estimated by the excess of the market price (*P*) of a product over the marginal cost (*MC*) to produce it, aggregated over all units sold.[13] Notice that producer surplus depends critically on two familiar concepts, market price (*P*) and the marginal cost (*MC*) of production.

Based on our discussion of supply decisions, we know that firms must charge a price for their product that covers *MC*. Further, we know that the competitive market supply curve is the horizontal sum of all firms' *MC* curves. Therefore, since market price is determined by the intersection of market supply and demand, it must be the case that *P* = *MC* at a competitive equilibrium. However, at every output level below equilibrium, *MC* is *lower* than *P*. So, firms are actually willing to supply these smaller quantities at prices below what is dictated by the market. The price that firms are "willing to accept" for each output level is their supply price, and it is this price that is reflected in the *MC* curve. Thus, at each quantity below equilibrium, firms accrue a net gain measured by the excess of *P* over *MC*.

This net gain is illustrated in Figure 2.7. The diagram shows the competitive market supply for mineral water, which is also the *MC* curve, and a reference line drawn horizontally at the equilibrium price of $2.50. For every unit of output supplied up *to* the equilibrium point at 900 units, producers receive a surplus equal to the excess of *P* over *MC*. For example, for the first unit of mineral water produced, the *MC* is $0.2525 based on the market supply

---

[13]Just as in the discussion of consumer surplus, producer surplus is defined here for the market level of analysis. It is, however, analogously applicable to the single firm.

FIGURE 2.7

*Producer surplus in
the competitive market
for bottled mineral
water*

For the first bottle of mineral water produced, the *MC* is $0.2525 based on an evaluation of the
market supply function at $Q_s = 1$. But since firms can sell this bottle at a price of $2.50, they
receive a net gain of $2.50 − $0.2525, or $2.2475, shown as the vertical distance *cd*. Aggregating
this gain over all units sold yields the measure of producer surplus represented by the triangular
area *XYZ*. The dollar value of this area is $(1/2 \cdot 900 \cdot \$2.25) = \$1,012.50$.

function.[14] But firms can sell this first bottle at the market-determined price
of $2.50. Thus, the net gain associated with this unit of output is the excess
of $2.50 over $0.2525, or $2.2475. Geometrically, this is the vertical distance
from the supply curve to the price line at $Q = 1$, labeled as distance *cd* in
Figure 2.7.

Just as on the demand side of the market, this net gain must be aggregated
over all units sold up to the equilibrium quantity to find the measure of producer surplus. Graphically, this is the sum of all the vertical distances between
the *MC* curve and the price line, or simply the triangular area bounded by the
MC curve and the price line, up to the equilibrium point. In Figure 2.7, this
is shown as the area labeled *XYZ*.

Using the same method as described for consumer surplus, the dollar value
of producer surplus can be found by calculating its representative triangular
area depicted in the graphical model. Referring to Figure 2.7, the base of *XYZ*
has a magnitude of 900, and its height is $2.25, found as the difference be-
tween the price line at $2.50 and the vertical intercept of the supply curve,
$0.25. Thus, producer surplus at equilibrium in the mineral water market is
$\frac{1}{2} \cdot 900 \cdot \$2.25 = \$1,012.50$. Notice that the magnitude of producer surplus,
just like consumer surplus, is based upon equilibrium price and quantity.
Hence, any market disturbance will change its value and thus provide a way
to assess any associated welfare gain or loss to firms.

---

[14]The supply price or *MC* of producing the first unit of output is found by evaluating the
market supply function at $Q_s = 1$, or $MC = 0.0025(1) + 0.25 = \$0.2525$.

Society's Welfare: Sum of Consumer and Producer Surplus

To assess the overall welfare of society, economists use the *sum* of consumer and producer surplus to capture the gains accruing to both sides of the market. Applying this concept to the market for bottled mineral water, we see that society enjoys a surplus valued at $4,050 + $1,012.50, or $5,062.50. It turns out that because this surplus is based on a competitive equilibrium, its value is maximized. This is so because of the efficient allocation of resources that characterizes a competitive market. Put another way, it is not possible to reallocate resources to improve society's welfare. By default, this implies that any market outcome that does not meet the criterion of allocative efficiency has a negative effect on society's well-being. In such an instance, the loss can be monetized by comparing the resulting value of the sum of consumer and producer surplus to what it *would* be if allocative efficiency were achieved.

Measuring Welfare Changes

By way of illustration, let's consider a hypothetical policy initiative in the mineral water market that forces price above *MC* up to $6.50 per unit. To measure the effect on society's welfare, we need to compare the post-policy level of consumer and producer surplus to the benchmark competitive level of $5,062.50. We begin by reproducing the model of the mineral water market in Figure 2.8, adding to the diagram the policy price and quantity of $6.50 and 500 respectively.[15] Capital letters A through F have been added to facilitate our discussion. The benchmark level of consumer surplus is represented in this diagram by the area (A+B+C) and producer surplus by the area (D+E+F).

Now, we determine the comparable surplus values under the policy-determined price and quantity. At the $6.50 price level, consumer surplus is reduced to the triangular area A valued at $1,250. This new value is $2,800 *lower* than it was before the policy, so we know that the policy generates a net *loss* to consumers. The producer surplus at the $6.50 price level is area (B+D+F) valued at $2,812.50, found by summing the area of the rectangle (B+D) and the area of the triangle (F). Since this magnitude is $1,800 *higher* than the original surplus, we see that producers enjoy a net *gain* as a result of the policy.

Finally, consider the overall effect. The total surplus under the new policy is $1,250 + $2,812.50, or $4,062.50, which is $1,000 less than the original value. Although producers enjoy a net gain of $1,800, it is outweighed by the loss to consumers of $2,800. Hence, the new pricing policy causes a decline

---

[15]At a price of $6.50, $Q_s > Q_d$, so the quantity exchanged in the market is Q_d. Thus, quantity is found by substituting $6.50 into the demand equation as follows: $Q_d = -100(6.50) + 1,150 = 500$.

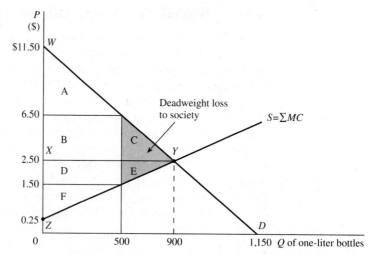

FIGURE 2.8

Deadweight loss to society under a pricing regulation in the bottled mineral water market

At the allocatively efficient equilibrium, area (A+B+C) is the consumer surplus valued at $4,050, and area (D+E+F) is the producer surplus valued at $1,012.50, for a total welfare measure of $5,062.50. Under a pricing policy that sets price at $6.50, consumer surplus falls to $1,250, shown as area (A), producer surplus increases to $2,812.50, shown as area (B+D+F), for a new total welfare measure of $4,062.50. Consumers incur a net loss of −(B+C) valued at $2,800, while producers gain +(B−E) valued at $1,800, Thus, as a result of this policy, there is a **deadweight loss to society** of −(C+E) valued at $1,000.

in society's welfare of $1,000. This change can be confirmed geometrically by looking at the areas representing surplus before and after the policy:

Change in consumer surplus: (A) − (A+B+C)   = −(B+C)

+ Change in producer surplus: (B+D+F) − (D+E+F)   = +(B−E)

Net loss to society: = −(C+E)

deadweight loss to society

The net loss of consumer and producer surplus due to some allocatively inefficient market condition.

Area (C+E), valued at $1,000, is referred to as the **deadweight loss to society** because it was once a part of the surplus accruing to producers and consumers under allocatively efficient conditions, but as a result of the policy is lost or unaccounted for. Notice that area B, while a loss to consumers, is a gain to firms. Thus, it is redistributed from one market sector to another. While some may view this outcome as unfair, the relevant point is that such transfers are not inefficient, since the amount is captured somewhere within the market system. What *is* problematic is that the policy generates a loss to society as a whole because it forces *P* above *MC*, violating the allocative efficiency criterion.

Conclusions

Understanding the fundamentals of how markets operate is an important basis for the study of environmental economics. To that end, we have limited our discussion in this chapter to the circular flow model—reviewing the mechanics of supply and demand, the signaling mechanism of price, and the importance of marginal analysis—all within the context of a classical competitive market system. Competitive markets establish a benchmark from which economists assess the effects of market failures and market disturbances, both of which are of critical importance to environmental economics. From a practical perspective, we can assess the effects of environmental pollution or any policy initiative using allocative efficiency as a criterion. Furthermore, these effects can be measured by quantifying the associated changes in consumer and producer surplus.

It is also the case that the competitive model illustrates how an economic system operates in the absence of any condition that impedes natural market forces. Recognizing how a fully functioning market performs is necessary to understanding the economic perception of environmental pollution as a market failure—the subject of our next chapter. To make this transition, we will expand our analysis to the full materials balance model, allowing for the interdependence of the circular flow with the natural environment. Using the modeling tools shown in this chapter and expanding on the concepts of marginal benefits and costs, we will develop more elaborate market models that explicitly account for this interdependence. These models will show *how* and *why* the market fails to correct environmental damage, which in turn will suggest approaches to finding effective policy solutions.

Summary

- In economic analysis, the concept of a market refers to the interaction between consumers and producers for the purpose of executing the exchange of a well-defined commodity.
- A competitive market model is characterized by a large number of independent buyers and sellers who cannot control market price, a homogeneous product, the absence of entry barriers, perfect information, and perfect mobility of resources.
- Demand is specified as a relationship between quantity demanded (Q_d) and price (P), holding constant all other factors that may influence this decision, such as consumer wealth and income, prices of related goods, preferences, and price expectations. The Law of Demand states that there is an inverse relationship between quantity demanded and price, *c.p.*
- The market demand for a private good is found by horizontally summing all individual demand data to determine aggregate quantity demanded at each and every price.
- Supply is specified as a relationship between quantity supplied (Q_s) and price (P), holding constant all other supply determinants such as production technology, input prices, taxes and subsidies, and price expectations. The Law of Supply states that there is a direct relationship between quantity supplied and price, *c.p.*
- The market supply for a private good is derived by summing all individual supply curves horizontally to determine aggregate quantity supplied at each and every price.

- Market equilibrium is determined by the simultaneous forces of supply and demand. The equilibrium or market-clearing price (P_e) is the price at which $Q_d = Q_s$. If the prevailing price is above (below) its equilibrium level, there is an excess supply (demand) of the commodity. The resulting surplus (shortage) will put pressure on the prevailing price to fall (rise) toward its equilibrium level.
- Allocative efficiency requires that the additional value society places on another unit of a good is precisely equivalent to what society must give up in scarce resources to produce it. This criterion is met at the market level under competitive conditions.
- All profit(π)-maximizing firms continue to expand (contract) output as long as the additional revenue (MR) from doing so is greater (lower) than the associated increase in costs (MC). The π-maximizing level of output occurs where $MR = MC$, or where marginal profit ($M\pi$) = 0.
- Competitive firms are price takers, accepting the market-determined price as a given. This means that price (P) is exactly equal to marginal revenue (MR). As a result, the π-maximizing output level for competitive firms at $MR = MC$ is also the point where $P = MC$, the condition signifying allocative efficiency.
- Technical efficiency arises when the maximum amount of output is produced from some fixed stock of resources. It is an application of the more general criterion known as cost-effectiveness. Competitive firms must be technically efficient to remain viable in the market, since they cannot raise price to cover the added costs of inefficient production.
- Consumer surplus is a measure of the net benefit accruing to buyers measured as the excess of what they are willing to pay over what they must actually pay, aggregated over all units bought in the market.
- Producer surplus measures the net gain accruing to sellers estimated by the excess of the market price of a product over the MC to produce it, aggregated over all units sold.
- Economists use the sum of consumer and producer surplus to assess the overall welfare of society. At a competitive equilibrium these surpluses are maximized because resources are being allocated efficiently. Hence, any market outcome that does not meet the criterion of allocative efficiency has a negative effect on society's well-being. The associated deadweight loss to society can be monetized by comparing the resulting value of consumer and producer surplus to what it *would* be if allocative efficiency were achieved.

Key Concepts

market	market demand
supply	Law of Supply
demand	total cost (TC)
private good	marginal cost (MC)
willingness to pay	supply price
demand price	market supply
marginal benefit (MB)	equilibrium price (P_e)
Law of Demand	equilibrium quantity (Q_e)

<table>
<tr><td>disequilibrium</td><td>technical efficiency</td></tr>
<tr><td>excess demand or shortage</td><td>marginal revenue (MR)</td></tr>
<tr><td>excess supply or surplus</td><td>marginal profit (Mπ)</td></tr>
<tr><td>allocative efficiency</td><td>consumer surplus</td></tr>
<tr><td>total profit (π)</td><td>producer surplus</td></tr>
<tr><td>total revenue (TR)</td><td>deadweight loss to society</td></tr>
</table>

Review Questions

1. Suppose in a given market, the following equations describe market demand and market supply: $Q_d = 200 - 4P$ and $Q_s = 100$.
   a. Algebraically find equilibrium price and quantity and support your answer graphically.
   b. What is unusual about this market? Give an example of a good or service that might be characterized by this unusual market attribute.

2. Recently, the Food and Drug Administration proposed tougher labeling standards for bottled water. Until now, bottlers could sell regular tap water under a bottled water label. As a matter of fact, the FDA estimates that approximately 25 percent of the current supply of bottled water is nothing more than ordinary tap water. Assume that these tougher standards are successful in eliminating this 25 percent of current supply. If market demand is unaffected, what directional impact would this labeling change have on the equilibrium price and quantity for bottled water? Support your answer with a graphical model.

3. Reconsider the implications of the change in labeling standards discussed in question 2 in the context of the hypothetical market for bottled water modeled in the text. Recall that the market demand and market supply equations are:

   $$Q_d = -100P + 1,150; \quad Q_s = 400P - 100;$$

   where

   $$P_e = \$2.50; \text{ and } Q_e = 900.$$

   Now, suppose the change in standards results in a new market supply of $Q_s' = 400P - 350$, with no change in market demand.
   a. Determine the new P_e' and Q_e' for bottled water. Do your results agree with your intuitive answer to question 2?
   b. Graphically illustrate the market for bottled water before and after the change in labeling standards. Be sure to label all relevant points.
   c. Compare the values of consumer and producer surplus before and after the change in labeling standards. Is this result expected? Why or why not?

4. a. Describe a specific real-world government policy that creates a market surplus. Be sure to carefully define the relevant market.
   b. Explain the efficiency implications of such a policy. Be specific.
   c. In the instance you have described, what is the government's motivation for intervening in the market in this way?

Additional Readings

Byrns, Ralph T. and Gerald W. Stone. *Microeconomics.* New York: Harper Collins Publishers, 1992.

Denzau, Arthur. *Microeconomic Analysis: Markets and Dynamics.* Homewood, Ill.: Richard D. Irwin, Inc., 1992.

Friedman, Milton. *Capitalism and Freedom.* Chicago: University of Chicago Press, 1962.

Heilbroner, Robert L. *The Worldly Philosophers.* New York: Simon and Schuster, 1980.

Hyman, David. *Microeconomics.* Homewood, Ill.: Richard D. Irwin, Inc., 1992.

3

MODELING MARKET FAILURE

According to the circular flow model, free markets provide desired goods and services to the market, resolve shortages and surpluses, and eliminate inefficiency through the pricing mechanism—all without government intervention. This is quite a remarkable result, given that consumers and producers are not motivated by altruistic goals but rather are driven by their own self-interest. As first described through Adam Smith's metaphor, the "invisible hand," this market outcome comes about as if consumers and firms are somehow guided to make decisions that ultimately enhance the well-being of all of society.[1] Recognizing the efficiency and social welfare implications of a competitive equilibrium underscores what is at stake whenever something impedes the market process that underlies it. A case in point is the persistence of environmental pollution.

When we consider the circular flow in the fuller context of the materials balance model, we become aware of how economic activity gives rise to residuals that can damage natural resources as they are released to nature. But we need to look further to understand the economics of why pollution *persists* absent any third-party intervention. Why is the market unable to respond to environmental pollution, or can it?

The most immediate answer is that pollution is a type of **market failure** that distorts the classical market outcome. From an economic perspective, environmental problems persist because they implicitly violate the underlying assumptions of a fully functioning market. Thus, the incentive mechanisms that normally achieve an efficient solution to market problems are unable to perform their function, and government has to intervene. However, if the concept of market failure is well understood, market incentives can be put to work by government in implementing environmental policy solutions. Conceptually, the idea is to ferret out the conditions that cause the pricing system to

---

[1]Smith (1937), p. 423, (originally published in 1776).

break down, make the necessary adjustments to the underlying conditions, and then let the power of the market work toward an ultimate resolution. Of course, implementing this process in practice can be fairly complex. Nonetheless, the important point is that market forces and the price system *can* be utilized to achieve greater efficiency once the market failure is identified and understood.

To that end, this chapter provides the requisite analytical tools for understanding market failure in the context of environmental problems. The discussion centers around the development of two economic models. The first of these is based on the public goods characteristics of environmental quality. The second uses what is known as externality theory to show how market incentives fail to capture the effects of pollution associated with production or consumption. Finally, the two models are linked together through an in-depth discussion of property rights and their role in environmental market failures.

Environmental Problems: A Market Failure

market failure
The result of an inefficient market condition such as imperfect competition, public goods, imperfect information, nonexistence of markets, and externalities.

Classical microeconomic theory predicts an efficient outcome given certain critical assumptions about pricing, product definition, cost conditions, and entry barriers. If any of these assumptions fails to hold, market mechanisms cannot operate freely. Depending on which assumption or set of assumptions is violated, the result will be any one of a number of inefficient market conditions, collectively termed **market failures.** These include imperfect competition, public goods, imperfect information, nonexistence of markets, and externalities. For example, if we relax the assumption of freedom of entry in the competitive market model, some degree of market power is allowed to develop, which in turn causes the market process to break down. As it does, society's welfare declines, and resources are allocated inefficiently.

Economists model environmental problems as market failures using either the theory of public goods or the theory of externalities. Each model is distinguished by how the relevant market is defined.

- If the market is defined as ''environmental quality,'' then the source of the market failure is that environmental quality is a **public good.**
- If the market is defined in terms of the good whose production or consumption generates environmental damage, then the market failure is due to the presence of an **externality.**

While each of these models suggests a different set of solutions to the problem, the theories are not totally unrelated. And it turns out that in the context of environmental problems, both are exacerbated by a third type of market failure, **imperfect information.** We begin by analyzing the market failure aspect of public goods.

Environmental Quality: A Public Good

public good
A commodity that is nonrival in consumption and yields benefits that are nonexcludable.

Economists distinguish public goods from private goods by examining their inherent characteristics—*not* by whether they are publicly or privately provided.[2] A **public good,** or more technically a *pure* public good, is one that possesses the following two characteristics: (1) the good is **nonrival** in consumption, and (2) the benefits of the good are **nonexcludable.**[3] At the other extreme is a pure private good, which is characterized by both rivalness and excludability. Recall that in the last chapter, one of the assumptions underlying the market model was that the commodity being exchanged was a private good.

Characteristics of Public Goods

nonrivalness
The characteristic of indivisible benefits of consumption such that one person's consumption of a good does not preclude that of another.

Nonrivalness refers to the notion that the benefits associated with consumption are *indivisible,* meaning when the good is consumed by one individual, another person is not prevented from consuming it at the same time. For example, consider the network television broadcast of the NBA championship finals. The benefits to the existing television audience are completely unaffected when another individual tunes in to view the broadcast. Contrast this result with what occurs when a private good is consumed, such as a personal computer. Once someone is using the computer, that consumption activity prohibits another person from using it at the same time.

nonexcludability
The characteristic that makes it impossible (or prohibitively costly in a less strict sense) to prevent others from sharing in the benefits of a good's consumption.

Nonexcludability means that preventing others from sharing in the benefits of a good's consumption is not possible (or prohibitively costly in a less strict sense). An example of a good with this characteristic is the provision of a jogging path in a local community. It would be virtually impossible to ration the use of the path only to a select group of runners. In contrast, consider the inherent excludability of a conventional private good such as hotel lodging. Exclusive rationing of hotel services to the consumer paying for them is easily accomplished, and the associated benefits accrue solely to that single consumer.

Although nonrivalness and nonexcludability may *seem* similar, they are not identical. A good way to distinguish them is as follows. Nonrivalness means that rationing of the good is not *desirable,* while nonexcludability means rationing of the good is not *feasible.*[4] In fact, it is possible for a good to possess one of these attributes but not the other. Reconsider the examples for each characteristic given above. While a televised NBA game is a nonrival good, it can be made excludable by broadcasting it via a cable network only to subscribers who have paid for the NBA telecast and by scrambling the signal to everyone else. Likewise, provision of the jogging path, while nonexcludable

---

[2]For a good discussion of this distinction, see Rosen (1995), Chapter 5.
[3]Much of the important work in the theory of public goods is credited to Samuelson (1954), (1955), and (1958).
[4]Stiglitz (1988), pp. 119–23.

absent prohibitively high costs, does not possess the nonrivalry attribute. Use of the path by more and more runners would lead to congestion, which would affect every consumer of the jogging path.

Two classic examples of public goods cited consistently in the literature are a lighthouse and national defense. Contemplate the services provided by these goods to see that the benefits of each are both nonrival and nonexcludable. A more contemporary and, from our perspective, more relevant example of a public good is environmental quality.[5] Just like the lighthouse, cleaner air, for example, is both nonexcludable and indivisible. Consider the futility of trying to restrict the benefits of air pollution abatement to a single individual. It's unreasonable to think that others could be excluded from the consumption of a cleaner air supply just because another person has paid for it. Moreover, once the air is made cleaner for one person, others could simultaneously enjoy the benefits of breathing more healthy air.

So, what then is the problem? Having accepted the assertion that environmental quality is a public good, we still need to explain why this, or any public good for that matter, is a market failure. To do this, we need to develop an economic model of a public good.

Modeling a Public Goods Market for Environmental Quality

Public goods generate a market failure because the nonrivalness and nonexcludability characteristics prevent natural market incentives from yielding an allocatively efficient outcome. To illustrate this assertion, we reintroduce the basic supply and demand model but redefine the market as the public good, air quality.[6] It turns out that by changing the market definition from a private to a public good, the conventional derivation of market demand is no longer viable. And, this modeling dilemma is at the root of the public goods problem.

Allocative Efficiency in the Market for a Public Good

Just as in the private goods case, achieving an allocatively efficient equilibrium in a public goods market depends upon the existence of well-defined supply and demand functions. We can develop these functions for air quality by first adjusting the market definition so that output can be quantified. Air quality can be defined as "an acceptable level of pollution abatement," which

---

[5]Alternatively, we could define environmental pollution as a public "bad."

[6]To direct attention solely to the public goods aspect of the model, we continue to assume competitive markets. This prevents confounding the market failure of public goods with that of imperfect competition. Further, the assumption of competitive markets allows the market supply curve to be modeled as the horizontal sum of all producers' marginal cost curves, just as was done for the private goods case in the previous chapter.

TABLE 3.1   **Hypothetical Supply Data in the Market for Air Quality Measured as a Percentage of Sulfur Dioxide (SO_2) Abatement per Year**

Quantity Supplied Q_s *(% of SO_2 abatement)*	*Market Supply Price* $P = 4 + 0.75Q_s$ *($ millions)*
0	4.00
5	7.75
10	11.50
15	15.25
20	19.00
25	22.75
30	26.50

we assume for discussion purposes is some percentage reduction in sulfur dioxide (SO_2) emissions per volume of air.

Market Supply for Air Quality.   Although the market supply of a public good often represents government's decisions about production as opposed to those of privately motivated firms, the general derivation of the supply function is analogous to what we developed in the previous chapter for a private good. We begin by positing that there is some number of hypothetical producers, each of which is willing and able to supply various reductions in SO_2 at different price levels, *c.p.* The aggregation of all these production decisions gives rise to market supply, which we assume is represented by the data given in Table 3.1. Price (P) is measured in millions of dollars, and quantity supplied (Q_s) is measured as a percentage of SO_2 abatement. The algebraic counterpart for these data is:

$$\text{Market supply: } P = 4 + 0.75Q_s.$$

Market Demand for Air Quality.   On the demand side of the market, the model for a public good is quite different than that for a private commodity. Recall from the previous chapter that the market demand for a private good is found by *horizontally* summing the demands of individual consumers. This procedure acknowledges that each consumer can choose the quantity that maximizes utility, based upon income, tastes, and so on. It is as if each consumer were asked: "What *quantity* of this good would you consume at each of the following prices?" But this question is not relevant to the demand for a public good because once such a commodity is provided, it is available at the *same quantity* to all consumers—a direct consequence of the nonrivalness characteristic. How then *is* market demand determined for a public good if quantity is not a decision variable?

TABLE 3.2   Hypothetical Demand Data in the Public Goods Market for Air Quality Measured as a Percentage of Sulfur Dioxide (SO_2) Abatement per Year

Quantity Demanded Q_d (% of SO_2 abatement)	Consumer 1's WTP $p_1 = 10 - 0.1Q_d$ ($)	Consumer 2's WTP $p_2 = 15 - 0.2Q_d$ ($)	Combined Demand Price for Consumers 1 and 2 $p_1 + p_2 = 25 - 0.3Q_d$ ($)
0	$10.00	$15.00	$25.00
5	9.50	14.00	23.50
10	9.00	13.00	22.00
15	8.50	12.00	20.50
20	8.00	11.00	19.00
25	7.50	10.00	17.50
30	7.00	9.00	16.00

WTP = Willingness to pay.

The key is to recognize that the *demand price* for a public good is variable, even though the quantity is not. So, the relevant question in deriving this demand must be: "What *price* would you be willing to pay for each of the following quantities?" In theory, each consumer should express a unique **"willingness to pay (WTP)"** for the public good based on the benefits each expects to derive from consumption. The **market demand for a public good** is the aggregate demand for all viable consumers in the market. It is derived by summing each individual demand *vertically* to determine the market price, $(P = \Sigma p)$, at each and every possible market quantity (Q), *c.p.*

market demand for a public good
The aggregate demand of all viable consumers in the market; derived by summing each individual demand *vertically* to determine the market price, $(P = \Sigma p)$, at each and every possible market quantity (Q), *c.p.*

To illustrate this procedure in the market for SO_2 abatement, we initially focus on only two consumers. The scenario is that we conduct a survey, asking the two consumers how much each would be willing to pay each year for various amounts of SO_2 abatement, *c.p.* The results of this hypothetical inquiry are given in Table 3.2. The quantity demanded (Q_d) column shows a selection of possible abatement levels to be provided to all consumers. The individual demand prices or WTP responses are labeled p_1 and p_2 for Consumer 1 and Consumer 2, respectively. These responses are based upon the following demand equations, which are expressed in inverse form to signify that price is the decision variable:

$$\text{Demand for Consumer 1: } p_1 = 10 - 0.1Q_d$$
$$\text{Demand for Consumer 2: } p_2 = 15 - 0.2Q_d$$

Notice that each consumer's price, or WTP, response for a given Q_d is unique. For example, for a 5 percent reduction in SO_2, Consumer 1 is willing to pay $9.50 per year, while Consumer 2 is willing to pay $14.00 per year. These responses are different because each consumer is distinguished by a unique level of such characteristics as income, wealth, expectations, and preferences. In this context, we might expect the two consumers to have distinct

FIGURE 3.1

*Combined demand of
two consumers for
air quality (SO₂
abatement)*

The demand curve labeled $(d_1 + d_2)$ represents the combined consumption decisions of two hypothetical consumers for air quality. For any given quantity on this curve, the corresponding price is equal to the vertical sum of the individual price responses for that same quantity as given on d_1 and d_2.

preferences for air quality and even disparate views about the associated benefits. For example, perhaps Consumer 2's WTP is higher because he or she is a member of an environmental group and is more aware of the benefits of cleaner air.

To find the combined demand for air quality, the individual price responses at each quantity level are simply added together. The far right column of Table 3.2 shows the result of this aggregation process. The algebraic counterpart is found by summing each pair of corresponding terms on the right-hand side of each equation:

	Demand for Consumer 1:	p_1	$= 10 - 0.1Q_d$
+	Demand for Consumer 2:	p_2	$= 15 - 0.2Q_d$
	Demand for Consumers 1 and 2:	$p_1 + p_2$	$= 25 - 0.3Q_d$

The graphical model is shown in Figure 3.1. For any given quantity on the combined demand curve, $(d_1 + d_2)$, the corresponding measure of price is equal to the vertical sum of the individual price responses for that same quantity based on the individual demand curves, d_1 and d_2.

Having developed the general procedure, we can now bring the demand relationship up to the market level by assuming that the combined demand of the two consumers actually represents the decisions of 1 million consumers. Notice that this conversion means that price (P) is now denominated in millions of dollars, which corresponds to the scale of the market supply function. More formally, the market demand function is specified as:

Market Demand: $P = 25 - 0.3Q_d$,

where P is measured in millions of dollars.

TABLE 3.3   Hypothetical Market Demand and Market Supply Data for Air Quality Measured as a Percentage of Sulfur Dioxide (SO$_2$) Abatement per Year

Quantity Q (% of SO$_2$ abatement)	Market Demand Price $P = 25 - 0.3Q_d$ ($ millions)	Market Supply Price $P = 4 + 0.75Q_s$ ($ millions)
0	25.00	4.00
5	23.50	7.75
10	22.00	11.50
15	20.50	15.25
20	19.00	19.00
25	17.50	22.75
30	16.00	26.50

Equilibrium in the Air Quality Market.   To find equilibrium in the market for SO$_2$ abatement, we consider supply and demand simultaneously. Assuming competitive conditions, the resulting equilibrium price (P_e) and quantity (Q_e) signify an allocatively efficient solution. To begin, we combine the market demand and market supply data in Table 3.3. We observe that Q_e is equal to 20 percent, the point where both the supply price and demand price are equal to $19 million, P_e. This result also can be found algebraically by solving the equations for market supply and demand simultaneously.[7] The corresponding graphical model is shown in Figure 3.2, where the intersection of market supply (S) and market demand (D) curves identifies P_e and Q_e.

Assessing the Implications

Determining P_e and Q_e for the abatement of any kind of pollution is a significant result. As will become apparent in upcoming chapters, it is this result to which economists refer when addressing market-based solutions to environmental pollution. Notice in Figure 3.2 that Q_e represents the efficient or optimal level of *abatement* measured from *left to right* and implicitly the optimal level of *air pollution* measured from *right to left*. And, as the model suggests, this optimal level is not necessarily zero.[8] Why is the efficient level of air pollution generally some positive value? Because there are opportunity costs associated with cleaning up the atmosphere, and these costs measured at the margin are rising.

From a general perspective, abating at the 100 percent level to reduce environmental pollution all the way to zero involves prohibitive opportunity

---

[7]Verify this assertion by setting the market demand equation, $P = 25 - 0.3Q_d$, equal to the market supply equation, $P = 4 + 0.75Q_s$, recognizing that $Q_s = Q_d$ at equilibrium.

[8]Of course, a zero optimal level of pollution is *possible* under certain conditions, though this is the exception rather than the rule.

FIGURE 3.2

*Market supply and
market demand for
air quality (SO$_2$
abatement)*

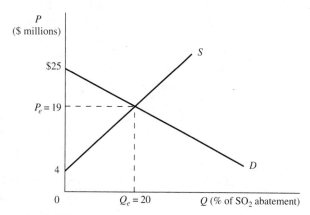

Assuming the market for SO$_2$ abatement is competitive, equilibrium price P_e of $19 million
and equilibrium quantity Q_e equal to 20 percent abatement represent an allocatively efficient
solution. Q_e represents the optimal level of *abatement* measured from *left to right* and
implicitly the optimal level of *air pollution* measured from *right to left*. Notice that the
optimal level of pollution is not zero.

costs. These include the forgone production and consumption of any good
generating even the smallest amount of pollution. Given our present technology, a zero-pollution world would be one without electricity, advanced
transportation systems, most mass-produced agricultural products, and virtually all manufactured products. Thus, it makes little practical sense to argue
for the elimination of all pollution in our environment. Economists have devoted years of research to conveying this point to government officials.[9] Only
recently have the results of these efforts begun to be incorporated into policy
formulation.

Accepting the outcome of a nonzero efficient level of pollution is important to policy analysis in environmental economics—an assertion that will be
well supported in upcoming chapters. For now, we need to address the market
failure of the public goods market we have developed.

Understanding the Market Failure of Public Goods Markets

As we stated at the outset, the achievement of an allocatively efficient outcome
in a public goods market depends upon the identification of well-defined
demand and supply functions. Although we developed both functions for our
hypothetical market for air quality, market demand was identified only because
we implicitly made one critical assumption—that consumers would reveal

---

[9]One of the classic research papers that discusses the economic view of pollution is Ruff
(1970).

their willingness to pay (WTP) for SO_2 abatement. But without some form of third-party intervention, the nonexcludability of this or any public good makes it difficult if not impossible to ascertain such information. And if consumers' WTP responses are unknown, market demand cannot be identified and an efficient outcome cannot be obtained. It is precisely the inability of free markets to capture the WTP for air quality or for any public good that explains why the market fails.

Consider the underlying meaning of demand in the context of private versus public goods. In general, market demand must capture the aggregate value of the expected benefits associated with consumption. If the good is private—that is, excludable—its associated benefits can be obtained only through purchase. Thus, the consumer's WTP for a private good is a suitable proxy for the measure of anticipated marginal benefits of consumption. However, in the case of a public good that is nonexcludable, the consumer can share in its consumption even when it is purchased by someone else. Hence, there is no market incentive for a rational consumer to volunteer a WTP for something he or she can consume without ever having to pay for it. Formally, this problem is referred to as **nonrevelation of preferences,** which in turn is due to the more basic dilemma of **free-ridership.** The rational consumer astutely recognizes that the benefits of a public good are accessible simply by allowing someone else to purchase it. So, the consumer becomes a "free-rider." Individual preferences about the public good remain undisclosed, and thus market demand is undefined. When the public good is environmental quality, the unfortunate consequence is often serious ecological damage. A case in point is the pollution that threatens Boston Harbor discussed in Application 3.1.

If we relax the conventional assumption of perfect information, adding more realism to the model, the identification of market demand becomes even more obscure. In many public goods markets, consumers are not fully aware of the benefits associated with consumption. This is certainly the case for environmental quality. Most people are not knowledgeable about the health, recreational, and aesthetic benefits associated with pollution abatement.[10] So, even if consumers could somehow be induced to honestly express their WTP for a cleaner environment, it is highly likely that the resulting demand price would underestimate the true benefits. This added complication is due to **imperfect information**—another source of market failure.

What can be concluded from all of this? As we initially claimed, natural market forces alone cannot provide an allocatively efficient level of a public good. This realization helps to explain what we observe in public goods mar-

nonrevelation of preferences
Arises if there is no market incentive for a rational consumer to volunteer a willingness to pay for something he or she can consume without having to pay for it.

free-ridership
Occurs when a rational consumer recognizes that the benefits of a public good are accessible by allowing someone else to purchase it.

---

[10]In fact, a critical issue in environmental economics is assessing and measuring the benefits of pollution abatement, a subject that will be investigated fully in subsequent chapters.

Application 3.1

Boston Harbor: The Changing Condition of an Environmental Public Good

During the 1988 presidential campaign, the environmental degradation of Boston Harbor became a highly charged political issue. Wanting to promote an image as the prospective "environmental president," then Vice President Bush focused the nation's attention on what he called the "dirtiest harbor in America." In retrospect, this was apparently an effective way to malign the image of his Democratic opponent, Michael Dukakis, then governor of Massachusetts, and to eventually defeat him in a landslide victory. Political motivations aside, Bush was, at least in spirit, accurate in his assessment of the famous harbor that for a century has suffered the ill effects of public and industrial waste dumping. Boston Harbor and its nine beaches have been fouled by pollutants ranging from raw sewage to heavy metals like lead and mercury.

Why did the condition of this vital natural resource decline to such a deplorable state? While the specifics are complex and entangled in the quagmire of public bureaucracy and local politics, the bottom line is that the harbor became seriously polluted because clean waterways are a public good. A cleaner Boston Harbor possesses the requisite characteristics of a public good, namely nonexclusivity and nonrivalness in consumption. Notice that it would be virtually impossible to exclude some users from enjoying a cleaner harbor once it was provided to others. In the context of a major waterway, exclusion could be achieved only through constant monitoring, which would be prohibitively costly at best. Similarly, an environmentally improved harbor is an indivisible commodity. That is, the consumption by a single Massachusetts resident of some aspect of a clean Boston Harbor, such as a day on one of its beaches, does not disallow another consumer from sharing in that very same consumption.

The result is the typical free-ridership problem that characterizes the market failure aspect of all public goods. No one is willing to reveal their preferences for a cleaner harbor and accept a share in the financial responsibility as long as the associated benefits can be enjoyed without having to pay for them. In addition, most harbor users are not fully aware of the benefits of cleaning it up. So no one accepts the responsibility for the preservation and protection of a waterway that is in a very real sense commonly owned. The unfortunate outcome is that industries have used the harbor as a dumping ground for toxic chemical discharges, and residents have carelessly left their trash on the harbor's beaches.

The abuses extend all the way back to 1820, when Boston residents were allowed to discharge human wastes into the city's storm drains. Due to the growth rate of the surrounding urban population, these types of wastes are a far more significant problem today, despoiling the harbor through discharges from sewer treatment plants and combined sewer overflows. Toxic wastes add to the pollution of Boston's now infamous waters. There is evidence of the presence of such contaminants as polychlorinated biphenyls (PCBs), mercury, lead, and benzene, which pose serious health and ecological risks.

One of the major polluting sources of Boston Harbor is the Massachusetts Water Resources Authority (MWRA) created in 1984. This independent water and sewer authority assumed the former responsibilities of the financially crippled and much maligned public agency, the Metropolitan District Commission (MDC). The independent status of the MWRA was believed to provide the flexibility and autonomy necessary to raise the funds needed to clean up the rapidly deteriorating harbor. In charge of the area's sewage system and waste management, both the MWRA and its predecessor have contributed to the dumping of contaminated wastes into the harbor.

As predicted by theory, third-party intervention—implemented in this case through a federal

Application 3.1 (concluded)

court order—was necessary to initiate corrective action to save the harbor. The federally mandated plan, to be spearheaded by the MWRA, calls for a $6.1 billion reconstruction of the area's sewage treatment facilities. To meet this major expenditure, the Massachusetts government has contributed the relatively meager sum of $29 million, and the federal government has committed only another $350 million. Consequently, the remaining $5.7 billion will be funded through increased rates charged by the MWRA to their 2.5 million customers.

While a plan of such proportions will take years to fully implement, interim results are encouraging. Thus far, discharges of toxic metal and PCBs by the MWRA have been reduced by some 50 percent.

Also, the MWRA has halted the destructive dumping of sludge into the harbor from its two major plants. The data below offer some evidence of the success of this third-party action.

While no one is ready to claim a complete victory, it is clear that at least the battle has begun. Perhaps the most important gain will be the lesson learned about the serious consequences that befall a city ignorant of the public goods dilemma.

Sources: Scott Allen, ''Boston Harbor's Waters Have Started to Heal: Cleanup Helping to Shed 'Dirtiest' Label,'' *Boston Globe*, September 6, 1992; Eric Jay Dolin, ''Boston Harbor's Murky Political Waters,'' *Environment* 34, no. 6 (July/August 1992), pp. 7–11, 26–33; D. Doneski, ''Cleaning Up Boston Harbor: Fact or Fiction?'' *Boston College Environmental Affairs Law Review* 12 (Spring 1985) p. 567.

Year	Toxic Metal Discharges (pounds per day)	Harbor Beach Closings (due to high bacteria)	Fish Liver Cancer (% of winter flounder)
1988	1,322	42	11.6
1989	982	55	3.2
1990	761	43	5.0
1991	741	49	2.8
1992	648	22	<3.0

Source: Woods Hole Oceanographic Institute, reported by Allen (September 6, 1992).

kets—intervention by some third party, typically government. But to what degree should government become involved in the market process, and what specific tasks should government perform to achieve an efficient solution? These are difficult questions, but the underlying theories that identify the public goods problem do suggest approaches to solving it.

The Solution: Government Intervention

In practice, a common means by which government responds to the dilemma of free-ridership and nonrevelation of preferences is through **direct provision of public goods.** Simple observation reveals that many public goods, such as fire protection, parks, and roadways, are provided by some level of government.[11] Likewise, government is involved in the preservation of natural resources and the provision of environmental quality. There are many government agencies whose responsibilities include addressing environmental issues. At the federal level, these include the Corps of Engineers, the Nuclear Regulatory Commission, the Federal Energy Regulatory Commission, and, of course, the Environmental Protection Agency (EPA).

An alternative government response is the use of **political procedures and voting rules** aimed at determining society's preferences about public goods.[12] For example, members of Congress are responsible for discerning their constituents' views on environmental issues and representing their interests in developing appropriate legislation. Other environmental laws such as ''bottle bills'' are enacted at the state level through majority voting rules on state referenda. Although these political processes are not without flaws, they do provide some means of identifying individual preferences about environmental issues and translating them into law.

Responding specifically to the problem of imperfect information, governments regularly provide **education and public information** to citizens about public goods. The EPA allocates a proportion of its resources to educating the public about the benefits of a cleaner, safer environment. And recently, the Federal Trade Commission (FTC) issued *Green Marketing Guidelines* to improve the accuracy of advertised environmental claims about products and product packaging—an important effort discussed in Application 3.2.

Government's effectiveness in correcting the market failure of environmental quality as a public good is a matter of considerable debate. Throughout upcoming chapters, an important objective will be to assess environmental policies and programs and to evaluate the associated efficiency implications. For now, we continue our preliminary work by examining an alternative market failure model of environmental problems.

Environmental Problems: Externalities

Another way to model environmental problems is through the use of **externality** theory, an approach that uses a different perspective to analyze the source of the market failure. Instead of defining the market as environmental quality or pollution abatement, this approach specifies the relevant market as

---

[11]There are of course exceptions. In some instances, private individuals have pooled their resources to support the provision of a public good. In fact, Coase (1974) makes reference to the private provision of a lighthouse, the classic case of a pure public good. However, as emphasized above, a public good is identified by its characteristics, not by what sector of the economy provides it to the market.

[12]Such approaches are suggested by public choice theory, a subdiscipline of applied microeconomics. For a concise but comprehensive overview of public choice theory, see Rosen (1995), Chapter 7 or Stiglitz (1988), Chapter 6.

Application 3.2

Informing the Public through Truth in Advertising: Green Marketing Guidelines

Provision of information about the public good environmental quality underlies the ongoing controversy about environmental advertising. Strategic labeling of products touting environmental attributes had become a growing business trend during the 1970s and early 1980s. This so-called green marketing was used by businesses to make their products more appealing to an emerging group of environmentally minded consumers. Using claims such as "environmentally safe," "biodegradable," or "made with 100% recycled material" on product packaging, firms could gain lucrative market share without having to cut product price. However, as consumers' awareness of environmental issues grew, so too did their demand for *accurate* "green" labeling and their skepticism about advertised ecological promises. As it turned out, many manufacturers' claims were at best deceptive, and in some cases, even downright false.

An often cited case of misleading advertising was Mobil Corporation's use of a biodegradable label to market its new line of Hefty trash bags in the late 1980s. Unfortunately for Mobil, its decision came right in the midst of controversy about the relevance of degradable products. Scientists had pointed out that the absence of oxygen and sunlight for wastes buried in a landfill would deter the degradation process. In response to this finding as well as to maintain some consistency with its public opposition of degradability claims, Mobil attempted to preempt any legal attacks by adding a disclaimer to its packaging. But the "green movement" was too strong, even for a giant like Mobil. In 1990, this major corporation was faced with several lawsuits, charging the company with deceptive advertising and consumer fraud for its claims (Lawrence 1991). Ultimately, Mobil paid $150,000 in damages to six states to settle the lawsuits.

Reacting to the Mobil case as well as countless other incidents of misleading ecological claims by manufacturers, consumers demanded that something be done. Their position was clear. If green marketing was here to stay as a competitive business strategy, environmental claims had to be accurate and independently substantiated. Would the marketplace resolve the problem on its own? Not likely. No single producer wanted to be the only one that qualified its environmental claims in the name of accuracy, only to run the risk of losing valuable market share. At the same time, the individual consumer lacked the needed information, not to mention the financial muscle, to take on corporate giants participating in this not-so-truthful eco-advertising. Absent litigation filed against each producer on a one-on-one basis, it became increasingly obvious that government had to step in to solve the dilemma.

In response to a call for action from consumer, industry, and environmental groups, the Federal Trade Commission (FTC) on July 28, 1992, announced environmental marketing guidelines for industry developed in consultation with the Environmental Protection Agency (EPA) and the Office of Consumer Affairs. In reference to the agency's actions, FTC chairperson Janet D. Steiger, said:

> Our goal is to protect consumers and bolster their confidence in environmental claims, and to reduce manufacturers' uncertainty about which claims might lead to FTC law-enforcement actions, thereby encouraging marketers to produce and promote products that are less harmful to the environment.

These important 1992 guidelines are summarized on the next page.

Application 3.2 (concluded)

General Guidelines for "Green Marketing"

- Product labels that state environmental claims should be clear and sufficiently prominent to avoid deception.
- It should be clear whether the environmental claim refers to the product, its packaging, or both.
- Claims of environmental benefits should not be overstated.
- Manufacturers that make environmental claims through the use of comparison with other products should clearly state the basis for comparison and be prepared to substantiate the claim.

The FTC guidelines also offer some broad-based definitions on the most commonly used environmentally oriented labels or descriptive phrases. A sample of these definitions is given below.

- Claims that products are **degradable, biodegradable, or photodegradable** should be substantiated by reliable scientific evidence that the entire product or package

will completely decompose and return to nature.

- A product or package labeled **recyclable** must be recoverable from the solid waste stream and subsequently usable as a raw material in the manufacture or assembly of a new product.
- Products advertised as **ozone-safe** or **ozone-friendly** must contain no ozone-depleting substances.

The FTC's action appears to be a step in the right direction. By offering some standardization of terminology and labeling practices, albeit in the form of *voluntary* guidelines, businesses will undoubtedly cooperate or risk losing their image as environmentally conscious enterprises. In so doing, accuracy of information about the product and the effects of its consumption on the environment should be improved.

*EPA*Sources: Adam Snyder, "The Color of Money," *SuperBrands*, 1992, pp. 30–31; Jennifer Lawrence, "Mobil," *Advertising Age*, January 29, 1991, p. 12; U.S. Environmental Protection Agency, Office of Solid Waste and Emergency Response, "FTC Announces Environmental Marketing Guidelines for Industry," *Reusable News*, Fall 1992; "State Your Claim," *EPA Journal* 18(3), July/August 1992, p. 10.

---

the good whose production or consumption generates environmental damage *outside of* the market transaction.[13] Any such effect that occurs *external to* the market is aptly termed an **externality.** To motivate this concept, we begin with a general overview of externality theory. Once done, we will explain the relevance of this theory to environmental economics. All of this lays the groundwork for building a model of an environmental externality associated with refined petroleum production.

The Basics of Externality Theory

Microeconomic theory argues that price is the most important signaling mechanism in the market process. Equilibrium price and the movement of price

---

[13]Recall from the materials balance model that residuals are generated by *both* producers and households.

toward its equilibrium level convey important information about consumer and producer behavior. In theory, equilibrium price communicates the marginal value consumers assign to a good and the marginal costs incurred by firms in producing it. Under ordinary conditions, this theory predicts the realities of the market remarkably well. But there are instances when price fails to capture all the benefits and costs associated with a market transaction. Market failures such as these occur when some third party is affected, either positively or negatively, by the production or consumption of a commodity. Such third-party effects are called **externalities.**

An **externality** is a spillover effect associated with either production or consumption of a good or service that extends outside the market to some third party other than the producer or consumer of that good or service. If the external effect generates *costs* to a third party, it is a **negative externality.** If the external effect generates *benefits* to a third party, it is a **positive externality.**

Although the notion of an externality may seem obscure, it is nonetheless very familiar conceptually. A good example of a positive externality is the technological knowledge gained by an entire industry as a result of one firm's research and development. A more mundane yet just as valid example is the external benefit of higher real estate values that accrues to homeowners when a neighbor's property is professionally landscaped. Conversely, an individual who purchases an unsightly satellite dish and installs it in his front yard imposes costs to neighbors in the form of a decline in their property values—a negative externality not absorbed by the price of the satellite dish.

Common to all of these examples is a spillover effect occurring *outside* the market transaction, which is *not* captured by the price of the commodity being exchanged. If price does not reflect *all* the benefits and costs associated with production and consumption, it is unreliable as a signaling mechanism, and the market fails. An important consequence is that scarce resources are misallocated. For example, if consumption generates external benefits, the market price undervalues the good, and *too little* of it is produced. On the other hand, if there is a negative externality, the market price does not reflect the external costs, and *too much* of the commodity is produced. An example of this latter phenomenon is the traffic congestion and pollution in Tokyo associated with merchants' pursuit of the ''just-in-time'' inventory system. Application 3.3 gives an inside look at this unusual dilemma.

externality
A spillover effect associated with either production or consumption of a good that extends outside the market to some third party other than the producer or consumer.

negative externality
An external effect that generates costs to a third party.

positive externality
An external effect that generates benefits to a third party.

Environmental Externalities

Of interest to environmental economists are externalities that damage the atmosphere, water supply, natural resources, and the overall quality of life. The classic case is the negative externality associated with *production* activities. For example, the provision of air transportation causes noise pollution and damages air quality. People living near airports experience an overall decline in their quality of life and a decrease in their property values. These are very real costs that are not considered by airlines or air travelers.[14] Since they are incurred by parties *outside* the market transaction, they are not captured in the price of airline tickets. There are also environmental externalities associated

Application 3.3

Tokyo's Just-in-Time Deliveries Create Negative Externalities

In an ironic turn of events, Tokyo's traffic congestion and air pollution have been worsened by local merchants' use of an efficiency-driven system known as "just-in-time" deliveries. The just-in-time (JIT) production system was developed and refined by the Toyota Motor Company during the late 1950s and early 1960s. This efficiency concept is based on the premise that firms should operate with a minimum amount of inventory to avoid waste and to minimize production costs. Raw materials and product components should arrive only just before they are needed in the manufacturing process. For the system to work, deliveries of productive inputs must be made frequently and in a timely manner to achieve maximum efficiency.

Over the years, the use of JIT production has allowed major Japanese manufacturers to bring their output to market at a substantially reduced cost. The system's success in Japan's industrial sector is responsible in part for the nation's dominant position in many international markets. Following the lead of their industrial counterparts, several Japanese service industries have begun to institute JIT delivery systems. Thousands of convenience stores, grocery markets, and department stores concentrated in Japan's capital city now maintain only a minimum stock, relying on frequent deliveries from suppliers—sometimes as often as every few hours. The result? Just-in-time delivery in this densely populated and already congested city has backfired. Adapted incorrectly, the system designed to save time is perversely wasting time. The parade of delivery trucks through the city

streets slows traffic to a crawl, contributes to the city's air pollution, and wastes fuel.

Few would question that *appropriate* use of the JIT concept generates tremendous gains in efficiency and resource productivity and thus substantially reduces private costs. However, Japan's local merchants have unwittingly compromised the integrity of the concept, as evidenced by delivery trucks filled to only half of their capacity. When the system is misused as is the case in Tokyo, there are external costs to society. These include the waste of fuel, increased urban air pollution, and longer commutes for workers—none of which is reflected in the price of convenience goods and grocery products. Hence, there is a true negative externality associated with the use of the JIT delivery system by Tokyo's merchants.

The Ministry of International Trade and Industry has begun to set up an advisory group to examine the current abuses of JIT by Japan's service sector and to suggest possible solutions. In a predictable move, the ministry has asked the management of Toyota to serve as a primary consultant on the project. That some third-party intervention is necessary to solve Tokyo's dilemma is not surprising. Just as theory predicts, the dilemma of negative externalities cannot be solved within the market system itself.

Sources: Michael Schrage, "In Tokyo, 'Just-in-Time' Deliveries in Need of Administrative Guidance," *Boston Globe,* March 22, 1992; Walter E. Goddard, *Just-in-Time: Surviving by Breaking Tradition* (Essex Junction, Vt.: Oliver Wight Limited Publications, Inc., 1986).

---

[14]There are studies in the literature that attempt to quantify the external costs of noise pollution. The interested reader should consult Nelson (1979), who provides a survey of some of this research.

with *consumption*. One example is the cost of waste disposal associated with the purchase of CD's in nonbiodegradable or excess packaging, an issue discussed in Application 3.4.

There are also positive externalities that help to explain the persistence of environmental problems. Consider the market for pollution abatement equipment, such as scrubbers. Scrubbers are elaborate systems used to clean emissions from producers' smokestacks. In practice, most are installed to reduce sulfur dioxide (SO_2) emissions. When a producer of electricity, for

---

Application 3.4

An Industry Response to a Negative Consumption Externality: CD Product Packaging

Product packaging is often as much a marketing tool as it is a means to protect a commodity during shipment. In either case, the explicit cost of *producing* such packaging is passed on to the consumer as part of the commodity's price. But there are other costs that are *not* passed on within the market transaction—the costs of *disposing* the packaging at the point of consumption. These external costs are not trivial, given the associated ecological effects of certain waste disposal practices. As environmental awareness has grown, so too have objections to excessive or nonbiodegradable packaging. In the market for compact disks (CDs), opposition to that product's wasteful packaging led to a controversy within the industry that involved music companies, recording artists, environmental groups, and the general public.

Introduced into the U.S. market in 1982, CDs originally were packaged in two boxes. The outer box was a 6-by-12-inch cardboard package, known in the industry as the "long box." Inside the long box was a 5-by-5 ½-inch "jewel box" constructed of clear plastic, which housed the CD. The jewel box, which continues in use today, generally is saved by the consumer as a protective storage container for the CD when not in use. However, the long box had virtually no practical value to the CD

buyer beyond identifying the contents at the point of sale. In fact, most consumers discarded the long box immediately after purchase, so this part of the packaging ended up in landfills or burned in municipal incinerators.

To give some credence to the disposal problem, consider the following. Of the 250 million CDs sold in 1990, an estimated 23 million pounds of CD packaging were discarded by consumers. Think about the costs associated with the generation and disposal of this amount of waste—costs that are external to the purchase and sale of CDs. The producer of the CD does not consider these external costs as part of its production expenditures, so they are not reflected in the CD's price. Who bears the costs of this waste? Society as a whole has to pick up the tab, the classic symptom of a negative externality—in this case, one associated with consumption.

Of course, the obvious question is to ask why the long box was used at all in packaging CDs. Music company executives defended this package design with two arguments. First, its large size helped to deter shoplifting, an ongoing problem for retail outlets. The second and most important justification was to facilitate the sale of CDs. The 6-by-12-inch long box allowed retailers to use existing display racks originally designed for 12-

Application 3.4 (concluded)

by-12-inch record albums. According to one industry official, the long box saved retailers an estimated $100 million in redesign costs for their display units.

Despite the industry's arguments, followers of the "green movement" began to pressure the industry to devise some alternative to the wasteful packaging. In 1991, a "Ban the Box" campaign materialized to eliminate the long box from CD packaging. Environmentally minded recording artists such as Sting, Peter Gabriel, and the Grateful Dead joined the crusade, demanding that a more environmentally friendly package design be developed. In a bold move, Gabriel's record company, Geffen Records, went so far as to ship his CD *Shaking the Tree* packaged in just the jewel box. The decision did not fare well with retailers, who had difficulty displaying it. While perhaps a coincidence, sales of Gabriel's new CD were markedly lower than his previous release, which sold over 2 million copies in conventional packaging.

Wanting to avoid similar retailing problems, industry officials aggressively searched for a new packaging design that would facilitate retailers' display needs *and* ameliorate environmentalists. Two industry-developed packages surfaced, both of which maintained the oversized dimensions demanded by retailers. One design is the Digi-Track, a folded cardboard shell that replaces the nonbiodegradable jewel box. Albeit for different reasons, this design met with dissatisfaction by both consumers and retailers. Consumers found the package too fragile for long-term storage use, and retailers complained about the additional plastic parts needed for display purposes. An alternative design, dubbed the Eco-Pak, was introduced by Time-Warner, Inc. The Eco-Pak is constructed mainly of recycled cardboard and is shrink-wrapped in recyclable plastic. For sale displays, it has the desirable long box size, and for consumer convenience, it can be folded into the smaller jewel box shape for storage purposes. A number of design entrepreneurs outside the industry also entered the

CD packaging race—not surprising in a multi-million-dollar industry such as this one. Two designs in particular were viewed favorably by the industry—the Laserfile and the Inch Pack. Both are adaptations of the jewel box design favored by consumers, but can be displayed in the open position to meet the retailers' long box size demands.

After weighing all the options, the recording industry in 1992 agreed to a voluntary ban on the long box, and since April 1, 1993, all new CDs are shipped without the objectionable packaging. As it turns out, the standard practice by most American music companies has become the use of the shrink-wrapped jewel box. Why this, instead of some of the newly itnroduced alternatives? Costs of converting to new machinery are the primary reason. Furthermore, since the jewel box has been adopted as the industry standard in Japan and Europe, recording firms shipping internationally would have had to carry duplicate packaging stock had they opted for a new design—adding still more to costs. Industry officials have indicated, however, that alternative packaging such as the Eco-Pak may be used for special releases or possibly for CD singles as a way to differentiate these from full albums.

The CD packaging controversy is an important example of how externalities persist in the marketplace. The ban on the long box *did* reduce the external costs of CD consumption. But notice that the externality associated with wasteful packaging practices persisted for a full decade before any action was taken. In this case, the third-party intervention came not from government but from environmentalists who made market participants aware of how their decisions affected the ecology. In so doing, the industry recognized the ramifications in terms of its long-term revenues and responded in a predictable manner.

Sources: Meg Cox, "Music Firms Try Out 'Green' CD Boxes," *The Wall Street Journal*, July 25, 1991; Peter Newcomb, " 'Ban the Box'," *Forbes*, May 13, 1991, p. 70; Debbie Galante Block, "CD Jewel Box Only, or Alternatives Too?" *Tape-Disc Business*, June 1993, p. 12.

example, purchases and installs a scrubber system, the benefits of cleaner air accrue to all people living in the nearby area. Since these individuals are not a part of the market transaction, the external benefits are not captured in the scrubber system's price. Resources are misallocated, and too few scrubbers are exchanged in the marketplace.

Notice that there is a qualitative relationship between the external benefits associated with pollution abatement goods and the external costs of pollution-generating commodities. They are just the inverse of one another. If the market is defined such that there is a *positive* externality, the external benefits are *improved* health, natural resources, aesthetics, and so on. If the market is defined such that there is a *negative* externality, the external costs are the *damages* to health, natural resources, scenic views, and so on. Which of the two is relevant depends solely upon which market is specified—the market for an abatement good or service or the market for a pollution-generating commodity.

The Relationship between Public Goods and Externalities

Environmental externalities are those affecting all environmental media—air, water, and land—all of which have public goods characteristics. What this implies is that while public goods and externalities are not the same concept, they are closely related. In fact, if the externality affects a broad segment of society and if its effects are both nonrival and nonexcludable, the externality *is* itself a public good.[15] If, however, the external effects are felt by a more narrowly defined group of individuals or firms, then those effects are more properly modeled as an externality.

The distinction between the two concepts, while defensible in theory, may not always be crystal clear when air and water supplies are the subject of analysis. However, since each model provides a different perspective to the same problem, each contributes to a better understanding of the issues at hand. The value added of the externality model will become clearer as our formal analysis develops.[16]

Modeling Environmental Damage as a Negative Externality

Having established a basic foundation of what externalities are conceptually, we now develop a formal economic model of a negative environmental

---

[15]Technically, if the externality provides *benefits* to a large component of society, it is a public *good*; if the opposite is true, the externality is a public "*bad*."

[16]For further discussion of the relationship between externalities and public goods, the interested reader is referred to Holtermann (1972).

externality. We elect to model an externality associated with *production,* since this approach more directly addresses the source of most environmental pollution.

Defining the Relevant Market

As always, one of the first steps in model building is the determination of the relevant market. In this case, we define the market as refined petroleum products. This is a fitting choice, since refined petroleum plants have been cited by the EPA as one of 627 industrial point sources polluting water supplies through direct discharge of toxic chemicals into rivers and streams. According to EPA statistics, an estimated 3.3 million pounds of toxic chemicals were released to surface waters by the refined petroleum industry in 1991.[17] Among the associated external costs are serious health risks for individuals using the rivers and streams. Moreover, fish and shellfish become contaminated, and over time their populations will decline. To illustrate this latter point, Application 3.5 discusses EPA trend data on the closings of shellfish beds from 1966 through 1990 due to water pollution.

Application 3.5

Closing of Shellfish Beds in the United States

In 1990, states submitted water quality assessment findings to the EPA as mandated by the Clean Water Act. These assessments were based upon 1988 and 1989 data and used physical, chemical, and evaluative methods, such as the use of questionnaires sent to fisheries and biologists. Part of this information reported on the effect of pollution on aquatic life, including fish and shellfish. Shellfish are a particular health concern because many are eaten raw, and cooking is known to be the most effective means to destroy many microorganisms. Varieties such as oysters, clams, and mussels are known as "filter-feeders," meaning that they extract their food from the water. As they do, they also take in contaminants, which accumulate on

their gills and in their digestive tracts. According to the EPA, the full story is not yet known on the health effects of the toxic pollutants found in fish and shellfish tissue. Some are linked to very serious health problems such as cancer, neurological disorders, and birth defects.

To assess the problem of contaminated fish and shellfish, states conduct tests on water samples and measure the most probable number (MPN) of total coliform and fecal coliform bacteria. These bacteria counts provide some indication of the presence of potentially pathogenic sewage-related microorganisms that can cause severe health problems such as dysentery, cholera, and infectious hepatitis. Shellfish harvesting is then restricted to

---

[17]See U.S. EPA, Office of Policy, Planning, and Evaluation (March 1991), p. 4–2; U.S. EPA, Office of Pollution Prevention and Toxics (May 1993), Table 1–21, p. 54.

Application 3.5 (concluded)

those areas that maintain total and fecal coliform levels below certain limits.

According to the 1990 National Water Quality Inventory, 20 states reported shellfish harvesting restrictions for the 1988 to 1990 period due to fecal coliform or viral contamination of coastal waters and estuaries. Twelve of these reported the restrictions by number of incidents, which totaled 340.

Eleven submitted data by geographical area, reporting some 2,108 square miles of estuarine waters affected by shellfish closures. As the following data indicate, the most frequently reported sources of shellfish harvesting restrictions were municipal wastewater treatment plants, urban runoff/storm sewers, on-site wastewater systems, marinas, and industrial dischargers.

At present, the U.S. government has identified 62 numeric human health criteria and 25 numeric aquatic life criteria for toxic water pollutants. These are designed to provide a basis of comparison for the testing of water samples. The problem is that not all states have adopted these criteria, and there are many more toxins than those for which criteria have been established. As a result, data on toxic contamination are reported in terms of "exceedances of state water quality standards," measures that are not the same across all states. This lack of consistency suggests that these data must be interpreted with caution. Nonetheless, the problem appears to be a serious one, as the following trend data on shellfish bed closings by region imply.

Sources: Primary source and all state-level data taken from U.S. Environmental Protection Agency, Office of Water, *National Water Quality Inventory: 1990 Report to Congress* (Washington, D.C., April 1992a); regional trend data on shellfish bed closures from U.S. Department of Commerce, National Oceanic and Atmospheric Administration, National Ocean Survey, Ocean Assessments Division, Strategic Assessment Branch, *Trends in Harvest-Limited Shellfish Areas* (Rockville, Md.: Data compiled from the National Estuarine Inventory database), cited in The Council on Environmental Quality, *Environmental Quality 22nd Annual Report* (Washington, D.C.: U.S. Government Printing Office, March 1992), Table 35, p. 266.

Sources Associated with Shellfish Harvesting Restrictions	Number of States Reporting
Municipal wastewater facilities	8
Urban runoff/storm sewers	4
On-site wastewater systems (septic)	3
Recreational activities (marinas)	2
Industry	2

	Prohibited Acres (thousands)			
Year	Northeast	Southeast	Gulf of Mexico	Pacific
1966	443.1	790.0	523.7	3.4
1971	710.4	1,702.4	592.1	317.4
1974	710.8	1,896.6	829.1	316.8
1980	781.8	877.9	889.1	317.5
1985	709.1	612.0	1,649.0	157.0
1990	1,020.0	630.0	2,405.0	183.0

Modeling the Private Market for Refined Petroleum

To avoid confounding the analysis with the market failure of imperfect competition, we assume that the private market for refined petroleum is competitive. The hypothetical supply and demand relationships for refined petroleum products are modeled as follows:

$$\text{Supply:} \quad P = 10.0 + 0.075Q$$
$$\text{Demand:} \quad P = 42.0 - 0.125Q,$$

where Q is measured in thousands of barrels of output per day and P is the price per barrel.

Recall from the previous chapter that supply represents the marginal costs of production and demand the marginal benefits of consumption, both based upon *private* or *internal* decision-making. In markets such as this one where there are also external costs associated with production, it is necessary to explicitly distinguish internal or private costs from external costs. Thus, we will formally refer to the supply function as the **marginal *private* cost (MPC)** of production. For consistency, we will analogously refer to the demand relationship as the **marginal *private* benefit (MPB)** function even though it is assumed that there are no external benefits, that is, no positive externality, associated with production or consumption of refined petroleum products. Hence, the two functions are restated as follows:

$$MPC = 10.0 + 0.075Q$$
$$MPB = 42.0 - 0.125Q$$

Inefficiency of the Competitive Equilibrium

Given the usual assumptions about the underlying motivations of supply and demand, the competitive market clears where $MPB = MPC$, or equivalently where marginal profit $(M\pi)$ or $(MPB - MPC) = 0$. Solving the MPB and MPC equations simultaneously yields a competitive market price, P_c, of $22 per barrel and market quantity, Q_c, of 160,000 barrels. The corresponding graphical model is shown in Figure 3.3, where equilibrium occurs at the intersection of the MPB and MPC curves.

The problem with this equilibrium is that it ignores the external costs to society of the contaminated water supplies caused by production of refined petroleum products. Remember, natural market forces motivate firms to satisfy their own interests, not those of society. The costs of the water pollution are *external* to the market exchange and consequently not factored into market decisions. The implications are serious, since an allocatively efficient equilibrium requires that marginal benefits be equal to *all* marginal costs of production. Since the external costs are not included in the decision-making process, the MPC specified by the supply function undervalues the true opportunity costs of production, and the resulting output level is too high.

FIGURE 3.3

Competitive equilibrium in the market for refined petroleum

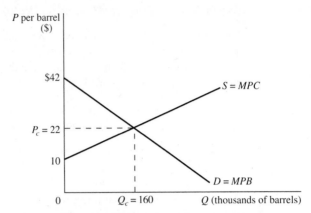

The intersection of the *MPB* and *MPC* curves identifies the competitive equilibrium in the refined petroleum market, where P_c = \$22 per barrel and Q_c = 160,000 barrels. This equilibrium ignores the external costs of contaminated water supplies caused by production of refined petroleum products. Therefore, the *MPC* undervalues the true opportunity costs of production, and the competitive output level is too high.

From a practical perspective, economists want to identify and monetize these external costs. But assigning a dollar value to negative externalities is difficult. Think about trying to monetize the damage to aquatic life from water pollution or the increased health risks from swimming in a polluted lake. Although there are economic methods to approximate these costs, they are not straightforward. So, we will defer discussion of these to later chapters. For now, we will simply argue that these costs do exist and assume for the present that they can be quantified.

Modeling the External Costs

To complete our exposition of the refined petroleum market, we will model the hypothetical **marginal external cost (MEC)** function as follows:

$$MEC = 0.05Q$$

Think about the economic interpretation of this equation. Based on the constant slope of 0.05, the function communicates that the *MEC* due to water pollution effects is increasing at a constant rate of 0.05 with respect to oil production. Since Q is measured in thousands of barrels, this magnitude implies that for every additional 1,000 barrels of refined oil produced, the marginal external costs of pollution rise by another \$0.05 per barrel.

These external costs must be accounted for in the determination of equilibrium price and quantity of refined petroleum to reach an efficient outcome.

marginal social cost (MSC)
The sum of the marginal private cost (*MPC*) and the marginal external cost (*MEC*).

To accomplish this, the *MEC* must be added to the firm's *MPC* to derive the **marginal social cost (MSC)** equation as shown below:

$$MSC = MPC + MEC$$
$$= 10.0 + 0.075Q + 0.05Q$$
$$MSC = 10.0 + 0.125Q$$

The *MSC* is the relevant consideration for production decisions, since it captures *all* of the costs of producing refined petroleum products—the private costs of production *and* the external costs of environmental damage to society.

marginal social benefit (MSB)
The sum of the marginal private benefit (*MPB*) and the marginal external benefit (*MEB*).

On the demand side of the market, there is an analogous benefit relationship called the **marginal social benefit (MSB)**, which is equal to the sum of the *MPB* and any **marginal external benefit (MEB).** Since we have assumed that there are no positive externalities in this market, the *MEB* is zero, so the *MPB* is equal to the *MSB* in this case.

The Efficient Equilibrium

Once determined, the *MSC* relationship must be set equal to the *MSB* function to solve for the efficient equilibrium price, P_e, and quantity, Q_e. In this case, the efficient level of refined petroleum products is 128,000 barrels per day sold at a market price of $26 per barrel. Compare this to the competitive equilibrium of $Q_c = 160,000$ and $P_c = \$22$. As we asserted, the competitive equilibrium in the presence of a negative externality is characterized by an overallocation of resources to production. Furthermore, the competitive price is too low, since the *MEC* is not captured by the market transaction.

The comparative results are shown graphically in Figure 3.4. Geometrically, the *MSC* curve is found by vertically summing the *MEC* curve and the *MPC* curve, since costs are measured on the vertical axis. The intersection of *MSC* and *MSB* identifies the efficient equilibrium point at $P_e = \$26$ and $Q_e = 128,000$. The graph also shows the competitive equilibrium points, $P_c = \$22$ and $Q_c = 160,000$, which corresponds to the intersection of *MPC* and *MPB*. Notice that at Q_c, *MSB* is *below* *MSC*. This signifies that society is giving up more in scarce resources to produce petroleum than it gains in benefits from consuming it. To restore the equality of *MSB* = *MSC*, signifying allocative efficiency, output must be decreased—precisely what is predicted by theory.

An alternative way to analyze the two equilibria is to examine the corresponding levels of *Mπ*. At the competitive equilibrium, we know that *Mπ* = 0, since that point is defined where *MPB* = *MPC*. At the efficient equilibrium, we know that *MSB* = *MSC*, which can be reexpressed as *MSB* − *MSC* = 0 or equivalently where *MPB* − *MPC* = *MEC*. Hence, we conclude that at

FIGURE 3.4

Comparing competitive and efficient equilibria using marginal benefit and marginal cost: the refined petroleum market in the presence of a negative externality

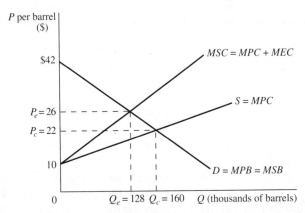

The *MSC* curve is found as the vertical sum of the *MEC* and the *MPC* curves. The intersection of *MSC* and *MSB* identifies the efficient equilibrium point at P_e = \$26 and Q_e = 128,000 barrels. Notice how this compares to the competitive equilibrium where P_c = \$22 and Q_c = 160,000, corresponding to the intersection of *MPC* and *MPB*. At Q_c, *MSB* is *below MSC*, which means that society is giving up more in scarce resources to produce petroleum than it gains in benefits from consuming it.

the efficient equilibrium point, $M\pi = MEC$. These derivations are summarized below:

competitive equilibrium
Occurs at the point where marginal private benefit (*MPB*) equals marginal private cost (*MPC*) or where marginal profit $(M\pi) = 0$.

efficient equilibrium
Occurs at the point where marginal social benefit (*MSB*) equals marginal social cost (*MSC*) or where marginal profit $(M\pi)$ = marginal external cost (*MEC*).

Competitive equilibrium:

$$MPB = MPC$$
$$MPB - MPC = 0$$
$$M\pi = 0.$$

Efficient equilibrium:

$$MSB = MSC$$
$$MPB + MEB = MPC + MEC$$
$$MPB - MPC = MEC \text{ (since } MEB = 0)$$
$$M\pi = MEC.$$

These $M\pi$ relationships are illustrated in Figure 3.5. There is a direct correspondence between the curves in this graph and those in Figure 3.4. The $M\pi$ function in Figure 3.5 is equivalent to the vertical distance between the *MPB* curve and the *MPC* curve shown in Figure 3.4. The *MEC* function in Figure 3.5 is equivalent to the vertical distance between the *MSC* and the *MPC* curves in Figure 3.4. The efficient equilibrium point, where Q_e = 128,000, occurs where $M\pi$ intersects the *MEC* function. At this intersection, both *MEC* and $M\pi$ are equal to \$6.40 per barrel:

$$MEC = 0.05Q = 0.05(128) = \$6.40;$$
$$M\pi = MPB - MPC = 42.0 - 0.125(128) - (10.0 + 0.075(128)) = \$6.40$$

The competitive equilibrium, where Q_c = 160,000, occurs where the $M\pi$ function crosses the horizontal axis or where $M\pi = 0$. Notice, however, that the *MEC* evaluated at this point is equal to \$8, [i.e., $MEC = 0.05(160) = \$8$].

FIGURE 3.5

*Comparing
competitive and
efficient equilibria
using marginal profit
and marginal
external cost: the
refined petroleum
market in the
presence of a
negative externality*

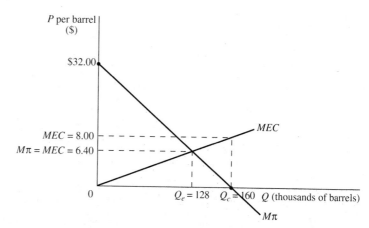

The efficient equilibrium is shown where $M\pi$ intersects MEC at $Q_e = 128,000$ barrels. At this point, both $M\pi$ and MEC equal \$6.40. The competitive equilibrium where $Q_c = 160,000$ occurs where the $M\pi$ function crosses the horizontal axis or where $M\pi = 0$. The MEC evaluated at this point is equal to \$8. Since at the competitive equilibrium $M\pi \neq MEC$, the result is not efficient.

Thus, at the competitive equilibrium, $M\pi \neq MEC$, indicating that the result is not efficient.

The interpretation of this result is as follows. In the presence of a negative externality, efficiency requires that firms set their production levels such that the price covers not only private costs at the margin but also the external costs at the margin. In this case, the external costs are the damages to the environment, and these should be accounted for by producing polluters in their profit decisions.

Measuring the Welfare Gain to Society

One important conclusion of the preceding analysis is that efficiency in the market for refined petroleum would improve if output were restricted by 32,000 barrels per day, (i.e., 160,000 − 128,000 barrels). Such an output adjustment would result in an increase in society's welfare. To illustrate this, the *MPC*, *MSC*, and *MPB* curves are reproduced in Figure 3.6 with some added notation. Study this model and consider the separate effects on the refineries and on society associated with this output restriction. From the firms' perspective, there is a loss in profits. Notice that as Q falls from 160,000 to 128,000, refineries lose profit, measured as the excess of *MPB* over *MPC* for each unit of output. Aggregating all of the $M\pi$ values between $Q_e = 128,000$ and $Q_c = 160,000$ defines the triangular area *WYZ*, representing the total loss in profits. However, from the vantage point of society, there is a measurable gain equal to the accumulated *reduction* in *MEC* associated with the output decline. This reduction in external costs represents the decrease in damages

FIGURE 3.6

Assessing the net gain to society of restoring efficiency in the refined petroleum market

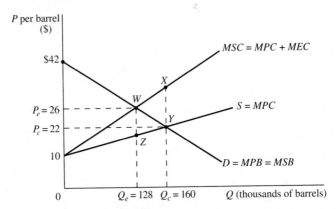

To restore efficiency, Q would have to be reduced from 160,000 to 128,000 barrels. As this output restriction occurs, refineries lose profit, represented as the triangular area *WYZ*. But at the same time, society gains the associated decline in damages to health and the ecology shown as area *WXYZ*. Thus, on net, society gains by the triangular area *WXY* due to the restoration of efficiency.

to health and the ecology. Geometrically, this gain is shown as area *WXYZ*. Hence, on net, society as a whole gains by an amount equal to the triangular area *WXY* due to the restoration of efficiency.

In sum, if production of a commodity generates a negative externality, the market will yield an inefficient solution with too many resources allocated to production of the good. If that externality were somehow accounted for within the market, society as a whole would gain. Of course, the operative issue is *how* to account for externalities such that efficiency can be restored.

Market Failure Analysis

It is important to understand the lack of incentive in the natural market process to explicitly account for external costs. Petroleum refineries are motivated by *private* gain, not *social* gain. Although these firms are undoubtedly aware of the environmental damage associated with their production process, there is no incentive—in fact there is a disincentive—for them to absorb these costs. Doing so would negatively affect profits. It would be as if firms offered to pay for the external costs on society's behalf. But there is no market incentive for any rational firm to incur higher costs than it has to, even if it is for the good of society. To expect firms to behave otherwise is to refute the underpinnings of the market process and the free enterprise system.

These assertions should not dissuade society's efforts to solve the problems of environmental damage. Quite the contrary. Market failure models give us a much better understanding of *why* we observe increasing damage to our physical environment as industrial production has intensified throughout the world. The theory also explains the persistence of environmental problems from a market perspective and the need for government regulation of markets where such problems arise. Finding appropriate policy solutions is not easy, but the process is facilitated by a clear understanding of how and why market failures arise. On that point, if we consider both the public goods problem and the externality model we have examined, an important common element leads us to the true underlying source of virtually all environmental problems—the **absence of property rights.** It is to this critical issue that we now direct our attention.

The Absence of Property Rights

property rights
The set of valid claims to a good or resource that permits use of that good or resource and the transfer of its ownership through sale.

In every model presented thus far in this chapter, the market has failed to provide an efficient solution. Using basic elements of economic theory, we have demonstrated *how* the market fails and even quantified the failure in terms of the overproduction of output. While in each case, the failure has been examined conceptually, we have not yet focused on the underlying root of the problem.

Reconsider the negative externality model, and recall the assertion that an externality *is* a public good if it affects a broad segment of society. In our model, the external cost is damage to water supplies, which indeed fits that characterization. Furthermore, clean water possesses the two distinguishing characteristics of a public good. Now recall our public goods model in which the relevant market was hypothetically defined as ''air quality.'' What do these two public goods have in common? The answer is that in each case, the **property rights** of the good are undefined, and as a result, markets for these goods are virtually nonexistent. **Property rights** are the set of valid claims to a good or resource that permits use of that good or resource and the transfer of its ownership through sale. These rights are generally limited by law and/or social custom.

In the context of environmental public goods, it is unclear who ''owns'' the rights to water supplies, or who ''owns'' the rights to the air. For example, do swimmers own the right to clean water or do refineries hold the rights to pollute it? Do individuals own the right to breathe clean air or do polluting firms own the right to contaminate it? Since there are no clear-cut answers to these questions, there is no built-in market mechanism to resolve environmental problems. It turns out that property rights are critically important to the sound functioning of the market system. In fact, as pointed out by Nobel laureate Ronald Coase (1960), the assignment of property rights alone can provide for an efficient solution even in the presence of an externality.[18]

---

[18]In 1991, Ronald Coase received the Nobel Prize in economics for his pioneering work in the theory of transactions costs and other concepts that link economic theory and the law. Much of his research is very relevant to the economics of environmental problems.

The Coase Theorem

Coase's exposition about property rights and their relevance to externality problems is so significant that it has come to be known as the **Coase Theorem.** This theorem posits that proper assignment of property rights to any good, even if externalities are present, will allow bargaining between the affected parties such that an efficient solution can be obtained, regardless of which party is assigned those rights. Two important caveats of this theory are noteworthy:

1. The predicted outcome is conditioned upon the assumption of costless transactions, that is, the requisite bargaining is unencumbered.
2. The result implicitly assumes that the damages associated with the externality are accessible and measurable.

The simplest way to illustrate the Coase Theorem is by way of a tangible example. To facilitate comprehension, we revisit our now familiar market model of refined petroleum to see how the assignment of property rights and bargaining can restore efficiency to the market. To operationalize the theory, we impose the assumptions given in (1) and (2) above, but test the theory's prediction by examining the outcome under two different assignments of rights of some hypothetical river. The alternatives are that private individuals can hold the rights to the river for recreational use or that refineries can hold the rights for the release of toxic chemicals from production.[19] The implications of points (1) and (2) are deferred to the end of the discussion.

Bargaining When Property Rights Belong to the Refineries

We begin by assigning the property rights to the petroleum refineries. This means that the refineries have the ''right to pollute'' the river as part of their production processes. While at first blush, this particular assignment of property rights may appear to be a perverse approach to an environmental problem, recall that according to the Coase Theorem this should have no effect on the outcome at all. Moreover, such an approach does emphasize the power of the theory.

Remember that the refineries are interested in producing petroleum products up to a level that maximizes profit—by itself, not an objectionable motive in a free enterprise system. The pollution they cause is an unintended ''by-product'' of the production process. Nonetheless, the recreational users of the river *are* harmed by the associated pollution, or more formally, their utility is negatively affected. Knowing that the refineries have the right to pollute and

---

[19]Although it would be more realistic to assume that only a single refinery were involved in a bargaining scenario about the use of a river, it is simpler to approach the problem from an industry perspective so that we can use the same data and graphical models developed in the negative externality discussion.

FIGURE 3.7

Bargaining in the refined petroleum market with the assignment of property rights

If the refineries own the rights to the river, bargaining begins at Q_c and continues to Q_e. This is so because at all output levels between these points, the payment ρ satisfies the condition: $MEC > ρ > Mπ$, which is acceptable to both parties. If the recreational users own the rights, bargaining begins at $Q = 0$ and continues up to Q_e. This occurs because at all output levels between these points, the payment ρ satisfies the condition: $Mπ > ρ > MEC$, which is acceptable to both parties.

given their own motivation to maximize utility, recreational users have a market incentive to negotiate. For each unit change in output, they would be willing to pay the refineries *not* to pollute up to an amount equal to the negative effect on their utility caused by the pollution. The refineries, on the other hand, would be willing to accept payment *not* to pollute as long as that payment were greater than the loss in profits from cutting back production.

The terms of the negotiation can best be understood by examining Figure 3.7, which is a replication of the negative externality model. As before, Q_c represents the profit-maximizing competitive equilibrium, and Q_e the efficient equilibrium. We assume that the market is at Q_c when the bargaining process begins, since this is the point that the owners of the rights, the refineries, would choose. Each party's bargaining position is given below in the context of the cost and benefit curves in the diagram:

Recreational users:　Willing to offer a payment, ρ,
　　　　　　　　　　 such that $ρ < (MSC − MPC)$
Refineries:　　　　　 Willing to accept a payment, ρ,
　　　　　　　　　　 such that $ρ > (MPB − MPC)$

Note that the value of $(MSC − MPC)$ measured vertically is simply the *MEC,* the value of the marginal damage incurred by the recreational users for each added unit of production. The vertical distance measured by $(MPB − MPC)$ is the *Mπ* earned by the refineries for each extra unit of output produced. In theory, the bargaining between the two groups should continue as long as the payment is greater than the refineries' loss in profit, but less than the recreational users' damage. In the context of the model, payment ρ will be acceptable to both parties as long as the following condition holds:

$$\text{If } (MSC - MPC) > \rho > (MPB - MPC) \text{ or equivalently,}$$
$$MEC \qquad > \rho > \qquad M\pi$$

Find these vertical distances on Figure 3.7. Note that at the competitive equilibrium, Q_c, the refineries' $M\pi$ equals zero, that is, $(MPB - MPC) = 0$. On the other hand, the MEC at Q_c is some positive value, that is, $(MSC - MPC) > 0$, represented on the graph as distance XY. Thus, bargaining between the parties is feasible at equilibrium, since $MEC > M\pi$ at Q_c. Moreover, since this condition holds for all output levels between Q_c and Q_e, the parties will continue to bargain all the way to Q_e, where negotiation ceases. The reason? Because at Q_e, $(MSC - MPC)$ is exactly equal to $(MPB - MPC)$, or $MEC = M\pi$, each measured as distance WZ. Output reductions beyond that point would generate a loss in profits to the refineries that is greater than what the recreational users would be willing to pay, or $M\pi > MEC$, so bargaining would break down.

This is a profound result. Under the assumptions of Coase's model, assigning the property rights to the refineries will lead to bargaining between the parties, which ultimately generates an efficient outcome without any third-party intervention.

Bargaining When Property Rights Belong to the Recreational Users

Now reconsider the model with the property rights assigned to the recreational users. Recall that according to the Coase Theorem, an efficient outcome can be obtained regardless of which of the affected parties controls the property rights. So we should expect to obtain the same result as before. The starting point at which bargaining begins, however, is different. If the recreational users hold the rights to the river, technically the refineries cannot produce at all unless they pay for the rights to pollute. Thus, we assume that the point at which bargaining begins is at $Q = 0$. All other assumptions of the model are the same.

The recreational users pursue their rights to a clean river, not to obstruct production of the refineries, but to maximize their utility. Nonetheless, the refineries' profit objective is detrimentally affected. Hence, it is they who have a market-based motivation to bargain with the recreational users in an attempt to get them to accept payment for their rights to the river. The terms of the bargaining are analogous to the previous scenario except that now the refineries are in the "offering" position and the recreational users are in the "accepting" position.

Refer back to Figure 3.7 and consider the two sides' relative positions at $Q = 0$. For each unit change in output, the refineries are willing to pay for the right to pollute, (and thus the right to produce output), up to an amount equal to the $M\pi$ received from production, measured as the vertical distance between MPB and MPC. The recreational users are willing to ''trade off'' their rights to clean water only if they receive payment greater than the damage they incur as the river becomes polluted. This damage is of course the MEC, measured as the distance between MSC and MPC. Thus, each party's bargaining stance is as follows:

Refineries:	Willing to offer a payment ρ such that $\rho < (MPB - MPC)$
Recreational users:	Willing to accept a payment ρ such that $\rho > (MSC - MPC)$

Hence, there is opportunity for bargaining to proceed as long as the following condition holds:

$$(MPB - MPC) > \rho > (MSC - MPC) \text{ or } M\pi > \rho > MEC$$

The model presented in Figure 3.7 confirms that this condition holds at $Q = 0$ and continues to hold for all output levels up to Q_e. At Q_e, bargaining ceases, since at that point $(MPB - MPC)$ is exactly equal to $(MSC - MPC)$, or $M\pi = MEC$, each represented by distance WZ. Note that beyond Q_e, the marginal damage associated with increased production exceeds the addition to profit that the refineries would receive, or $MEC > M\pi$, so bargaining would break down. Thus, the assignment of property rights, this time to the recreational users, leads to an efficient outcome without any government intervention.

Limitations of the Coase Theorem

Coase's model yields an extremely powerful result and one that underscores the significance of property rights to the market process, regardless of which party is assigned those rights. However, as was stated at the outset, the model's prediction of an efficient outcome depends upon two very limiting assumptions: (1) that transactions are costless, and (2) that damages are accessible and measurable. Thus, for the theory to hold in practice, at minimum it must be the case that very few individuals are involved on either side of the market.

The reality of the refinery market, and in fact of most markets, is that there are many affected parties on both sides of the market. There would be nontrivial costs associated with attempting to reach a consensus within each group about the bargaining terms even before the negotiation could begin. Undoubtedly, legal counsel would be necessary, adding still more to the transactions costs. Then there is the difficult problem of ascertaining the sources of the damage and attempting to assign a value to that damage. As more parties are involved, this task would become increasingly difficult. However, there does seem to be evidence that when rights are more clearly defined, the affected parties have a stronger incentive to move toward a resolution.

Common Property Resources

It turns out that the delineation of property rights need not be completely missing for a market problem to exist. If property rights exist in some form but are ill defined, the outcome will also be an inefficient one. Such is the case for what are termed **common property resources,** which represent another source of externalities and therefore market failures. **Common property resources** are those for which property rights are shared by some group of individuals.

Notice that according to this definition, common property resources fall somewhere on a continuum between the extremes of pure public goods and pure private goods. Unlike pure public goods, common property resources are not accessible to everyone, meaning there is some measure of excludability.[20] However, since the property rights extend to more than one individual, they are not as clearly defined as they are for pure private goods. Some classic examples of common property resources are fisheries and animal populations.

In the case of common property resources, the problem is that public access without any control leads to resource exploitation, which in turn generates a negative externality. The problem arises because each co-owner makes decisions about using the resource based only on private costs and benefits, ignoring how that decision would affect other owners. For example, consider a lake stocked with fish for use exclusively by members of a local community. Unless the catch is limited in some way, each person would fish from the lake based on private motivations, ignoring how the associated decline in the fish population would negatively affect others' ability to share in the benefits. Furthermore, each individual would have no incentive to consider the ultimate cost of restocking the lake, since their personal share of that cost would be very small. The result is overuse or depletion of the scarce resource.

The Solution: Government Intervention

From an economic perspective, the general solution to externalities, including those affecting the environment, is to *"internalize the externality"*—force the market participants to absorb the external costs or benefits. One way this can be accomplished is through the assignment of property rights. In our model, when the refineries owned the rights to pollute, the recreational users internalized the externality through their payment offer. Conversely, when the recreational users owned the rights to clean water, the refineries internalized the external cost by paying for the right to pollute. But how do these rights get assigned in the first place? In practice, the government would have to make this determination as well as enforce limitations on these rights for the good of society.

---

[20]Put another way, one can think of public goods as an extreme case of common property resources, when the group that shares the property rights consists of all individuals.

Other approaches to internalizing environmental externalities are policies that change the effective price of a product by the amount of the associated external cost or benefit. In the petroleum refinery market, for example, the price per barrel of oil could be forced up by the amount of the *MEC*. More recent policy prescriptions involve the most direct form of internalizing environmental externalities, which is to establish a market and a price for pollution. These approaches will be investigated in later chapters, all of which are rooted in market failure theory.

Conclusions

From an economic perspective, environmental problems persist because they are market failures. Whether we model pollution as a negative externality or as damage to environmental public goods, we observe conditions that impede natural market forces. At the root of the dilemma is the absence of property rights. Because no one owns the atmosphere or the earth's water bodies, there are no market incentives to pay for the right to protect these resources or for the right to pollute them. The result is a misallocation of economic resources and a decline in society's welfare. Some third-party mediation, typically government, is necessary to correct the market failure and reach an efficient equilibrium.

How strong a presence should government be in affected markets? And how should government go about the difficult task of developing effective policy solutions? Although market failure models communicate what the overall approach should be, there are many practical issues that have to be addressed. In theory, we know that the value of an environmental externality must be internalized so that the efficient solution can be identified. But, *how* in practice is this accomplished, and is this a practical solution? Are there methods that determine some proxy measure of the costs and benefits of pollution abatement? Or are there better alternative solutions or more reasonable objectives that should be pursued?

In the next two chapters, we will begin to address these questions by investigating various types of policy solutions, ranging from legislated regulations to various types of market-based initiatives. Using the analytical modeling tools developed thus far, we will critically evaluate different policy approaches to mitigating environmental pollution. Beyond their use in a theoretical inquiry, models of policy solutions prepare the way for the more pragmatic analyses to follow. These will consider both the environmental and economic implications of major U.S. policies, various government-sponsored programs, and international treaties—all aimed at protecting the earth's natural resources.

Summary

- There are two basic explanations for the economic assessment of environmental problems as market failures. If the market is defined as environmental quality, then the market failure arises because environmental quality is a public good. If the market is defined as a pollution-generating commodity, then the market failure is due to the presence of an externality.
- A pure public good is one that is both nonrival and nonexcludable in consumption.
- Market demand for a public good is found by vertically summing individual demand curves, since the market quantity is the same for all consumers but the perceived benefit of consuming the good is likely to be different across individuals.
- If the market demand for environmental quality could be determined and considered simultaneously with market supply, the efficient level of pollution would be identified.
- The market failure of public goods exists because demand is not readily identified. Since a public good is nonexcludable in consumption, there is no incentive for consumers to reveal their willingness to pay for it. The dilemma is known as nonrevelation of preferences, which in turn is due to the more fundamental problem of free-ridership.
- Because of imperfect information, consumers lack knowledge about the benefits of public goods consumption. Hence, even if they did reveal their willingness to pay, it is likely that the resulting price would underestimate the good's true value.
- Government can respond to the dilemma of free-ridership, nonrevelation of preferences, and imperfect information through direct provision of public goods, political procedures and voting rules, and the provision of education and information to society.
- An externality is a third-party effect associated with either production or consumption of a good. If this effect generates costs to the third party, it is a negative externality; if it yields benefits, it is a positive externality.
- In the presence of a negative (positive) externality, the competitive equilibrium is characterized by an overallocation (underallocation) of resources such that too much (too little) of the good is produced.
- In a negative externality model, the resulting competitive price is too low since the marginal external cost (MEC) is not captured by the market transaction. The MEC must be added to the firm's MPC to derive the marginal social cost (MSC), which must be set equal to the marginal social benefit (MSB) to identify the efficient equilibrium.
- The underlying source of the problem in public goods markets as well as in private markets where externalities are present is that property rights are not defined.
- The Coase Theorem argues that under certain conditions the assignment of property rights, even if externalities exist, will lead to bargaining between the affected parties such that an efficient solution can be obtained, regardless of which party is assigned those rights.
- If property rights exist but are ill defined, such as in the case of common property resources, the market solution is inefficient because of the presence of externalities.

- Solutions to market failures typically involve some type of intervention in the market by government. This intervention takes a variety of forms, including legislated regulation, taxation policy, and more recently the implementation of market-based solutions.

Key Concepts

market failure	positive externality
public good	marginal private cost (*MPC*)
externality	marginal private benefit (*MPB*)
imperfect information	marginal external cost (*MEC*)
nonrivalness	marginal social cost (*MSC*)
nonexcludability	marginal social benefit (*MSB*)
willingness to pay (WTP)	marginal external benefit (*MEB*)
nonrevelation of preferences	absence of property rights
free-ridership	Coase Theorem
negative externality	common property resources

Review Questions

1. Use economic analysis to evaluate the following statement: ''The only amount of acceptable pollution is no pollution at all.''

2. Using the theory of public goods, explain the logic of *why* in some resort communities, the ownership of waterfront homes also includes some defined area along the beach.

3. Recall the model of the refined petroleum market given in the text. Use the following graph to answer the questions below.

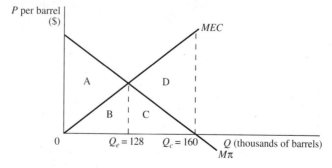

a. Give the economic interpretation of areas *A, B, C,* and *D.*

b. What area in the graph represents the loss to the petroleum refineries due to the restoration of efficiency? To which area in Figure 3.6 in the text is this area equivalent?

c. Which area represents the net gain to society? Should the reduction in output from Q_c to Q_e take place? Why or why not?

4. Using the graph presented in question 3, carefully describe the bargaining process between the refineries and the recreational water users, assuming the refineries have the rights to pollute.

5. Suppose you serve on an environmental policy planning board for the federal government. Your task is to propose a policy initiative aimed at reducing urban air pollution, using the assignment of property rights according to the Coase Theorem. Assume that the major polluters to be targeted are commuter bus companies and that the major parties affected are the collection of city dwellers, that is, residents and workers. Describe your proposal in detail, and include the following:

a. Whether the rights are to be assigned to city dwellers or to bus companies.

b. How these "rights" are to be defined.

c. How the rights are to be distributed to the parties.

d. Whether the rights are to be auctioned or sold, and if so at what price.

Additional Readings

Bator, F. M. "The Anatomy of Market Failure." *Quarterly Journal of Economics* 72 (1958), pp. 351–79.

Braden, John B. and Charles D. Kolstad, eds. *Measuring the Demand for Environmental Quality.* Amsterdam: North Holland, 1991.

Cornes, Richard and Todd Sandler. *The Theory of Externalities, Public Goods, and Club Goods.* Cambridge: Cambridge University Press, 1987.

Dasgupta, Partha. "The Environment as a Commodity." In Dieter Helm, ed., *Economic Policy Towards the Environment.* Cambridge: Blackwell Publishers, 1991.

Hardin, Garrett. "The Tragedy of the Commons." *Science* 162 (December 13, 1968), pp. 1243–48.

Head, John G. "Public Goods and Public Policy." Reprinted in *Public Goods and Public Policy,* ed. John G. Head. Durham, N.C.: Duke University Press, 1974.

MODELING SOLUTIONS TO ENVIRONMENTAL PROBLEMS

Recognizing the risks of environmental degradation helps us to appreciate what's at stake if the problem of pollution goes unchecked. Knowing how the market functions helps us to accept its inability to correct the problem on its own. Hence, solutions to reduce the ill effects of polluting residuals must come from outside the market, generally in the form of government policies and programs. But how does government go about the process of designing policy to address the complex problem of environmental pollution? What objectives does it establish to protect society's health and welfare, and what kinds of policy instruments does it use to implement those objectives? These are tough questions, and in this two-chapter module, we will only begin to answer them.

At the outset, we know that government solutions will not eliminate pollution entirely. The laws of science and the materials balance model tell us that much. However, determining exactly where environmental targets should be set is one of the more difficult and even controversial elements of policy development. So too is the specific approach undertaken by government to intervene in pollution-generating markets. Governments all over the world use a variety of policy instruments aimed at reducing environmental risks—some more successful than others. These range from regulations that directly control the activities of polluters to incentive-based plans that attempt to use market forces and the price mechanism to achieve a cleaner environment.

In this module, we introduce this broad range of policy alternatives by exploring both conventional and economic solutions to environmental degradation. Conventional policy is the subject of Chapter 4, where we investigate the traditional use of standards to define environmental objectives along with the command-and-control approach to implementing these standards. In Chapter 5, we examine the market approach, which has recently been adopted by the United States and other nations as a secondary form of environmental control policy. Using economic modeling and the criteria of allocative efficiency and cost-effectiveness, we evaluate the implications of using these very different regulatory strategies to solve the complex problem of environmental pollution.

CONVENTIONAL SOLUTIONS TO ENVIRONMENTAL PROBLEMS

The Command-and-Control Approach

In the previous chapter, the public goods model and the theory of externalities were used to show how pollution is the result of market failures—failures that arise because of the absence of property rights. Since no one owns the atmosphere or the earth's surface waters, there is no market incentive to prevent or correct contamination of these natural resources. According to the Coase Theorem, assigning property rights *would* solve the dilemma, but only under certain limiting assumptions. The bottom line is that government is needed to act as a third-party mediator in those markets where the more serious pollution problems arise.

Recognizing the need for government to correct environmental market failures is an important observation gained through economic modeling, but it is only a first step. We can also use these models to determine *how* government should respond to achieve effective policy solutions. For example, economic theory maintains that government should set abatement targets to achieve allocative efficiency, balancing social benefits and costs at the margin. It also identifies the tasks needed to achieve this criterion in practice, such as estimating the benefits of improving environmental quality and resolving the discrepancy between social and private costs. Although it is unlikely that these benefits and costs can be exactly determined, the efficiency criterion is useful in assessing how policy-makers set environmental objectives *relative* to their optimal level. In addition, the criterion of cost-effectiveness can be used to evaluate how *any* objective is being implemented—even one set at something other than its efficient level.

To establish a foundation for understanding government's response to environmental market failures, our objective in this chapter is to study what can be termed *conventional* policy solutions. First, we provide an overview of environmental standards and their role in most policies. We then use allocative efficiency to assess the level at which standards are set to define environmental objectives. Next, we provide an overview of the two broadly defined approaches to *implementing* these standards-based objectives—the **command-and-control approach** and the **market approach.** Finally, we investigate the cost-effectiveness of the command-and-control approach, the more conventional of the two, deferring an analysis of the market approach to the next chapter.

The Use of Standards in Environmental Policy

Standards are the fundamental basis of most environmental policies. In the United States, setting standards follows a rather lengthy set of procedures involving scientific research and a series of review processes. The EPA is charged with the oversight of these tasks and for making a formal recommendation about how these standards are to be defined. Ultimately, environmental standards are legislated by Congress and subsequently monitored for compliance and enforced by the EPA.[1]

Types of Environmental Standards

When standards are defined within environmental law, they are specified in one of two ways, either as **technology-based standards** or as **performance-based standards.** As its name implies, a **technology-based standard** stipulates the type of abatement control that must be used by all regulated polluting sources. As we will discuss in later chapters, the use of such standards is not uncommon under U.S. law. In practice, the EPA is responsible for researching available technologies and evaluating their relative effectiveness in accordance with certain criteria outlined in the law. It then selects the "best" technology, which subsequently must be adopted by all regulated polluters.[2] The motivation is straightforward—to assure a specific limit on pollution releases by controlling *how* that limit is to be achieved. For example, to reduce sulfur dioxide emissions, the EPA might require all coal-burning electric power plants to use a scrubber system, forcing each one to achieve the same level of abatement in precisely the same way.

The alternative type of environmental standard is performance-based. A **performance-based standard** specifies an emissions limit to be achieved by every regulated polluter, but does not stipulate the technology to be used to achieve that limit. By definition, performance-based standards are more flexible than their technology-based counterparts. They implicitly allow polluting sources to choose *how* they will reduce pollution releases as long as they meet the statutory emissions limit.

technology-based standard
Designates a specific type of abatement equipment or method to be used by polluting sources in reducing emissions or effluents.

performance-based standard
Specifies a pollution limit to be achieved by every regulated polluter, but does not stipulate the technology to be used to achieve that limit.

---

[1]In subsequent chapters, we will elaborate on these important processes that define environmental policy development under U.S. law.

[2]The meaning of "best" in the context of environmental legislation is one that is often the subject of debate, an issue we will investigate in upcoming chapters.

The Economic Implications of Using Standards

Although the use of mandated standards sounds straightforward enough, there are two important economic implications to be considered. The first has to do with the *level* at which these standards are set—an important issue, since standards define environmental quality objectives. For example, a legislated standard that sets a limit on carbon monoxide emissions defines an ''acceptable level'' of that particular pollutant for society. From an economic perspective, the relevant issue is whether that level has been set to achieve **allocative efficiency.** If not, there is a tangible welfare loss to society.

A second implication of using standards is in *how* they are implemented across polluting sources. Policy implementation is concerned with the use of specific **control instruments** such as pollution limits or taxes. The selection determines not only whether the objectives are realized but also whether they are achieved in a **cost-effective** manner. If not, economic resources are being wasted, which imposes costs to society.

We can investigate these implications through a two-part economic evaluation, which centers around the following important questions:

- In using standards to define environmental objectives, are these standards set at a level that is **allocatively efficient?** That is, does the marginal social cost of pollution abatement equal the marginal social benefit?
- Given some predetermined environmental objective, is the implementation of that objective conducted in a **cost-effective** manner?

Addressing each of these questions will help us assess the effectiveness of environmental policies based upon well-defined economic criteria. We begin with the first part of our investigation, focusing on the *level* at which standards are set by policy-makers.

Are Environmental Standards Set at an Allocatively Efficient Level?

allocatively efficient standards
Environmental standards set such that the associated marginal social cost (MSC) of abatement equals the marginal social benefit (MSB) of abatement.

Since standards are used to define environmental objectives, it is important to determine whether these objectives are set to achieve **allocative efficiency.** As is the case for any market, this condition holds if resources are allocated such that the associated benefits and costs to society are equal at the margin. Hence, we need to develop these benefit and cost concepts specifically for the pollution abatement market, expanding upon what was presented in the previous chapter. Our objective is to learn precisely what is required to identify an allocatively efficient abatement level so that we can assess the likelihood of the government achieving such an outcome by setting a standards-based environmental objective.

The Marginal Social Benefit of Pollution Abatement

marginal social benefit (MSB) of abatement
A measure of the additional gains accruing to society as pollution is reduced, such as improvements in human health and the ecology.

As pollution is abated, the gains accruing to society are all the benefits associated with a cleaner environment, such as improvements in human health, ecosystems, aesthetics, recreation, and property. If we measure how these benefits increase relative to increases in abatement, we arrive at the relationship known as the **marginal social benefit (*MSB*) of abatement.** It is equally correct to think of this *MSB* as a measure of the *reduction in damages* caused by pollution.[3] We have actually modeled damage reduction, though in a limited context, in our discussion of bargaining in the previous chapter. By paying refineries to pollute less, recreational users of the river gained the *reduction* in the marginal external cost (*MEC*) associated with refined petroleum production. A real-world case where damages were shown to be directly attributable to industrial pollution is in the town of Catano, Puerto Rico, the subject of Application 4.1. In theory, if we were to add up all of the marginal reductions in environmental external costs across every market where pollution is reduced, we would arrive at the *MSB*.

From a market perspective, the *MSB* of abatement is society's *demand* for pollution abatement, or equivalently its demand for environmental quality.[4] Just as the recreational users were *willing to pay* the refineries for a cleaner river, society is *willing to pay* for a cleaner environment or additional amounts of pollution abatement. We expect that this willingness to pay declines with increasing levels of abatement, just as the law of demand predicts. If the abatement level is low, or equivalently if pollution is high, we would expect society to place a relatively high value on any marginal change in abatement. But as the environment becomes cleaner and abatement increases, this value at the margin would likely decline. Hence, the *MSB* is modeled as a negatively sloped relationship.

The Marginal Social Cost of Abatement

marginal social cost (MSC) of abatement
Includes the marginal costs of every polluter's abatement activities plus the marginal cost incurred by government to monitor and enforce those activities.

On the supply side, we need to model the costs incurred by society as all polluting sources reduce their releases of contaminating residuals. This relationship is referred to as the **marginal social cost (*MSC*) of abatement.** To gain a more tangible sense of what the *MSC* represents, it is easier to think of it as comprising two parts: (1) an aggregation of the marginal costs of every individual polluter's abatement activities; *plus* (2) the marginal costs government incurs to monitor and enforce those activities. Let's begin with the first

---

[3]Technically, the *MSB* also includes the reduction in costs to society from attempting to avoid the effects of pollution, such as the costs of air purification systems, bottled water, and water filtration systems.

[4]Although we generally model demand as the *MPB,* which differs from the *MSB* by the amount of any marginal external benefits (*MEB*), in this context there is no *MEB,* since the demanders are *all* of society. Thus there are no third parties to which any external benefits could accrue.

Application 4.1

Industrial Pollution and Damages to Human Health: Catano, Puerto Rico

For years, the people of Catano, Puerto Rico, blamed their persistent health problems on the town's severe air pollution. The residents live with a barrage of emissions generated by a nearby oil refinery, a sewage sludge incinerator, passing ships in San Juan Bay, and a parade of 18-wheelers transporting goods from nearby docks. According to the island dwellers, however, most of the problem is caused by two giant power plants operated by the Puerto Rico Electric Power Authority. Together, the two facilities house 10 generating units with a combined capacity of 1,086 megawatts, and they release an average of 100 million pounds of sulfur dioxide emissions into Catano's air supply each year. One of the town's residents leading the charge against the utility says that Catano's air supply can be likened to a "toxic soup."

Acting on the residents' complaints, several agencies conducted health studies. Findings by a Puerto Rico Medical Association study showed that cancer rates in Catano were nearly twice the national average. The report found approximately 362 incidents of cancer for every 100,000 residents in Catano in the 1987–88 study year—a dismal statistic compared to Puerto Rico's average rate of 199 in 100,000. Still more disturbing evidence came from a U.S. public health service investigation, which found an alarming rate of respiratory disease among the people of Catano. Since it is well known that long-term exposure to sulfur dioxide causes respiratory ailments, this latter report validated the suspicion that the utility's emissions were the primary cause of health damages in the town.

Responding to these disturbing medical reports, the EPA initiated its own study of the area, focusing on the two power plants' emissions. What they found confirmed the accusations of Catano's residents. Pollutant releases from the electric power plants were in violation of air quality regulations. The EPA conducted what are called opacity tests, which measure the amount of light that can pass through emissions. The results showed that the opacity levels of the power plants' emissions were two to four times the allowable limit. The test results were forwarded to the U.S. Justice Department to bring Puerto Rico's utility back into compliance. As this occurs, Catano's residents should enjoy the benefits of better health.

There is little doubt that Catano's residents were right. Few would suggest that the utility's emission violations and the town's health statistics are mere coincidence. Air pollution is known to cause serious health damages. Unfortunately in this case, being right is little solace to some 300,000 individuals that have long suffered the consequences that have already befallen their community.

Source: Karl Ross, "Some Foul Air in Puerto Rico," *Boston Globe,* January 7, 1993.

part by considering a representative polluter and how it goes about the task of abating its emissions.

Referring once again to our discussion of bargaining under the Coase Theorem, recall that refineries reduced their toxic releases by decreasing output. In that case, the marginal cost to refineries of abating pollution was forgone profit, modeled as a movement from right to left along the marginal profit ($M\pi$) curve. Hence, if the decision variable is output, each polluting firm faces a marginal abatement cost equal to its *forgone $M\pi$*. However, such a model implicitly assumes that polluters can meet an environmental standard *only* by reducing output—a very limiting assumption. Since other methods are also available, we need to expand upon this output-based specification.

As a profit-maximizer, the polluting firm is implicitly a cost-minimizer. Thus, to meet an emissions standard, it will consider *all* available abatement options and select the *least-cost* method. In addition to reducing the level of production, these options may include installing a type of abatement technology, altering a production process, and fuel switching. To allow for the fact that polluters choose from a full menu of available abatement methods, we model what conventionally is called a **marginal abatement cost (*MAC*)** function. This relationship measures the change in economic costs associated with reducing pollution using the least-cost method of abatement at some point in time. Application 4.2 discusses the importance of choosing a least-cost abatement technology in the context of cleaning up contaminated sites from oil spills and hazardous wastes.

marginal abatement cost (*MAC*)
Measures the change in economic costs incurred by the firm associated with reducing pollution using the least-cost abatement method.

Application 4.2

Abatement Costs:
The Promise of Remediation Technology

Soil contamination is an environmental problem of major proportions. This seemingly esoteric subject has captured world attention in large part because of the damage caused by major oil spills. The 1989 *Valdez* incident, for example, despoiled Alaskan shorelines with 11 million gallons of oil. Such disasters are national and international news both because the environmental implications are so severe *and* because the abatement costs are so staggering. Adding to these concerns is the well-publicized problem of deliberate hazardous waste dumping. Many landfill sites have become contaminated with cancer-causing substances, ranging from polychlorinated biphenyls (PCBs) to heavy metals. Based on EPA estimates, there are more than 30,000 contaminated sites scattered throughout the United States, and cleanup has only just begun.

Projected abatement costs to clean up the 1,200-plus worst U.S. hazardous waste sites bears an impressive price tag that might be as high as $750 billion, according to some estimates. As of 1992,

actual expenses accumulated by the EPA were at $11 billion to clean up only 84 of these sites. Oil spill abatement expenses are no less disturbing. Exxon spent $3 billion to clean up the beaches damaged by its devastating oil spill, an amount said to be modest given that much of the cleansing was achieved naturally from the effect of winter storms.

Facing such prohibitive damage estimates, research is being directed toward technologies that can lower abatement costs for major environmental hazards. Recently, scientists have made important strides in contaminated soil abatement using a technology called **bioremediation.** Bioremediation is a relatively low-cost abatement technique that relies on bacteria that naturally consume waste materials. Fertilizer sprays are used to stimulate the feeding of these microorganisms, which accelerates the usually lengthy process of returning soil to its original state. Used for some 50 years to clean wastewater treatment plants, the process is now being employed to abate toxic contaminants. In its most

Application 4.2 (concluded)

successful application to date, bioremediation was used to help clean up the oily mess left by the *Valdez* on Alaskan beaches. Within a scant three weeks, the soil was restored down to a foot below the surface. While there are still problems to be solved, such as bacteria that feed on only a single contaminant, bioremediation holds great promise for the environment. And, from a financial perspective, the costs of using this technology relative to conventional methods are remarkably low.

While the use of bioremediation in toxic abatement is still limited, existing data show that contractors are charging in the range of $50 to $100 per ton for this innovative process—a significant cost savings over the standard charge for more conventional methods. Soil abatement technologies used at waste sites have consisted primarily of either on-site or off-site incineration. On-site soil incineration can be done for $300 per ton, while the costs for off-site abatement can run as high as $1,000 per ton. Both use the same basic technology, but the higher costs of off-site abatement reflect its added expenses such as the cost of transport.

Abatement Method	Per Unit Abatement Cost
On-site soil incineration	$ 300
Off-site soil incineration	1,000
Bioremediation	50–100

The lesson is clear. Technology offers a solution to controlling what are often prohibitively high abatement costs. As technology advances, decision-makers are offered a wider range of alternatives to abate pollution. The result? Both public officials and polluting sources are better able to meet environmental objectives in a cost-effective manner—an outcome that serves all of society.

Sources: U.S. Environmental Protection Agency, Office of Communications, Education, and Public Affairs, *Securing Our Legacy, An EPA Progress Report 1989–1991,* Washington, D.C., April 1992, p. 27; Peter Hong and Michele Galen. "The Toxic Mess Called Superfund," *Business Week,* May 11, 1992, pp. 32–34; Robert D. Hof, "The Tiniest Toxic Avengers," *Business Week,* June 4, 1990, pp. 96, 98; Associated Press, "Updating Previous Big Spills," *Boston Globe,* January 6, 1993.

Each polluting source likely faces a unique *MAC* curve. The firm's location, the type of contaminants it releases, the nature of its production, and the availability of technology are among the factors that affect the shape and position of the *MAC* curve. However, a typical *MAC* curve is positively sloped and increasing at an increasing rate, as shown in Figure 4.1. At low levels of abatement, such as at A_1, the marginal cost to remove pollution is relatively low, measured as MAC_1. As the firm continues to abate from A_1 to A_2, the marginal cost increases by a proportionately greater amount from MAC_1 to MAC_2. Think about the intuition of this model. When pollution levels are high, the addition of virtually any type of abatement technology will likely be quite effective. So, although costs are rising, they are doing so at a fairly slow rate relative to the abatement being accomplished. But, as this process continues and the environment becomes cleaner, it becomes very difficult to remove still more pollution. Thus, the added costs relative to the abatement achieved increases at a much faster rate.

Should a firm's abatement options change, the position of its *MAC* would be affected. For example, the introduction of a new cost-saving abatement

FIGURE 4.1

The single polluter's marginal abatement cost (MAC)

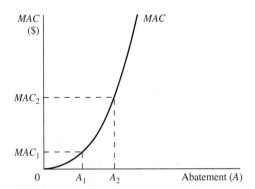

A typical *MAC* curve is positively sloped and increasing at an increasing rate. Notice that as the firm continues to abate from A_1 to A_2, the *MAC* increases by a proportionately greater amount from MAC_1 to MAC_2. This reflects the fact that as the abatement process continues and the environment becomes cleaner, it becomes increasingly difficult and therefore more costly to remove each additional unit of pollution.

FIGURE 4.2

The effect of cost-saving technology on the polluter's MAC curve

Changes in a firm's abatement options change the position of the *MAC* curve. For example, this model shows how the introduction of a new cost-saving abatement technology would pivot the *MAC* downward to *MAC'*.

market-level marginal abatement cost function (MAC_{mkt})
The horizontal sum of each polluter's *MAC*.

technology would pivot the *MAC* downward, as shown in Figure 4.2.[5] Notice that at each abatement level, *MAC'* is below *MAC*. Likewise, a polluter's *MAC* for one pollutant might be lower than that of another. Thus, an *MAC* function generally is defined for a particular contaminant at a *given* level of technology.

The aggregate of all polluters' *MAC*s represents the **market-level *MAC* function (MAC_{mkt})** defined as the horizontal sum of each polluter's *MAC*, or $MAC_{mkt} = \Sigma MAC_i$ for all i firms. This is exactly the same procedure we used

[5]Since a firm's *total* abatement costs are represented as the area under the *MAC* up to the abatement level required by the standard, the effect of the cost-saving technology on total abatement costs is implicitly shown as the reduction in the area under the firm's *MAC*.

FIGURE 4.3

*The allocatively
efficient amount of
pollution abatement*

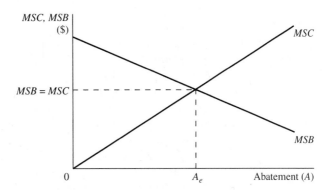

In the market for pollution abatement, the efficient level, A_e, occurs at the intersection of the *MSB* and *MSC* curves.

to derive market supply in Chapter 2. In this context, the horizontal summing assures that the MAC_{mkt} maintains the notion of least-cost decisions, since it effectively sets each *MAC* equal at every abatement level. We will come back to this point of equal *MAC*s across firms later on in the chapter.

Now, consider the second element of the *MSC*. To the MAC_{mkt}, we need to add the marginal costs incurred by government for enforcement and monitoring of abatement activities. The result of this final step in the aggregation process is the **marginal social cost (*MSC*) of abatement.**

Are Abatement Standards Set Optimally?

From our discussion in Chapter 3, we know that the *MSB* and the *MSC* simultaneously determine the socially optimal level of pollution abatement. This result is illustrated in Figure 4.3 where, for simplicity, it is assumed that both functions are linear. The efficient level of abatement, A_e, occurs at the intersection of the two curves. Whether or not the government sets environmental quality standards to achieve this level depends on a variety of considerations. There are three factors in particular that suggest this outcome is highly unlikely: (1) the existence of legislative constraints; (2) imperfect information; and (3) regional differences.

**benefit-based
standard**
A standard set at a
level to improve
society's well-being
with no allowance for
a balancing of the
associated costs.

Legislative Constraints.   First of all, the reality of a standards-based approach is that it does not necessarily set pollution limits to account for both the associated benefits and costs. In fact, under U.S. environmental law, many national standards are said to be **benefit-based,** meaning they are set at a level to improve society's well-being with no allowance for a balancing of the associated costs. For example, under the U.S. Clean Air Act, air quality standards are motivated solely by the anticipated benefits of improved public health and welfare. As long as costs are not accounted for in the standard-setting process, resources likely will be overallocated to abatement.

Imperfect Information.   Even when a cost-benefit balancing *is* called for by law, the absence of full information would likely prevent the government from identifying the *MSB* and *MSC* of abatement. Let's consider the *MSB* relationship first. Recall from our discussion of market failure in Chapter 3 that pollution abatement is a public good. As such, its demand, which *is* the *MSB* curve, is not readily identified due to the problem of nonrevelation of preferences. Government would have to somehow circumvent this problem to define the *MSB* for any type of pollution abatement. There are methods used in practice to *estimate* the value society places on the damage reductions associated with abatement. However, given the inherent difficulties of attempting to monetize such intangibles as health improvements and longevity of life, the probability of accurately modeling *MSB* is quite low.

There are similar problems in attempting to identify the *MSC*. In addition to estimating the marginal costs of monitoring and enforcement, the government would have to know the *MAC* for every polluter. Obtaining this firm-level information would be a virtually impossible undertaking, given the diversity of production and abatement techniques across polluting sources. Furthermore, the *MAC* must also account for the *implicit* costs of abatement, which are difficult to determine. In this context, implicit costs would have to capture any unemployment associated with production declines, the potential loss of consumer choice if products were eliminated or altered, and any associated price and income effects arising from abatement requirements.[6]

In the absence of perfect information, it is highly probable that the government will unknowingly establish the abatement standard at some level other than the allocatively efficient one, even if that was the legislated intent. Figure 4.4 reproduces the market for abatement at equilibrium, comparing the allocatively efficient outcome, A_e, along with two other possible abatement levels, A_0 and A_1. If the standard is set at A_0, the *MSB* would be greater than the *MSC*, meaning that society places a higher value on reducing pollution than it must give up in resources to achieve it. Hence, society would consider the A_0 standard to be too lenient. Conversely, a standard set at A_1 would be considered too restrictive. Only at A_e would society accept the legal limit as allocatively efficient. However, the information needed to find this optimal level of pollution abatement is immense.

Regional Differences.   Finally, even if the law permits a balancing of costs and benefits *and* if full information were available, there is a qualifier on the use of A_e as a national standard across all polluting sources. Why? Because this optimal level is determined from *MSB* and *MSC,* both of which assume the absence of regional-specific abatement benefits and costs. The only way A_e would be allocatively efficient in all locations is if the respective *MSB* and *MSC* functions defined for those locations were identical.

---

[6]In a later chapter, we will investigate the methods used in practice to estimate the benefits and costs of improving environmental quality.

FIGURE 4.4

Setting an environmental quality standard: Is it allocatively efficient?

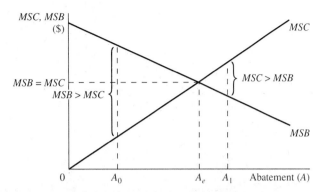

If the government were to set an abatement standard at A_0, the *MSB* would be higher than the *MSC*, meaning that society places a higher value on the gain from reducing pollution than the resources needed to achieve it. Hence, the A_0 standard would be too lenient. On the other hand, if the standard were set at A_1, it would be considered too restrictive. Only at A_e would society accept the legal limit as allocatively efficient.

FIGURE 4.5

The effect of regional differences on achieving allocative efficiency

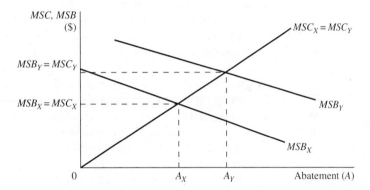

This model shows how regional-specific conditions can give rise to different optimal levels of abatement. Although the *MSC*s are identical, that is, $MSC_X = MSC_Y$, the *MSB* in region X is *lower* than for that of region Y, that is, $MSB_X < MSB_Y$. Thus, the allocatively efficient abatement level for region X, A_X, is lower than for region Y, A_Y. Consequently, a single national standard of abatement cannot be optimal for both regions.

By way of example, consider two hypothetical regions X and Y that have identical *MSC* functions, that is $MSC_X = MSC_Y$, but different *MSB* functions such that MSB_X is *lower* than MSB_Y at all abatement levels. Such a disparity might be due to differences in income, education, or population across the two locations. In any case, at most, only one of the two locations would consider a nationally-determined A_e as efficient. Look at Figure 4.5, which superimposes the *MSB* and *MSC* for each region on the same diagram. The allocatively efficient level of abatement in region X, A_X, is much lower than that for region Y, A_Y. So, there is no way that a single national standard of abatement—even one that *is* efficient on a national level—would be optimal for both regions.

What we can surmise from this assessment is that in most real-world applications, at least one of the factors—legislative constraints, imperfect information, or regional differences—will be present. Hence, there is a very small probability that pollution abatement standards will be set at an allocatively efficient level. Accepting this, we must rely on a different criterion to evaluate, not where the standards are set, but how they are implemented.

General Approaches to Implementing Environmental Policy

cost-effective policy
A policy initiative that meets an environmental objective at the lowest possible cost, using the least amount of economic resources.

command-and-control approach
An environmental policy approach using pollution limits or technology-based restrictions to directly control the release of pollutants.

market approach
An environmental policy approach using incentive-based instruments to motivate pollution abatement based on natural market forces.

Our preceding analysis makes a strong case that a government-established environmental standard will be set at something other than its optimal level. While this outcome is unfortunate, it *is* possible that even a nonoptimal environmental standard can be implemented using the least amount of resources. If so, the policy is said to be **cost-effective.** Whether or not this criterion is met depends upon the method used to bring about the desired reduction in pollution. Most governments, including that of the United States, use a number of different policy tools to achieve environmental quality, as Application 4.3 explains. However, it is helpful at the outset to collapse these down into two broadly defined categories. One is the **command-and-control approach,** which uses pollution limits or technology-based restrictions to directly regulate polluting sources. The second is known as the **market approach,** since it uses incentive-based policy tools to motivate abatement through normal market forces.

Of the two, command and control is the more conventional approach, dominating environmental policy in most nations. This nearly universal reliance on direct regulation seems to have evolved from an attempt to gain immediate control of what was initially an unfamiliar and urgent social dilemma. Though well intentioned, the use of inflexible regulations and emissions limits—often imposed uniformly across all polluters—has not met with consistent success. Hence, over time policy-makers began to look for alternatives.

Recently, a change has been observed in the United States and other industrialized countries that shows a gradual shift toward the use of more market-based solutions. Combining incentive-oriented control instruments with more conventional methods seems to be indicative of a trend in environmental policy. Economists have long been proponents of such a change, advocating the use of a market approach to achieve environmental objectives. However, the *relative* gains of market-based solutions cannot be fully appreciated without an understanding of the command-and-control approach and its effectiveness in solving environmental problems.

Application 4.3

Methods Used by Government to Reduce Environmental Pollution

According to the Relative Risk Reduction Strategies Committee of the EPA's Science Advisory Board, there are six categories of risk-reducing policy tools that governments should consider when addressing any environmental problem. Two of these are the more conventional broad-based categories of *conventional regulations,* such as standards, use restrictions, and product design, and *market incentives,* such as pollution charges and permit systems. The other four major groups are described as follows:

- **Scientific and Technical Measures**

  Research and development to suggest promising solutions and to improve understanding of problems like the potential for global warming.

  Innovations in pollution prevention and pollution control technology, such as the development of ecologically safe, cost-effective methods to manage contaminated sediments.

- **Provision of Information**

  Improving communication to producers, consumers, and/or state and local governments about risks of environmental problems and threats to communities. (For example, new home buyers could be provided with the results of radon tests, and state and local governments could be given

technical information to support their efforts in addressing indoor air pollution.)

- **Enforcement**

  Implement more vigorous enforcement of existing laws and regulations. (Suggested options include: (1) the use of statistical techniques in enforcement to ensure that all classes of potential violators are properly inspected; and (2) the imposition of penalties that create incentives for compliance with existing environmental laws.)

- **Cooperation with Other Government Agencies and Nations**

  Promotion of interagency cooperation to reduce environmental risk. (Environmental authorities typically have limited jurisdiction, but other government bodies make decisions that affect the environment. This necessitates a cooperative approach to environmental issues.)

  Promotion of cooperation with other nations through such means as international conventions aimed at problems like global warming or acid rain.

Source: U.S. Environmental Protection Agency, Science Advisory Board, *Reducing Risk: Setting Priorities and Strategies for Environmental Protection* (Washington, D.C., September 1990), p. 15.

Is the Command-and-Control Approach Cost-Effective?

The practical basis for assessing the command-and-control approach according to the cost-effectiveness criterion is to assure that society is not incurring higher costs than necessary to achieve a given level of environmental quality. For discussion purposes, let's consider the abatement standard as the socially desirable (as opposed to optimal) outcome, perhaps motivated solely to protect human health. To achieve cost-effectiveness, policy-makers must determine the relative costs of all available policy instruments that can achieve this socially desirable objective and select the one that minimizes costs. By confining the options only to those that meet the abatement standard, the government's decision about which instrument to use has no effect on social benefits. Only the costs incurred are within the policy-maker's choice set.

Given this general premise, we can identify two aspects of the command-and-control approach that may violate the cost-effectiveness criterion. The first is the use of a technology-based standard, and the second is the conventional use of standards imposed *uniformly* across polluting sources. We discuss each of these issues in turn.

The Cost-Ineffectiveness of the Technology-Based Standard

Recall from the beginning of the chapter that there are two types of standards imposed under a command-and-control framework—the **performance-based** standard and the **technology-based** standard. Take a minute to reread the definitions of each of these control instruments, and think about the cost implications of each. What should be apparent is that the technology-based standard potentially prevents the polluter from minimizing the costs of achieving a given abatement level. Remember that the *MAC* curve is defined under the assumption that the polluter selects the *least-cost* available method. If the government *forces* polluters to use a specific technology to meet an emissions limit, it is directly impeding the firm's natural incentive to abate in a cost-effective manner. Unless the mandated technology happens to be the least-cost abatement approach for *all* polluters, at least some will be forced to operate *above* their respective *MAC* curves. This in turn means that society is incurring costs higher than the *MSC* of abatement. The unfortunate consequence is a waste of economic resources with no additional benefits accruing to society.

If instead a performance-based standard were used, each polluter could select the means by which it achieves a given objective. Without further guidance, it would follow its self-interest and choose the least costly abatement method. Assuming compliance with the law, society would still gain the benefits of a cleaner environment, but fewer resources would be used to achieve that gain. A word of caution is in order, however. Although there are potential cost advantages to using performance-based standards over technology-based standards, this selection does not by itself assure a cost-effective policy solution. In fact, regardless of which type of standard is used, resources will be wasted if they are imposed *uniformly* across polluters.

The Cost-Ineffectiveness of Uniform Standards

Under a strict command-and-control framework, standards often are imposed *uniformly* across groups of polluting sources.[7] The operative question is whether such a policy approach is cost-effective. The answer? The use of uniform standards across polluting sources will waste economic resources as long as abatement cost conditions differ among those sources. Of course, the reality is that there are many factors that might give rise to such differences. One is the age of the polluter's physical plant. Newer facilities typically are designed and built with the most advanced pollution control equipment, making them capable of meeting an abatement standard at a much lower marginal cost than their less modern counterparts. Another relevant factor is regional differences in input prices. There is no reason to expect firms in different locations to face the same costs of labor, land, and capital, and as long as input prices vary, so too will polluters' costs to achieve a given abatement standard.

Accepting the likelihood of abatement cost differences among polluters, why should this set of conditions make the use of uniform standards cost-ineffective? The problem is that uniform standards under a command-and-control framework force high-cost abaters to reduce pollution as much as low-cost abaters, so more resources than necessary are used to achieve the benefits of a cleaner environment. Cost savings could be achieved by having more of the abatement accomplished by polluters who are capable of doing so at a relatively lower cost. We use a simple model to illustrate this important assertion.

To begin, assume there are only two polluting sources in a given region, each of which generates 10 units of pollution for a total of 20 units released into the environment. The government determines that emissions must be reduced by 10 units across the region to achieve the "socially desirable level of pollution." Each firm faces different abatement cost conditions modeled as follows:[8]

Polluter 1's Marginal Abatement Cost (MAC_1): $MAC_1 = 2.5(A_1)$;
Polluter 1's Total Abatement Costs (TAC_1): $TAC_1 = 1.25(A_1)^2$,

   where $A_1 =$ the amount of pollution abated by Polluter 1.

Polluter 2's Marginal Abatement Cost (MAC_2): $MAC_2 = 0.625(A_2)$;
Polluter 2's Total Abatement Costs (TAC_2): $TAC_2 = 0.3125(A_2)^2$,

   where $A_2 =$ the amount of pollution abated by Polluter 2.

---

[7]In some contexts, pollution limits vary across major industrial groups but are applied uniformly *within* each of these.

[8]The total abatement costs (*TAC*) for a given abatement level, *A*, are simply the aggregation of the *MAC* at each abatement level up to *A*. Graphically, *TAC* for abatement level *A* is the area under the *MAC* curve up to point *A*.

Now, assume that the government implements the 10-unit standard *uniformly,* requiring each polluter to abate by 5 units, (i.e., $A_1 = A_2 = 5$). At this abatement level, the *MAC* for Polluter 1 is \$12.50, [$MAC_1 = 2.5(5) = \$12.50$], and its *TAC* is \$31.25 [$TAC_1 = 1.25(5)^2 = \$31.25$]. For Polluter 2, MAC_2 is \$3.13, and TAC_2 is \$7.81. Thus, the total abatement costs for the region (absent the costs of monitoring and enforcement), equal \$39.06, which represents the value of resources used by polluters to meet the standard. The question is, could the same standard be achieved at a lower cost?

Notice that Polluter 2 has an abatement cost advantage over Polluter 1. For example, the fifth unit of abatement cost Polluter 2 \$9.37 less than Polluter 1. Therefore, it would be cheaper if Polluter 2 were to do more of the abating. Of course, it would have to have an incentive to do this, and the two firms would have to negotiate to arrive at some mutually beneficial agreement.[9] But no such opportunity is allowed when the government forces every polluter to abate by the same amount. Thus, we conclude that the use of uniform standards under a conventional command-and-control approach does not achieve the cost-effectiveness criterion as long as *MAC* conditions differ across polluters.

Could the government reallocate abatement levels across the two polluters to achieve a cost-effective solution? The answer is yes, and it turns out that economic theory conveys exactly how this result can be achieved. If each polluter abates to the point where the corresponding level of *MAC* is equal across firms, the environmental standard would be met at minimum cost. This solution is one application of what microeconomic theory calls the **equi-marginal principle of optimality.**

equi-marginal principle of optimality
Asserts that the cost-effective allocation of abatement responsibilities across polluting sources occurs at the point where the *MAC*s for each source are equal.

To illustrate the cost savings of such an approach, let's return to our two-polluter model. We need to find the abatement levels for each polluter where their respective *MAC*s are equal, holding the combined abatement level at 10 units to meet the standard. Algebraically, the solution is:

(1)   Set $MAC_1 = MAC_2$: $2.5A_1 = 0.625A_2$

(2)   Set $A_1 + A_2$ = Abatement Standard: $A_1 + A_2 = 10$

(3)   Solve the equations simultaneously: $A_1 = 2; A_2 = 8.$

This same result is shown graphically in Figure 4.6. Both firms' *MAC* curves are plotted on the same diagram. For Polluter 1, A_1 is measured horizontally *left to right,* while for Polluter 2, A_2 is measured *right to left.* The horizontal axis measured in either direction ranges from 0 units of abatement up to the 10-unit requirement imposed by the regulatory authority. Thus, every point on this axis represents a *combined* abatement level that satisfies the standard. Notice that the intersection of the two *MAC* curves yields the cost-effective solution, $A_1 = 2$ and $A_2 = 8$. At this point, $MAC_1 = MAC_2 = \$5.00$.

---

[9]In a real-world setting, there would also be transactions costs associated with the negotiations between the two firms.

FIGURE 4.6

The cost-effective solution in a two-polluter model

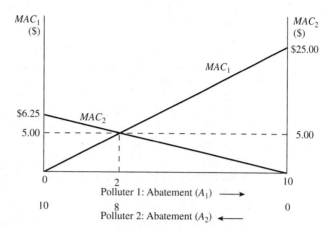

The model shows the *MAC* curves for two firms, Polluter 1 and Polluter 2, diagrammed on the same graph. Polluter 1's abatement level, A_1, is measured left to right on the horizontal axis, and Polluter 2's abatement, A_2, right to left. The horizontal axis measures from 0 units of abatement up to the 10-unit limit imposed by the regulatory authority, so that every point represents a *combined* abatement level that satisfies the standard. In accordance with the equi-marginal principle of optimality, the intersection of the two *MAC* curves yields the cost-effective solution, where $A_1 = 2$ and $A_2 = 8$. At this point, notice that $MAC_1 = MAC_2 = \$5.00$.

If each polluter were given these firm-specific abatement targets, the total costs of achieving the environmental objective would be minimized. The dollar value of these costs can be calculated from each firm's *TAC* equation, substituting in the cost-effective abatement levels:

$$TAC_1 = 1.25(2)^2 \quad = \$ \ 5.00$$

$$TAC_2 = 0.3125(8)^2 = \$20.00$$

By following the equi-marginal principle of optimality, the total cost to society of achieving the 10-unit abatement standard is \$25.00—a \$14.06 savings over the uniform standards approach. Equivalently, this \$14.06 represents the unnecessary costs incurred by society when a uniform standard is imposed across nonidentical polluters to implement the environmental objective.

As a final point, it is reasonable to ask how in practice the government could arrive at these firm-specific abatement standards within a command-and-control framework. The answer is that it would have to know the abatement cost conditions for every firm it was regulating. Of course, this kind of information would be virtually impossible to determine, particularly when thousands of individual sources are being controlled. But there is a way around the problem—though not within the command-and-control approach. As we will discover in the next chapter, there are instruments under the market approach that can arrive at this same cost-effective solution without specific knowledge of polluters' costs. How? By using natural market incentives and the price mechanism in place of inflexible rules.

Conclusions

In this chapter, we have begun to evaluate solutions to environmental problems by focusing in on the more conventional policy tools used in practice—the use of standards to define environmental objectives and the command-and-control approach to implementing those objectives. Even at this introductory level, we were able to reach some important conclusions. It is apparent, for example, that government-mandated environmental standards are not likely to be set at an efficient level. Beyond those instances when the law does not allow for the requisite balancing of benefits and costs, there is still an information problem. Policy-makers would need extensive and highly detailed data to accurately measure the marginal costs and benefits of pollution abatement. Hence, in all likelihood, the level at which governmental environmental objectives are set will not be allocatively efficient.

Accepting this realization, cost-effectiveness becomes the relevant criterion by which to assess the command-and-control approach and ultimately compare it to the market approach. Thus far, our investigation shows that the use of *uniform* standards under a command-and-control framework likely wastes economic resources. Cost savings can be realized if the equi-marginal principle of optimality is applied to the problem, whereby polluters reduce emissions up to the point where their marginal costs of doing so are equal. But, how can such a result be achieved in practice? The answer requires an investigation of alternative control instruments, in particular those characterized as part of the market approach to environmental policy.

In sum, although our findings in this chapter are important, they are nonetheless incomplete. We still must learn how market-based initiatives are designed and how they compare to their command-and-control counterparts—precisely the agenda of our next chapter. This part of our analysis is particularly relevant given the recent move by the United States and other nations to integrate market-based instruments into what had been an exclusively command-and-control approach to environmental policy. To appreciate this trend and what it means for society, we must understand how market instruments operate and evaluate their effectiveness in achieving environmental goals.

Summary

- Standards are the fundamental basis of most environmental policies. There are two basic types of standards used in environmental control policy. One is a technology-based standard, which designates the abatement method to be used by polluters. The second is a performance-based standard, which specifies an emissions limit to be achieved by polluters.
- The level at which standards are set is critical since standards implicitly define environmental quality objectives for society. From an economic perspective, the relevant issue is whether that level has been set to achieve allocative efficiency.

This criterion is met if resources are allocated to abatement such that the marginal social benefit (*MSB*) of abatement is equal to the marginal social cost (*MSC*) of abatement.

- The *MSB* is a measure of the additional gains to society associated with the reduction in damages caused by pollution. It is effectively society's demand for pollution abatement or equivalently its demand for environmental quality.

- The *MSC* can be specified as the horizontal sum of every polluter's marginal abatement cost (*MAC*) *plus* the marginal costs government incurs to monitor and enforce those activities. Each polluter's *MAC* function measures the change in costs associated with reducing pollution, using the least-cost method of abatement at some point in time.

- Three factors suggest that a government-mandated abatement standard is not likely to meet the allocative efficiency criterion: (1) the existence of legislative constraints; (2) imperfect information; and (3) regional differences.

- Another important issue is to consider whether an environmental objective—even one that is nonoptimal—is implemented by government in a cost-effective manner.

- Governments generally use one of two general approaches to implement environmental policy: the command-and-control approach, which relies on pollution limits or restrictions to directly regulate polluting sources; or the market approach, which utilizes incentive-based policy tools to motivate a pollution reduction through normal market forces.

- Two aspects of the command-and-control approach may violate the cost-effectiveness criterion: the use of technology-based standards; and the use of uniform standards across nonidentical polluting sources.

- Since technology-based standards dictate a specific abatement method to polluting sources, their use potentially prevents the polluter from minimizing the costs of achieving a given abatement level.

- The use of uniform standards across polluting sources will waste economic resources as long as marginal abatement cost conditions differ among those sources. Uniform standards force high-cost abaters to reduce pollution as much as low-cost abaters, so more resources than necessary are used to achieve the benefits of a cleaner environment.

- To achieve a cost-effective outcome, the allocation of pollution abatement responsibilities across polluting sources must be such that the corresponding level of *MAC* is equal across polluters. This is an application of the equi-marginal principle of optimality.

Key Concepts

technology-based standard
performance-based standard
control instruments
allocative efficiency
marginal social benefit of abatement (*MSB*)
marginal social cost of abatement (*MSC*)

marginal abatement cost (*MAC*)
benefit-based standard
cost-effectiveness
command-and-control approach
market approach
equi-marginal principle of optimality

Review Questions

1. One of the major problems in applying the Coase Theorem in practice is the existence of high transactions costs. Propose an approach that a third party could institute which would reduce these costs sufficiently so that the bargaining process could proceed. How likely is the solution to be efficient and why?

2. Using a graph of the pollution abatement market, model a situation where the allocatively efficient level of abatement occurs at 100 percent, or equivalently where pollution is zero. Using the relative position of the *MSC* and *MSB* curves, explain such an outcome intuitively.

3. *a.* Under a strict command-and-control framework, abatement standards are set equally across polluters. Assume the total abatement target is set at 30 units and show the cost implications using three graphs, each of a different polluter with a unique *MAC* curve drawn to depict a ''low-cost abater,'' a ''moderate-cost abater,'' and a ''high-cost abater.'' On each graph, identify the abatement level corresponding to a uniform standards approach and show the level of *MAC* at that point and the area corresponding to *TAC*.

   b. Now, refer directly to your model and explain what would happen *qualitatively* to the abatement levels of each firm if the equi-marginal principle of optimality were used and explain intuitively why this would be cost-effective.

4. It is well documented that the emissions of carbon monoxide (CO) from combustible engines, (e.g. automobile engines), increase in colder climates. This in turn implies that damages associated with CO emissions are expected to be less severe in summer months than in winter. However, air quality control authorities use a standard for CO that is uniform throughout the year with no allowance for seasonal effects. Use this information and the following model to answer the questions below:

$$MSB \text{ of CO abatement in winter} = 350 - 0.5A$$

$$MSB \text{ of CO abatement in summer} = 140 - 0.2A$$

$$MSC \text{ of CO abatement} = 0.2A$$

where A is the level of CO abatement.

a. Graph the *MSB* and *MSC* functions on the same diagram.

b. Assume the government sets a uniform standard for both winter and summer at $A = 500$. Support or refute this policy based on the criterion of allocative efficiency, using your model to explain your response.

c. If you were in charge of setting policy for CO emissions, what action would you recommend to assure an allocatively efficient outcome across the two seasons?

Additional Readings

Kneese, Allen V. and Charles Schultz. *Pollution, Prices, and Public Policy.* Washington, D.C.: The Brookings Institution, 1975.

Portney, Paul R. "EPA and the Evolution of Federal Regulation." In Paul R. Portney, ed. *Public Policies for Environmental Protection.* Washington, D.C.: Resources for the Future, 1990, pp. 7–25.

Spence, A. M. and M. L. Weitzman. "Regulatory Strategies for Pollution Control." In A. E. Friedlander, ed. *Approaches to Controlling Air Pollution.* Boston: MIT Press, pp. 199–219.

Stavins, Robert N. "Harnessing Market Forces to Protect the Environment." *Environment* 31, no. 1 (January/February 1989), pp. 5–7, 28–35.

U.S. Environmental Protection Agency, Science Advisory Board. *Reducing Risk: Setting Priorities and Strategies for Environmental Protection.* Washington, D.C., September 1990.

ECONOMIC SOLUTIONS TO ENVIRONMENTAL PROBLEMS

The Market Approach

Though the market fails to correct environmental problems on its own, the incentives that define the market process can be put to work by policy-makers. Recommended for some time by economists, the **market approach** to environmental policy has begun to be adopted by governments as part of their overall response to the risks of pollution. Distinct from the more traditional use of emissions limits and output restrictions, the market approach uses price or other economic variables to provide incentives for polluters to reduce their harmful emissions.

Economists are strong proponents of the market approach because it can achieve a cost-effective solution to environmental problems, unlike the exclusive use of command-and-control instruments. How? By designing policy initiatives that allow polluters to respond according to their own self-interest. Market instruments are aimed at bringing the external costs of environmental damage back into the decision-making of firms and consumers. The strategy used to accomplish this takes its cue directly from the theory of market failure. Unregulated markets cannot correct pollution because of the absence of property rights and hence the absence of market forces. To remedy the problem, the market approach attempts to restore these forces by assigning a value to environmental quality or equivalently by pricing pollution. Once done, normal market incentives take over, and firms and consumers adjust their optimizing behavior to the government-induced change in market conditions.

Awareness of the gains associated with market-based instruments is growing in both the private and public sectors. Thus, it is important to understand this alternative approach to environmental policy and its advantages over more traditional forms of regulation. To that end, this chapter examines both the theory and the practical implications of pollution control instruments that are based on market incentives. As we have done to this point, economic modeling will be the primary tool of analysis, and the economic criteria of efficiency and cost-effectiveness will serve as the means by which assessments are made.

To provide a framework for our investigation, we begin with a brief overview of the major categories of market-based instruments: pollution charges, subsidies, deposit/refund systems, and pollution permit trading systems. We then use these categories to structure the economic analysis. Taking each one in turn, we develop models of specific instruments, assess the results, and provide examples of how each is used in practice. As we proceed, keep in mind that even as the market approach becomes more commonplace, most governments will likely use a combination approach to environmental policy. Thus, it is important to perceive market-based initiatives more as complements than as substitutes for the more traditional command-and-control instruments.

A Descriptive Overview

market approach
An environmental policy approach using incentive-based instruments to motivate pollution abatement based on natural market forces.

What distinguishes the **market approach** from the command-and-control approach is the way in which environmental objectives are *implemented* as opposed to the *level* at which those objectives are set. As we pointed out in the last chapter, common practice is to use standards to define a target level of environmental quality. From a practical perspective, standards-based objectives are set at a socially desirable rather than optimal level, regardless of the approach used to achieve them. Where the market approach parts company with the command-and-control approach is in how it attempts to achieve those objectives, that is, in its design of policy instruments.

Identifying Types of Market Instruments

Since there are many types of control instruments that use market incentives, it is helpful to classify these into major categories. As described in Table 5.1, these categories are: **pollution charges, subsidies, deposit/refund systems, and pollution permit trading systems.** Nations all over the world have begun to use these market-based instruments to help control pollution. In fact, an international survey of 14 nations found that 11 market instruments on average were being used in each country as of 1987.[1] Every type of economic instrument—from pollution charges to tradeable permit systems—was identified by the survey as part of national policy across all environmental media. Although the market approach continues to be a secondary form of control, its use in national policy prescriptions speaks to its importance as part of the full range of available solutions to environmental problems. A brief description of each of the major categories of market instruments follows.

---

[1]OECD (1989a).

TABLE 5.1   A Taxonomy of Market-Based Instruments

Market Instrument	Description
Pollution charge	A payment or fee charged to the polluter, which varies with the quantity of pollutants being emitted. It can be implemented through any one of the following:
	Effluent or emission charge: A fee based on the actual discharge of pollution.
	Product charge: An upward adjustment to the price of the pollution-generating intermediate or final product based on either its quantity or some characteristic responsible for the pollution. Product charges may be implemented through *tax differentiation,* that is, levying different taxes on goods based on their potential effect on the environment.
	User charge: A fee levied on the user of the environmental resource based on the costs for treatment of emissions or effluents that adversely affect those resources.
	Administrative charge: A service fee for implementation or monitoring of a regulation or for registering a polluting substance with an authority.
Subsidy	A payment or tax concession that provides financial assistance either for emission or effluent reductions or plans to mitigate pollution in the future.
Deposit/refund	A system that imposes an up-front charge to pay for potential pollution damages which is returned for positive action taken by the potential polluter, such as returning a product for proper disposal or recycling.
Pollution permit market	The establishment of a trading system of "rights to pollute," using either credits or allowances.
	With a **credit system,** polluters earn marketable credits for emitting below an established standard.
	Under an **allowance system,** some number of allowances is allocated to each polluting source, which can then be increased or decreased through trading.

Source: U.S. EPA, Office of Policy, Planning, and Evaluation, *The United States Experience with Economic Incentives* (Washington, D.C., July 1992); Organisation for Economic Co-Operation and Development, *Economic Instruments for Environmental Protection* (Paris: OECD, 1989a).

Pollution Charges.

Pollution charges are fees imposed on polluting sources that vary directly with the amount of contaminants released to the environment. These pricing instruments have broad applicability, since they can be executed in a variety of ways. Among these are **effluent or emission fees** assessed directly on pollution releases, **product charges** levied on pollution-generating commodities, **user charges** imposed on users of natural resources, and **administrative charges** levied for services such as the registration of hazardous chemicals. The type of pollution charge employed in practice depends on the environmental media and the nature of the problem. For example, effluent charges are used primarily to control noise and water pollution, whereas user charges are commonly employed to control wastewater treatment and solid waste disposal.

Subsidies.   **Subsidies** are payments or other forms of financial assistance awarded for reducing pollution levels or for developing plans to do so in the future. Sometimes referred to as the ''carrot'' versus the ''stick'' approach, subsidies give polluting sources an *incentive* to increase abatement activity— just the opposite of charges, which penalize polluting activities. They might be effected through direct payments, grant programs, loans at below-market interest rates, or tax concessions.[2]

Deposit/Refund Systems.   A **deposit/refund system** imposes an up-front charge, the **deposit,** to pay for *potential* environmental damage to the environment, which is later returned as a **refund** for some positive action undertaken by the potential polluter. This positive action might be returning a product for proper disposal or recycling a good for some alternative use.

Pollution Permit Trading Systems.   A fairly recent addition to the market approach is the **pollution permit trading system.** Under such a system, the government issues a fixed number of permits or ''rights to pollute'' in a given region and then allows a market to develop by letting polluters trade these rights among themselves. In practice, pollution permits are defined either as **credits** or **allowances.** Under a credit system, a polluter earns marketable credits only if it emits below an established standard. If instead the trading system uses allowances, each permit gives the bearer the right to release some amount of pollution. These too are marketable, so that polluters can buy and sell allowances as needed based on their internal abatement technologies and cost conditions.

pollution charge
A fee charged to the polluter that varies with the amount of pollutants released; implemented through an effluent or emission fee, a product charge, a user charge, or an administrative charge.

Pollution Charges

The theoretical premise of a **pollution charge** is to internalize the cost of environmental damages by pricing the pollution-generating activity. The motivation follows what is known as the **''Polluter-Pays Principle (PPP)''**—a position rooted in the belief that the polluter should bear the costs of control measures to maintain an acceptable level of environmental quality.[3] We begin by modeling a **product charge** implemented as a tax—the classical solution to negative externalities.

---

[2]OECD (1989a), p. 15.
[3]OECD (1989a), p. 27.

FIGURE 5.1

*The implementation
of a Pigouvian tax to
achieve efficiency*

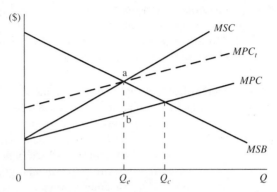

The model illustrates the use of a Pigouvian tax to achieve efficiency in the market for some pollution-generating product, Q. By setting the per unit tax exactly equal to the *MEC* at Q_e, shown as distance ab, the *MPC* shifts up to MPC_t. Equilibrium output is then determined by the intersection of MPC_t and *MSB*, which establishes an allocatively efficient production level at Q_e.

Modeling a Product Charge as a per Unit Tax

product charge
A fee added to the price of a pollution-generating intermediate or final product based either on its quantity or some attribute responsible for pollution.

Pigouvian tax
A per unit charge imposed on a good whose production generates a negative externality, such that the charge equals the *MEC* at the efficient output level.

Consider a good in a competitive market whose production generates a negative environmental externality. Because producers base their decisions solely on the marginal private cost (*MPC*) of production, ignoring the marginal external cost (*MEC*) of the environmental damage, too many resources are allocated to production. As shown in Figure 5.1, firms produce at output level Q_c, where the marginal social benefit (*MSB*) associated with consuming the good is exactly equal to the marginal private cost (*MPC*) of producing it.[4] Notice that the equilibrium output, Q_c is higher than the efficient level, Q_e, which corresponds to the point where the *MSB* equals the marginal social cost (*MSC*).

The policy motivation of a **product charge** is to induce firms to internalize the externality by taking account of the *MEC* in their production decisions. One way this can be done is by imposing a per unit tax on the pollution-generating product exactly equal to the *MEC* at the optimal output level, Q_e. This type of tax is called a **Pigouvian tax,** named after the English economist A. C. Pigou, who initially formulated the theory. As illustrated in Figure 5.1, this policy instrument effectively shifts the *MPC* curve up by distance ab to MPC_t, which generates an equilibrium at the efficient output level.

Assessing the Model.   In theory, the Pigouvian tax forces firms to lower production to the efficient output level, Q_e. While theoretically pleasing, this instrument is difficult to impose in practice and is not commonly used. Why?

---

[4]As we have done in previous discussions, we are implicitly assuming that there is no marginal external benefit (*MEB*) in the market for this good, so that *MPB* = *MSB*.

One problem is the difficulty of identifying the dollar value of *MEC* at Q_e and hence the level of the tax. A second is that the model implicitly allows only for an output reduction to abate pollution—an unrealistic restriction. To address both of these reservations in this context, we consider a more practical alternative. The pollution charge can be implemented as an **emission charge,** a tax levied on the pollution, instead of as a product charge. By moving out of the product market, the model does not restrict the polluter's response to output reductions.

Modeling an Emission Charge: The Single Polluter Case

emission or effluent charge
A fee imposed directly on the actual discharge of pollution.

An **emission or effluent charge** assigns a price to pollution, typically through a tax. Once this price mechanism is in place, the polluter can no longer ignore the effect of its environmental damages on society. The pollution charge forces it to confront those damages, pay for them, and in so doing, consider the damages as a part of its production costs. Faced with this added cost, the polluting firm can either continue polluting at the same level and pay the designated charge, or it can invest in some type of abatement technology to reduce its pollutant releases and lower its tax burden. Based on normal market incentives, it will choose whatever action minimizes its costs.

It is fairly simple to model an emission charge that allows polluters to make cost-minimizing decisions. To begin, we assume that the government sets a pollution abatement standard at some "acceptable level," A_s. Now, we consider a policy that presents the polluting source with the following options to be undertaken either singularly or in combination:

- The polluter must pay a constant per unit tax, *t,* on the difference between its existing abatement level, A_i, and the standard, A_s, such that Total Tax $= t(A_s - A_i)$; and/or
- The polluter incurs the cost of abating.

In Figure 5.2, we graph these options from a single firm's perspective using marginal curves. Since the per unit tax is constant, the marginal tax (*MT*) curve is a horizontal line at the per unit level, *t.* The cost of abating at the margin is shown as the marginal abatement cost (*MAC*) curve. At each unit of *A*, the cost-minimizing firm will compare *MAC* to *MT* and choose the lower of the two. In our model, the firm will abate up to A_o, since up to that point *MAC* is below *MT*. Total abatement costs (*TAC*) are represented by the area under *MAC* up to A_o, or area $0aA_o$. Notice that these costs are lower than what the taxes would be up to A_o, shown as area $0taA_o$. Beyond A_o and up to A_s, the firm will opt to pay the tax, since *MT* is lower than *MAC* in that range. The firm's total tax payment for not abating between A_o and A_s is

FIGURE 5.2

*Modeling an emission
charge for the single
firm*

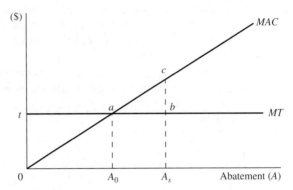

The model illustrates the decisions of a single polluter, faced with the options of either paying a tax $= t(A_s - A_i)$ and/or incurring the cost of abating. The tax burden is represented by the marginal tax (MT) curve, and the firm's marginal cost of abating is shown as the MAC curve. In this case, the cost-minimizing firm will abate up to level A_o, since up to that point $MAC < MT$. Its total abatement costs (TAC) are represented by area $0aA_o$. Beyond A_o and up to the standard, A_s, the firm will opt to pay the taxes, since $MT < MAC$ in that range. Its tax burden is represented by area $A_o abA_s$. Hence, the total costs to the polluter of complying with this policy are shown as area $0abA_s$.

represented by area $A_o abA_s$, which is smaller than the cost of abating that amount, which is area $A_o acA_s$. In sum, the total costs to the polluter of complying with this policy are area $0abA_s$, which comprises the following two elements:

1. Area $0aA_o$, the total cost of abating A_o units of pollution; and
2. Area $A_o abA_s$, the cost of the tax on the pollution not abated up to A_s.

Assessing the Model.   Be sure to recognize that the emission charge stimulates the natural market incentives of the polluter. At any point in time, there are *static* incentives that motivate the firm to choose among the available options given its existing technology. Seeking to satisfy its own self-interest to maximize profit, the polluter makes a least-cost decision between paying the tax for the damage it causes or abating. The result is that the externality is internalized using the least amount of economic resources.

There are also *dynamic* incentives that motivate the firm to advance its abatement technology. More efficient abatement techniques would allow the firm to reduce pollution more cheaply and enjoy the cost savings associated with doing so. Furthermore, the lower abatement costs might even allow the firm to avoid paying any emission charges. Consider the effect of a hypothetical technological advance, shown in Figure 5.3 as a downward pivot in the MAC to MAC'. In this case, if the firm were faced with the same set of policy options based on A_s, it would be better off abating all the way up to that standard. We now have to illustrate how the emission charge operates across a group of nonidentical polluting sources.

FIGURE 5.3

*The effect of
technology
improvement on the
firm's least-cost
decision-making*

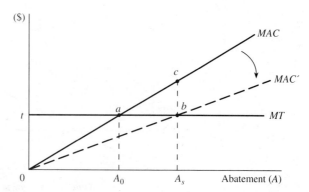

A technological advance causes the *MAC* to pivot downward to *MAC'*. As a result, if the firm is faced with the option of abating or paying the unit tax at each abatement level up to A_s, it would be better off abating all the way up to A_s. Hence, the technological change helped the firm avoid paying any emission charges.

Modeling an Emission Charge: The Multiple Polluter Case

To evaluate the cost-effectiveness of an emission charge across multiple polluters, we return to the two-polluter model used in the last chapter. As before, we assume that the government imposes a 10-unit abatement standard for the region. The cost functions are repeated below to facilitate discussion:

Polluter 1's Marginal Abatement Cost (MAC_1): $MAC_1 = 2.5(A_1)$;
Polluter 1's Total Abatement Costs (TAC_1): $TAC_1 = 1.25(A_1)^2$,

where A_1 = the amount of pollution abated by Polluter 1.

Polluter 2's Marginal Abatement Cost (MAC_2): $MAC_2 = 0.625(A_2)$;
Polluter 2's Total Abatement Costs (TAC_2): $TAC_2 = 0.3125(A_2)^2$,

where A_2 = the amount of pollution abated by Polluter 2.

Let's assume that the government imposes the same emission charge specified in the single firm case, that is, Total Tax = $t(A_s - A_i)$. In this case, since $A_s = 10$, the emission charge becomes, Total Tax = $t(10 - A_i)$. We also assume that the tax rate, t, is set at \$5, so Total Tax = \$5(10 - A_i)$ for each polluter.

Now, consider each firm's response to the tax. As we proceed, refer to Figure 5.4, which reproduces the model used in Chapter 4, adding a horizontal line (*MT*) at \$5 to represent the emission charge. When faced with the \$5 per unit charge, Polluter 1 would compare the relative cost of *MT* and MAC_1 for each incremental unit of abatement, just as in the single firm case discussed above. It would abate as long as $MAC_1 < MT$, and pay the tax when the opposite is true. Thus, Polluter 1 would abate up to the point where $MAC_1 = MT$, which occurs at $A_1 = 2$ and pay the tax on the remaining 8 units. Polluter 2 would proceed in the same manner, abating to the point where $MAC_2 = MT$

FIGURE 5.4

Effect of an emission charge in a two-polluter model

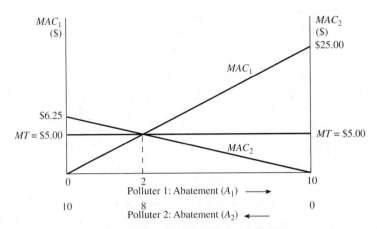

The model shows the *MAC*s for Polluter 1 and Polluter 2 and the emission charge imposed as a unit tax of $5 represented by the *MT* curve. The horizontal axis measures the 10-unit abatement standard imposed by government. Each firm abates as long as its *MAC* < *MT*, and pays the emission charge on all units of pollution not abated. In this case, Polluter 1, the high-cost abater, abates 2 units and pays $40 in taxes on the remaining 8. Polluter 2, the low-cost abater, abates 8 units and pays taxes of $10 on the remaining 2. At this point, $MAC_1 = MAC_2$ = $5, which indicates the least-cost allocation of abatement responsibilities across the two firms.

at $A_2 = 8$ and paying the tax on the remaining 2 units. The corresponding calculations are:

Polluter 1:
    Abates up to the point where $MAC_1 = MT$: $2.5(A_1) = \$5$, or $A_1 = 2$
    Incurs Total Abatement Costs of: $TAC_1 = 1.25(2)^2 = \$5.$
    Incurs Total Tax payment of: Total Tax = $5(10 - 2) = \$40.$

Polluter 2:
    Abates up to the point where $MAC_2 = MT$: $0.625(A_2) = \$5$, or $A_2 = 8$
    Incurs Total Abatement Costs of: $TAC_2 = 0.3125(8)^2 = \$20.$
    Incurs Total Tax payment of: Total Tax = $5(10 - 8) = \$10.$

Combined Values for the Region:
    Total level of abatement = $10 = A_s$
    Total Abatement Costs = $25
    Total Tax Payments = $50

    There are two important observations to make about these results. First, the $5 unit tax does achieve the 10-unit abatement level. Secondly, this objective has been achieved using the most cost-effective allocation of abatement resources across polluters.[5] Since each polluter abates to the point where its *MAC* equals *MT*, all *MAC*s are equal—precisely in accordance with the

---

[5]Recall from the previous chapter that using a uniform standard under a command-and-control approach, the total abatement costs are $39.06.

equi-marginal principle of optimality. Notice that most of the abating is done by the low-cost abater, Polluter 2. The high-cost polluter, Polluter 1, abates less but pays much higher emission charges in the form of taxes.

Assessing the Model.   It is the market orientation of the emission charge that provides the flexibility to achieve a cost-minimizing solution across all firms. The tax instrument exploits each polluter's natural incentive to pursue a least-cost strategy. As a result, the low-cost abaters do most of the cleaning up, and the high-cost abaters pay more in taxes to cover the greater damages they cause. Remember that the objective of the policy instrument is to improve environmental quality. The associated benefits to society are not affected by *who* does the pollution abating, but the costs are. In this case, costs are minimized because Polluter 2 does most of the abating. It does so, not because it is motivated by society's objectives, but because it is in *its* best interest to do so. An added advantage of this approach is that the tax instrument generates revenues to the government, which could be used in a real-world setting to help finance the costs of enforcement and monitoring.

Having said this, there are nonetheless several caveats that deserve mention. The first concerns the setting of the emission charge itself. Realistically, the government will not know the tax rate at which all polluters' selected abatement levels collectively meet the standard and will likely have to adjust the tax until the environmental quality objective is achieved.[6] Such an adjustment process can be time-intensive. In the interim, firms would have difficulty planning and executing their abatement strategies. A second consideration is the potential effect on monitoring costs. Monitoring is likely to be more complex when each polluting source responds to a policy based on its own internal operations. There are also distributional implications to be considered. As polluting firms pay higher taxes, part of the tax burden is shared with consumers in the form of higher product prices. There may also be negative effects on workers who may lose their jobs as a consequence of polluters' making adjustments to absorb the tax burden and/or changing production technology to abate their emissions. Finally, there is a concern that firms may attempt to evade a pollution tax by illegally disposing of pollutants. To minimize the potential of such activities, the government may have to strengthen its monitoring program, which of course adds to administrative costs.

Pollution Charges in Practice

Internationally, the pollution charge is the most commonly used market-based instrument. For example, the OECD survey of 14 nations found that 81

---

[6]For example, if the government had set the tax at too low a level, say $4, each polluter would have abated to the point where its *MAC* equals $4. The result would have been $A_1 = 1.6$, and $A_2 = 6.4$. The combined level of abatement would have been 8.0 units—too low to satisfy the objective. So, the government would have had to raise the tax until the combined total achieved the 10-unit abatement standard.

pollution charges were in use during 1987 out of a total of 153 identified market instruments. Some of these charges are intended to be true incentives for environmental improvement, others are designed to be revenue-producing, and still others serve both purposes. For example, several countries use **effluent charges** to control the noise pollution generated by aircraft, including Japan and Switzerland. These fees typically are based on aircraft weight and sound level. Another use of effluent charges is in controlling water pollution. Germany and Italy are among the nations employing such an instrument to protect water resources.[7]

user charge
A fee levied on the user of an environmental resource based on the costs for treatment of emissions or effluents that adversely affect those resources.

A common application of a **user charge** is in pricing solid waste disposal, a practice that has already been adopted by several U.S. municipalities. In Seattle, Washington, for example, consumers of waste disposal services are charged higher prices as the volume of their disposal activity increases. The intent is to give households a financial incentive to reduce waste generation either through recycling, changes in consumption patterns, or yard waste composting.[8]

Since **product charges** are generally implemented through a tax, they provide both an incentive for environmental improvement and a revenue source to governments. A common use of a product charge is as a tax levied on lubricant oils, such as that employed in Finland, France, Germany, Italy, and the Netherlands. Finland also uses a product charge to encourage its deposit-refund system by heavily taxing beverage containers that are *not* returnable. Other targeted products include pesticides, fertilizers, mercury- or cadmium-containing batteries, and fuels.[9] Application 5.1 gives an overview of the international experience with gasoline taxes aimed at internalizing the external costs of gasoline consumption.

Environmental Subsidies

environmental subsidy
A payment or tax concession provided for abatement equipment purchases or pollution reductions.

An alternative market approach to mitigating environmental damage is to pay polluters not to pollute through an **environmental subsidy.** At first blush, such an approach may seem counterintuitive, but the underlying premise actually is rooted in the theory of property rights. From a purely objective vantage point, suppose that prior to any form of pollution control, polluters had the free use of the environment. (Recall that we made such an assumption in our analysis of the Coase Theorem in Chapter 3.) It could be argued that during this unregulated period, society had implicitly given polluting sources the ''right to pollute'' as part of their production processes. To ask these polluting sources to pay for what seemingly had been their ''right'' might be viewed as

---

[7]OECD (1989a), pp. 31–50.
[8]Wirth and Heinz (1991), pp. 48–53.
[9]OECD (1989a), pp. 55–60.

Application 5.1

Taxing Gasoline Consumption: An International Comparison

According to Kazuo Aichi, former chief of Japan's environmental agency, "Gasoline is too cheap in the United States and should be taxed more to cut energy use." Aichi's argument is motivated in part by ongoing disagreements between the United States and some of its industrialized counterparts about the appropriate response to problems like resource depletion and global air pollution. Fueled by the alleged lack of U.S. cooperation at the 1992 Rio Earth Summit, Aichi's criticism of U.S. policy on fuel taxes points out the importance of the price mechanism to encourage much-needed conservation measures.

To better understand the objection to American policy, consider how the U.S. tax on gasoline compares to what is imposed by other industrialized countries, as shown in the table below.

These data validate Aichi's claim that the price of gasoline in the United States *is* cheap in a relative sense, and much of the difference is due to a lower tax rate. Notice that the gasoline tax is 69 to 77 percent of the unit price in the European nations and 47 percent in Japan. The comparatively low tax rate of 28 percent in the United States underscores its fuel tax policy.

Beyond this cursory assessment of Aichi's commentary, there is the more important issue of the economic intent of a gasoline tax. In addition to boosting government revenues, taxing a commodity like gasoline is designed to internalize the negative externalities associated with gasoline consumption. External to the market for gasoline are air pollution problems caused by operating gasoline-powered motor vehicles. The adverse effects include impairment to health and visibility caused by urban smog and the potential for global warming associated with burning carbon-based fuels. Other negative externalities are highway congestion and the higher risk of traffic accidents. These adverse effects have one thing in common—they extend to parties beyond those directly engaged in the market transaction. Consequently, the costs of these damages are not reflected in gasoline prices, and too much gasoline is brought to market.

As other nations have apparently learned, raising the tax on gasoline can help bring the social costs and benefits of gasoline consumption closer together. While the suggestion for higher tax rates is never one embraced by consumers, in this case such a proposal could bring about a more socially desirable outcome in the long run.

Sources: Associated Press, "Japanese Environmentalist Says Gas Too Cheap in U.S.," *Brockton Enterprise,* February 2, 1992; James Tanner, "Carbon Tax to Limit Use of Fossil Fuels Becomes Embroiled in Global Politics," *The Wall Street Journal,* June 9, 1992.

Gasoline Prices and Taxes by Country

Country	Total Gasoline Price per Gallon (U.S. dollars)	Tax Rate % of Price
United States	$ 1.19	28%
Britain	3.69	69
France	3.85	77
Germany	3.85	71
Italy	5.00	75
Japan	3.75	47
Spain	3.75	69

Source: International Energy Agency, cited in James Tanner, "Carbon Tax to Limit Use of Fossil Fuels Becomes Embroiled in Global Politics," *The Wall Street Journal,* June 9, 1992.

an unjust use of government intervention. Hence, an alternative form of environmental control could be to give **subsidies** to polluting sources as payments not to pollute. In general, there are two forms of subsidies, **abatement equipment subsidies** and **per unit pollution reduction subsidies.** We briefly discuss each of these in turn.

Modeling an Abatement Equipment Subsidy

Subsidies on abatement equipment are aimed at reducing the costs to polluters of abatement technology. Since subsidies are "negative taxes," they have a similar incentive mechanism to pollution charges except that they reward for *not* polluting as opposed to penalizing for engaging in polluting activities. In practice, abatement equipment subsidies are implemented through the use of grants, low-interest loans, or investment tax credits, all of which provide an incentive for polluting sources to invest in abatement technology.

From a theoretical perspective, we can argue that these subsidies attempt to internalize the *positive* externality associated with the consumption of abatement activities. If a subsidy were offered for the installation of a specific type of abatement equipment, such as scrubbers, the impact of the subsidy would be to encourage a higher quantity demanded of this equipment by lowering the effective price. To achieve an efficient equilibrium, the subsidy would have to equal the amount of the marginal external benefit (*MEB*) associated with scrubber consumption measured at the efficient output level. Notice that the premise is analogous to that of a Pigouvian tax, and in fact this type of subsidy is known as a **Pigouvian subsidy.**

Pigouvian subsidy
A per unit payment offered on a good whose consumption generates a positive externality, such that the subsidy equals the *MEB* at the efficient output level.

A model of a hypothetical competitive market for scrubbers would be:

$$MSC = 70.0 + 0.5Q, \quad MPB = 350.0 - 0.9Q$$
$$\underline{+ \ MEB = \ \ 56.0 - 0.2Q}$$
$$MSB = 406.0 - 1.1Q,$$

where Q is the number of systems produced in a year and *MSC, MPB,* and *MEB* are denominated in millions of dollars.[10] The corresponding graph is illustrated in Figure 5.5. The competitive equilibrium is found where $MPB = MSC$, or at $Q_c = 200$ scrubber systems per year sold at a market $P_c = \$170$ million each. However, the efficient equilibrium occurs where $MSB = MSC$, or at $Q_e = 210$, and $P_e = \$175$. In an unregulated market, too few scrubbers are exchanged at too low a price because the external benefits associated with a cleaner environment are not recognized by the market participants. If a subsidy (s) were provided to demanders, that is, polluters, equal to the *MEB* at the efficient output level, more scrubbers would be traded. In this case, the Pigouvian subsidy would equal $MEB = 56.0 - 0.2(210) = \$14$ million, shown

---

[10]For simplicity, we are assuming that there are no marginal external costs (*MEC*) in the market for this good so that the $MPC = MSC$.

FIGURE 5.5

*A Pigouvian subsidy
in the market for
scrubbers*

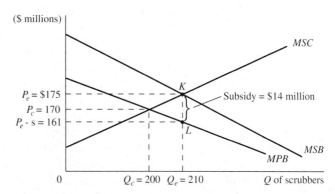

In the market for scrubbers, there is a positive externality associated with their consumption. Hence, the true measure of benefits to society is given by the *MSB*, which is the vertical sum of the *MPB* and the *MEB*. If a Pigouvian subsidy were provided to purchasers of scrubber systems equal to the *MEB* at the efficient output level, 210 scrubbers would be traded in the market instead of the competitive output level of 200. In this case, the Pigouvian subsidy is $14 million labeled as distance *KL*. Notice that the effective price to polluters would be the efficient market price *less* the amount of the subsidy paid by the government, which in this case is ($175 − $14) or $161 million.

as distance *KL* on the graphical model. The effective price to polluters would be the efficient market price *less* the amount of the subsidy, that is, $(P_e - s)$, which in this case is ($175 − $14) or $161 million.

Assessing the Model. Just as in the case of a Pigouvian tax, one problem with implementing a Pigouvian subsidy is in measuring the value of *MEB*. Monetizing the marginal external benefits of such intangibles as better health and more stable ecosystems is difficult at best. Hence, because of practical considerations, it is not likely that subsidies of abatement equipment will arrive at an allocatively efficient solution. However, the effect of encouraging greater consumption because of an effectively lower price should still occur.

Even setting aside the difficulty in achieving an efficient outcome, equipment subsidies may have other drawbacks. One commonly cited criticism is that this type of control instrument biases polluters' decisions about how best to reduce their harmful releases to the environment. Subsidies affect relative prices, making other alternatives less attractive to polluters from a profit perspective. However, some of these alternatives might be more effective in reducing pollution. For the same set of reasons, technological development in abatement technology may likewise be biased. Innovation of a potentially superior type of abatement system could be discouraged as long as the government is subsidizing and therefore discounting the price of existing equipment. Finally, subsidies must be financed either through taxes or government borrowing. Thus, they effectively redistribute income from society to polluters, an outcome that is not viewed as acceptable by some even in light of the gains associated with a cleaner environment.

Modeling a per Unit Subsidy on Pollution Reductions

An alternative type of subsidy can be based upon emission or effluent reductions. With this type of policy instrument, the government agrees to pay the polluter a per unit subsidy (s) for every unit of pollution removed below some predetermined level, Z_o. Hence, we can model the subsidy as follows:

$$\text{Per unit subsidy} = s(Z_o - Z_i),$$

where Z_i is the actual level of pollution. Suppose, for example, the standard Z_o is set at 200 tons of emissions per month, and the subsidy (s) is set at $100 per month. Then, if a polluter reduces its emissions to 180 tons per month, it would receive a subsidy of $100(200 − 180), or $2,000.

Assessing the Model. On the plus side, a per unit pollution reduction subsidy *might* be less disruptive than an equipment subsidy, since it is established independent of the abatement method used and thus avoids any technological bias. On the other hand, per unit subsidies can have the perverse effect of elevating pollution levels in the aggregate. How does such a paradox arise? Because a per unit subsidy effectively lowers a polluter's unit costs, which in turn raises its profits. If the industry has limited entry barriers, these profits would signal entrepreneurs to enter what has become a more lucrative industry. In the long run, although each individual polluter reduces its emissions, the subsidy may cause the market to expand such that aggregate emissions end up higher than they were originally.[11]

The per unit subsidy is designed to alter the decisions of *existing* polluting sources, and indeed market incentives should give rise to that result. The problem is that the subsidy has *market-level* effects that work against the intended outcome. In theory, the dilemma could be solved if entry were prohibited, or at least limited in some way. Whether or not this is feasible, or even desirable, is a difficult and controversial issue that depends on the particular industry structure, the extent of environmental damage, and the costs of implementing such a market adjustment.

Environmental Subsidies in Practice

There are many instances where environmental subsidies are used in practice. One example is found in Italy's *Decree of August 31, 1987,* which allows for direct subsidies to industries that are changing manufacturing technologies to reduce waste disposal.[12] In the United States, the most common use of subsidies has been to provide federal financial assistance for public environmental projects such as publicly owned wastewater treatment works (POTWs).[13]

---

[11]For further detail, see Baumol and Oates (1975), Chapter 12.
[12]OECD (1989a), pp. 79–80.
[13]U.S. EPA, Office of Policy, Planning, and Evaluation (July 1992), p. 6-1.

Subsidies are also used to encourage the use of energy-saving products, such as "green lights" (i.e., energy-efficient lighting). State governments are also putting subsidies to work as part of their environmental policy plans. For example, during 1990 to 1992, Louisiana provided tax exemptions based on a polluter's environmental track record. Any firm who applied for this exemption was assigned a rating based on such factors as the amount of chemical contaminants it released and the number of environmental violations it had received. The better the track record and hence the higher the rating, the larger the tax exemption the firm received.[14] Today, many state governments use subsidies in the form of tax incentives to encourage recycling activities. An overview of some of these programs is given in Application 5–2.

Deposit/Refund Systems

deposit/refund system
Imposes an up-front charge to pay for potential pollution damages which is reimbursed for positive action such as returning a product for proper disposal or recycling.

The potentially perverse consequences of abatement subsidies suggest that pollution charges might be a better alternative. In some contexts, however, pollution charges can be costly to administer because of the associated expense of monitoring and enforcement. Recall that one of the drawbacks of pollution charges is that they may encourage polluters to illegally dispose of their contaminants as a way to avoid paying emissions fees. This potential problem is an important motivation for the use of a **deposit/refund system.** This market instrument effectively combines the incentive characteristic of a pollution charge with a built-in mechanism for controlling monitoring costs. It is used primarily to capture the difference between the private and social costs of improper waste disposal, with its most common targets being beverage containers and lead-acid batteries. Operationally, deposit/refund systems attach a front-end charge—the deposit—for the *potential* occurrence of a damaging activity, and guarantee a return of that charge—the refund—upon assurance that the activity has not been undertaken.

The Economics of a Deposit/Refund System

Improper or illegal waste disposal gives rise to a negative externality. The external costs include health damages, such as lead contamination from discarded lead-acid batteries, and aesthetic impairment from unsightly litter and trash accumulation. Deposit/refund systems are intended to force the potential polluter to account for both the marginal private cost (MPC) and the marginal external cost (MEC) of improper waste disposal, should that activity be undertaken.

Like the pollution charge, the deposit component of the system is intended to capture the MEC of improper waste disposal. In so doing, it forces the

---

[14]Glenn (1992), as cited in U.S. EPA, Office of Policy, Planning, and Evaluation (July 1992), p. 6-2.

Application 5.2

State Subsidies for Recycling Programs

Some state governments have elected to implement subsidy instruments as a way to encourage recycling by their constituents. Many of these subsidies are being imposed as one-time tax incentives rather than as ongoing policies extending over the life of a recycling program. Among the more common subsidy instruments are investment tax credits for recycling facilities and sales tax exemptions on the purchase of recycling equipment. The premise for these particular applications is that once the incentives establish the infrastructure to support recycling efforts, these activities should become self-directed.

The following summary itemizes some of the innovative fiscal approaches being used in state governments throughout the United States.

State	Description of the Tax Incentive
California	Tax credits for the cost of equipment used to manufacture recycled products. Development bonds for manufacturing products with recycled materials.
Colorado	Income tax credits for investments in plastics recycling technology.
Florida	Sales tax exemptions on recycling machinery purchased after July 1, 1988. Tax incentives to encourage affordable transport of recycled materials from collection centers to processing sites.
Illinois	Sales tax exemptions for recycling equipment.
Indiana	Property tax exemptions for buildings, equipment, and land used in recycling waste into new products.
Iowa	Sales tax exemptions.
Kentucky	Granting property tax exemptions to recycling industries.
Maine	Tax credits to businesses of 30 percent of the cost of recycling equipment. Subsidies to municipalities for transport costs of scrap metal.
Maryland	Income tax deduction of 100 percent of expenses for the cost of furnace conversion to burn used oil and for the purchase and installation of equipment for recycling used Freon.
New Jersey	50 percent investment tax credit to businesses for recycling vehicles and equipment. Six percent sales tax exemption on recycling equipment purchases.
North Carolina	Corporate income tax credits and exemptions for recycling equipment and facilities.
Oregon	Income tax credits for recycling equipment and facilities. Special tax credits for property or machinery used to collect, transport, or process reclaimed plastics.
Texas	Franchise tax exemptions for sludge recycling corporations.
Utah	Payment of $21 per ton to tire recyclers for tires recycled or incinerated for energy recovery.
Virginia	Tax credit of 10 percent of the cost of any machinery or equipment used for processing recyclable materials.
Washington	Exemption from motor vehicle rate regulation for vehicles used to transport recovered materials.
Wisconsin	Sales tax exemptions for waste reduction and recycling equipment and facilities. Property tax exemptions for certain equipment.

Source: Drawn from National Solid Waste Management Association (NSWMA), *Recycling in the States: Mid-Year Update 1990*, (Washington, D.C.: NSWMA, October 1990) with permission of National Solid Waste Management Association.

polluting source to internalize the cost of any damage it may cause by making it absorb this cost *in advance*. Unique to the deposit/refund system is the refund component, which introduces an incentive to properly dispose of wastes, preventing environmental damage from ever taking place at all. Taken together, the deposit/refund system effectively targets the *potential* polluter instead of just penalizing the *actual* polluter, using the refund to reward appropriate behavior.

Modeling a Deposit/Refund System

A model of a deposit/refund system is shown graphically in Figure 5.6. From left to right, the horizontal axis represents *improper* waste disposal (*IW*) measured as the percentage of all waste disposal activity. Implicitly, then, the percentage of *proper* waste disposal (*PW*) is measured right to left. Thus, if 25 percent of all wastes are improperly disposed of, by default 75 percent are disposed of appropriately and safely.

The MPC_{IW} includes expenses for collecting and illegally dumping wastes into a stream or at a roadside, plus the costs of improperly disposing recyclable wastes, such as the expense of trash receptacles, collection fees paid to a refuse company, and the opportunity costs of forgone revenue associated with recycling. The MSC_{IW} includes the MPC_{IW} plus the MEC_{IW}, which is implicitly represented as the vertical distance between MSC_{IW} and MPC_{IW}. The MPB_{IW} represents demand for improper waste disposal. It is motivated by the avoidance of the time and resources needed to collect the wastes, bring the

FIGURE 5.6

Modeling a deposit/ refund system in the market for waste disposal

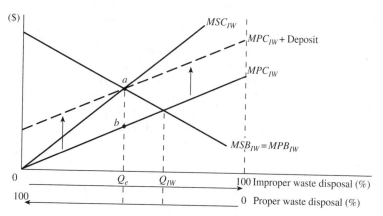

Improper waste disposal (*IW*) is measured left to right on the horizontal axis as a proportion of all waste disposal activity. Hence, the percentage of proper waste disposal (*PW*) is measured right to left. To correct the negative externality associated with improper waste disposal, a deposit/refund system is instituted with the deposit set equal to the MEC_{IW} measured at Q_e. The deposit, labeled as distance *ab*, elevates the MPC_{IW} up to MSC_{IW}, forcing the market participants to establish a new equilibrium at the socially optimal level. The result is an increase in the proportion of wastes properly disposed of from Q_{IW} to Q_e.

nonrecyclables to a landfill, and haul the recyclables to a collection center.[15] Since there are assumed to be no external benefits in this case, $MPB_{IW} = MSB_{IW}$. In the absence of environmental controls, market equilibrium is determined by the intersection of MSB_{IW} and MPC_{IW}, or Q_{IW}. The efficient equilibrium occurs where MSC_{IW} equals MSB_{IW}, or at Q_e, which is smaller than Q_{IW}. Once again, we observe that in the presence of a negative externality, too much improper waste disposal, Q_{IW}, is produced because market participants are not made to consider the full impact of their actions.

To correct the negative externality, assume that a deposit/refund system is instituted whereby an up-front deposit is charged to all potential disposers equal to the MEC_{IW} at the efficient amount of disposal, Q_e. The deposit is labeled as distance ab in Figure 5.6. Once imposed, the deposit effectively elevates MPC_{IW} up to MSC_{IW}, forcing the market participants to a new equilibrium at the socially optimal level, Q_e. In so doing, a percentage of overall waste disposal is converted from improper methods to appropriate ones measured by $(Q_{IW} - Q_e)$. At this point, the deposit serves the same function as a per unit pollution charge. The critical difference is that the refund helps to deter improper waste disposal. The potential polluter has an explicit incentive to properly dispose of wastes, since doing so allows it to reclaim the deposit. Should disposers choose instead to illegally discard their wastes, at least they will have paid for the external cost of their actions in advance. Authorities also have the flexibility to adjust the deposit or refund amounts to enhance the built-in incentives.[16]

Assessing the Model.   The primary objective of encouraging proper waste disposal is to reduce the inherent risks to human health and the physical environment associated with careless dumping of dangerous substances. The major value added of the deposit/refund system is that the refund encourages environmentally responsible behavior without adding significantly to government's monitoring and compliance costs. What makes this instrument unique is that once established, the incentives operate with limited supervision.

Another advantage of the deposit/refund instrument is that it can be used to encourage more efficient use of raw materials. An inordinate amount of used products and materials ends up in landfills or burned in waste disposal incinerators, when they could be recycled for use in economic production. The availability of recycled products and materials can help slow the depletion of such virgin raw materials as aluminum and timber and may result in associated

---

[15]Given its meaning, the MPB_{IW} measured left to right is equivalent to the MPC_{PW} measured right to left.

[16]This analysis could equivalently be modeled by specifying the market as ''proper waste disposal.'' In such a specification, there would be a *positive* external benefit from *proper* disposal of wastes, which would be equivalent to the reduction in external costs from reducing *improper* waste disposal.

price declines as well.[17] Charging firms a deposit on raw materials acts as a tax on productive inputs, encouraging more efficient use of resources *during* the production process. The refund encourages proper disposal or recycling of raw material waste at the *end* of the production phase. Firms that elect to ignore this incentive face not only conventional disposal costs but also the opportunity cost of the forgone refund.

Deposit/Refund Systems in Practice

Perhaps the best known applications of deposit/refund systems are those used to encourage proper disposal of beverage containers. In the United States, such programs typically are initiated through state "bottle bills." As of 1993, 10 states had passed legislation requiring deposits on beer and soft drink containers. Application 5.3 discusses the mechanics of these state-level initiatives.

Application 5.3

The Mechanics of a Deposit/Refund System: "Bottle Bills"

The main objective of a "bottle bill" is to discourage the illegal disposal of certain types of beverage containers. Notwithstanding the validity of this motivation, there are also important secondary benefits that arise from recycling the collected containers. One is energy conservation. Manufacturing new beverage containers from recycled aluminum consumes about 95 percent less energy than what is used when the containers are produced from raw ore. Another benefit is the reduced extraction of scarce virgin raw material.

Currently, 10 states have passed bottle bills—California, Connecticut, Delaware, Iowa, Maine, Massachusetts, Michigan, New York, Oregon, and Vermont. While each state's law is unique, there are similarities that characterize how a deposit/refund system is designed for beverage containers. The following is a brief description of the phases outlining the general structure of such a system.

Phase 1: Depending on the product, a deposit (e.g., 5 or 10 cents), is paid by the retailer to the bottler or wholesaler for each beverage container received. If the product is a soft drink, retailers pay the deposit to the bottler; for beer containers, the retailer pays the wholesaler.

Phase 2: Consumers of the product pay the same deposit to the retailer as part of the product's purchase price.

Phase 3: After the beverage is consumed, the consumer returns the used container to the retailer who refunds the consumer for the amount of the initial deposit. (If the consumer chooses instead to discard the container—either legally or illegally—the deposit is forfeited, acting as payment for the social cost of improper disposal.)

---

[17]As an exercise, model the demand and supply of aluminum. Now assume that a deposit/refund system has been imposed on aluminum containers. Show how an increase in recycled aluminum is expected to affect this market.

Application 5.3 (concluded)

Phase 4:   Retailers reclaim the deposit from either the bottler or wholesaler when they return the empty container. In addition, bottlers and wholesalers typically pay a per unit handling fee (e.g., 2 cents), to retailers to cover their costs to collect and return the containers.

Notice from this four-step process that bottle bills are self-implementing. Once the deposit system is in place, market forces take over. There is a natural incentive for consumers and retailers to return used containers so that they can recover their deposits.

So, why haven't more states passed bottle bills? Voter opposition to these bills exists for a variety of reasons. One is the perverse effect caused by the availability of substitute containers not covered by a bottle bill. For example, some beverages are packaged both in plastic bottles and in aluminum cans. If a bottle bill requires a deposit only on aluminum containers, some consumers may purchase the product in plastic containers just to avoid the deposit. Such a response occurred in New York, where consumption of soft drinks in plastic containers rose from 39 to 52 percent following the passage of the state's bottle bill. The response is problematic because plastic is not as recyclable as aluminum. Furthermore, disposal of plastic containers adds more to the *volume* of the solid waste stream than other types of beverage containers. While this argument is a common one, the problem could be resolved by making the law cover *all* types of containers.

Another reason for voter opposition is the opportunity cost of participating in a deposit/refund program—the value of time to collect, clean, store, and transport used containers to retailers. Some consumers view these costs as outweighing the value of refunds. As cost-minimizers, these individuals would make the rational decision *not* to participate in a deposit/refund program. It has been suggested that if states make a concerted effort to minimize consumers' costs of compliance, they will realize a higher return rate on beverage containers *independent* of the dollar value of the deposit.

Finally, there is uncertainty about the overall effectiveness of bottle bills. There is some controversy about what proportion of collected containers actually are recycled versus the proportion that ends up in landfills. Other skeptics believe that bottle bills have a relatively small effect on the size of the solid waste stream.

How valid are these concerns? To answer this, deposit/refund systems for beverage containers must be evaluated using benefit-cost analysis. The appraisal should make use of information from those states that *do* have bottle bills about the associated energy savings, reduction in littering, recovery rates, and changes in consumption patterns. As these data are examined, consumers and industry will be better able to make informed decisions about proposals in their own states and to tailor a deposit/refund system to better meet the needs of their regions.

Sources: U.S. Environmental Protection Agency, Office of Policy, Planning, and Evaluation, *Economic Incentives: Options for Environmental Protection* (Washington, D.C., March 1991), Chapter 2; U.S. Environmental Protection Agency, Office of Policy, Planning, and Evaluation, *The United States Experience with Economic Incentives to Control Environmental Protection* (Washington, D.C., July 1992), Chapter 4.

Oregon, the first state to enact a "bottle bill," reports that roadside litter was reduced by 75 to 85 percent just two years after its bill became law.[18] The state of Michigan reported a 95 percent return rate in the first year after it instituted its program.[19] Similar results have been observed in other countries

---

[18]U.S. EPA, Office of Policy, Planning, and Evaluation (July 1992), p. 4-1.
[19]Porter (1983), pp. 177–94.

as well. Finland, Norway, the Netherlands, and Sweden report return rates on beverage containers ranging from 70 to 90 percent after instituting a deposit/ refund system.[20]

Other state initiatives are aimed at encouraging responsible disposal of used tires and lead-acid batteries. Proper discard of lead-acid batteries is of particular concern due to the associated health risks of lead exposure. According to the EPA, lead-acid batteries represent approximately 65 percent of the lead found in municipal solid wastes.[21] Sweden and Norway have had some success using deposit/refunds to reduce the improper disposal of junk cars. Interestingly, both charge a deposit that is actually less than the refund, presumably to further enhance the incentive to return unwanted vehicles to designated locations for proper disposal or recycling.[22]

Pollution Permit Trading Systems

pollution permit trading system
Establishes a market for "rights to pollute" through the issuance of tradeable pollution credits or allowances.

pollution credits
Tradeable permits issued to polluters for emitting below an established standard.

pollution allowances
Tradeable permits that indicate the maximum level of emissions or effluents polluters may release based on a preestablished environmental objective.

Thus far, we have illustrated that market instruments can be used to set prices for polluting and abatement activities. In so doing, the market quantity of these activities is simultaneously controlled. It is also possible for government to use the price-quantity relationship in the opposite direction—by establishing the quantity of pollution or abatement to be achieved and letting the market determine the appropriate price level. With perfect information, either approach is viable, and both will lead to the same outcome. However, pricing instruments can be problematic in that the government will not know in advance what price level will achieve a quantity-based environmental objective. Consequently, it has to monitor the quantity response to some initially established price and continually make adjustments until the proper pollution level is achieved—essentially a "trial and error" process. It may be more efficient to use a policy instrument that operates from the *known* variable, that is, the socially desirable quantity of pollution or abatement, and let the market adjust to establish the price. Such is the underlying premise of a **pollution permit trading system,** which can be implemented through the use of **credits** or **allowances.**

The Structure of a Pollution Permit Trading System

A system of marketable pollution permits has two essential components: (1) the issuance of some fixed number of pollution permits in a given region; and (2) a provision for trading of these permits among polluting sources within that region. The total number of permits issued is bound by whatever level of pollution is mandated by law as "acceptable." For example, if the level were

[20]U.S. EPA, Office of Policy, Planning, and Evaluation (July 1992), pp. 9-4–9-5.
[21]U.S. EPA, Office of Policy, Planning, and Evaluation (March 1991), p. 2-18.
[22]U.S. EPA, Office of Policy, Planning, and Evaluation (July 1992), p. 9-5.

set at 200 units of emissions, a maximum of 200 one-unit permits could be issued. Any polluter releasing emissions not authorized by permits would be in violation of the law. Once the permits are distributed, polluters are allowed to trade them with one another. A bargaining process should develop, which gives rise to a *market* for "pollution rights." Following their own self-interest, polluters either purchase these "rights to pollute" or abate—whichever is the cheaper alternative. High-cost abaters will have an incentive to bid for available permits, while low-cost abaters will have an incentive to abate and sell their permits on the open market. The result is a cost-effective allocation of abatement responsibilities.[23]

The tradeable permit system accommodates environmental objectives defined at an aggregate level. For example, in the United States, air pollution policies are designed to achieve national ambient air quality standards within well-defined regions. Within any such region, some polluters might perform above the standard and others below it, as long as in the aggregate the region is in compliance. This is exactly how the permit system operates—controlling the total amount of emissions allowed in a region, but not the releases for each source within that region.[24] The trading component of the permit system capitalizes on differences in polluters' abatement technologies and opportunities. Sources that can abate efficiently are given the incentive to do so because they can sell their unused permits to their less efficient counterparts. As long as the environmental goal is achieved in the aggregate, the benefit to society is the same whether every firm does an equal amount of abating or if the task is undertaken by a select few. However, the costs will be markedly lower if abatement is undertaken by more efficient polluting sources.

Modeling a Pollution Permit System for Multiple Polluters

To illustrate the operation of a permit system, we return to our former two-polluter model, where each firm faces distinct abatement cost conditions:

Polluter 1: $TAC_1 = 1.25(A_1)^2$
$MAC_1 = 2.5(A_1)$

Polluter 2: $TAC_2 = 0.3125(A_2)^2$
$MAC_2 = .625(A_2)$

Prior to any government intervention, we assume that each firm releases 10 units of pollution into the environment for an aggregate amount of 20 units

---

[23]Trading is critical to the cost-effective outcome. For example, if the permits were allocated equally across all polluters and no trading were allowed, the result would be no different than a command-and-control system of uniform standards.

[24]Contrast this scenario with a command-and-control instrument that forces every polluting source to meet identical standards of emission or effluent levels. Such instruments equalize the *level of control* across polluters rather than equalizing the *marginal costs of control*.

for the region in which they are located. The government has determined that the "acceptable" level of pollution for this region is 10 units, and it decides to reach this objective by using a tradeable pollution permit system. It therefore issues 10 permits, each of which allows the bearer to emit one unit of pollution. For simplicity, assume that the government allocates five permits to each polluter.[25] Under the rules of the tradeable pollution permit system, each firm is required to: (1) hold a permit for each unit of pollution released into the environment; and (2) undertake abatement on all remaining units of pollution.

Based on the *initial* allocation of permits in our model, each polluter must abate five units of pollution. This initial condition, termed Round 1 of the permit system, is summarized as follows:

Round 1:   *Government issues five permits to each polluter*

Polluter 1:   Current pollution level: 10 units

     Number of permits held: 5
     Abatement required: 5 units

$$MAC_1 = 2.5(A_1) = 2.5(5) = \$12.50$$
$$TAC_1 = 1.25(A_1)^2 = 1.25(5)^2 = \$31.25$$

Polluter 2:   Current pollution level: 10 units

     Number of permits held: 5
     Abatement required: 5 units

$$MAC_2 = 0.625A_2 = 0.625(5) = \$3.125$$
$$TAC_2 = 0.3125(A_2)^2 = 0.3125(5)^2 = \$7.81$$

If the permit system did not allow for trading, each firm would have no choice but to abate five units each. While the environmental objective would be met, it would not be achieved in a cost-effective manner. The combined abatement cost for both sources without trading is \$39.06.[26]

Now, consider how the result changes when permit trading is allowed. Since the two firms face different *MAC*s at their respective abatement levels at the end of Round 1, there will be an incentive for trade. Polluter 1 has an economic incentive to buy permits from Polluter 2 as long as the purchase price of each permit is less than its MAC_1. Likewise, Polluter 2 has an economic incentive to sell permits to Polluter 1 as long as it can obtain a price

---

[25]The government could have introduced the permits into the system through a direct sale by assigning an initial price to each permit, or through an auction, letting the polluters bid on the permits. Either method has the advantage of generating revenue to the government, which could be used to absorb some of the administrative costs of the permit system.

[26]Recall from the last chapter that this is precisely the same expenditure incurred by the two polluters if a uniform standard is used under a command-and-control approach.

greater than its MAC_2. Suppose that at Round 2 of the trading process, the two firms agree on the purchase and sale of one permit at a price of $8.00.[27] Polluter 1 purchases one permit from Polluter 2, giving Polluter 1 the "right" to pollute a total of 6 units and the obligation to abate 4 units. Polluter 2 now possesses the "right" to pollute a total of 4 units of pollution, which means it must undertake abatement for 6 units of pollution. Round 2 is summarized as follows:

Round 2:	*Polluter 1 purchases one permit from Polluter 2*	
Polluter 1:	Current pollution level:	10 units
	Number of permits held:	6
	Abatement required:	4 units

$$MAC_1 = 2.5(A_1) = 2.5(4) = \$10.00$$
$$TAC_1 = 1.25(A_1)^2 = 1.25(4)^2 = \$20.00$$
Cost of one permit purchased = $ 8.00

Polluter 2:	Current pollution level:	10 units
	Number of permits held:	4
	Abatement required:	6 units

$$MAC_2 = 0.625A_2 = 0.625(6) = \$3.75$$
$$TAC_2 = 0.3125(A_2)^2 = 0.3125(6)^2 = \$11.25$$
Revenue from one permit sold = $ 8.00

This outcome can be analyzed from two perspectives—that of society and that of the firm. From the vantage point of society, the total costs of abating the 10 units of pollution are now $31.25, which is $7.81 *less* than what they were without permit trading. Qualitatively, this is exactly what should result, since trading has brought the two firms' MAC values closer together. Polluter 1 now faces a lower MAC_1 of $10, (compared to $12.50 in Round 1), and Polluter 2, a higher MAC_2 of $3.75, (compared to $3.125 in Round 1). Recall that the **equi-marginal principle of optimality** indicates that the MACs are equal at the cost-effective allocation of abatement responsibilities.

Next, consider the gains that accrue to each firm as a result of the trade. Polluter 1 is better off, since its total expenditures have decreased. Its outlay for abating plus the cost of the added permit is $28.00 (i.e., TAC_1 of $20.00 *plus* the cost of the additional permit at $8.00), which is $3.25 less than its TAC_1 in Round 1. Likewise, Polluter 2 is better off, since its net expenditures associated with abating and trading are $3.25 (i.e., TAC_2 of $11.25 *less* the revenue received from selling one permit at $8.00), which is $4.56 less than its TAC_2 at the end of Round 1.

---

[27] Any negotiated price between MAC_1 and MAC_2 would be acceptable. The ultimate selling price within that range would be determined by the two firms' relative bargaining strengths.

Since there is an incentive for trade as long as the two firms face different *MAC* levels, it should be apparent that Round 2 does not represent an equilibrium. After the initial exchange of one permit, Polluter 1 still faces a higher *MAC* than Polluter 2 at their respective abatement levels, that is, $10.00 for Polluter 1 versus $3.25 for Polluter 2. Thus, it is in each polluter's best interest to continue to trade. The "rule of thumb" is that in the presence of differing *MAC*s among polluting sources, high-cost abaters have an incentive to purchase permits from low-cost abaters, and low-cost abaters have an incentive to sell them. The result? Low-cost abaters will do what they do best—clean up the environment—and high-cost abaters will pay for the "right" to pollute by buying more permits. Trading will continue until the incentive to do so no longer exists—when the *MAC*s across both firms are equal. At precisely this point, the cost-effective solution is obtained.

Applying this equi-marginal principle to our two-firm model, the final round or the equilibrium point is as follows:

Final Round: *Polluter 1 purchases a total of three permits from Polluter 2: Equalization of* **MAC** *across Polluters Is Achieved*

Polluter 1:   Current pollution level: 10 units
                Number of permits held: 8
                Abatement required: 2 units

$MAC_1 = 2.5(A_1) = 2.5(2) = \$ 5$
$TAC_1 = 1.25(A_1)^2 = 1.25(2)^2 = \$ 5$
Cost of three permits purchased[28] $= \$20$

Polluter 2:   Current pollution level: 10 units
                Number of permits held: 2
                Abatement required: 8 units

$MAC_2 = 0.625A_2 = 0.625(8) = \$ 5$
$TAC_2 = 0.3125(A_2)^2 = 0.3125(8)^2 = \$20$
Revenue from three permits sold $= \$20$

At this point, each polluter faces an *MAC* of $5, and society's total cost to achieve the environmental objective of 10 units of pollution is $25. (Notice that the $20 payment for permits should not be included in society's abatement costs, since this amount is just a *transfer* from one firm to another.) As predicted, the low-cost abater, Polluter 2, is doing most of the abating at 8 units, while the high-cost abater, Polluter 1, abates only 2 units.

Assessing the Model.   It is no coincidence that the final abatement allocation for these two firms is identical to what results if a $5 pollution charge is imposed. The outcome is logically the same because both instruments use

---

[28]We assume that the second permit was sold for $7 and the third for $5. These values plus the $8 price for the first permit results in a total payment of $20 for permits.

incentives that operate through the *MAC*s of each polluter. There are, however, three important differences. First, with a pollution charge instrument, the government has to search for the price that will bring about the requisite amount of abatement. In the permit system, bargaining and eventual trading between the polluters establishes the price of a ''right to pollute'' without any outside intervention. Secondly, the pollution charge generates tax revenues on all units of pollution not abated, while there are none from the permit system. This distinction may be a critical one in jurisdictions facing tight fiscal budgets. However, a trading system *can* be designed to generate revenues, if the government sells or auctions off the original allocation of permits. Thirdly, the trading system is inherently more flexible in that the number of permits can be adjusted to satisfy any change in the environmental objective. If the objective is too stringent, more permits can be introduced into the market. If it is too lenient, the government, environmental groups, or concerned citizens can enter the market and buy up permits, effectively reducing the amount of pollution legally allowed in the affected region.

There is some measure of controversy surrounding the use of trading systems. Economists typically tout the advantages of a system that so explicitly uses the market process. Noted economist Alan Blinder has argued publicly in favor of market-based environmental policy instruments for years. He points to the inherent cost savings, the elimination of bureaucratic interference, and the potential for much-needed government revenues.[29] On the other side of the coin, opponents argue that trading systems can create ''pollution hot spots''—localized areas facing high concentrations of pollutants where most of the permit buying takes place. Another objection is the potential for elevated administrative costs to keep records of trades and the emissions of buyers and sellers.[30] Hypotheticals aside, the true test will be in observing how these permit systems perform in practice.

Pollution Permit Trading Systems in Practice

Of all the available control instruments, tradeable permit systems are by far the most market-oriented form of environmental policy. Proposed for years by economists,[31] these systems are still in the embryonic stage of development, with much of the evolution taking place in the United States. As yet, there is only limited evidence of how effective these instruments are in establishing viable markets for pollution rights. This will likely change in the near future, as we observe the results of a comprehensive trading plan mandated by the Clean Air Act Amendments of 1990. Attempting to combat the adverse effects of acid rain, these amendments establish an allowance-based program to con-

---

[29]See, for example, Blinder (July 10, 1989, and August 24, 1987).
[30]Mandel (May 22, 1989).
[31]See, for example, Ruff (1970).

trol sulfur dioxide emissions.[32] Other examples of how this innovative market instrument has been introduced into government policy efforts are discussed in Application 5.4.

Application 5.4

Pollution Permit Trading Systems:
Credits versus Allowances

Marketable permit systems specify the quantity of emissions or effluents that can be released into the environment and let the market determine the price. In practice, these markets for "rights to pollute" involve the trading of pollution **credits** or **allowances,** which differ in the intent of the initial allocation. Credit-based systems, the most common of the two, allocate permits to polluting sources based upon their *current* emission levels relative to the allowable limit. For every unit of pollution emitted below the standard, the polluter receives a credit. Allowance-based systems, which are starting to gain acceptance, are based on *future* pollution levels. The number of allowances communicates the maximum emission level the polluter must achieve to satisfy an environmental objective. If it emits less than what is mandated, it can either hold the unused allowances for future use or sell them to another polluter. If it cannot achieve the limit, it must buy allowances from another source.

Credit Trading in Phosphorus Reduction Rights

In 1984, Summit County, Colorado, implemented a credit trading program to control phosphorus levels in the Dillon Reservoir, a body of water that represents 50 percent of Denver's water supply. This reservoir had been polluted by wastes discharged by a collection of point sources, including several municipal treatment plants and an industrial source, as well as nonpoint sources such as urban runoff. The area suffers from high levels of phosphorus from fertilizer use on golf courses and agricultural crop lands. Given the importance of Dillon Reservoir to the city's water supply, officials initiated a market-based program to abate the reservoir's pollution through a system of credits for phosphorus reductions.

Several characteristics in the Dillon Reservoir case motivated the use of a tradeable credit system. First, there was only one major contaminant that needed to be controlled—in this case phosphorus. Second, the polluting sources were identifiable, thus facilitating the allocation of credits. Finally, the polluters faced different abatement cost conditions. Officials estimated that the incremental control costs for phosphorus discharges were substantially higher for point sources than for nonpoint sources. Cost differences such as these motivate trading among polluting sources, which can lead to a cost-effective solution.

Allowance Trading in Chlorofluorocarbon Production Rights

A relevant example of an allowance-based trading system is the one currently being used by the U.S. EPA to control chlorofluorocarbons (CFCs). CFCs are organic chemicals used as industrial solvents, in the manufacture of plastic foam, and as refrigerants in air conditioners, home refrigerators, and freezers. The release of CFCs into the atmosphere has been linked to the breakdown of the earth's ozone layer, which serves as a protective shield against ultraviolet radiation. In September 1987,

---

[32]These important amendments and the specific legislation dealing with emissions trading will be discussed at length in upcoming chapters.

Application 5.4 (concluded)

the United States and 34 other nations signed the Montreal Protocol, an international agreement aimed at protecting the earth's ozone layer through a phaseout plan for production and consumption of CFCs. Effected through amendments to the Protocol in 1992, the participating countries agreed to eliminate the production and consumption of ozone-depleting substances by 1996.

To meet the objectives of the Montreal Protocol, the United States established a tradeable allowance system for CFCs. To set the plan in motion, all major U.S. producers of CFCs were issued allowances according to a baseline allocation set by the EPA. This initial allocation was expected to bring about trading among CFC producers based on the usual market forces. To accommodate the phaseout called for in the Protocol, the EPA instituted a plan to gradually reduce the number of allowances available for trading. Inter-

estingly, the reductions are tied to trading transactions. When any trade takes place, the transferor must deduct 1 percent of the amount transferred from its remaining allowances.

Whether these pollution permit trading systems will encourage their use on a broader scale remains to be seen. Some have predicted that these systems will become more prevalent in the coming decade. More conservative analysts suggest that the future of this approach depends on the success of existing trading programs, particularly the highly publicized acid rain trading program mandated under the 1990 Clean Air Act Amendments.

Source: U.S. Environmental Protection Agency, Office of Policy, Planning, and Evaluation, *The United States Experience with Economic Incentives to Control Environmental Pollution* (Washington, D.C., July 1992).

Conclusions

No environmental policy instrument is without flaws. In fact, the same could be said of all types of regulation aimed at correcting market failures. In truth, this less-than-perfect outcome should be expected. The market process works as well as it does because it operates autonomously, without external guidance. Hence, it should not be surprising that any attempt to correct a market problem by imposing third-party controls is likely to have its share of pitfalls.

This line of defense is precisely the motivation of market-based approaches to pollution control. The aim of such policies is not to add more restraint but to restore the market forces that broke down in the first place. What all economic instruments have in common is that they attempt to utilize the natural incentives of the market to work toward a solution that benefits all of society. In one form or another, market-based instruments effectively assign a price to environmental goods like clean air and water. In the absence of prices, polluters have no incentive to account for the effect of their decisions on the environment. Once this signaling mechanism is assigned to environmental resources, polluters are forced to internalize the costs of pollution damage and adjust their decisions accordingly.

Of course, not all market-based instruments are well suited to all environmental problems. Both the nature of the environmental problem and the market context must be well understood before any policy can be implemented with success. Environmental problems are complex, both in origin and in implication. Likewise, today's markets are highly sophisticated and dynamic. However, evidence is beginning to accumulate that the link between the two is a fundamental step toward finding solutions.

Summary

- The market approach to pollution control uses economic incentives and the price mechanism to achieve a government-mandated environmental standard. The major categories of these market-based instruments are: pollution charges, subsidies, deposit/refund systems, and pollution permit trading systems.
- A pollution charge is a payment or fee charged to the polluter that varies with the quantity of pollutants released into the environment. If it is implemented as a per unit tax on the pollution-generating product equal to the *MEC* at the efficient level of production, it is called a Pigouvian tax.
- An alternative type of pollution charge is an emission charge, which can also be implemented as a tax. Given a choice of abating, paying the tax, or employing a mix of abatement technology and tax payments, the profit-maximizing polluter will choose the most cost-effective strategy.
- In the case of multiple polluters with different *MAC* functions, the emission charge yields an allocation of abatement responsibilities at the point where the *MAC*s for all sources are equal.
- A subsidy is a payment or tax concession that provides financial assistance for emission or effluent reductions. Abatement equipment subsidies are implemented through the use of grants, low-interest loans, or investment tax credits. If the subsidy is equal to the *MEB* at the efficient level of production, it is called a Pigouvian subsidy. Per unit pollution reduction subsidies pay the polluter for abating beyond some predetermined level. Because profitability is enhanced, such an instrument can paradoxically lead to higher pollution levels, since profits encourage new firms to enter the market.
- A deposit-refund system imposes an up-front charge to pay for potential pollution damage, which is eventually refunded for activities such as returning a product for proper disposal or recycling. The deposit component is intended to capture the *MEC* of improper disposal, and the refund component is aimed at introducing an incentive to properly dispose of or recycle wastes.
- A pollution permit trading system involves the issuance of some number of permits based upon an environmental objective and interfirm permit trading. The trading activity gives rise to a market for "pollution rights." Following natural incentives, polluters will either purchase these rights or abate—whichever is the cheaper alternative.

Key Concepts

market approach
pollution charge
Polluter-Pays Principle
product charge
Pigouvian tax
emission or effluent fee
user charge
environmental subsidy

abatement equipment subsidy
Pigouvian subsidy
per unit pollution reduction subsidy
deposit/refund system
pollution permit trading system
pollution credits
pollution allowances

Review Questions

1. In an article entitled, "Environmentalist Predicts Marked Change in U.S. Policy," which appeared in the December 7, 1992, issue of the *Boston Globe*, Jessica Mathews, then vice president of the World Resources Institute, is quoted as saying that U.S. environmental policy will be undergoing major changes. She argues that subsidies encouraging the use of scarce resources will be abandoned and that the prices of goods using these resources will rise to reflect their true environmental cost.

   a. Illustrate Mathews's prediction by using appropriate market diagrams, both before and after a subsidy is in use.

   b. Mathews also asserts that future policy will include tax differentials, whereby taxes will be reduced or removed on productive activity such as savings and imposed on nonproductive negative externalities like pollution.
      (1) Give the economic intuition of this tax proposal.
      (2) Give an example of a *current* polluting activity that might be taxed in the future. Graphically illustrate your example and explain its significance to environmental quality control.

2. Despite economists' support of a market approach to environmental quality control, command-and-control continues to dominate the policy of most nations. Explain why this is the case. In your response, cite and then comment on some of the common criticisms of market-based initiatives.

3. Assume that there are two firms each emitting 20 units of pollutants into the environment for a total of 40 units in their region. The government sets an aggregate abatement standard of 20 units. The polluters' cost functions are as follows:

   Polluter 1: $TAC_1 = 10 + 0.75(A_1)^2$ Polluter 2: $TAC_2 = 5 + 0.5(A_2)^2$
   $MAC_1 = 1.5(A_1)$ $MAC_2 = A_2$

   a. What information does the government need to support an assertion that the 20-unit abatement standard is allocatively efficient?

   b. Suppose the government allocates the abatement responsibility equally such that each polluter must abate 10 units of pollution. Graphically illustrate this allocation and analytically assess the cost implications.

   c. Now, assume that the government institutes an emission fee of $16 per unit of pollution. How many units of pollution would each polluter abate? Is the $16 fee a cost-effective strategy for meeting the standard? Explain.

   d. If instead the government used a pollution permit system, what permit price would achieve a cost-effective allocation of abatement? Compare this allocation to the equal allocation standard described in part (b).

Additional Readings

Bohm, Peter. *Deposit-Refund System: Theory and Application to Environmental, Conservation, and Consumer Policy.* Baltimore: Johns Hopkins University Press for Resources for the Future, 1981.

Feldman, Stephen L. and Robert K. Raufer. *Emissions Trading and Acid Rain: Implementing a Market Approach to Pollution Control.* Totowa, N.J.: Rowman and Littlefield, 1987.

Hahn, Robert W. and Gordon L. Hester. "Where Did All the Markets Go? An Analysis of EPA's Emission Trading Program." *Yale Journal on Regulation* 6, no. 109 (1989), pp. 109–53.

Kelman, Steven. *What Price Incentives? Economists and the Environment.* Boston: Auburn House Publishing Company, 1981.

Kneese, Allen V. and Charles Schultz. *Pollution, Prices, and Public Policy.* Washington, D.C.: The Brookings Institution, 1975.

National Solid Wastes Management Association (NSWMA). *Recycling in the States: Mid-Year Update 1990.* Washington, D.C.: NSWMA, October 1990.

Nichols, Albert L. *Targeting Economic Incentives for Environmental Protection.* Cambridge, Mass.: MIT Press, 1984.

Repetto, Robert, Roger C. Dower, Robin Jenkins, Jacqueline Geoghegan. *Green Fees: How a Tax Shift Can Work for the Environment and the Economy.* Washington, D.C.: World Resources Inc., November 1992.

Stavins, Robert N. "Harnessing Market Forces to Protect the Environment." *Environment* 31, no. 1 (January/February 1989), pp. 5–7, 28–35.

Stavins, Robert N. and Bradley W. Whitehead. "Dealing With Pollution: Market-Based Incentives for Environmental Protection." *Environment* 34, no. 7 (September 1992), pp. 6–11, 29–42.

Tietenberg, T. H. *Emissions Trading: An Exercise in Reforming Pollution Policy.* Washington D.C.: Resources for the Future, 1985.

Wirth, Timothy E. and John Heinz. *Project 88: Harnessing Market Forces to Protect Our Environment: Initiatives for the New President.* Washington, D.C.: December 1988.

PART

III

ANALYTICAL TOOLS FOR ENVIRONMENTAL PLANNING

Economics uses powerful models to explain environmental market failures and the policy solutions used to address them. With these models as a foundation, we can now move beyond the theory to the practical implications of environmental planning—the process through which government identifies environmental risks, prioritizes them, and drafts a policy plan in response. This planning process involves difficult decisions—determining which hazards pose the greatest threat to society, where to set policy objectives, and which control instruments to use. Although there are no easy answers, these decisions are guided by analytical tools designed to evaluate environmental risks and assess the costs and benefits of minimizing them.

The planning or decision-making process is actually part of a broader paradigm known as public policy development—a series of events that typically begins at the grassroots level of society and eventually leads to scientific investigation, congressional debate, and legislative enactment. Every segment of society and virtually every discipline plays a role. Understanding the entirety of public policy development gives context to environmental decision-making and explains how it is affected by science, technology, politics and the law, and fiscal constraints.

In this module, we conduct an in-depth investigation of environmental planning and the analytical tools of decision-making, all within the broader framework of government policy development. In Chapter 6, we present a conventional public policy model, which we tailor to environmental issues. This customized model identifies the planning phase as one called environmental decision-making and risk analysis. In Chapter 7, we study the two components of risk analysis known as risk assessment—the identification of risk, and risk management—the formulation of a risk response. Among several risk management strategies available to policy-makers is benefit-cost analysis, an economic tool used in guiding environmental policy decisions. Because of its potential significance, the final two chapters of the module are devoted to an investigation of this important analytical tool. Chapter 8 explains how economists measure and monetize environmental benefits and costs, and Chapter 9 shows how the results are used in a comparative evaluation to guide policy decisions.

6

ENVIRONMENTAL DECISION-MAKING

Public Policy Development

As we learned in the last module, there are many types of policy instruments government can employ to control pollution, ranging from uniform standards to tradeable pollution permits. Now, we are prepared to investigate *how* such policies are designed and implemented in practice. It turns out that the means by which government first becomes involved in any market failure and how it ultimately responds through policy are elements of a highly complex process. Our goal is to understand how this process works in the context of **environmental public policy development.** How does the government first become aware of an environment problem? What information does it use to decide which environmental problems most merit government resources? And, what guides the decision-making that gives rise to such sophisticated policy initiatives as the Clean Air Act, the Superfund Amendments, and the Clean Water Act?

Logically, it makes sense that policy-makers have to start by understanding the extent of the environmental damage. Then, they must establish an environmental quality objective and begin to consider various policy options capable of achieving it. Once a course of action is selected, it must be formally adopted through the legislature and then implemented by various government agencies and departments. Finally, the policy is monitored through an ongoing evaluation process. Collectively, these tasks define environmental public policy development and the decision-making process that supports it.

In this chapter, we explore this series of events using an established model of public policy development tailored to highlight environmental decision-making by the public sector. Of course, in practice policy development rarely follows the same path, nor is it an entirely objective procedure. Nonetheless, a general model can guide us through what is usually a complicated and often politically charged process. Think of it as a sort of blueprint that shows how the pieces fit together and what supports the structure rather than all the detail of complex reality.

Our primary objectives are twofold. The first is to explain how environmental decision-making fits into the big picture of public policy development. A step-by-step approach is used to trace the evolution of policy from the point in time when an environmental problem is first identified up through the ongoing appraisal of policy. The second objective is to show how environmental policy depends on an elaborate exchange of information drawn from many disciplines. Here, it is important to recognize the interdependence of the many participants in the public policy development process and the need for a collaborative effort in developing and supporting environmental protection initiatives.

A Model of Environmental Public Policy Development

In the United States, environmental public policy development typically does not originate at the White House or on Capitol Hill or even at a local town hall. Well before any governing body begins to take action on a public issue, the environmental problem must first be identified—something that usually occurs at the grassroots level of society. Following this, the problem has to be communicated to the public sector. The objective is to elicit government's help by convincing the appropriate public official or agency that the problem should be added to what is usually an already crowded agenda. Once done, the decision-making begins—a process that involves analyzing and assessing the damages to society, setting an objective, considering possible solutions, and selecting and implementing some type of initiative. Finally, once the policy has been set in motion, monitoring and enforcement activities take over to assure that the policy is achieving its stated objective.

In practice, the process we have just described in a few sentences is a complex one. In fact, for major environmental policies aimed at pervasive problems like air pollution or hazardous waste dumping, the full series of steps can take years to accomplish. Because of this, public policy analysts have developed models that give some structure to the process and make it easier to understand. One fairly general paradigm of public policy development is illustrated in Figure 6.1.[1] Notice from the graphic that this model breaks down the public policy process into a series of more manageable steps: problem formation, policy agenda, policy formulation, policy adoption, policy implementation, and policy evaluation.

Adapting this model to investigate environmental public policy development can be accomplished by grouping the six steps into a more compact three-phase procedure. This customized approach is presented in Figure 6.2. First,

---

[1]See Anderson, Brady, and Bullock III (1978) and Anderson (1975).

*The public policy
process*

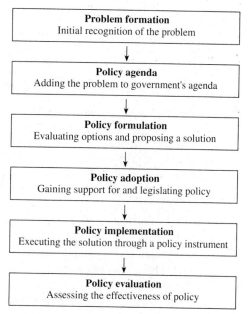

Sources: Adapted from James E. Anderson, David W. Brady, and Charles Bullock III, *Public
Policy and Politics in America* (North Scituate, Mass.: Duxbury Press, 1978); James E.
Anderson, *Public Policy-Making: Decisions and Their Implementation* (New York: Praeger,
1975).

FIGURE 6.2

*Environmental public
policy development*

problem formation and policy agenda define **Phase I: Identification of the
environmental problem.** The next three steps—policy formulation, policy
adoption, and policy implementation—are combined into **Phase II: Environmental decision-making and risk analysis.** Finally, policy evaluation is
classified as **Phase III: Environmental policy appraisal.** This approach

shows that, while decision-making in Phase II is the operational basis of environmental policy development, it is but one part of an interdependent progression of events.

Phase I: Identification of the Environmental Problem

**identification
of the
environmental
problem**
Involves initial
awareness of an
existing or potential
environmental hazard
and the process of
convincing
government to
respond to the
problem.

Identification of an environmental issue begins with **problem formation**— the recognition of a *public* dilemma, meaning one that affects some segment of society as opposed to a single individual. Sometimes, the signs of a problem are obvious, like medical wastes washed up on local beaches or heavy smog that impairs breathing and visibility. In other instances, the signals are more subtle— so much so that it takes people a long time to notice that there might be a problem. For example, residents of a community might begin to realize that there has been a higher than normal number of unexplained birth defects within its population or that the incidence of cancer is suspiciously high. If an environmental problem is the suspected cause, such as a contaminated water supply, citizens will most likely elicit government's help to identify the source of the problem and discover ways to correct it.

Recognizing a problem or a potential hazard is a significant step, but it is just the beginning. What must happen next is that citizens must convince public officials that the issue is sufficiently important to be added to government's **policy agenda.** In theory at least, there are a variety of ways for this to be accomplished. For example, depending on the scope of the problem, individuals might express their grievances at a town meeting, or they might contact the mayor of their town or even the governor of their state. Larger and potentially more damaging problems will most likely require federal intervention. In such instances, individuals might bring the problem to the attention of one of their senators or congressional representatives. Of course, in practice, it is difficult for a single individual to summon government action, particularly at the federal level. Consequently, private individuals often form coalitions to strengthen their chances of success, a practice that has been effective in bringing environmental issues to national attention. As environmental awareness has grown, so too have the ways in which concerns are communicated from the grassroots level to public officials. Application 6.1 reports on some recent survey results about what American citizens are doing to influence the environmental agenda of both public and private decision-makers.

Once government officials are first made aware of a suspected environmental problem, they have to make certain that any claim of environmental damage can be substantiated. Even if that is achieved, there are no guarantees that the problem will be placed on an official agenda. For one thing, government has to make a judgment about which of the many problems it learns about are most in need of an official response. Resources are limited—even at the federal level of government. Given an already busy agenda, the public sector might have no alternative but to take no action at all or at least defer any intervention to a later date. Its evaluation of the *relative* importance of a

How American Citizens Are Influencing Environmental Agenda

Since the first Earth Day in 1970, Americans have become increasingly active in environmental issues and more aggressive in influencing environmental agenda. According to recent public opinion polls, approximately 78 percent of Americans consider themselves to be environmentalists. But, are such self-acclamations supported by bona fide actions? Survey results suggest that they are. Individuals report that they are recycling newspapers, glass, and aluminum, and that their communities are orchestrating coordinated efforts to clean up polluted beaches and littered roadsides. Even more telling are survey statistics showing rising participation rates in "green" activities over time. Between March 1989 and March 1991, the proportion of individuals recycling newspapers nearly doubled, and those returning beverage bottles and cans grew from 41 to 48 percent. More recent polls indicate that this latter statistic is continuing to rise, estimated at 58 percent in 1992.

Beyond these activities, individuals and consumer groups also have begun to use the market influence of their attitudes toward environmentally damaging products. By purchasing only commodities produced by environmentally responsible firms and by avoiding those offered by less diligent firms, consumers are sending important market signals to the business community. Recognizing the

potential profit implications, some firms are responding by eliminating wasteful packaging and minimizing the use of toxic substances in their production processes.

Private citizens also are becoming more involved in the political process that guides environmental policy decisions. Some are contributing money to environmental groups and other organizations whose agenda matches their own. Often, these contributions support lobbying efforts aimed at communicating specific environmental concerns to Congress and other government officials. Other individuals choose a more direct route by contacting their government representatives either to voice their opinion or to volunteer their services to some environmental endeavor.

All told, it seems that Americans are making a commitment to protect and preserve the environment. To better understand the broad range of efforts at the grassroots level, consider the following survey data collected by the Roper Organization for the 1991–92 period.

Sources: Frederick Allen and Gregg Sekscienski, "Greening at the Grassroots: What Polls Say about America's Environmental Commitment," *EPA Journal* 18, no. 4, September/October 1992, pp. 52–53; U.S. Environmental Protection Agency, Office of Communications, Education, and Public Affairs, *Securing Our Legacy: An EPA Progress Report 1989–1991* (Washington, D.C., April 1992), p. 9.

Activity	1992	Percentage Change from 1991
Return bottles and cans to a store and recycling center	58	10%
Recycle newspaper	43	6
Sort trash to separate from recyclable material/garbage	35	3
Use biodegradable, low-phosphate detergents	29	0
Buy products in pumps, not aerosols	28	−3
Use biodegradable plastic garbage bags	28	2
Check labels for environmental safety	24	NA
Buy products made of/packaged in recycled paper	19	1
Buy products in refillable packages	18	NA
Compost household/yard waste	18	NA
Avoid products from companies not environmentally responsible	12	−2
Take bags to the market	10	−2
Cut back on auto use	8	−2
Avoid restaurants using Styrofoam containers	8	−1
Contribute money to environmental groups	8	0
Write letters to politicians on environmental issues	4	−2

public problem and its inherent risks involves not only a systematic appraisal but also some subjective value judgments. There are also political pressures that affect how a policy agenda is set. Every public official knows that this agenda becomes a track record by which constituents evaluate political accomplishments and failures. Hence, the process that connects policy formation to policy agenda is not without its share of gray areas. In any event, once an environmental problem does reach an official public agenda, government must begin the task of formulating an appropriate policy response.

Phase II: Environmental Decision-Making and Risk Analysis

environmental decision-making and risk analysis
Involves assessing the magnitude of the environmental problem and developing an appropriate policy response.

risk assessment
The qualitative and quantitative evaluation of the risk posed to health or the ecology by an actual or potential environmental hazard.

risk management
The decision-making process of evaluating and choosing from alternative policy responses to environmental risk.

Policy formulation is the first step in environmental decision-making. It is during this stage that two important and highly interrelated functions are performed. First, the government must make a formal assessment of the magnitude of the environmental problem and the degree of risk it poses to society—a procedure referred to as **risk assessment.** Second, public officials must develop an appropriate policy response to the environmental risk—part of the process known as **risk management.** In the next chapter, we will elaborate on these important risk-based procedures. For now, we consider the issues that are at stake when these processes are undertaken as part of environmental policy development.

Perhaps the most important decision made during policy formulation is determining what is to be accomplished by government regulation. For comprehensive initiatives, policy goals often are stated in very general terms, such as achieving cleaner water to protect human health and welfare. More refined objectives are defined as the process evolves and as more specific provisions are proposed. Implicitly, these objectives dictate how stringent the ultimate policy response will have to be. In extreme cases of environmental degradation, the goal might be an outright ban of the suspected contaminant.[2] In the United States, such an uncompromising approach has been used to control some cancer-causing substances, such as polychlorinated biphenyls (PCBs) and dichloro-diphenyl-trichloroethane (DDT). Although such hardline policies are disruptive to economic activity, the objective-setting decision is clear-cut. If the threat to society is so severe as to warrant such action, there is no room for compromise and debate.

Aside from such extremes, the conventional case calls for seeking a middle ground somewhere between status quo and an outright ban. In these instances, government officials are faced with the tough decision of setting a goal at some ''acceptable'' level of pollution. But, what exactly is meant by an ''acceptable'' level of pollution, and how is such a determination made? Economic theory argues that ''acceptable'' should be guided by allocative

---

[2]Such an objective would be justified on economic grounds only if the *MSC* of abatement were less than or equal to the *MSB* of abatement at the 100 percent abatement level.

efficiency—setting the target where the *MSC* and *MSB* of abatement are equal. In practice, however, the uncertainties associated with measuring these costs and benefits leave public officials with the difficult dilemma of making inferences or using some alternative criteria. About all that can be said from a general perspective is that the determination of an acceptable pollution level comes about only through consulting with a myriad of experts, such as medical researchers and other scientists, and through soliciting input from virtually every sector of society.

Once environmental objectives are defined, public officials begin to consider alternative control instruments capable of realizing these goals. As we have learned from Chapters 4 and 5, available options range from command-and-control approaches to more flexible market-based instruments. Economic theory can and sometimes does guide the policy-maker in selecting from among alternative control policies, using the criteria of allocative efficiency or cost-effectiveness. However, because of the inherent difficulty in measuring the expected benefits of improved environmental quality, officials most often are guided by cost-effectiveness—choosing control instruments that achieve an objective using the least amount of economic resources.

Following the selection of an appropriate policy proposal, the **policy adoption** stage begins. Adopting public policy into law is a complex undertaking, particularly at the federal level of government. In the United States, the customary procedure is for the proposal to be submitted to Congress where it is debated and discussed for a time before a vote is called for. The proposal must be approved by the House of Representatives and the Senate, and finally by the president of the United States.[3] Of course not all proposals are adopted, and among those that eventually do become law, most are amended along the way.

Many factors influence this process—national economic conditions, international trade implications, politics, and public opinion. Beyond the importance of national and global interests, regional economic impacts must also be considered. A case in point was President Clinton's 1993 plan to preserve the ecology of our national forests and protect certain endangered species such as the northern spotted owl. The Clinton plan met with strong resistance from congressional representatives from the northwestern United States and from the logging industry, both of whom shared a common concern about the potentially adverse economic effects on the Northwest region. Special-interest groups are also a highly visible and often influential element of the environmental policy process—among them, environmentalists, corporate officials, and labor unions. In fact, a strong lobbying force for the United Mine Workers biased certain of the provisions in the 1977 Clean Air Act Amendments to protect the jobs of high-sulfur coal miners. Consequently, that particular

---

[3]Some policies are issued directly through executive order by the president or handed down by the Supreme Court.

aspect of U.S. clean air policy imposed much higher costs than necessary on all of society.[4]

Once an environmental policy is ratified by Congress, it then must be executed, monitored, and enforced—all part of **policy implementation.** In the United States implementation is conducted by administrative agencies, and it generally involves coordination between federal and state governments. As it applies to the environment, this coordination is referred to as **environmental federalism.** Included among the U.S. agencies responsible for environmental policy implementation are the Food and Drug Administration (FDA), the Office of Safety and Health Administration (OSHA), and, of course, the Environmental Protection Agency (EPA)—the largest federal agency in the United States[5]

To assure compliance, monitoring systems must be established. As environmental regulations have become more sophisticated, so too have monitoring and enforcement procedures. According to the EPA, criminal enforcement has become a powerful means to assure compliance. For example, during 1991, a record number of 104 individuals and corporations were charged in EPA criminal cases, 48 of which resulted in conviction and sentencing. In 1992, 174 criminal indictments were handed down with $163 million in fines imposed, including $125 million from the *Exxon Valdez* incident.[6]

There are important economic implications associated with monitoring and enforcement activities. Reconsider the market for pollution abatement, which is reproduced in Figure 6.3. The efficient level of abatement is determined by the intersection of the *MSC* and *MSB* curves, which is labeled A_e. Recall that the *MSC* includes the aggregate of all polluters' marginal abatement costs (MAC_{mkt}) plus government's marginal cost for monitoring and enforcement, commonly referred to as the **marginal cost of enforcement** (*MCE*). In Figure 6.3, the *MCE* is represented by the vertical distance between MAC_{mkt} and *MSC*. Notice that this distance is increasing with higher abatement levels. As pollution standards become more stringent, polluters have a greater tendency to evade the law, which in turn calls for more sophisticated and thus more costly monitoring and enforcement programs. If the *MCE* is not accounted for in setting an objective level of abatement, too many resources will be allocated to that activity. Referring to the diagram in Figure 6.3, notice that such an omission would cause the target abatement level to be set at A_1, determined by the intersection of *MSB* and MAC_{mkt}, which is well above A_e.

environmental federalism
The coordination and delegation of tasks among various levels of government to develop and implement environmental policy.

marginal cost of enforcement (MCE)
The additional costs incurred by government associated with monitoring and enforcing more stringent environmental regulations.

---

[4]We will elaborate on this historical and highly controversial issue in our study of clean air policy in upcoming chapters.

[5]Within the EPA, the Office of Policy, Planning, and Evaluation (OPPE) is assigned the overall responsibility for implementation, a major undertaking given that the EPA now administers nine comprehensive environmental protection laws.

[6]U.S. EPA, Office of Communications, Education, and Public Affairs (April 1992), p. 28; Council on Environmental Quality (January 1993), p. 82.

FIGURE 6.3

The economic implications of monitoring and enforcement costs

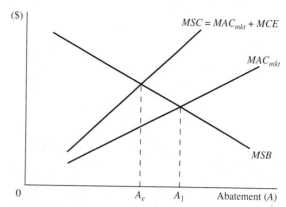

A_e signifies the efficient level of abatement, which is determined by the intersection of *MSC* and *MSB*. The *MSC* includes all polluters' marginal abatement costs (MAC_{mkt}) plus the government's marginal cost of enforcement (*MCE*). The *MCE* is represented by the vertical distance between MAC_{mkt} and *MSC*. If the *MCE* is not accounted for in setting an abatement objective, too many resources will be allocated to that activity. The result of such a decision is shown as A_1, determined by the intersection of *MSB* and MAC_{mkt}.

Phase III: Environmental Policy Appraisal

environmental policy appraisal
The ongoing process of evaluating environmental policy using criteria such as allocative efficiency, cost-effectiveness, or equity.

The final step in the planning process, **policy evaluation,** is aimed at appraising the overall effectiveness of environmental initiatives and initiating minor revisions or major reform as needed. The operative issues in this phase are to determine how well the policy is achieving its objectives and whether there have been any unanticipated negative impacts on society. Consider, for example, provisions in the 1990 Clean Air Act Amendments, which call for the use of cleaner gasolines. These are expected to reduce harmful air pollutants in nine of the nation's dirtiest cities by at least 15 percent.[7] Part of the evaluation of this set of provisions will be to determine whether the targeted pollution reduction has been achieved and whether there have been any unexpected and thus unaccounted-for effects on society, such as worker displacement or other financial loss caused by fuel switching.

environmental equity
Concerned with the fairness of the environmental risk burden across segments of society or geographical regions.

An *economic* ex-post policy appraisal uses benefit-cost analysis guided by the same criteria used in policy formulation, that is, allocative efficiency and cost-effectiveness. Relying on well-defined criteria such as these provides a way to quantify the evaluation and to lend objectivity to what is a very difficult process. While both efficiency and cost-effectiveness are rooted in resource allocation, another criterion called **environmental equity** has a different perspective. It considers the *fairness* of the ultimate risk burden across various geographical regions or across segments of the population. In the United States and elsewhere, policy officials have begun to place an increasing emphasis on environmental equity. Pollution problems such as exposure to

---

[7]Council on Environmental Quality (January 1993), p. 12.

FIGURE 6.4

*Players in the
environmental public
policy process*

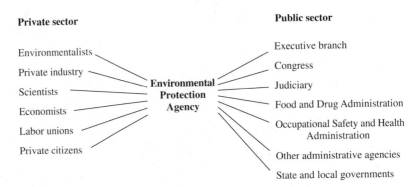

Source: Adapted from James W. Vaupel, ''Truth or Consequences: Some Roles for Scientists and Analysts in Environmental Decisionmaking,'' in Wesley A. Magat, ed., *Reform of Environmental Regulation* (Cambridge, Mass.: Ballinger Publishing Company, 1978), Figure 5-3, p. 75.

hazardous waste sites and urban smog are by definition locationally oriented, and there is some evidence to suggest that income and cultural factors are linked to the locational decisions of certain population groups. Consequently, public officials are trying to rectify existing inequities across segments of society and to incorporate the equity criterion into decision-making procedures to avoid such problems in the future.[8]

The Key Players in Environmental Decision-Making

One of the more important observations to be made from studying environmental policy development is the interdependence of many individuals or groups from both the private and public sectors. Each group of participants, albeit from a different vantage point, plays an important role in environmental decision-making and the formulation of policy. Not unlike the more general model of an economic system, each set of players in the policy development process operates from a unique set of motivations, yet each offers much-needed expertise and skill to the outcome. On balance, the process would suffer immeasurably without any one of them.

There are any number of ways to categorize the individuals who are instrumental to environmental policy development. Using the broadest classification, there are two major groups—the public sector and the private sector. The schematic in Figure 6.4 shows the different parties included in each sector, with the EPA acting as a sort of liaison between them. At the other extreme

[8]For a collection of articles on the issue of environmental equity, see Heritage (March/April 1992).

is a classification of these participants according to their professions or disciplines—a very long list indeed. Seeking a middle ground, we consider five broadly defined groups of key players in environmental public policy development. These are: **environmentalists, private industry, scientists, economists,** and **government and its agencies.**[9] Notice that this classification is a comprehensive cross section of society with many professions implicitly represented within each category—an observation that speaks to the interdisciplinary nature of environmental decision-making. Although government leaders have the final say in determining policy, their decisions are influenced by virtually every segment of society. This assertion will become clearer as we look at the five identified groups in a bit more detail.

Environmentalists

Private citizen interest in environmental issues has evolved considerably over the last century.[10] Beginning in the late 1800s, society became concerned with the preservation of natural resources and wilderness areas, a period referred to as the conservationist era. It was during this time that environmental groups such as the Sierra Club (1892) and the National Audubon Society (1905) were founded. While this interest in conservation was distracted at times by political and economic crises, such as the two world wars and the Great Depression, the stream of consciousness was never completely broken. Maintaining society's interest in nature and resource preservation was largely the result of efforts by active, high-visibility groups like the Sierra Club.

During the 1950s, more complex issues like overpopulation and pollution began to gain national attention. This shift in focus signified that conservationism was beginning to evolve into the environmentalist movement that continues to thrive today. But it was the decade of the 1960s that witnessed a surge in public awareness of environmental pollution. Rachel Carson's notable book, *Silent Spring* (1962), warned of the dangers of the pesticide known as DDT. Carson's was not the only ominous report of the effects of environmental damage. Across the Atlantic at about the same time, Britain's Nature Conservancy revealed that all of the seabirds' eggs it had collected along England's coastlines had been contaminated with organochloride pesticides. A similar report was released in 1969, when the dumping of PCBs was blamed for the discovery of between 50,000 and 100,000 dead seabirds on Britain's beaches.

Public reaction to these and other troubling accounts was direct and aggressive. In the United States, several new environmental groups were formed.

---

[9]Of course, from a technical perspective, these groups are not mutually exclusive. That is, an individual who is a member of an environmental group might also be a scientist or an industry official. However, the purpose of the groupings is not to divide the population into distinct categories but rather to consider the motivation and importance of those who most influence environmental public policy.

[10]For a more detailed analysis of this evolution, see Dunlap and Mertig (1992).

Among them were the Environmental Defense Fund (1967), Friends of the Earth (1969), and the Natural Resources Defense Council (1970). A parallel reaction occurred in other parts of the world. In the United Kingdom, for example, a British chapter of Friends of the Earth was founded, along with Greenpeace and the Conservation Society.[11] Meanwhile, membership in existing environmental groups skyrocketed throughout the 1960s. The environmental movement was fully under way, further evidenced by the celebration of the first Earth Day in 1970—a public acclamation that preserving the earth's resources was to be a top priority.

Of course, there are differences in the *relative* effectiveness of environmental groups. According to public policy analysts, membership size, power, and status are important determinants of a group's ability to influence government decisions and business practices.[12] Following this line of thought, Table 6.1 gives membership and budget data for some of the major environmental organizations as of 1990. Much of the observed variability across associations is related to the kinds of activities that dominate each group's agenda. For example, most of the nonlobbying groups control smaller budgets than their lobbying counterparts. Furthermore, groups whose focus is relatively narrow, such as the Citizen's Clearinghouse for Hazardous Waste, operate with considerably less money than those whose agenda is more comprehensive. Greenpeace USA, which has a varied and aggressive agenda, has about 2.3 million memberships—over 30 percent of the total—and controls a budget of $50.2 million.

Although environmentalists continue to influence public policy today, two emerging trends suggest that a new phase may be evolving in the environmentalist movement. One is the formation of cooperative efforts between environmentalists and corporations. Both groups have recognized the advantages of working together even though their primary objectives are different. This new phenomenon has given rise to some productive alliances, as Application 6.2 explains. A second trend is an apparent slowdown in society's support of environmental groups. Starting in the early 1990s, membership in and financial support of major associations like Greenpeace and the Sierra Club began to drop. The reported reasons are many—economic decline, a perception that environmentalism is already well entrenched in the public agenda (due in part to the Clinton-Gore platform), and a belief that other social issues such as homelessness and crime are now more in need of support.[13] Even acknowledging a possible slowdown in the environmentalist movement, there is little question that environmental groups will continue to have an effect on policy development all over the world.

---

[11]Vogel (1986), pp. 40–41.
[12]Anderson, et al. (1978), p. 9.
[13]Aeppel (October 21, 1994).

TABLE 6.1 Selected Environmental Organizations

Organization	Year Founded	1990 Membership	1990 Budget ($millions)
Lobbying Groups			
Sierra Club	1892	560,000	35.2
National Audubon Society	1905	600,000	35.0
National Parks and Conservation Association	1919	100,000	3.4
Wilderness Society	1935	370,000	17.3
National Wildlife Federation	1936	975,000	87.2
Defenders of Wildlife	1947	80,000	4.6
Environmental Defense Fund	1967	150,000	12.9
Friends of the Earth	1969	30,000	3.1
Natural Resources Defense Council	1970	168,000	16.0
Environmental Action	1970	20,000	1.2
Nonlobbying Groups			
Land and Wildlife Preservation and Nature Conservancy	1951	600,000	156.1
World Wildlife Fund	1961	940,000	35.5
League of Conservation Voters	1970	55,000	1.4
Greenpeace USA	1971	2,300,000	50.2
Sea Shepherd Conservation Society	1977	15,000	0.5
Earth First!	1980	15,000	0.2
Citizen's Clearing House for Hazardous Waste	1981	7,000	0.7
National Toxics Campaign	1984	100,000	1.5
Rainforest Action Network	1985	30,000	0.9
Rainforest Alliance	1986	18,000	0.8
Conservation International	1987	55,000	4.6
Total		7,188,000	468.3

Source: Adapted from Robert Cameron Mitchell, Angela G. Mertig, and Riley E. Dunlap, ''Twenty Years of Environmental Mobilization: Trends among National Environmental Organizations,'' in Riley E. Dunlap and Angela G. Mertig, eds., *American Environmentalism: The U.S. Environmental Movement, 1970–1990* (Philadelphia, Pa.: Taylor and Francis New York, Inc., 1992), pp. 13 and 18.

Application 6.2

Working Together:
Strategic Environmental Partnerships

Corporate America and environmental groups often are perceived as archenemies, with the business sector's profit motive pitted against the social objectives of environmentalists. Although the two groups are still at odds on many issues, a relatively recent phenomenon is beginning to take hold. Private industry and environmental groups are starting to work together instead of battling it out in the courtroom. Through government-sponsored programs and various independent organizations, the two are coordinating their efforts to find environmental solutions that are also good for business.

Application 6.2 (continued)

Why the about-face? The move is mutually beneficial. Firms continue to be motivated by their bottom line—that much hasn't changed. What *is* different is that environmentally responsible decision-making has become a critical determinant of a firm's profit position. Consumers are no longer tolerant of businesses that ignore the ecological and health implications of their actions. The bad PR that accompanies a lawsuit brought by an environmentalist group is not something any firm can afford. Furthermore, environmental regulations are adding significantly to firms' operating costs. Such cost increases give businesses a direct market incentive to function more efficiently and to *prevent* pollution rather than absorb the costs of cleaning it up—decisions that can yield an important competitive advantage. These strategic adjustments and changes in corporate culture set up the perfect opportunity for firms and environmentalists to learn from one another and to find a common ground.

For its part, government is fostering such cooperative relationships wherever it can. A good example is the President's Commission on Environmental Quality (PCEQ) formed in 1991. Its membership comprises 23 entities, representing both the corporate world and nonprofit organiza-tions, each of which has achieved some acclaim for its commitment to the environment.

The PCEQ is an effective vehicle for bringing businesses and environmentalists together. Since its inception, the commission has formed a network of over 200 organizations. Members participate in joint environmental projects, share their expertise, and experiment with new concepts. In 1992, the organization advanced 12 initiatives, which span a wide range of environmental issues such as energy efficiency, biodiversity, quality environmental management, water conservation, and waste management.

Beyond the cooperative efforts fostered through national affiliations, there are also environmental partnerships developing independently between corporations and environmental groups. A case in point is alliances formed between the nonprofit environmental group, Environmental Defense Fund (EDF), and several major corporations. No stranger to working for or against corporations, the EDF has been active in influencing environmental policies since it was founded in 1967, including its instrumental role in the U.S. 1972 decision to ban DDT. In 1990, EDF began a collaborative waste management program with the fast-food giant, McDonald's Corporation. As a result, the corporation has made

Member Affiliations of the 1991 President's Commission on Environmental Quality

Proctor & Gamble Company	Bechtel Group, Inc.
Pacific Gas and Electric Company	American Recreation Coalition
Waste Management, Inc.	Council on Environmental Quality
Chevron Corporation	Resources for the Future
World Wildlife Fund	International Paper Company
Massachusetts Institute of Technology	National Geographic Society
3M Company	Environmental Defense Fund
Enron Corp.	Kraft Foods North America
Conservation Fund	Ford Motor Corporation
The Dow Chemical Company	Browning-Ferris Industries, Inc.
John D. and Catherine T. MacArthur Foundation	Merck & Co., Inc.
General Electric Company	

Application 6.2 (concluded)

waste reduction an integral part of its management decisions. McDonald's now purchases more recycled supplies, uses more environmentally responsible packaging, and is experimenting with reusable versus disposable products in its food preparation.

More recently, EDF formed a strategic alliance with another major corporation, General Motors (GM)—this one aimed at improving air quality. The focus of the EDF-GM agenda is to find more market-based motivations for firms to reduce pollution. One example of the new partnership's endeavors is the development of an incentive-based program to encourage the removal of older, polluting cars from the nation's highways. Based on a concept suggested by the federal government dubbed "Cash for Clunkers," the plan would provide an incentive, such as pollution credits, to firms that buy up vintage vehicles and scrap them. EDF is also planning to study GM's internal environmental programs with the objective of finding more cost-effective solutions to pollution control.

So far, environmental partnerships like these seem to be succeeding. Environmentalists are winning battles against pollution, and firms are finding ways to support corporate environmentalism while trimming significant sums from their operating and compliance costs. All in all, these alliances seem like win-win situations.

Sources: Council on Environmental Quality, *Environmental Quality, 23rd Annual Report* (Washington, D.C.: U.S. Government Printing Office, January 1993), pp. 183–92; Rose Gutfeld, "Environmental Group Doesn't Always Lick 'em; It Can Join 'em and Succeed," *The Wall Street Journal,* August 20, 1992.

Private Industry

Another important influence on environmental decision-making is private industry. As regulatory controls have been put in place, firms have had to internalize at least part of the environmental damage they cause. In so doing, industry has had to absorb the costs of adopting abatement technologies into their production processes. Table 6.2 presents abatement cost data for a selection of U.S. manufacturing industries over the 1980 to 1991 period. The magnitude of these costs as well as their growth rate over time confirms that private industry has a vested interest in how environmental policy is formulated and put into effect. Of course, some industries are more directly affected than others. Look at the expenditures for the chemicals and allied products group. These costs account for the largest industrial share of abatement expenditures— a direct reflection of the amount and toxicity of polluting residuals released by this industry to all environmental media.

Increased awareness of environmental issues, better enforcement, and technological advances in pollution abatement all have contributed to a growing amount of cooperation between industry and other sectors of the economy. In the United States, a number of corporate-government partnerships have evolved with the specific aim of developing innovative methods to help reduce pollution. One of these is an EPA-sponsored program called Green Lights. This plan encourages industry to install energy-efficient lighting that conserves energy *and* reduces operating costs. Another is a toxic chemical reduction plan called the 33/50 Program. This project is so named because it

TABLE 6.2   **Pollution Abatement Expenditures for Selected Industries ($millions)**

Year	Chemicals and Allied Products	Petroleum and Coal Products	Primary Metals Industries	Paper and Allied Products	Rubber and Misc. Plastic Products	Textile Mill Products
Current Dollars						
1980	2,632.5	1,949.9	2,417.3	1,101.7	129.9	175.3
1981	2,800.6	2,276.1	2,640.0	1,115.2	140.1	156.5
1982	2,734.1	2,512.9	2,083.4	1,109.4	115.4	96.7
1983	2,593.6	2,378.7	1,840.9	1,135.2	189.4	119.8
1984	2,763.5	2,395.2	2,043.7	1,322.4	201.4	143.1
1985	3,278.1	2,353.8	2,115.9	1,453.2	222.8	173.6
1986	3,278.7	2,429.5	1,947.8	1,425.9	262.2	187.1
1988	4,169.9	2,488.3	2,118.8	1,761.0	268.6	195.9
1989	4,704.0	2,587.6	2,338.1	2,257.2	481.5	215.4
1990	5,799.0	3,622.0	2,553.0	2,682.0	522.0	244.0
1991	6,115.0	4,312.0	2,675.0	3,068.0	523.0	271.0
Constant 1986 Dollars						
1980	3,557.7	2,635.2	3,266.9	1,488.9	175.6	236.9
1981	3,439.5	2,795.4	3,242.3	1,369.6	172.1	192.2
1982	3,161.5	2,905.7	2,409.1	1,282.8	133.4	111.8
1983	2,882.1	2,643.3	2,045.7	1,261.5	210.5	133.1
1984	2,942.7	2,550.5	2,176.2	1,408.1	214.5	152.4
1985	3,364.9	2,416.1	2,171.9	1,491.7	228.7	178.2
1986	3,278.7	2,429.5	1,947.8	1,425.9	262.2	187.1
1988	3,889.0	2,320.7	1,976.1	1,642.4	250.5	182.7
1989	4,205.0	2,313.1	2,090.1	2,017.7	430.4	192.5
1990	4,977.2	3,108.7	2,191.2	2,301.9	448.0	209.4
1991	5,064.5	3,571.2	2,215.4	2,540.9	433.2	224.4

Note: Data for 1987 not available. GDP Price deflator (1987 = 100) used to convert current dollars to constant dollars.

Source: Council on Environmental Quality, *Environmental Quality, 23rd Annual Report* (Washington, D.C.: U.S. Government Printing Office, January 1993), Table 11, citing U.S. Department of Commerce, Bureau of the Census, *Pollution Abatement Costs and Expenditures, Current Industrial Reports, MA-200* (Washington, D.C.: Department of Commerce, Annual).

calls for the voluntary reduction of the release of 17 highly toxic industrial chemicals into the environment—33 percent by 1992 and 50 percent by 1995.[14] (We will have much more to say about these innovative partnership programs in upcoming chapters.)

These cooperative arrangements will likely continue to be a part of environmental policy development in the future. Both industry and government have an important stake in the outcome, and each has a significant contribution to make along the way. Industry has the technological expertise to find cost-effective ways to abate pollution and the knowledge to anticipate any market implications of policy initiatives. Government has the resources and the span

---

[14]U.S. EPA, Office of Communications, Education, and Public Affairs (April 1992), p. 21–22. For a full discussion on industry's participation in a variety of cooperative and proactive programs, see U.S. EPA, Office of Pollution Prevention (October 1991).

TABLE 6.3 Selected Environmental Laws in the United States and Britain

Selected U.S. Legislation	Year Enacted	Selected U.K. Legislation	Year Enacted
Clean Air Act	1963	Comprehensive Environmental Response,	
Clean Air Act Amendments	1965	Compensation and Liability Act	1980
Solid Waste Disposal Act	1965	Clean Air Act	1956
The Air Quality Act of 1967	1967	Estuaries and Tidal Water Act	1960
National Environmental Policy Act	1969	Radioactive Substances Act	1960
The Resource Recovery Act	1970	Rivers (Prevention of Pollution) Act	1961
Clean Air Act Amendments	1970	Water Resources Act	1963
The Federal Water Pollution Control Act of		Medicines Act	1968
1972	1972	Countryside Act	1968
The Federal Environmental Pesticide Control		Clean Air Act	1968
Act of 1972	1972	Town and Country Planning Act	1968
Safe Drinking Water Act	1974	Deposit of Poisonous Waste Act	1972
Toxic Substances Control Act	1976	Water Act	1973
The Resource Conservation and Recovery		Dumping at Sea Act	1974
Act of 1976	1976	Health and Safety at Work Act	1974
Clean Air Act Amendments	1977	Control of Pollution Act	1974
The Federal Environmental Pesticide Control		The Conservation of Wild Creatures and	
Act Amendments	1977	Wild Plants Act	1975
Clean Water Act Amendments	1977	Endangered Species (Import and Export) Act	1976
		Town and Country Planning Act	1980

of control to gather and assimilate market data and information on new technologies, which can help firms make sound decisions about how best to respond to environmental policy. With profit at stake, industry cannot afford to risk the stiff penalties imposed for noncompliance with environmental regulations, nor can it risk the unfavorable press that such behavior would elicit. Likewise, public officials cannot afford to jeopardize the success of policy initiatives by failing to invoke the cooperation of industry.

Government and Its Administrative Agencies

Throughout the world, governments are giving high priority to environmental issues. In the United States, this commitment is apparent at every level of government—from local jurisdictions to the executive branch of the federal government. This shift in emphasis began to take hold in the 1960s and 1970s, just as the environmental movement was gaining strength. Some evidence of this change is the number of comprehensive environmental laws passed during that time period, as Table 6.3 indicates. To illustrate that this legislative trend is not just a U.S. phenomenon, the table also lists some of the laws passed in the United Kingdom during this same period.[15]

---

[15]The dates given show the year in which the original legislation was passed. Many of these laws are still in force, but have undergone numerous reauthorizations and revisions over time.

TABLE 6.4   Nixon's Consolidation Plan to Form the EPA in 1970

Executive Department or Government Agency	Component Transferred to the EPA
Department of Health, Education, and Welfare (now Department of Health and Human Resources)	Air pollution control Solid waste management Radiation control Drinking water program
Department of the Interior	Federal water pollution control program Part of pesticide research program
Department of Agriculture	Authority to register and regulate use of pesticides
Food and Drug Administration	Responsibility to set tolerance levels for pesticides
Atomic Energy Commission	Some responsibility for setting environmental radiation protection standards
Federal Radiation Council	All duties

Source: U.S. Environmental Protection Agency, Information Access Branch, Information Management and Services Division, *Access EPA* (Washington, D.C., 1991).

At the federal level of government in the United States, there is a complex infrastructure responsible for public policy design and implementation. In addition to the three branches of government and the vast array of committees, subcommittees, and commissions, there is also a contingent of administrative agencies dedicated to these tasks. Federal agencies are created by Congress, which also defines their power and responsibilities. From a practical perspective, these agencies are established to carry out tasks that are too detailed and too specialized to be handled effectively by Congress. They act as a conduit through which scientific, economic, and industry data can be collected, synthesized, and interpreted for use in administering policy. Some agencies report to a cabinet department, while others function independently. All must answer to Congress and operate under specific procedural guidelines.

Major environmental policy issues are of course the responsibility of the EPA. Established in 1970, the EPA was created by President Nixon's Reorganization Plan #3—a plan that formed the elaborate agency from various components of existing federal agencies and executive departments, as shown in Table 6.4. Today, the EPA operates as an independent agency headed by a president-appointed administrator who oversees its vast infrastructure. To gain a general sense of the EPA's organization and internal hierarchy, refer to the schematic in Figure 6.5.[16] The growth rate of the EPA since its creation has been substantial. Look at the rise in its budget authority and workforce shown

---

[16]Recently, Congress has debated whether to elevate the agency to cabinet status as the Department of Environmental Protection.

FIGURE 6.5

Structure of the U.S. Environmental Protection Agency

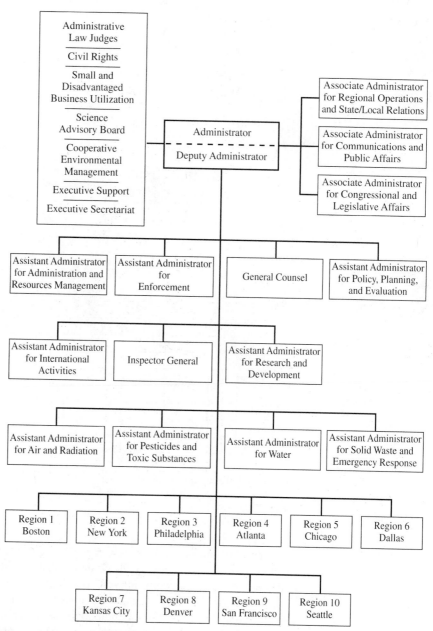

Source: U.S. Environmental Protection Agency, Information Access Branch, Information Management and Services Division, *Access EPA* (Washington, D.C., 1991), p. 8.

FIGURE 6.6

EPA budget and staff data

(a) EPA budget authority

(b) EPA workforce growth

Source: U.S. Environmental Protection Agency, Office of Communications, Education, and Public Affairs, *Securing Our Legacy, An EPA Progress Report 1989–1991* (Washington, D.C., April 1992), p. 46.

in the graphics presented in Figure 6.6. During the Bush administration, the agency's staff grew by nearly 20 percent and its funding for operating programs by 24 percent in constant 1982 dollars.[17]

Some environmental issues do fall under the jurisdiction of federal agencies other than the EPA. For example, policies aimed at occupational-specific environmental hazards, such as worker exposure to asbestos, are assigned to the Occupational Safety and Health Administration (OSHA), an agency that reports to the Department of Labor. One of OSHA's primary responsibilities

[17]U.S. EPA, Office of Communications, Education, and Public Affairs (April 1992), p. 46.

is to implement and monitor the provisions of the Occupational Safety and Health Act of 1970. Issues relating to the contamination of foods or the use of food additives such as saccharine are the responsibility of the Food and Drug Administration (FDA). This agency reports to the Department of Health and Human Resources and is responsible for administering the Federal Food, Drug and Cosmetic Act (FFDCA).

Integration of environmental policy efforts across the various administrative agencies, executive departments, and branches of government is directed by the National Environmental Policy Act (NEPA) of 1969. This legislation provides the basis for formulating all federal environmental policy and mandates ongoing awareness of and responsibility for the environmental implications of all public policy decisions. Among its many provisions, the act calls for the following:

> The Congress authorizes and directs that, to the fullest extent possible . . . all agencies of the Federal Government shall—
>> Utilize a systematic, interdisciplinary approach which will insure the integrated use of the natural and social sciences and the environmental design arts in planning and in decision making which may have an impact on man's environment; . . .
>> Include in every recommendation or report on proposals for legislation and other major Federal actions significantly affecting the quality of the human environment, a detailed statement by the responsible official on the environmental impact of the proposed action, . . . [18]

The provisions of the NEPA are not just political rhetoric. In fact, there has been a history of complaints filed against government agencies for failing to comply with this act, particularly its requirement for submitting an "Environmental Impact Statement (EIS)" on any proposed legislation or major federal initiative. (The EIS is referred to as the "detailed statement" in the second paragraph quoted above.) Application 6.3 presents some survey data on the litigation history of the NEPA and discusses its recent role in negotiating international trade agreements.

Scientists

The research of chemists, biologists, and other scientists is critical to the development of sound environmental public policy. For example, government decision-makers rely on the scientific community to study health effects from human exposure to contaminants and to identify population-specific sensitivities, such as the higher susceptibility of young children to lead poisoning. This research is guided by the science of **toxicology,** that is, the study of poisons and their effects. This relatively young discipline has grown in significance as chemicals have become more prevalent in our society and as synthetic chemicals have been developed—a trend that has led to more complex and serious pollution problems. In fact, coincident with the surge of

toxicology
A scientific discipline concerned with studying poisons and their effects.

---

[18]Title I. "Declaration of National Environmental Policy"; Sec. 102(1)(A) and Sec. 102.(1)(E) of the National Environmental Policy Act of 1969 as amended.

Application 6.3

Assuring Compliance with the National Environmental Policy Act (NEPA)

The National Environmental Policy Act (NEPA) is a broad-based set of rulings, which outlines the nation's overall position on environmental issues. Its statutory purposes are intentionally general. Included among them is the following:

> To declare a national policy which will encourage productive and enjoyable harmony between man and his environment; to promote efforts which will prevent or eliminate damage to the environment and biosphere and stimulate the health and welfare of man; . . .

Beyond this general mission, some of the NEPA's provisions are quite specific, and none are taken lightly. One mandate in particular has been the focus of many lawsuits, specifically Sec.102(C), which requires the submission of what has become known as an Environmental Impact Statement (EIS). The law is clear about what an EIS is to entail:

> The Congress authorizes and directs that, to the fullest extent possible: . . . all agencies of the Federal Government shall—
>> Include in every recommendation or report on proposals for legislation and other major Federal actions significantly affecting the quality of the human environment a detailed statement by the responsible official on—
>
> (i) The environmental impact of the proposed action,
> (ii) Any adverse environmental effects which cannot be avoided should the proposal be implemented,
> (iii) Alternatives to the proposed action,
> (iv) The relationship between local short-term uses of man's environment and the maintenance and enhancement of long-term productivity, and
> (v) Any irreversible and irretrievable commitments of resources which would

be involved in the proposed action should it be implemented.

Since the NEPA was passed in 1969, literally thousands of EISs have been completed by a variety of federal agencies. During 1991, approximately 456 EISs were completed by major federal agencies and executive departments. Most were executed by the Department of Agriculture, which filed 145 such statements that year. However, not all federally proposed actions have complied with the law, and in some of these cases lawsuits have been filed. The table on the next page provides a partial history of complaints against federal agencies for failure to meet the requirements of the NEPA.

As these data indicate, the most common complaint is the failure of the federal agency or department to prepare an EIS. Notice also that the complaints are filed most often by private citizens or environmental groups, indicative of their influence on environmental policy.

In a stunning federal court decision handed down in 1993, a judge ruled that the filing of an EIS was required for negotiations of the North American Free Trade Agreement (NAFTA), the trade agreement between the United States, Mexico, and Canada. The case originally had been brought before the District Court of Washington, D.C., in August 1992 as *Public Citizens* v. *Office of the U.S. Trade Representative* for failure to file an EIS for NAFTA and for the Uruguay Round of negotiations under the General Agreement on Tariffs and Trade (GATT). Among the plaintiffs in the case was the Sierra Club, a major lobbying environmental group. The district court dismissed the case, and a subsequent court of appeals ruling stated that the plaintiffs had failed to identify a final agency action. Responding to President Bush's announcement of an agreement on NAFTA on September 12, 1992, a new court action was filed—this time arguing the need for an EIS only for NAFTA.

Application 6.3 (concluded)

Cumulative NEPA Litigation Survey

Year	Cases Filed	Most Frequent Plaintiff	Most Common Complaint	Most Frequent Defendant
1975	152	nr	nr	nr
1980	140	Individuals or citizens groups; environmental groups	No EIS	DOT, DOI, DOD, HUD, EPA.
1985	77	Environmental groups; individuals or citizens groups	No EIS	DOT, DOI, COE, FERC.
1990	85	Environmental groups; individuals or citizens groups	No EIS	DOT, COE, EPA.
1991	94	Individuals or citizens groups; environmental groups	No EIS	DOT, DOI, ARMY.

Notes:

nr = not reported.

DOT = Department of Transportation; DOI = Department of Interior; DOD = Department of Defense; HUD = Department of Housing and Urban Development; COE = Council on Environmental Quality; FERC = Federal Energy Regulatory Commission; DOE = Department of Energy.

Source: Council on Environmental Quality, *Environmental Quality, 23rd Annual Report* (Washington, D.C., January 1993), pp. 164–65.

The 1993 decision by Judge Charles B. Richey stirred up another round of debate centered on the economic and environmental implications of open trade among the three nations. Judge Richey was assertive about his position, writing in his decision:

An impact statement is essential for providing Congress and the public with the information needed to assess the present and future environmental consequences of . . . the NAFTA.

Critics complained that filing an EIS could take years—a delay they believed could mean the end of NAFTA. Responding to Judge Richey's ruling, U.S. trade representative Mickey Kantor stated that the government would appeal the decision. Interestingly, in September of 1993, Judge Richey's ruling was reversed—not because of the anticipated delays, but because NAFTA is a presidential action not covered by the NEPA. In December 1993, President Clinton signed NAFTA into law.

Sources: Council on Environmental Quality, *Environmental Quality, 23rd Annual Report* (Washington, D.C.: U.S. Government Printing Office, January 1993), pp. 164–65; Dianne Dumanoski, ''Activists Cite Trade Rules as a Force Shaping Nature,'' *Boston Globe*, July 1, 1993; Peter G. Gosselin, ''Environmental Ruling Blocks Free Trade Pact,'' *Boston Globe*, July 1, 1993; Michael York, ''President Wins One on NAFTA; Court Reverses Order to Study Environment,'' *The Washington Post*, September 25, 1993, p. A1.

public concern with environmental degradation was the formation of the Society of Toxicology in 1961, an association that specifically acknowledges scientists who study the effects of environmental pollutants, drugs, and food additives.[19]

In addition to toxicologists, scientists from virtually all subdisciplines are needed to research the issues targeted by environmental policy. For example,

---

[19]Kamrin (1988), Chapter 1.

policy-makers rely on marine biologists and chemists to assess the impact of surface water contamination on aquatic life and marine ecosystems. Such research helps public officials understand the implications of water pollution, which in turn guides the formulation of policy solutions. As a direct consequence of this kind of scientific study, the U.S. government has allocated significant amounts of resources to the restoration of threatened water bodies, including the Great Lakes, the Gulf of Mexico, Puget Sound, and Chesapeake Bay.[20]

The role of science in policy development has grown in importance as environmental problems have become more complex. A recent EPA report cites several instances in which science is influencing U.S. policy.[21] Thanks to new scientific findings on the extent of human exposure to pesticides, the EPA was able to extend the permitted use of a group of important fungicides commonly used for food crops. Scientific research in bioremediation (i.e., the use of microorganisms to clean up hazardous substances), was put to work in dealing with the damages caused by the *Exxon Valdez* accident. Billions of dollars have been spent in the United States to support scientific research on climate change, as more information is needed to support initiatives on what continues to be a highly debated issue. There is little question that environmental policy would be ill defined without the evidence that can be provided only through scientific research and analysis.

Economists

Over the last decade or so, economic theory and the use of market forces have become increasingly important to the design of environmental policy solutions. Recent revisions to major U.S. legislation, such as the 1990 Clean Air Act Amendments, incorporate more market-based instruments than ever before. Observing the federal government's success with this type of approach, many state governments have begun to follow suit, using incentives to *encourage* abatement rather than *imposing* command-and-control limits or restrictions. As this trend has evolved, the role of economists in policy development has become more prominent.

The use of economic analysis in public policy decisions is in large part the result of President Reagan's Executive Order 12291 issued in 1981—a mandate that explicitly calls for federal government decision-makers to consider the benefits and costs of all major regulatory acts.[22] Why is benefit-cost analysis so important in this context? The answer is simple economics. Industrialized nations are having to allocate scarce resources among the needs of many pressing national problems. Thus, efficiency and cost-effectiveness

---

[20]U.S. EPA, Office of Communications, Education, and Public Affairs (April 1992), p. 29.

[21]U.S. EPA, Office of Communications, Education, and Public Affairs (April 1992), p. 36.

[22]See *Federal Register*, February 17, 1981, pp. 13193–13194. We will discuss this executive order in more detail in an upcoming chapter.

have become the relevant criteria in deciding how best to use the available stock of resources. Yet, these criteria can be applied in practice only if measures of the associated costs and benefits have been estimated. Hence, as environmental policy has advanced, so too has the need for economists to define, measure, and interpret these concepts in the context of evaluating proposed environmental initiatives. In this relatively new application, benefit-cost analysis is still very much in its infancy, and there is much new ground to break. In upcoming chapters, we will investigate this important work and examine how economists actually arrive at these estimated values and where new research is being directed.

Conclusions

Environmental degradation affects all of society, and there is little doubt that government is needed to assess the damages, evaluate the implications, and formulate a policy response. By itself, the public policy process is a complex one. However, the task is that much more difficult when the objective is to reduce environmental damage. Environmental problems are not easy to solve, and there continues to be much scientific uncertainty about many of the underlying issues. What *is* certain is that policy decisions have implications about the quality of life for today's society and for future generations. Recognizing both the challenge and the significance of environmental decision-making is in large part why *all* segments of society must participate in the public policy process.

Private citizens are often the catalyst for environmental policy development. Through their efforts in identifying environmental problems, both as individuals and as members of environmental groups, many new laws have been passed to protect and preserve the natural environment from the effects of pollution. Scientists provide the research results needed to identify health and ecological risks—a critical element of environmental decision-making. As a result of scientists' laboratory and field research, public officials gain valuable information about the nature of environmental contaminants and the associated risks of exposure. Armed with this scientific data, government agencies can make better and more informed policy decisions.

For its part, industry also contributes to public policy development through technological advance and through cooperative endeavors with environmental groups and with government agencies. These and other efforts show how expansive the network of participants has become in environmental policy development. In their search for better solutions, governments also are calling upon the expertise of economists to analyze and assess the use of market-based control instruments in environmental policy. Economists are also needed to estimate the social benefits and costs of major policy proposals in keeping with Reagan's Executive Order 12291. Such efforts are instrumental not only to policy formulation, but also to the important appraisal stage during which strategic initiatives are assessed and often amended.

Taken together, it is apparent that all segments of society can and do contribute to every phase of environmental public policy development. In the next chapter, we will learn more about this collective effort by focusing in on Phase II of our model—environmental decision-making and risk analysis. In our study of risk assessment, we will explore how many scientific fields, including biology, toxicology, and medicine, contribute to policy-makers' understanding of the dangers of environmental hazards. Even more disciplines are called upon in risk management—among them, economics and the law. Such an interdisciplinary collaboration has become the cornerstone of environmental decision-making and the key to achieving environmental quality.

Summary

- Public policy development can be modeled as a series of six steps: problem formation, policy agenda, policy formulation, policy adoption, policy implementation, and policy evaluation.
- Tailoring the model to environmental policy development, the six-step paradigm can be recast as a three-phase model as follows: Problem formation and policy agenda define Phase I: Identification of the environmental problem. Policy formulation, policy adoption, and policy implementation characterize Phase II: Environmental decision-making and risk analysis. Policy evaluation represents Phase III: Environmental policy appraisal.
- The first step in Phase I: Identification of the environmental problem is the recognition of an environmental hazard, referred to as problem formation. The second step is government's official acknowledgment of the problem signified by its being placed on the policy agenda.
- Phase II: Environmental decision-making and risk analysis begins with policy formulation, a step concerned with assessing the magnitude of an environmental problem and developing a policy response to the inherent risk. Policy adoption refers to the passage of a proposal into law. The next step is policy implementation, which involves the execution, monitoring, and enforcement of policy.
- Phase III: Environment policy appraisal is the ex-post evaluation of the overall effectiveness of environmental policy. An economic ex-post policy appraisal uses the criteria of allocative efficiency and cost-effectiveness. Another criterion, environmental equity, considers the fairness of the risk burden across geographical regions or population groups.
- There are five groups of major players in environmental policy development: environmentalists, private industry, scientists, economists, and government and its agencies.
- Environmental groups have a long history of activism that began during the conservationist era in the late 1800s. These coalitions continue to influence public policy today. According to analysts, membership size, power, and status are key determinants of their overall strength.

- Private industry exerts an important influence on environmental policy decisions. The corporate sector has a vested interest in these matters, particularly because of the high costs of abatement. Today, business and government are beginning to work together to control pollution.

- At the U.S. federal level of government, there is a complex infrastructure responsible for environmental policy formulation and implementation. Integration of effort across administrative agencies, executive departments, and branches of government is directed through the National Environmental Policy Act (NEPA) of 1969.

- Scientific research is critical to sound environmental decision-making, particularly in assessing environmental risk. The role of science in policy development has grown in importance as environmental problems have become more complex.

- Over the last decade, economic theory and the use of market forces have become increasingly important to environmental policy. This is due in part to President Reagan's Executive Order 12291, which mandates that government decision-makers consider the benefits and costs of all major regulatory acts. As a consequence, economists have come to play a more important role in the public policy process.

Key Concepts

identification of the environmental problem
problem formation
policy agenda
environmental decision-making and risk analysis
policy formulation
risk assessment
risk management

policy adoption
policy implementation
environmental federalism
marginal cost of enforcement (MCE)
environmental policy appraisal
policy evaluation
environmental equity
toxicology

Review Questions

1. Use economic theory to explain why the ''acceptable'' level of pollution established by policy-makers is rarely set at a zero level. Graphically illustrate a case where a zero level of pollution would be allocatively efficient.

2. Find a recent example of how an environmental group has influenced the direction of public policy. Discuss why in this instance the group was successful in its efforts.

3. Look at the membership of the President's Commission on Environmental Quality given in Application 6.2. Choose any two of the affiliates and contrast their motivations for being in this group.

4. Discuss the possible trade-offs that may exist between abatement and enforcement activities. How will these trade-offs affect the allocatively efficient level of pollution abatement?

Additional Readings

Gutfeld, Rose. "Environmental Group Doesn't Always Lick 'em; It Can Join 'em and Succeed." *The Wall Street Journal,* August 20, 1992.

Landy, Marc K., Marc J. Roberts, and Stephen R. Thomas. *The Environmental Protection Agency: Asking the Wrong Questions.* New York: Oxford University Press, 1990.

Portney, Paul R. "EPA and the Evolution of Federal Regulation." In Paul R. Portney, ed. *Public Policies for Environmental Protection.* Washington, D.C.: Resources for the Future, 1990, pp. 7–25.

ENVIRONMENTAL RISK ANALYSIS

7

In our model of environmental public policy development, we identify Phase II of the model as environmental decision-making and risk analysis. It is during this phase that scientists must identify and evaluate the risks of an identified environmental hazard and communicate their findings to policy-makers. Based on this communication of risk, public officials must decide an appropriate course of action to reduce that risk. These two processes, known as risk assessment and risk management, involve difficult and sometimes controversial decisions. The decision-making is difficult because there is much uncertainty about environmental hazards and the implications for the ecology and human health—particularly over the long term. The controversy arises because there is no clear consensus about how government should respond to what *is* known about a given hazard. Accepting the reality that all environmental risk cannot be eliminated, policy-makers have to determine how much risk society can tolerate—a decision about which there is likely to be much debate. They also must decide what policy approach to use to achieve whatever risk level is deemed acceptable. How do public officials justify choosing one policy instrument over another? What criteria are used to guide this decision-making process, and are they the appropriate ones?

From an economic perspective, managing environmental risks should be guided by the costs and benefits associated with abating environmental damages. Unfortunately, there is often insufficient data to fully assess the benefits and costs of environmental risk reduction. Thus, policy-makers have to either rely on best available estimates or use an alternative risk management strategy to guide this set of decisions in public policy development. What are these alternative strategies, and what criteria are used to motivate them? These and other issues in risk analysis comprise our agenda in this chapter.

To begin our investigation, we explore the concept of risk from a general perspective and then develop it in the context of environmental hazards. We then study the multistep process of risk assessment following a paradigm currently in use by the EPA. Once done, we shift our focus to risk management, where we study how government officials design and implement a policy response to environmental risk. In this part of our discussion, we introduce the strategies used in practice to support policy decisions, such as risk-benefit analysis and benefit-cost analysis.

Concept of Risk

risk
The chance of something bad happening.

Risk is a somewhat obscure notion, yet all of us have some intuitive sense of what it is. After all, while most of us choose not to dwell on it, risk—or the chance of something bad happening—is part of life. Accepting that risk is a pervasive, albeit an unpleasant, phenomenon, we also know that some risks can be minimized or even avoided, provided they have been clearly recognized. This realization suggests that dealing with risk involves two important tasks. The first is *identifying* the degree of risk, and the second is *responding* to it. Individuals participate in both activities, although usually not in any systematic fashion. As a matter of course, they usually formulate a *perception* of risk, not based on any scientific data, but rather on a subjective or even instinctive level. These perceptions, however unscientific, are what determine how an individual responds to risk. A person might choose to accept the risk as is, find ways to reduce it, or attempt to avoid it entirely.

While all of this seems to imply that dealing with risk is strictly a private exercise, it turns out that risk analysis is also an important part of public policy development. Why? Because at its very core, policy is a formal response to the risks faced by society. Since the government is devising a response for society as a whole, it cannot rely on individual perceptions of risk that are highly subjective, often uninformed, and possibly off the mark. Instead, the policy-maker must depend on a systematic assessment of risk before devising a policy response. Of course, the extent to which the public sector becomes involved through setting policy depends upon the type of risk involved and the proportion of society exposed to that risk.

Classifying Risk: Voluntary and Involuntary Risk

Attempting to impose structure on obscure concepts is always difficult. Yet, it is precisely in these instances that order is needed in what otherwise could be little more than vague description. That there are a number of ways researchers and other analysts classify risk seems to bear out this observation. One of the more common approaches is to consider two broad risk categories: **voluntary risk** and **involuntary risk.**

Voluntary Risk.   As the label suggests, **voluntary risks** are those that are deliberately assumed at an individual level. That is, they are the result of a

voluntary risk
A risk that is deliberately assumed at an individual level.

conscious decision. Every day, we make personal decisions to engage in activities that implicitly add or subtract some amount of risk that we as individuals elect to accept. Often, the risk is self-evident, and hence decisions are made with full information, at least in a qualitative sense. On the other hand, some activities, although entered into willingly, have unknown or hidden risks.

Most voluntary risks arise from participating in personal activities, such as driving a car, flying in an airplane, smoking cigarettes, or drinking coffee. Because the risks associated with these personal activities are self-imposed, individuals can and do make decisions to respond to them. In particular, they adjust their personal exposure level to the underlying hazards. For example, skydiving is a personal activity associated with the risks of serious injury or premature death. An individual might choose to respond to these known risks by avoiding the activity entirely. In so doing, exposure to the hazard and the risks to that single individual are reduced to zero.

Since voluntary risks are self-imposed and since the potential outcome is confined to a single person, the public sector typically is not involved or at most plays a very limited role. When government *does* intervene, it is usually confined to identifying conditions or products that are potentially dangerous and communicating that information to society. By doing so, the government is helping individuals with the tasks of identifying and assessing risk, but it is *not* imposing a response decision. Providing information helps individuals perceive risks more accurately, so that *they* can make more informed private decisions about how to minimize or avoid them. This communication can be accomplished through such means as product labeling, a sort of one-on-one information stream directly to the consumer, or through public service announcements that inform the general population about certain hazards. Aside from these activities, however, government generally does not attempt to intervene in private risk response decisions.

Involuntary Risks.   People are also exposed to hazards that are beyond their control. Here, the risks are considered **involuntary,** since they do not arise because of a willful decision. A classic example of involuntary risk is the likelihood of property damage and personal injury caused by a natural disaster. The risk of being harmed by a hurricane or an earthquake is not self-imposed, yet the chance of such an event, while relatively small, nonetheless exists.[1] Environmental hazards, such as air pollution or toxic waste sites, are another important source of involuntary risk. Here, the hazard is often chemical exposure that arises as an externality of production. In such cases, the risk is considerable because the effects are pervasive and the potential harm extends to human health and the ecology.

involuntary risk
A risk that is beyond one's control and not the result of a willful decision.

Characteristic of involuntary risk is that individual responses to it are limited. Although personal exposure to the underlying hazard can be adjusted, absent extreme behavior the risk cannot be reduced to zero. For example, to

---

[1]Scheuplein (January/February/March 1993).

reduce personal risk of harm from an earthquake, an individual can avoid living in places prone to such occurrences like the San Francisco area. Such a response would decrease that individual's risk of harm from earthquakes, but the risk still exists at some nonzero level. Similarly, to decrease one's personal risk of the effects of dirty air, one could avoid living in cities like Los Angeles or Mexico City. Again, the risk of harm is reduced, but not eliminated.

Because the sources of involuntary risk are hazards beyond the control of private individuals, the associated threat is a type of *public* problem. Hence, government tries to control society's exposure to some involuntary risks. For chemical contaminants, government assumes most of the responsibility for reducing society's exposure to these hazards through legislated controls. Occasionally, officials pass regulations that forbid both the production and consumption of an environmental contaminant. By banning a dangerous chemical, government reduces society's risk of exposure to that substance to zero. In the more conventional and less extreme cases, the public sector limits the use of the chemical or restricts its release into the environment.

Distinguishing between Voluntary and Involuntary Risks.   To illustrate the difference between voluntary and involuntary risk, consider the following contemporary environmental issue. Until fairly recently, the full extent of the voluntary risk of smoking cigarettes was not completely known. As researchers learned more about the associated health risks like lung cancer and heart disease, the government disseminated this information through public service announcements and by placing warnings on cigarette packages. But the individual decision to smoke, or in this context the response to the voluntary risk, remained a private decision because at that time the risk was believed to extend *only* to the individual smoker. As research continued, it became apparent that there were risks associated with cigarette smoking that extended beyond the person who chose to smoke. It was learned that "passive" or "secondhand" smoke (that which comes from the end of a lit cigarette and the exhalation of the smoker), poses a risk to persons other than the smoker. This discovery meant that what was originally perceived as a voluntary risk posed a threat to others that was very much beyond their control—an involuntary risk. As such, passive smoke was considered a public problem, and government began to assume a more aggressive position on the matter. For more on the risks of passive smoke and the controversy surrounding new regulations, see Application 7.1.

environmental risk
A measure of the probability that damage to life, health, property, or the environment will occur due to exposure to a given hazard.

Defining Environmental Risk

One of the more important concerns of environmental decision-makers is determining the involuntary risk of exposure to hazards such as pollutant emissions and toxic substances, known as **environmental risk. Environmental risk** is a measure of the likelihood or probability that damage to life, health,

Application 7.1

EPA Declares Secondhand Smoke a Carcinogen

Tobacco smoke is known to contain such contaminants as inorganic gases, heavy metals, and carbon monoxide. Scientists have known for some time that direct inhalation of tobacco smoke causes lung cancer and other health problems such as respiratory and heart disease. Even the tobacco industry acknowledges that smoking is a factor in the risk determination of these health effects, though it stops short of the U.S. surgeon general's assertion that smoking *causes* them. Since the first Surgeon General's Report on Smoking and Health in 1964, many people have made the decision to avoid the voluntary risks and have quit smoking. However, a separate issue is the involuntary risk to nonsmokers from the effects of environmental tobacco smoke, also known as ''passive'' or ''secondhand'' smoke, which consists of sidestream smoke from the lit end of a cigarette and exhaled mainstream smoke. Published risk estimates indicate that passive smoke is responsible for somewhere between 500 and 5,000 cancer deaths every year. Yet it was not until recently that the EPA took a firm official position on the matter.

In January 1993, the EPA released a long-awaited report, giving its conclusion that environmental tobacco smoke is a human carcinogen, which causes the death of about 3,000 nonsmokers per year from lung cancer. Other reported risk estimates include the increased incidence of asthma in children and the higher risk of bronchitis and pneumonia in infants under 18 months old. The EPA's report is based on the findings of a scientific advisory panel, which reviewed evidence from a collection of U.S. studies.

As one would expect, the EPA's announcement alarmed the general public, but it also stimulated debate about the EPA's treatment of the matter. Some harsh criticism has been mounted about the two-year delay between the EPA's initial draft report on environmental tobacco smoke and its formal announcement. In 1990, the EPA concluded

its review of the risks of passive smoke and prepared a first draft report. However, the final report was delayed while the agency and the tobacco industry disputed the validity of its findings. At that same point in time, the EPA's indoor air research program terminated its work on tobacco smoke. According to the agency's critics, this halt in tobacco research *and* the delay in announcing its conclusions were the result of the EPA's succumbing to pressure exerted by the tobacco industry. The EPA denied the allegation, asserting that its research on tobacco ended because the work had been completed and it wished to move on to study other pollutants. EPA officials further argued that the 1993 announcement was connected to their risk assessment division, whose research was not affected by any changes within the agency's indoor air program.

Other questions have been raised about the methods employed by the EPA to arrive at the risk estimates used to support its decision. Among the most vocal of the critics is the tobacco industry, which asserts that the studies forming the basis for the agency's report do not provide statistically significant evidence of a passive smoke health risk to nonsmokers. In July 1993, tobacco growers and cigarette manufacturers jointly filed suit against the EPA in U.S. District Court in Greensboro, North Carolina. The objective was to obtain a declaration that the agency's January report is null and void as it is based on faulty scientific evidence, invalid procedures, and manipulated data. Notwithstanding the obvious motivation of the plaintiffs, it has been reported that the agency *did* adjust the statistical confidence level of the scientific studies down from 95 percent to 90 percent. This adjustment allowed one of the studies to show a statistically significant increased risk of lung cancer in nonsmokers from exposure to passive smoke. Without the adjustment, no single study arrives at such a conclusion. Responding to the allegation, EPA administrator

---

Application 7.1 (concluded)

Carol Browner said she stands firmly behind the report. In July 1993, the Justice Department filed a motion to dismiss the lawsuit.

No one disputes that the stakes are high. Health risks, particularly those associated with children, are a serious matter. Hence, a barrage of lawsuits will likely be filed because of the EPA's 1993 announcement. Most observers expect that suits filed by nonsmokers claiming damages from passive smoke will be more successful than those filed by smokers for damages from inhaled smoke. Why? Because juries are more likely to be sympathetic to involuntary risks. In fact, since the EPA has no jurisdiction over indoor air pollution, it acknowledges that it is relying upon private sector responses to initiate self-imposed antismoking regulations to avoid such lawsuits. While many employers already prohibit smoking in the workplace, the EPA is hoping that OSHA will move ahead to more stringently regulate this practice. As of this writing, 44 states have issued restrictions on smoking in the workplace. Nearly 150 cities have prohibited smoking in public areas, with 19 states in the process of considering the same kind of restrictions.

Absent a complete overturn of the EPA's report by the courts, it is likely that the agency's intent to raise public awareness of the risks of passive smoke and to encourage self-regulations will be realized. Despite the allegations about its interpretation of data and scientific results, most will likely err on the side of conservatism, both to avoid the personal health risk of exposure to passive smoke *and* to avoid the risk of liability from exposing others to this hazard. However, while the EPA's motivation to protect the public health may be well placed, its decision to adjust scientific findings to support a policy decision is not one that will be lightly dismissed. In this case, it is likely that the agency's lack of power to directly regulate indoor air pollution influenced its actions. But given the responsibility of this important and powerful federal agency, most would still question whether the end justified the means.

Sources: U.S. Environmental Protection Agency, *Environmental Progress and Challenges: EPA's Update* (Washington, D.C., August 1988), p. 32; National Research Council, Committee on Passive Smoking, Board on Environmental Studies and Toxicology, *Environmental Tobacco Smoke: Measuring Exposures and Assessing Health Effects* (Washington, D.C.: National Academy Press, 1986); Timothy Noah, "EPA Declares 'Passive' Smoke a Human Carcinogen," *The Wall Street Journal*, January 6, 1993; Andrea Shalal-Esa, "Tobacco Industry Sues EPA over Secondhand Smoke Report," *Boston Globe*, June 23, 1993; Associated Press, "EPA Warns of Exposure to Smoke," *Boston Globe*, July 23, 1993; Associated Press, "Quietly, EPA Drops Some Tobacco Research," *Boston Globe*, January 7, 1993.

---

hazard
The source of the environmental damage such as poisonous emissions or toxic effluents.

exposure
The pathways between the source of the damage and the affected population or resource.

property, and/or the environment will occur due to **exposure** to a given **hazard.** Notice from this definition that two elements determine the extent of environmental risk—the hazard itself and exposure to that hazard. The **hazard** is the source of the damage or the negative externality, such as poisonous emissions from factories and automobiles or toxic chemicals dumped into a river or stream. **Exposure** refers to the pathways between the source of the damage and the affected population or resource. While both hazard and exposure define environmental risk, each can independently affect the outcome. That is, some hazards are relatively minor but affect a large part of the population; others, like certain chemicals, are highly dangerous, but exposure to them is limited. In either case, notice that environmental risk quantifies the potential damage posed by a negative environmental externality.

Because risk analysis is so central to environmental decision-making, policy-makers have devised methods to assess, characterize, and respond to environmental risk. These interdependent methods are referred to as **risk assessment** and **risk management,** each of which will be investigated in some

FIGURE 7.1

The risk assessment process

Source: National Academy of Sciences, *Risk Assessment in the Federal Government: Managing the Process* (Washington, D.C.: U.S. Government Printing Office, 1983).

detail. We begin by examining the role of risk assessment in environmental policy formulation.

Risk Assessment in Environmental Decision-Making[2]

risk assessment
The qualitative and quantitative evaluation of the risk to health or the environment by the actual or potential presence and/or use of pollutants.

To understand environmental risk, policy-makers rely upon the information derived through **risk assessment,** a systematic approach to characterizing the risk of exposure to an environmental hazard. More formally, **risk assessment** refers to the qualitative and quantitative evaluation of the risk posed to human health or the environment by the actual or potential presence and/or use of certain pollutants.

In practice, environmental risk assessment is conducted by scientists who gather, analyze, and interpret data about a given contaminant. In the United States, the EPA uses a paradigm of this process first presented by the National Academy of Sciences (NAS) in 1983.[3] This model specifies risk assessment as a series of four steps, or ''fields of analysis,'' as they are known. These are as follows: **hazard identification, dose-response analysis, exposure analysis,** and **risk characterization.** Figure 7.1 shows the flow of information through these four steps as well as between risk assessment and risk management. An overview of each field of analysis follows. As we proceed, notice

---

[2]Much of the following is drawn from Patton (January/February/March 1993).
[3]National Academy of Sciences (1983).

how each performs a particular function, which is then used in the subsequent step of this highly interdependent process.

Hazard Identification

hazard identification
Scientific analysis aimed at determining if a causal relationship exists between a pollutant and any adverse effects on health or the ecology.

The first step of risk assessment is known as **hazard identification.** It is in this stage that scientists analyze existing data to determine if a causal relationship exists between an environmental pollutant and adverse effects on the ecology and/or human health. Causality in this context refers to a linkage between an environmental agent and the observed effect that is *believed* to exist based on a consensus within the scientific community.[4]

Ecological effects are any impacts on the natural environment, such as crop damage, forest declines, soil contamination, fish kills, or destruction of ecosystems. While under most public policies, ecological effects from environmental pollution are viewed as secondary to human health effects, the two are *not* independent. Over time, human health is adversely affected if ecological health deteriorates. For example, damage to soil and agricultural crops may have a direct negative impact on economic productivity, human fitness, and the quality of life. In fact, a recent report on environmental risk conducted by the EPA's Science Advisory Board (SAB) recommends that the EPA devote more attention to reducing ecological risks and to recognizing the important link between ecological health and human health. Read Application 7.2 for more on these issues.[5]

Identifying the health consequences of exposure to an environmental contaminant is a high priority. Health effects can be classified as either mortality (i.e., death) or morbidity (i.e., illness). Morbidity effects range from minor health problems like skin or eye irritations to more serious health risks, such as those that are carcinogenic (i.e., cancer producing) or mutagenic (i.e., causing alteration in genetic material). Beyond identifying a link between contaminant exposure and any adverse effects, the scientist must also determine how these effects vary with the *length of exposure* to the contaminant. This part of the analysis distinguishes between *acute effects,* those associated with short-term exposure, and *chronic effects,* those due to longer-term exposure.

case clusters
A scientific method to identify a health hazard based on the observation of an abnormal pattern of health effects within some population group.

Several scientific methods are used to gather the evidence needed to identify an environmental *health* hazard, some more reliable than others. Three common methods are **case clusters, bioassays,** and **epidemiology.**[6] The use of **case clusters** refers to the observation of an abnormal pattern of health effects within some population group. This is the simplest method of hazard

---

[4]Kuhn (1970), cited in Lave (1982b), pp. 36–37. The interested reader should refer to Lave (1982a) for more detail on the problems of establishing causality in the context of hazard identification.

[5]U.S. EPA, Science Advisory Board (September 1990).

[6]For more detail on these and other hazard identification methods, see Lave (1982b), which also provides a thorough analysis of the strengths and weaknesses of each approach.

A Model for Assessing Ecological Risks

The primary objective of U.S. environmental policy is to reduce the health risks associated with pollution. While no arguments have been made about this priority per se, there is concern that the EPA has not given enough attention to *ecological risks* in its policy decisions. In its 1990 report, the EPA's Science Advisory Board makes a strong argument that the EPA's lack of response to environmental threats to ecosystems is inappropriate, since there is very little difference between human life and the ecology in the natural environment. According to the report:

Human beings are part of an interconnected and interdependent global ecosystem, and past experience has shown that change in one part of the system often affects other parts in unexpected ways. National efforts to evaluate relative environmental risks should recognize the vital links between human life and natural ecosystems. Up to this point, they have not. (U.S. EPA, Science Advisory Board, September 1990, p. 9.)

In response to this criticism, the EPA began to develop guidelines aimed specifically at ecological risk assessment. Published in a 1992 report entitled *Framework for Ecological Risk Assessment,* the agency outlines the following three-stage process:

Problem formulation: This phase is aimed at identifying the goals of risk assessment as well as its overall extent and focus. Ultimately, the objective is to formulate a conceptual model, which identifies the ecological resources to be protected, the data needed to complete the assessment, and the analytical methods to be employed.

Analysis: This step studies the extent of ecological contamination and the relationship between the stressor (i.e., contaminant) and the affected resource. The aim is to determine the cause-and-effect relationship and the degree of damage.

Risk characterization: In this final step, the results of the analysis are assimilated and evaluated to identify the probability of harm associated with a given stressor.

While this model is only a prototype, it nonetheless signifies the nation's intention to improve its policy response to ecological damage.

Much of what defines the new framework came from a study of Puget Sound's Commencement Bay in Tacoma, Washington. The Puget Sound area is one of the most threatened of the nation's coastal resources. Commencement Bay suffers from pollution generated by some 280 sources, which include petroleum refineries, sewage treatment plants, a pulp mill, and an ocean port. Responding to the problem, a Remedial Investigation/Feasibility Study was launched to identify the health and ecological risks caused by the pollution of Commencement Bay. One of the major problems faced by scientists studying the region was that the natural movement of the waters diluted the chemical contaminants, making an accurate risk assessment impossible. With no existing model to guide them, the scientists devised a two-pronged approach to complete their ecological risk assessment. First, they established two "reference sites" to use as a basis of comparison for their work, selecting two waterways based on their low contamination levels. Secondly, they used an apparent effects threshold approach, using certain preselected forms of aquatic life as biological indicators of the bay's contamination level.

As a result of the scientists' efforts at Commencement Bay, eight of the nine areas identified as problems were selected for remedial treatment, and several strategies have been proposed for implementation over the next 15- to 20-year abatement period. Joint efforts by the EPA and the state of Washington's Department of Ecology are continuing the work of this pioneering research team. On a broader scale, the methods devised during the Commencement Bay project have helped the development of ecological risk assessment for all natural resources damaged by pollution.

Sources: Patricia Cirone and Matthew Coco, "The Lessons of Commencement Bay," *EPA Journal* 19, no. 1 (January/February/March 1993), pp. 33–34; U.S. Environmental Protection Agency, Risk Assessment Forum, *Framework for Ecological Risk Assessment* (Washington, D.C., February 1992); "A Step Toward Ecological Risk Guidelines," *EPA Journal* 19, no. 1 (January/February/March 1993), p. 33.

identification, but it is effective only if the observed health symptoms are very unusual or if the frequency of occurrence is extremely high. However, in either case, formal analysis and follow-up testing are needed to validate a causal relationship.

animal bioassays
Studies based on the comparative results of laboratory experiments on living organisms before and after exposure to a given hazard.

A more sophisticated hazard identification method uses **animal bioassays,** which are studies based on the comparative results of laboratory experiments on living organisms both before and after exposure to a given hazard. This is a costly method, and there are concerns about the reliability of its findings. One concern is that an observed linkage between exposure and a biological response in an animal subject does not necessarily mean that the same response will occur in humans. Another is that most animal bioassays use much larger doses of an environmental contaminant than what would normally be encountered by the affected human population, sometimes as much as thousands of times greater. Researchers exaggerate the dosage to assure that the experiment will produce some measurable adverse effect. If a lower dose were used, the scientist would have to perform the same experiment on hundreds or even thousands of animal subjects before any effect could be observed. What all of this means is that animal bioassays do not provide *direct* evidence of identified hazards to humans. Instead, statistical models are used to *extrapolate* information gathered from laboratory animal responses to approximate how humans might respond. These models often make assumptions that are conservative and sometimes arbitrary, which further diminishes the reliability of any conclusions.

epidemiology
The study of the distribution of a health-related condition in human populations based on such characteristics as age, gender, occupation, ethnicity, and economic status.

There *are* contexts in which scientists study human populations to identify environmental hazards. The discipline that examines the effect of harmful substances on human health is known as **epidemiology.** Technically, it is the study of the *distribution* of disease or other health-related conditions in human populations based on such characteristics as age, gender, occupation, ethnicity, and economic status. Because epidemiology research is based on the direct observation of humans, there is no need for extrapolation of results from animals to humans as is necessary when animal bioassays are used. Furthermore, epidemiology studies are more systematic than case clusters, since they attempt to control for extraneous information that can confound the results. However, because epidemiology studies draw directly from reality, they are not fully controlled experiments. In a fully controlled experiment, exposure and dose amounts are carefully monitored so that only these factors are responsible for any observed response.

An important application of epidemiology was its use in identifying a link between exposure to benzene and the incidence of leukemia. In the 1970s, researchers studied data on individuals who worked in industries that used benzene in their production processes. What they found was a pattern between worker exposure to benzene and the incidence of leukemia. Notice that by limiting the population of subjects to those who were occupationally exposed to benzene, the researchers attempted to control for other types of exposure. Interestingly, however, attempts by OSHA to impose a standard based on these findings were fought in the courts until additional quantitative evidence supported by animal bioassays was obtained.[7]

Dose-Response Analysis

dose-response
A quantitative relationship between various doses of an identified hazard and the ecological and/or human responses to that hazard.

threshold
The level of exposure to a hazard up to which no response exists based on scientific evidence.

Once a chemical substance has been identified as a hazard, scientists must investigate the potency of the hazard by quantifying the ecological and/or human responses to various doses of the identified hazard. This element of the risk assessment process determines what is called the **dose-response** relationship, also known as the **exposure-response** relationship. Using data collected in the hazard identification stage, the dose-response analysis attempts to derive a complete profile of the effects of an environmental pollutant. An important aspect of this analysis is to identify if some level of exposure to the hazard is "safe." More formally, scientists attempt to discern what is called a **threshold** level of exposure, which is the point up to which no response exists based upon scientific evidence.

To determine the dose-response relationship, researchers must first conduct two types of extrapolations from the data obtained through hazard identification:

1. The high-to-low dose extrapolation—to adjust for the high exposure levels used in laboratory or other test conditions.
2. The laboratory-to-natural extrapolation—to infer how the effects observed in the laboratory or test environment would differ under conditions existing in nature. (This includes the adjustment to infer a human response from the results of laboratory animal studies.)

Then, the researcher assigns some general functional form to the expected relationship between exposure and response, and uses a statistical model to quantitatively estimate that relationship.

Consider for example, estimating the dose-response relationship associated with exposure to carbon monoxide (CO), a gas released from the incomplete engine combustion of carbon-based fuels such as gasoline. At relatively small doses of CO, the individual may experience drowsiness. At higher exposure levels, visual perception may be impaired as well as learning ability. As the exposure level increases, death results. It is the purpose of the dose-response analysis to quantitatively estimate at what exposure levels each of these effects occurs and all the intermediate dose to response relationships as well.

Like any statistical study, estimating a dose-response relationship requires the researcher to make some initial assumptions. These include which factors are being controlled when defining the relationship and what the underlying relationship looks like.[8] Figure 7.2 (a), (b), and (c) illustrates three hypothetical

---

[7]Kamrin (1988), pp. 96–97.
[8]For more detail on this issue, see Lave (1982b), pp. 43–47.

FIGURE 7.2

Hypothetical dose-response relationships

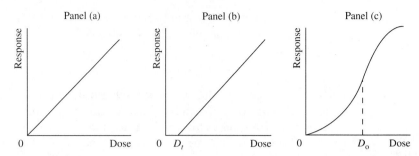

These graphs illustrate three hypothetical dose-response functional forms. Panel (a) shows a linear dose-response function, meaning that the rate of increase between dose and response is constant. Because the function starts at the origin, it implies that no threshold level has been observed. The relationship in panel (b) also shows a constant rate of change between dose levels and response but only beyond dose level D_t. Up to and including that point, there is no response at all, meaning that there is an identified threshold at D_t. Panel (c) depicts a cubic relationship drawn from the origin, showing that the response level initially increases at an increasing rate up to dose level D_o and then increases at a decreasing rate thereafter.

dose-response functional forms. Common to each depiction is a positive relationship between dose level and response. What differs among them is the *rate* at which the response increases as the dosage increases. For example, in panel (a) of Figure 7.2, the dose-response relationship is linear, meaning that the rate of increase between dose and response is constant. Notice also that this curve begins at the origin. This means that a response is expected no matter how small the dose, or equivalently that no identifiable **threshold** level has been observed. Contrast this with the relationship shown in panel (b). In this case, there is also a constant rate of change between dose levels and response but only beyond dose level D_t. Up to and including that point, there is no response at all, meaning that the hazard represented by this relationship has an identified threshold at D_t. Finally, panel (c) shows a cubic (or S-shaped), relationship drawn from the origin. Here, the response level initially increases at an increasing rate up to dose level D_o and then increases at a decreasing rate beyond that point.

   The scientific results derived from hazard identification and dose-response analysis provide general information about the risks of an environmental hazard based on some *known population* as defined by the laboratory or test conditions. This generalized information can then be used as a basis for assessing the risk to a *potentially exposed population* in a specific context. The population might be workers in some industrial setting, an ecological system under natural conditions, or even the general population of an entire nation. The EPA has established a database of identified environmental hazards and their estimated dose-response relationships for use by researchers and the general public. Referred to as the Integrated Risk Information System (IRIS), this database is designed to improve risk assessment by lending consistency and efficiency to what is a difficult and time-intensive process. See Application 7.3 for more on what IRIS offers and how it is used in practice to facilitate the remaining steps of the risk assessment process.

Application 7.3

EPA's IRIS: A Health Effects Database

Risk assessment of environmental health hazards has become a well-structured process over the last decade or so. In large part, this is a direct consequence of the paradigm presented by the National Academy of Sciences (NAS) in its 1983 publication, *Risk Assessment in the Federal Government: Managing the Process*. Of the four steps outlined in this model, hazard identification, dose-response analysis, exposure analysis, and risk characterization, the first two provide general scientific findings about the risk associated with a given contaminant based on laboratory studies. By design, these findings then can be used to assess the specific risk posed by that same contaminant under actual conditions, using the latter two steps of the NAS model.

Because of the applicability of the information provided by hazard identification and dose-response analysis, the EPA added more structure to the risk assessment process by creating a repository of all EPA consensus views on the health risks of environmental contaminants. Established in 1986, the comprehensive database of these consensus opinions comprises the Integrated Risk Information System, referred to by its acronym IRIS. Originally accessible only to EPA officials and staff, IRIS was made available to the general public in 1988.

There are three sections in the database: carcinogen assessment data for oral and inhalation exposure, noncancer health effects from oral exposure, and noncancer health effects from inhalation exposure. The database was developed and is maintained by two work groups: the Carcinogen Risk Assessment Verification Endeavor (CRAVE) and the Oral Reference Dose/Inhalation Reference Concentration Work Group. Each group consists of a panel of EPA scientists representing a multitude of disciplines and several agency program areas.

As each group arrives at a consensus on a given pollutant, a summary is prepared and then added to IRIS. Each summary includes a risk assessment table, which gives a risk number or relative risk value [i.e., a probability value for carcinogenic effects, a reference dose (RfD) for oral exposure to noncarcinogenic effects or a reference concentration (RfC) for inhalation exposure to noncarcinogenic effects]. The risk value is supported by a synthesis and discussion of the relevant preliminary scientific data used to form the consensus. A full reference listing is also provided to direct the reader to the primary studies upon which the consensus is based. Drinking water health advisories and any EPA regulatory actions relevant to the pollutant are itemized along with supplemental data, which may include acute health hazard information, chemical and physical properties of the substance, and major uses of the pollutant. These summaries assure consistency and efficiency in conducting exposure analysis and risk characterization. Currently, there are about 500 substances for which summaries are given within IRIS.

As part of its ongoing efforts to improve IRIS, the EPA has launched a formal review of the database, involving an appraisal of its technical content and its applicability to risk evaluation. Public comment on this review process has been solicited by the agency in a *Federal Register* notice on February 25, 1993 (58 FR 11490). This self-directed review is indicative of the EPA's plan to make IRIS a mainstay in the important process of risk assessment.

Source: Linda Tuxen, "EPA's IRIS Data Base: Accessing the Science," *EPA Journal* 19, no. 1 (January/February/March 1993), pp. 22–23; U.S. Environmental Protection Agency, Environmental Criteria and Assessment Office, *IRIS Data Base* (Research Triangle Park, N.C.: U.S. EPA, 1993).

Exposure Analysis

exposure analysis
Characterizes the
sources of an
environmental
hazard, the
concentration levels
at the source point,
the pathways from
the source to the
affected population,
and sensitivities
within the population
group.

The process through which a generalized dose-response relationship is applied
to specific conditions for an affected population is called **exposure analysis.**
Exposure analysis is concerned with characterizing the following: the specific
sources of the environmental hazard, the concentration levels at the source
point, the specific pathways from the source to the affected population, and
any sensitivities within the population group. Some of this information is
obtained through direct measurements, and some is estimated through mathematical models.

Understanding the pathways by which a contaminant reaches humans or
natural resources is an important component of exposure analysis. In the
human body, there are three major pathways by which an environmental
hazard can be absorbed: **inhalation** of contaminated air, **ingestion** of contaminated liquids or foods, and **dermal absorption** through the skin. In the
ecology, there are different types of pathways. For example, for forests and
crops, the pathways include uptake by **photosynthesis, absorption by foliage,**
and **modification of soil chemistry.**[9] Since the extent and degree of exposure
are not the same for all pathways, researchers must determine which pathways
are relevant, and of these, which are more important. Biological organisms
have natural mechanisms that cleanse their systems of hazardous substances.
For example, sneezing is a response that clears the upper respiratory track,
and coughing performs the same function for bronchial airways.[10] Hence, exposure analysis has to account for differences between the concentration level
of the contaminant at the source and the actual dosage received by the affected
population.

To illustrate, consider the case of human exposure to lead. The potentially
affected target group is the general population. The sources of lead are many,
including painted surfaces, factory emissions, improperly fired ceramic cookware, automobile lead-acid batteries, lead water pipes, and lead-soldered food
cans. Since lead is ubiquitous, there are many pathways by which sources of
this contaminant reach the population. Lead exposure can occur through inhalation of contaminated air, ingestion from drinking contaminated water or
eating contaminated food, and direct ingestion of lead particles from paint or
other sources. Furthermore, existing research shows that sensitivity to lead
exposure is greater for unborn babies, infants, and young children. All of these
findings are part of an exposure analysis for lead.

Risk Characterization

The final phase of environmental risk assessment is called **risk characterization**—the objective of the entire process. **Risk characterization** is a complete
description of the form and dimension of the expected risk based upon the

---

[9]U.S. National Acid Precipitation Assessment Program (November 1991), pp. 47–48.
[10]Lippmann and Schlesinger (1979), p. 197.

risk characterization
A complete description of expected risk based upon the assessment of the identified hazard and exposure to that hazard.

assessment of its two components—the identified hazard and exposure to that hazard. More than just an assimilation of the analyses and data from the previous steps, the description includes both a quantitative and qualitative risk evaluation.

The **quantitative** component helps to identify the magnitude of an environmental risk and provides a way to compare one risk with another. Risk can be measured as a **probability** that an event will occur, using a numerical value that quantifies the likelihood of occurrence in some time period. Some of these probabilities are based on what are called **actuarial risks,** those determined from factual data. Actuarial risk measures are found by calculating the number of victims of a given hazard relative to the total number exposed. For example, the actuarial risk of death per year from the personal activity of driving an automobile has been estimated at approximately 24 in 100,000, or 0.024 percent. The likelihood of premature death from the natural hazard of being struck by lightning is approximately 0.00005 percent, or 5 people for every 10 million. Other probability measurements such as the carcinogenic risks associated with exposures to chemicals are based, not on actual data, but on **inferences** derived from animal bioassays or epidemiological studies. For example, the risk of getting cancer in a given year from drinking chlorinated water has been estimated to be 0.0008 percent or 8 in 1 million persons exposed.[11]

Other environmental risks such as noncarcinogenic health risks are quantified as the exposure level to a hazard that can be tolerated over a lifetime without harm. This exposure level is communicated as a **reference dose (RfD),** which is generally expressed as follows:

RfD = milligrams of a pollutant per body weight per day.

Thus, the hypothetical RfD for pollutant X of 0.005 milligrams/kilogram/day means that exposure to 0.005 milligrams of pollutant X per kilogram of body weight each day over a lifetime should cause no harm.

The **qualitative** element of the characterization gives context to the numerical risk value. It gives a description of the hazard, an assessment of exposure noting any susceptible population groups, an identification of the data used, the scientific and statistical methods employed, and all underlying assumptions. Any scientific uncertainties, data gaps, or measurement errors that distinguish the findings should be pointed out as well. All of this information characterizes the reliability of the results and facilitates further research that may call for revisions to the assessment.

It is important to realize that risk assessment is not a fixed evaluation, but rather part of a dynamic process. The assessment changes as new information and better analytical methods become available—exactly what has occurred in assessing the risk of exposure to dioxin, the subject of Application 7.4. In sum, no commentary can better emphasize the importance of a thorough and

---

[11]The estimates of risk presented in this section are given in Scheuplein (January/February/March 1993).

Application 7.4

The Dynamics of Risk Assessment:
The Case of Dioxin

A family of chemical compounds called dibenzo-p-dioxins are considered by some scientists to be the single most deadly of all synthetic compounds. Named as one of the contaminants responsible for the evacuation of residents in Love Canal, New York, in 1980 and Times Beach, Missouri, in 1983, dioxins were classified by the United States in 1985 as probable, highly potent, human carcinogens. Over time, new evidence has called this initial risk assessment into question, suggesting the need for further scientific inquiry—a process that has already been initiated. In a broad sense, what this reevaluation implies is that risk assessment is a dynamic process. As scientific research continues, using advanced methods and better measurement techniques, risk assessments must be adjusted to reflect new discoveries.

The chronicle of events surrounding the reassessment of dioxins is a good case study of this dynamic process in action. A summary is given below.

Time Period	EPA Actions
1980–1985	Following the disaster at Love Canal, the EPA begins to assess the risks of exposure to dioxins. Relying on data from animal studies and investigating only carcinogenic effects, the EPA concludes in 1985 that dioxin is a probable human carcinogen.
1988	Based mainly on scientific judgment, the EPA writes a draft document to revise its initial risk assessment of dioxin. The draft suggests that dioxin may not be as potent as originally stated in the 1985 assessment, but that existing scientific methods are inadequate to properly determine the associated health risks. The EPA's Science Advisory Board finds no basis for a reassessment but recommends that a new model be devised to deal with the multiple biological responses known to accompany exposure to the substance.
1990	A conference of 30 scientific experts agrees that the health effects of dioxin in humans can be predicted from the measured effects obtained through animal studies. They further agree that a new risk assessment model needs to be developed to accommodate current understanding of how dioxin affects the human body.
1991	In January, the National Institute for Occupational Safety and Health (NIOSH) releases new data relating to the cancer mortality of dioxin-exposed workers.
	In April, the EPA Administrator directs the EPA to begin work on a reassessment of *all* risks of dioxin in a cooperative framework to involve both EPA and external scientists. As part of its tasks, the agency is to develop a biologically based dose-response model with the help of outside prominent scientists.
	The EPA holds meetings to inform the public of its progress and to ask for public comment.
1992	In August, the EPA issues drafts of both human health and exposure assessment documents. As part of the review process, the EPA schedules a series of public meetings.
	During September, the EPA holds two public meetings aimed at discussing the draft reports. The meetings consist of scientific peer reviews of both draft assessment documents and an appraisal of the progress in developing the new dose-response model. In addition to those directly participating in the forums, over 200 members of the general public attend the meetings.
1993–1994	The EPA releases its draft report, reaffirming its earlier findings that human exposure to dioxin at high levels may cause cancer and at low levels may lead to serious health consequences. The study is to be reviewed by the agency's Science Advisory Board.

Application 7.4 (concluded)

The open forum under which the dioxin reassessment is being conducted speaks to the EPA's efforts to elicit the best available scientific information. It also indicates the agency's intent to promote better communication of environmental risk and the EPA's assessment procedures to the general public.

At the completion of the dioxin project, the EPA plans to evaluate this open approach to risk assessment. Thus far, the commentary from both the scientific community and the participation by the general public suggest that the new approach holds great promise.

Source: Peter W. Preuss and William H. Farland, "A Flagship Risk Assessment: EPA Reassesses Dioxin in an Open Forum," *EPA Journal* 19, no. 1 (January/February/March 1993), pp. 24–26; Associated Press, "Study: Dioxin Health Threat Much Worse Than Suspected," *Brockton Enterprise,* September 12, 1994.

accurate risk characterization than to recognize it as the vehicle that links risk assessment to risk management, the next phase of environmental decision-making.

Risk Management in Environmental Decision-Making: Responding to Risk

risk management
The process of evaluating and selecting from among available regulatory and nonregulatory responses to risk.

While the objective of risk assessment is to *identify* risk, it is the goal of risk management to *respond* to it. More to the point, **risk management** is concerned with formulating and implementing policy to reduce society's risk of a given hazard.

To evaluate various policy options, the decision-maker must consider, not only the information given by the risk characterization, but also such factors as technological feasibility, implementation costs, and other economic implications. Notice from Figure 7.3 that while risk assessment is dominated by the work of natural scientists, risk management relies upon information from many fields. Its interdisciplinary makeup reflects the need for risk managers to consider the legal, economic, political, and social implications of policy along with the data provided by the scientific community.

Implementation of the risk management process involves a series of decisions aimed at two major tasks: (1) to determine what level of risk is "acceptable" to society; and (2) to evaluate and select the "best" policy instrument to achieve that risk level. None of the underlying decisions are unidimensional, and realistically none can be made with complete objectivity. However, there are strategic approaches used to guide the decision-making, some of which are mandated by law. We begin with a brief discussion of these

FIGURE 7.3

Disciplines in risk analysis

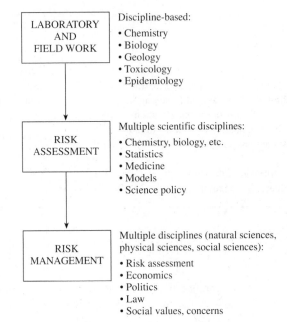

Source: Dorothy E. Patton, "The ABCs of Risk Assessment: Some Basic Principles Can Help People Understand Why Controversies Occur," *EPA Journal* 19, no. 1 (January/February/March 1993), p. 12.

two major tasks of risk management, which lays the groundwork for an analysis of risk management strategies.

The Tasks of Risk Management

Determining "Acceptable" Risk. The universal objective of all risk management strategies is to reduce risk. However, for each policy proposal, the public official must decide how much of a reduction is appropriate. Although risk is a function of both the hazard and exposure to that hazard, only one of these—exposure—can be controlled. So, when the risk manager decides the amount of risk reduction to be achieved, the exposure level is implicitly determined. This in turn dictates how stringent public policy must be. In setting the level of **"acceptable" risk,** the policy-maker confronts a difficult but necessary decision. The operative question is as follows. Should the policy eliminate the risk by reducing exposure to zero, or should some compromise be struck at some positive risk level, and if so, where?[12]

"acceptable" risk
The amount of risk determined to be appropriate or tolerable for society.

---

[12]For an excellent discussion of the political and legal processes involved in environmental standard-setting as it applies to the concept of acceptable risks, see Marchant and Danzeisen (1989).

If the acceptable risk level is set at zero, the policy must reduce society's exposure to the environmental hazard to zero (assuming there is no threshold level). While this action eliminates the associated health and ecological damage, such a stringent policy is likely to cause economic problems. For example, if the hazard is a toxic chemical used in manufacturing, reducing exposure to that chemical to zero means that its use must be prohibited. Such a ban may force plant closings and create job losses. Despite the economic consequences, there are a few environmental laws that *do* call for a "zero-risk" standard. One commonly cited and controversial example is the "Delaney Clause" of the Federal Food, Drug, and Cosmetic Act. This clause prohibits the use of any food additive found to pose *any* carcinogenic risk in humans or animals with no implicit exception for even negligible risk.[13] This risk-based objective is to be achieved regardless of the costs to attain it. Hence, the Delaney Clause is said to be entirely benefit-based.

Conversely, if some positive level of risk is deemed "acceptable," then the decision-maker is setting policy that allows some amount of exposure and therefore some amount of damage. Such a decision puts some segment of society and/or some natural resource or ecological system at risk—a responsibility most of us would like not to think about. To help guide this difficult decision, policy-makers sometimes use the concept of **de minimis risk** as a baseline for where to set the acceptable level. *De minimis* risk refers to a negligible level of risk such that reducing it further would not justify the costs of doing so.[14] This concept is sometimes equated to the risk of a natural hazard like a lightning strike or an earthquake.[15] Once the baseline is established, the decision-maker might use **comparative risk analysis** to evaluate how the positive risk level of an environmental hazard compares to other risks currently faced and "accepted" by society. This sort of analysis has been used to communicate the relatively unfamiliar risks associated with exposure to radon, a naturally occurring gas that can be harmful when trapped indoors. See Application 7.5 for a discussion of how the risks of radon exposure are expressed in terms of the risks from more familiar activities such as X-rays and cigarette smoking.

de minimis risk
A negligible level of risk such that reducing it further would not justify the costs of doing so.

Evaluating and Selecting a Policy Instrument.   Once the degree of risk and hence the stringency of policy have been determined, the second task of risk management is to decide what type of policy instrument to use. Here, the decision-maker has to first evaluate alternative policies that can achieve the "acceptable" risk level and then select the "best" option from among them.

---

[13]Kimm (January/February/March 1993); and *EPA Journal* (January/February/March, 1993), p. 15.

[14]For example, the United States generally does not regulate cancer risks measured at less than 1 additional case per 1 million people. This does not mean that they will never intervene if the risk is smaller—only that as a general rule they choose not to.

[15]Krimsky and Golding (1991), p. 105.

Application 7.5

Using Comparative Risks to Communicate the Dangers of Radon

As recently as 10 years ago, the average person knew virtually nothing about radon. Today, public awareness of this environmental hazard has improved, but many people still are unaware of the potential risks involved. The result? Government is faced with a difficult public policy problem. Although the risk of exposure to radon is involuntary, government cannot directly intervene because radon pollutes a part of the environment that is beyond its jurisdiction—the indoor air.

Radon presents an involuntary risk because it is a natural hazard. It is a radioactive gas caused by the decaying of uranium found in soil deposits and rocks. Outdoors, as radon is released, it dissipates quickly and poses no adverse health effects to humans. It becomes a potential problem only if it enters homes and buildings through cracks in basements or foundations. If radon is trapped indoors, it can accumulate to dangerous levels. It is odorless and colorless, so people are unaware of its presence and are exposed to it quite involuntarily. Research studies suggest that long-term exposure to radon causes lung cancer. The EPA estimates that chronic exposure may be responsible for 7,000 to 30,000 lung cancer deaths per year, ranking it second only to smoking as a cause of lung cancer.

Because the potential risk of radon exposure is significant, government needs to take action yet remain within the bounds of its authority. While it cannot regulate the air quality in people's homes, it *can* communicate information about radon risk so that people can manage the risk themselves. Notice that this approach is precisely what the government uses to inform the public about certain voluntary risks, like the potential hazards of using garden pesticides.

The EPA along with the surgeon general and various national health associations have joined forces to educate society about the little-known but potentially dangerous problem of radon. In 1986, national guidelines were issued to explain the associated health risks and to recommend ways to reduce exposure. A national media campaign was launched to encourage people to measure the level of radon in their homes using readily available test kits. Various guides also have been prepared by government and other associations to disseminate the facts about radon to home owners and building managers. Yet all of this well-intentioned information is useful only if it is communicated in a way that is meaningful to the general public. To accomplish this, the government uses **comparative risks.**

Radon concentration levels are measured in units of picocuries per liter (pCi/l). Risk estimates for lifetime exposure to various levels are given as the number of lung cancer deaths in a given population. To communicate these estimates more effectively, comparable lifetime risks of more familiar activities are provided. For example, lifetime exposure to a radon level of 10 pCi/l is estimated to cause 30 to 120 lung cancer deaths out of 1,000 people so exposed. This is *comparable* to the risk of smoking one pack of cigarettes per day over a lifetime. Notice that the unfamiliar measure of picocuries per liter is translated into a meaningful risk measure—precisely the objective of good risk communication. The table on the next page gives a more thorough depiction of how comparable risk is used to explain the problem of radon exposure.

Application 7.5 (concluded)

Radon (pCi/l)	Risk of Dying from Radon (Number of persons out of 1,000)	Comparative Risk
200	440–700	More than 60 times nonsmoker risk
100	270–630	4-pack-a-day smoker
40	120–380	2,000 chest X-rays per year
20	60–210	2-pack-a-day smoker or 100 times the risk of drowning
10	30–120	1-pack-a-day smoker or 100 times the risk of dying in a home fire
4	13–50	5 times a nonsmoker risk or 100 times the risk of dying in a plane crash
2	7–30	200 chest X-rays per year or 2 times the risk of dying in a car crash
1 (Average indoor level)	3–13	Nonsmoker risk of dying of lung cancer
0.2 (Average outdoor level)	1–3	20 chest X-rays per year

If the indoor radon level is measured at 4 pCi/l or above, the EPA recommends that some action be taken to correct the problem. The results of EPA's National Residential Radon Survey of 57,406 homes showed that 1 out of every 5 homes tested had elevated levels of radon. This implies that as many as 6 million homes in the United States may have radon levels exceeding 4 pCi/l. Fortunately, there are a number of ways to lower indoor levels of radon, and most are relatively easy and inexpensive. But the first step is proper risk communication. Using comparative risks to explain an otherwise unfamiliar hazard can be an effective means to help society recognize and respond to the health risk of radon exposure.

Sources: U.S. Environmental Protection Agency, *Environmental Progress and Challenges: EPA's Update* (Washington, D.C., August 1988), pp. 35–37; U.S. Environmental Protection Agency, Office of Communications, Education, and Public Affairs, *Securing our Legacy: An EPA Progress Report 1989–1991* (Washington, D.C., April 1992), p. 15; U.S. Environmental Protection Agency, U.S. Department of Health and Human Services, and U.S. Public Health Service, *A Citizen's Guide to Radon: The Guide to Protecting Yourself and Your Family from Radon,* (Washington, D.C., May 1992), p. 12.

Recall from Chapters 4 and 5 that the options likely will include some that are command-and-control in motivation and others that are market-based. In making the decision, the risk manager considers the magnitude of risks, benefits, and/or costs associated with each available control instrument. In fact, there are risk management strategies that define exactly how this evaluation is to be done. In some instances, the law mandates which of these strategies must be used.

TABLE 7.1   **Scientific Rankings of Environmental Problems**

Environmental Problem	*Relative Risk Ranking*
Ambient air pollutants	High risk to human health
Worker exposure to chemicals in industry and agriculture	High risk to human health
Indoor pollution	High risk to human health
Contamination of drinking water	High risk to human health
Habitat alteration and destruction	High risk to natural ecology and human welfare
Species extinction and loss of biological diversity	High risk to natural ecology and human welfare
Stratospheric ozone depletion	High risk to natural ecology and human welfare
Global climate change	High risk to natural ecology and human welfare
Herbicides/pesticides	Medium risk to natural ecology and human welfare
Contamination of surface waters	Medium risk to natural ecology and human welfare
Acid deposition	Medium risk to natural ecology and human welfare
Airborne toxics	Medium risk to natural ecology and human welfare
Oil spills	Low risk to natural ecology and human welfare
Groundwater contamination	Low risk to natural ecology and human welfare
Radionuclides	Low risk to natural ecology and human welfare
Thermal pollution	Low risk to natural ecology and human welfare
Acid runoff to surface waters	Low risk to natural ecology and human welfare

Source: U.S. Environmental Protection Agency, Science Advisory Board, *Reducing Risk: Setting Priorities and Strategies for Environmental Protection* (Washington, D.C., September 1990); U.S. Environmental Protection Agency, Office of Communications, Education, and Public Affairs, *Securing Our Legacy, An EPA Progress Report 1989–1991* (Washington, D.C., April 1992), p. 9.

Risk Management Strategies

Executing the two tasks of risk management—determining the ''acceptable'' risk level and choosing the appropriate policy instrument—requires a systematic evaluation of available options. From an economic perspective, the most important considerations are: (1) the level of risk established; (2) the benefits that accrue to society from adopting the policy; and (3) the associated costs of implementing the policy. Several risk management strategies have developed over time, each of which outline *how* these factors are to be evaluated. The most prevalent of these are: **comparative risk analysis, risk-benefit analysis,** and **benefit-cost analysis.**

comparative risk analysis
An evaluation of relative risk, also referred to as risk-risk analysis.

Comparative Risk Analysis.   Just as **comparative risk analysis** helps the risk manager select an ''acceptable'' risk level, it can also be used to prioritize environmental hazards needing policy solutions. Given that public policy decisions are constrained by budget limitations, assessing relative risk helps officials identify which risks are in most need of an official response. The EPA's Science Advisory Board (SAB) recently prepared a ranking of environmental problems by degree of risk, shown in Table 7.1.[16] The ranking was

---

[16]U.S. EPA, Science Advisory Board (September 1990); *EPA Journal* (January/February/March 1993), p. 19.

TABLE 7.2   Public Perceptions of Environmental Problems

Environmental Problem	*Percent Responding that Problem Is Very or Extremely Serious*
Hazardous waste	89
Oil spills	84
Air pollution	80
Solid waste disposal	79
Atmospheric damage	79
Nuclear waste	78
Contaminated water	77
Forest destruction	76
Ocean pollution	75
Endangered species	67
Threats to wildlife	65
Pesticide use	60
World population	57
Poor energy use	56
Global warming	56
Reliance on coal/oil	53
Wetland development	50
Radon gas	35
Indoor air pollution	27
Electromagnetic fields	19

Source: U.S. Environmental Protection Agency, Office of Communications, Education, and Public Affairs, *Securing Our Legacy, An EPA Progress Report 1989–1991* (Washington, D.C., April 1992), p. 9.

---

based on the best available data and scientific information, (although as the SAB cautions, these data are not always complete), and considered such factors as the severity of effects and the number of people exposed. The purpose of this analysis is to guide the EPA in setting risk-based priorities. The SAB specifically advises that EPA programs should be guided by the principle of **relative risk reduction,** meaning the agency should order its policy decisions to reduce the most severe environmental risks first. The board's view on this use of comparative risk analysis is clear. In its report, the SAB asserts:

> If priorities are established based on the greatest opportunities to reduce risk, total risk will be reduced in a more efficient way, lessening threats to both public health and local and global ecosystems . . .

One difficulty risk managers face in setting risk-based priorities for environmental policy is that the rankings set by government are often different from how society *perceives* relative environmental risks. Look at Table 7.2 to see the ranking of environmental problems based on general public perception, and compare it to the SAB's ranking given in Table 7.1. This dichotomy of views presents a dilemma to government officials attempting to gain support for policy proposals. Not unaware of the problem, the SAB recognizes that in a democratic society, laws often are driven more by public perception of risk than by expert risk assessments. Therefore, it is important that government communicate scientific findings to the public to improve its understanding of environmental risk. It also must be cognizant of and receptive to public perceptions, particularly society's views on issues such as environmental equity and social values, which are difficult to quantify and incorporate in objective analyses.[17]

Not only can comparative risk analysis be used to prioritize all environmental problems needing a policy solution, but it can also be used to select among alternative control instruments aimed at any one of these. Used in this context, this approach is generally called **risk-risk analysis.** This risk management strategy involves a comparison of the estimated risk probabilities or risk ranking scores from two or more policy options. For example, the decision-maker might compare the relative risks of two different mandates for hazardous waste treatment, such as land disposal versus incineration, and propose whichever approach is more effective in reducing risk.[18] Implicitly, the objective of a risk-risk strategy is risk minimization, with no explicit consideration allowed for associated costs.

Risk-Benefit Analysis.   An alternative risk management strategy, called

risk-benefit analysis
An assessment of the risks of an environmental hazard along with the benefits to society of not regulating that hazard.

risk-benefit analysis, simultaneously considers the benefits to society of *not* regulating a given environmental hazard along with the level of associated risk. Here, the objective is to simultaneously maximize expected benefits *and* minimize risk. Although it may seem perverse, it is nonetheless accurate that the source of some environmental hazards offers benefits to society even though it also poses an ecological or health risk. Think about gasoline, which during combustion gives off harmful emissions that present a health risk. Nonetheless, gasoline *does* benefit society by fueling motor vehicles. Hence, if the risk manager were to consider only the risks, the solution to the problem of hazardous gasoline emissions might be to ban the use of gasoline. Yet, if the risk-reduction strategy were balanced with a consideration of the benefits of gasoline consumption, then the risk manager would have to assess how a reduction in gasoline usage would diminish society's well-being. Hence, a risk-benefit strategy would guide the risk manager to search for a solution that would balance these two factors.

The use of a risk-benefit management strategy is commonly mandated in environmental laws. An example is found in the Toxic Substances Control Act (TSCA). This act requires the EPA to respond if a chemical substance is found to ''present an unreasonable risk of injury to health or the environment.'' However, the law also requires the agency to simultaneously consider the health and environmental effects, the degree of exposure to the substance,

[17]U.S. EPA, Science Advisory Board (September 1990), p. 12.
[18]U.S. Congress, Office of Technology Assessment (OTA) (1983), pp. 226–27.

and the benefits the substance provides to society in use. A similar mandate is called for in the Federal Insecticide, Fungicide, and Rodenticide Act (FIFRA), which requires the EPA to register pesticides that will not cause "unreasonable adverse effects on the environment." This phrase refers to "any environmental risks to man or the environment taking into account the economic, social, and environmental costs and benefits of the use of any pesticide."[19]

benefit-cost analysis
A strategy that compares the marginal social benefit (*MSB*) of a risk reduction policy to the associated marginal social cost (*MSC*).

Benefit-Cost Analysis.   President Reagan's Executive Order 12291 issued in 1981 is largely responsible for the more intensified use of **benefit cost analysis** in formulating environmental policy. President Clinton's Executive Order 12866 of September 1993 continues to support this decision-making strategy. In risk management, benefit-cost analysis can be used to identify an "acceptable" risk level based on the criterion of **allocative efficiency.** For incremental risk reductions, the decision-maker would compare the monetized value of the social benefits with the associated costs to find the efficient level of risk where the *MSB* and *MSC* of risk reduction are equal. Equivalently, this point corresponds to the risk level that maximizes the difference between total social benefits and total social costs.

Often, environmental law establishes the risk reduction to be achieved, which means that the level of associated benefits has been predetermined. In such cases, the risk manager still can use benefit-cost analysis but with a different objective in mind. Here, the goal would be to select a policy instrument that achieves the legislated risk objective at least cost. If the selection is made properly, the initiative will achieve the economic goal of **cost-effectiveness** rather than allocative efficiency.

Finally, benefit-cost analysis can be used in the policy appraisal stage much in the same way as it is used in finding an "acceptable" risk level. At this stage of policy development, allocative efficiency is used to evaluate the effectiveness of any ongoing initiative. In practice, estimates of the *MSB* and *MSC* at the risk level achieved by policy are compared to see if they are equivalent. If not, the risk manager knows that the policy needs to be amended to correct the resource misallocation.

Conclusions

While most policy decisions are difficult and even controversial, those made in the context of environmental issues are particularly so. There is still much uncertainty about the causes and effects of many pollution problems. Moreover, the determination of how best to protect human health and natural resources is often subjective and emotionally charged. With so much at stake

---

[19]*EPA Journal* (January/February/March 1993), p. 15. We will have much more to say about TSCA and FIFRA in later chapters.

and so many sensitive issues involved, policy-makers have had to find ways to add consistency and clarity to what otherwise could become a continuous debate with no hope of resolve. Indeed, much of what environmental policy-makers struggle with is how to deal objectively and fairly with the risks posed by environmental hazards. Such is the purpose of risk analysis and its two components, risk assessment and risk management.

Scientists provide the fundamental data and analysis needed for risk assessment. As a result of their laboratory and field research, public officials gain valuable information about the nature of environmental hazards and the risks of exposure. Armed with a characterization of the risks involved, government officials can make better and more informed policy decisions. Through risk management strategies, such as comparative risk analysis and benefit-cost analysis, "acceptable" risk levels can be determined and alternative policy instruments can be evaluated in an objective way using well-defined criteria. Independent of how the "acceptable" risk level is determined, estimates of the social benefits and costs of a policy are useful in evaluating the effectiveness of policy initiatives after they have been adopted into law. These data can guide proposals for legislative amendments and revisions that have come to characterize the dynamic process of environmental policy development.

The use of benefit-cost analysis as a decision rule is becoming more prevalent in public policy decision-making. While monetizing environmental costs and benefits is an attempt to provide an impartial guideline to the risk manager, the task can be difficult to execute in practice. It also has been the source of some controversy. Think about the dilemma of assigning a dollar value to saving a human life or restoring coastal waters. Consequently, economists are continuing to research better methods and more comprehensive data to improve their estimates of benefits and costs. In the next two chapters, we will explore the fundamental steps of a benefit-cost analysis and assess the contribution of this risk management strategy to environmental decision-making.

Summary

- Voluntary risks are those that are deliberately assumed at an individual level. Since the potential outcome is confined to a single person, the government's role in risk reduction is usually confined to identifying potentially dangerous conditions or products and communicating that information to society. Involuntary risks arise from exposure to hazards beyond the control of individuals. Because these represent a public problem, government tries to control society's exposure to some of these.

- Environmental risk is a measure of the likelihood that damage to life, health, property, and/or the environment will occur as a result of exposure to a given hazard. The hazard is the source of the damage or the negative externality; exposure refers to the pathways between the source of the damage and the affected population or resource.

- Risk assessment is the qualitative and quantitative evaluation of the health or ecological risk posed by an environmental hazard. In the United States, the EPA uses the National Academy of Sciences' risk assessment model, which specifies the process as a series of four steps: hazard identification, dose-response analysis, exposure analysis, and risk characterization.

- Hazard identification uses scientific data to determine if a causal relationship exists between an environmental agent and adverse health or ecological effects. Several methods are used, including case clusters, bioassays, and epidemiology.

- A dose-response relationship quantitatively shows how a biological organism responds to a toxic substance as its exposure to the substance changes. An important objective is to identify if there is a threshold level of exposure, the point up to which no response is observed.

- Exposure analysis is concerned with characterizing the conditions faced by the potentially affected population. It identifies the sources of the hazard, the concentration levels at the source point, the pathways from the source to the affected population, and any sensitivities within the population group.

- Risk characterization is a quantitative and qualitative description of the form and dimension of the expected risk based upon the assessment of both the hazard and the exposure.

- The quantitative component of risk management provides a means to gauge the relative magnitude of the risk. Risk can be measured as a probability. Some probabilities are based on actuarial risks, while others are inferences derived from scientific laboratory studies. An alternative risk measure is a reference dose (RfD), which is the level of exposure to a given hazard that can be tolerated over a lifetime without harm.

- The qualitative component of risk management gives context to the numerical measure of risk and includes a description of the hazard, an assessment of exposure, an identification of the data used, the scientific and statistical methods employed, and any uncertainties in the findings.

- Risk management is concerned with formulating and implementing a policy response to reduce society's risk of a given hazard. Its tasks are to determine an "acceptable" risk level and to evaluate and select from alternative policy responses to risk. Several risk management strategies are used in practice, including comparative risk analysis, risk-benefit analysis, and benefit-cost analysis.

- Comparative risk analysis, known in some contexts as risk-risk analysis, involves an evaluation of relative risk. This strategy can be used to set risk-based priorities among different environmental hazards or to find which of the alternative policy options for a given hazard is most effective in reducing risk. Implicitly, the objective of a risk-risk strategy is risk minimization with no explicit consideration allowed for associated costs.

- Risk-benefit analysis is aimed at simultaneously maximizing expected benefits *and* minimizing environmental risk. Its use is commonly mandated in environmental laws.

- Benefit-cost analysis evaluates alternative risk levels by comparing the value of the expected gains with the associated costs. If the "acceptable" risk level maximizes the difference between social benefits and social costs, the outcome will be allocatively efficient. If the law establishes the risk level to be achieved, a cost-effective solution can be achieved by selecting the least-cost policy instrument that achieves the risk objective.

Key Concepts

voluntary risk	bioassays
involuntary risk	epidemiology
environmental risk	threshold level of exposure
exposure	actuarial risks
hazard	reference dose (RfD)
risk assessment	risk management
hazard identification	"acceptable" risk
dose-response analysis	*de minimis* risk
exposure analysis	comparative risk analysis
risk characterization	risk-benefit analysis
case clusters	benefit-cost analysis

Review Questions

1. Refer to Tables 7.1 and 7.2 and investigate how the public's perception of the risk of indoor pollution compares with the ranking given by the EPA's Science Advisory Board. How is this comparison relevant to the use of comparative risk analysis in communicating the hazards of radon as discussed in Application 7.5?

2. Comment on the following statement: "Without exposure, there is no risk."

3. Other than those mentioned in the chapter, give several real-world examples of how government has provided public information to enhance the identification of a voluntary risk.

4. *a.* Interpret the shape of the dose-response function in Figure 7.2 (c).
   b. Does this dose-response relationship suggest the presence of a threshold level? If so, where is it? If not, why not?

5. *a.* Verbally describe what an RfD of 0.002 for some pollutant Z means.
   b. Graphically sketch a dose-response function for pollutant Z, assuming that the dose-response relationship increases at a decreasing rate throughout. Label the RfD on your diagram.

6. Suppose you are using risk-benefit analysis to evaluate a policy aimed at limiting the use of a pesticide applied to grain crops. Describe the risks and benefits that would have to be estimated to conduct this analysis properly.

Additional Readings

Ahearne, John F. "Integrating Risk Analysis into Public Policymaking." *Environment* 35, no. 2 (March 1993), pp. 16–20, 37–39.

Carnegie Commission on Science, Technology, and Government. *Risk and the Environment: Improving Regulatory Decision Making.* New York: Carnegie Commission, June 1993.

Chess, Caron and Billie Jo Hance. "Opening Doors: Making Risk Communication Agency Reality." *Environment* 31, no. 5 (June 1989), pp. 11–15, 38–39.

Davies, Terry. ''Congress Discovers Risk Analysis.'' *Resources,* Winter 1995, pp. 5–8.

Johnson, F. Reed, Ann Fisher, V. Kerry Smith, and William H. Desvouges. ''Informed Choice or Regulated Risk? Lessons from a Study in Radon Risk Communication.'' *Environment* 30, no. 4 (May 1988), pp. 13–15, 30–35.

Kates, R. W. *Risk Assessment of Environmental Hazards.* New York: John Wiley & Sons. 1978.

Lave, Lester B. and Eugene P. Seskin. *Air Pollution and Human Health.* Baltimore: Johns Hopkins University Press, 1977.

Manes, Christopher. *Green Rage.* Boston: Little Brown & Co., 1990.

Smith, Kirk R. ''Air Pollution: Assessing Total Exposure in the United States.'' *Environment* 30, no. 8 (October 1988), pp. 10–15, 33–38.

ASSESSING BENEFITS AND COSTS FOR ENVIRONMENTAL DECISION-MAKING

Risk assessment and risk management are central to the decision-making process that guides environmental policy. Once the extent and degree of environmental risk have been identified by the scientific community, public officials begin the critical task of formulating policy. Ultimately, the objective is to minimize risk, which represents a benefit to society. But meeting this objective is not an unconstrained decision. Implementing a risk-reducing policy has a cost—an opportunity cost to be precise. Resources are needed to execute every policy action, and once allocated to that specific use, they are no longer available for alternative needs. Public officials have to recognize that resources used to reduce smog are no longer available to clean the Great Lakes or to save the California condor or to educate our children. How do policy-makers come to grips with such tough decisions? There is no simple answer, and in fact most would argue that the public sector wrestles with this problem on an ongoing basis. Yet, there are decision-making strategies that seem to be effective in environmental policy development—among them, benefit-cost analysis. This risk management strategy has begun to play a major role in environmental control policy, making it an important subject of inquiry and investigation.

Conceptually, benefit-cost analysis underlies much of economic theory. Consider how the theory of the firm uses this notion to explain how businesses make profit-maximizing decisions. The balancing of revenues and costs at the margin is an application of benefit-cost analysis. Consumer decisions also are rooted in the same concept, except that the balancing of benefits and costs is done in terms of marginal utility. In the broader context of policy decisions, benefit-cost analysis is used to evaluate the associated gains and losses to society as a whole. In every case, the basic principle is the same—an efficient solution results if benefits and costs are balanced at the margin.

Having said this, it should be apparent that the theoretical footing of ben-efit-cost analysis is sound and virtually indisputable. However, applying this theory in practice is not so clear-cut. In order to use benefit-cost analysis to guide environmental decisions, the associated social benefits and costs have to be *quantified.* Yet there are many intangibles involved that are difficult to measure in monetary terms, such as longevity of human life, improved aes-thetics, and the preservation of ecosystems. Although the process is difficult, it is critically important. Governments everywhere are spending huge sums to develop and implement environmental policy. In the United States alone, the annual expenditure is about $100 billion. Such large appropriations cannot be made without understanding the economic implications on both sides of the ledger. Hence, there is no debate that policy-makers need reliable measures of social benefits and costs to help guide these important decisions.

In this chapter, we explore both the motivation and the mechanics of methods used to measure environmental benefits and costs. We start by pre-senting the conceptual issues of how and why society values natural resources and environmental quality. This theoretical framework supports our subse-quent investigation of the methods economists use to measure and monetize environmental benefits. Once this side of the analysis is complete, we conduct an analogous study of the cost side, presenting both the theory and the esti-mating techniques. All of this lays the groundwork for studying how the two elements come together in a benefit-cost analysis—the subject of the next chapter.

Identifying and Valuing Environmental Benefits: Conceptual Issues

incremental benefits
The reduction in health, ecological, and property damages associated with an environmental policy initiative.

As a starting point, we need to establish the appropriate level of analysis for assessing policy-induced environmental benefits. From previous chapters, we know that these health and environmental improvements can be assessed as damage reductions. The key is to recognize that the relevant measure is the *change* in damage reductions brought about by the policy. In practice, these changes are called **incremental benefits.**

Defining Incremental Benefits

To assess the social benefits attributable to environmental policy, decision-makers must find out how health, ecological, and property damages *change* as a consequence of that initiative. This focus on the *change* in damages in-stead of their absolute level is not new. Economic theory is concerned with effects that occur *at the margin.* These too are changes, though they are infin-itesimal—measured *at a point.* When the relevant change is over a discrete range, it is referred to as **incremental** rather than **marginal.** Since policy evaluation is concerned with identifying damage reductions over some discrete time period, the appropriate measure of benefits is incremental.

To identify these incremental benefits, the analyst must compare the actual or expected benefits to society *after* some policy is implemented to a baseline measure of *current* conditions. Environmental benefits are commonly separated into categories, such as improvements in human health, aesthetics, the economy, recreation, property values, and the ecology. Application 8.1 discusses how incremental benefits were estimated to support a revision in U.S. air quality standards for particulate matter.

Application 8.1

Incremental Benefit Estimates for Revising U.S. Particulate Matter Standards

During 1983, the EPA prepared what is called a Regulatory Impact Analysis (RIA)* for a proposal to tighten the U.S. air quality standard for particulate matter. Particulate matter (PM) refers to a broad class of contaminants that are emitted into the air as small particles. Examples are road dust and fly ash from combustion. As part of the requirements of the RIA, the EPA had to estimate the incremental benefits of the proposal. According to the Clean Air Act, air quality standards are to be set based on "scientific criteria relating to the level of air quality needed to protect public health and welfare." Thus, to arrive at a measure of incremental benefits, the EPA had to quantify the health and welfare damage reductions expected to arise from the more stringent PM standard.

Relying on the findings of existing scientific studies, the EPA determined that exposure to PM is linked to such human health problems as respiratory and cardiovascular disease. The agency further found that the associated welfare effects include: (1) soiling of physical property such as buildings and materials; (2) increased acidic deposition through releases of sulfate particles; and (3) visibility impairment. Using this qualitative assessment as a basis, the EPA had to estimate *how much* these damages would be reduced by the proposed change in the PM standard and then monetize its findings. The aggregate result would be the agency's estimate of the incremental benefits needed to evaluate the proposal.

To illustrate the inherent variability in quantifying environmental benefits, the table below presents the series of benefit estimates actually used in the EPA's evaluation. Six sets of values are shown, each based on a different estimation procedure and each broken down by the relevant categories of health and welfare effects.

	Incremental Benefit Estimates by Aggregation Procedure (billions of 1980 dollars)					
Benefit Class	*A*	*B*	*C*	*D*	*E*	*F*
Mortality	1.12	1.12	1.12	12.72	12.72	13.84
Acute morbidity	0.00	1.32	10.65	10.65	10.65	11.97
Chronic morbidity	0.12	0.12	0.12	0.12	11.40	11.40
Soiling and materials (household sector)	0.00	0.00	0.73	0.73	3.14	13.85
Soiling and materials (manufacturing sector)	0.00	0.00	0.00	0.00	1.30	1.30
TOTAL incremental benefits	1.24	2.56	12.63	24.24	39.22	52.36

Application 8.1 (concluded)

For each benefit class, the letters A through F distinguish the series of estimates derived from each procedure. Procedure A is the most conservative, since its total of $1.24 billion includes only the benefits of reduced mortality and chronic illness. At the other end of the spectrum, Procedure F is the most comprehensive. It includes *all* of the expected health and welfare benefits—the reductions in mortality and morbidity plus the reduced soiling and material damages. According to this latter approach, the incremental benefits of tightening the PM standard are valued at $52.36 billion.

Beyond the differences in aggregation across the six procedures, there is also variability in how the individual benefit categories are valued. For example, according to Procedures A through C, mortality benefits are monetized at $1.12 billion, but Procedures D and E place a value on this same category of $12.72 billion, and Procedure F an even higher value of $13.84 billion. This disparity reflects the different scientific studies used across procedures to assess the benefit classes.

An important inference to be made from this discussion is that benefit assessment is not an exact science. Rather it relies on approximations based on a consensus of experts and supported by available scientific evidence. Often, as is the case here, a *range* of benefit estimates is considered, each based on certain assumptions. Although the absence of a single measure adds uncertainty to the process, the range of values actually helps the policy-maker understand the sensitivity of benefit estimates to even slight changes in expected outcomes—important information for sound environmental decision-making.

*An RIA was required under President Reagan's Executive Order 12291. More detail on this requirement will be provided in Chapter 9.

Source: Mathtech Inc., *Benefit and Net Benefit Analysis of Alternative National Ambient Air Quality Standards for Particulate Matter, Volume I.* Prepared for U.S. Environmental Protection Agency, Economic Analysis Branch, Office of Air Quality Planning and Standards (Research Triangle Park, N.C.: U.S. EPA, March 1983), pp. 1–52; U.S. Environmental Protection Agency, Office of Policy Analysis, Office of Policy, Planning, and Evaluation, *EPA's Use of Benefit-Cost Analysis, 1981–1986* (Washington, D.C., August 1987).

Defining Primary and Secondary Environmental Benefits

primary environmental benefit
A damage-reducing effect that is a direct consequence of implementing environmental policy.

secondary environmental benefit
An indirect gain to society associated with environmental policy.

Within the broad category of incremental benefits are two types of damage-reducing effects, **primary environmental benefits** and **secondary environmental benefits.** A **primary environmental benefit** is a damage-reducing effect that is the *direct* consequence of implementing environmental policy. Compare this with the concept of a **secondary environmental benefit,** which is an *indirect* gain to society associated with the implementation of environmental policy. This indirect gain may arise from some stimulative effect of the primary benefits or from some demand-induced effect caused by spending on inputs to implement the policy.[1]

While the difference between primary and secondary benefits may seem simple enough, it turns out that this refinement in benefit analysis has been a source of some controversy. To understand why, we consider what each of these concepts means from a theoretical perspective. Once done, the practical problems associated with this delineation will become apparent.

Primary Environmental Benefits.   Most environmental policy actions are aimed at increasing primary benefits, particularly those associated with human

---

[1]Haveman and Weisbrod (1975), p. 50.

health. Health benefits include both decreased mortality, such as a reduction in the risk of cancer deaths, and reduced morbidity, such as a lower incidence of respiratory ailments. Other primary benefits include more stable ecosystems and improved aesthetics. Still others are economic, such as a more prosperous fishing industry due to the enactment of clean water regulations. What all of these benefits have in common is that they are a *direct* outcome of environmental policy.

Secondary Environmental Benefits.   Secondary environmental benefits arise *indirectly* from a policy change. One source might be the stimulative effect of a primary benefit, such as higher worker productivity that results from the primary benefit of improved human health. Higher productivity increases the availability of goods and services, which may lead to a decline in product prices. Since these gains are stimulated by a primary benefit and arise indirectly, they are considered secondary benefits. An alternative source is a demand-induced change, such as the increased demand for labor to implement a new policy. In this case, the economic gains of an improved labor market are secondary benefits.

Theoretically, the difference between primary and secondary benefits seems reasonable. So, why the controversy? Much of the debate has to do with whether secondary benefits ought to be considered in the assessment of public policy proposals. According to one analysis, the existence of secondary benefits depends in part on employment conditions. In a fully employed economy, the reallocation of resources to newly created markets is simply a transfer from one market to another. Thus, although the reallocation would generate an incremental secondary benefit in one sector, it would be offset by a reduction in another. Even in the case of idle resources, the same conclusion is possible. If unemployment is stable and equal across markets, the same trade-off occurs.[2] Although the debate cannot be settled here, it is certain that *measuring* secondary benefits is problematic from a practical perspective. In fact, as we will discover in later chapters, most analyses assume that these indirect benefits are offset by losses in other areas.

Even absent secondary benefits, the identification of environmental primary benefits is only a first step to measuring them, albeit a critical one. What must be achieved next is an understanding of how society values these benefits in terms of its overall welfare. This perspective uses a conceptual characterization of value that relies on basic economic theory.

Conceptually Valuing Environmental Benefits

What is the value to society of cleaner air or water? What value does society place on cleaning up a hazardous waste site? As we have discussed in previous chapters, both of these questions could be answered directly *if* the commodity

---

[2]Haveman and Weisbrod (1975).

FIGURE 8.1

Marginal social benefit (MSB) *and total social benefits* (TSB) *of air quality (% SO₂ abatement)*

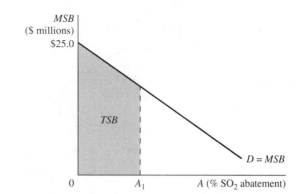

The market demand curve for SO_2 abatement represents the marginal social benefit (*MSB*) of air quality. At the hypothetical level of abatement, A_1, the corresponding *MSB* is the vertical distance from the horizontal axis at that point up to the curve. The total social benefits (*TSB*) associated with A_1 are shown as the shaded area under the *MSB* up to that point.

in each case were a private good traded in the open market. If so, demand prices would convey the marginal benefit society places on each additional unit of the good. The problem is that environmental quality is a public, non-marketed commodity. The absence of prices and the dilemma of nonrevelation of preferences cloud a determination of how society values a cleaner environment. In theory, if we could *infer* society's demand for environmental quality, we could then measure the incremental benefits associated with any policy initiative.

To illustrate this assertion, we return to our model of air quality based on SO_2 pollution abatement, which we introduced in Chapter 3. Recall that since demand for this public good represents society's decisions, it is both the marginal private benefit (*MPB*) and the marginal social benefit (*MSB*) of air quality. Thus, we can refer to the demand for SO_2 abatement as $MSB = 25 - 0.3A$, where *MSB* is measured in millions of dollars and A is the percentage of SO_2 abated.[3] The graphical model of this relationship is shown in Figure 8.1. At each level of abatement, *MSB* is shown as the vertical distance from the horizontal axis up to the demand curve. The total social benefits (*TSB*) for any abatement level are measured as the aggregation of these vertical distances, or the area under the *MSB* up to that point. In Figure 8.1, the *TSB* for some hypothetical abatement level, A_1, is shown as the shaded area under the demand curve up to A_1. Using this model, we can measure the incremental benefits from a policy-induced increase in SO_2 abatement in three steps: (1) find the baseline level of *TSB before* the policy is undertaken; (2) find the new level of *TSB* that would arise *after* the new policy is implemented; and

---

[3]Recall that market demand for a public good is modeled as the vertical summation of each individual's demand. The student may wish to review this derivation in Chapter 3.

FIGURE 8.2

*Modeling incremental
social benefits for air
quality (% SO₂
abatement) using the
MSB function*

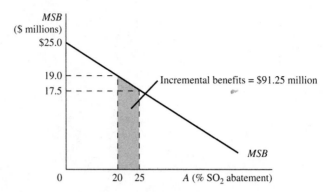

The *MSB* at the baseline abatement level of 20 percent is $19 million, and *TSB* is the area under the *MSB* up to that point, or $440 million. If a policy were proposed to increase SO₂ abatement to 25 percent, *MSB* would be $17.5 million and *TSB* would rise to $531.25 million. Therefore, the incremental benefits associated with the proposed policy are measured as the difference between the two *TSB* values, which is $91.25 million. In this model, incremental benefits are shown as the shaded area under the *MSB* between the two abatement levels.

(3) subtract the baseline *TSB* from the postpolicy *TSB* to determine incremental benefits.

Suppose that the current level of SO₂ abatement is 20 percent and that we wish to find the incremental benefits of a policy proposal to increase abatement to 25 percent. First, we find the baseline *TSB* for our model. Referring to Figure 8.2, notice that *MSB* at the 20 percent abatement level is $19 million. *TSB* at this level is the area under the *MSB* up to that point, or $440 million.[4] This dollar value represents society's **willingness to pay (WTP)** for the benefits achieved when 20 percent of SO₂ emissions are abated from the atmosphere. Next, we do the analogous calculations for the proposed abatement increase to 25 percent. At this postpolicy abatement level, *MSB* is $17.5 million and *TSB* is $531.25 million. Finally, the incremental benefits associated with the proposed policy are found as the difference between the two *TSB* values, or $91.25 million. This is shown as the shaded area in Figure 8.2.[5]

An alternative model of the same result is shown in Figure 8.3 where *TSB* is graphed directly with SO₂ abatement. In this model, the *TSB* associated with a given abatement level is measured simply as the *vertical distance* up to the curve and *not* as an area. Find on the graph the pre- and postpolicy levels of *TSB* corresponding to the 20 and 25 percent abatement levels. Notice that the

---

[4]Recall from Chapter 2 that the area beneath the demand curve and above the market price is consumer surplus, or the *net* benefit enjoyed by consumers. Notice that this net benefit is exactly equal to the total benefits received minus the total dollar value paid for the good. In fact, if a commodity has a zero market price, total benefits would be exactly equal to consumer surplus.

[5]To test this result, calculate the shaded area directly from the graphical model.

FIGURE 8.3

Modeling incremental social benefits for air quality (% SO₂ abatement) using the TSB *function*

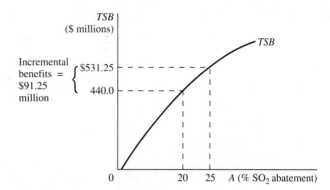

An alternative way to model the incremental benefits of improving air quality is to graph the relationship between *TSB* and various levels of SO₂ abatement. At each abatement level, *TSB* is measured as the vertical distance from the horizontal axis up to the curve. The model shows the *TSB* for the 20 percent baseline abatement level and for the 25 percent postpolicy abatement level as $440 million and $531.25 million respectively. The incremental benefits associated with the proposed policy are shown as the vertical distance between the two points on the *TSB* curve, which is $91.25 million.

incremental benefits of $91.25 are shown as the vertical distance between these two *TSB* levels.

Both models assume that society's valuation of environmental quality, or equivalently its demand for pollution abatement, can be identified. However, since there is no explicit market for this commodity, the valuation cannot be obtained from observing market-determined prices. Instead, inferences must be made about *how* society derives value or utility from various levels of environmental quality.

User versus Existence Value[6]

Discovering how society values a good is difficult in the absence of market prices. Even if the dilemma of nonrevelation of preferences could be overcome, the value of a good like clean air or water is difficult to quantify because of the many intangibles involved. While economists recognize that some of these intangibles are immeasurable, they still need some sense of how the benefits of environmental quality are *perceived* by society. Fortunately, theories have been advanced that can help.

user value
The utility or benefit derived from physical use or access to an environmental good.

existence value
The utility or benefit received from the continuance of an environmental good.

From a purely conceptual vantage point, it is generally recognized that society derives utility from environmental quality through two sources of value: **user value** and **existence value. User value** refers to the utility or benefit received from physical utilization or access to an environmental good or service. **Existence value** is the utility or benefit received from an environmental good through its continuance as a good or service. Collectively, these

------

[6]Much of the following is drawn from Mitchell and Carson (1989), Chapter 3.

two components yield a measure of society's total valuation of an environmental good, expressed as follows:

Total value of environmental quality = User value + Existence value

To clarify the meaning of these concepts, we illustrate them through simple examples, beginning with user value.

User Value.   Consider the benefits derived from using a lake. If an individual swims in the lake, that person is deriving utility by physically using it. Likewise, a commercial fishing fleet derives user benefit from catching fish from the lake. Notice that in both cases, benefits are derived from directly consuming services provided by the environmental resource. These types of activities, both recreational and commercial, generate benefits that are said to yield **direct user value.** This valuation helps to determine what the individual or the fishing fleet would be willing to pay to maintain or improve the lake's quality.

direct user value
Derived from directly consuming services provided by an environmental good.

Continuing with the same example, it is also possible that an individual might receive utility from simply looking at the view of the lake. Here, the utility is derived from the lake's aesthetic qualities. This type of activity involves using the lake in a less immediate way than swimming in it or fishing from it. Hence, it is said to yield **indirect user value.** Both direct and indirect user value are elements of society's total valuation of environmental quality.[7]

indirect user value
Derived from indirect consumption of an environmental good such as the aesthetic value it provides.

Existence Value.   Society also receives benefits from environmental goods beyond the utility associated with direct or indirect use. Think about how people value such natural resources as the great rainforests, the Grand Canyon, or the bald eagle. Use or direct consumption does not explain how or why society values these resources. Yet, we know that society as a whole is willing to pay to preserve and protect them. In such circumstances, benefits accrue to society from simply knowing that these resources exist and are being preserved. This component of total valuation is referred to as **existence value.**

While seemingly abstract, existence value is an important motivation for privately funded conservation efforts and for many environmental public policy initiatives. A case in point is the Endangered Species Act of 1973, which provides for the protection and preservation of certain animals, birds, fish, and plant life that are threatened by extinction. As discussed in Application 8.2, this act is an example of the U.S. government's official recognition of existence value. Other tangible evidence is the willingness of society to

---

[7]While these examples involve present period consumption, economists also have begun to examine how society expects to benefit from consumption in some future period. This valuation concept, which adds uncertainty to the benefit assessment process, is referred to as option value. For detail on the concept of option value, the interested student is referred to Mitchell and Carson (1989), Chapter 3 and Johansson (1991).

The Endangered Species Act of 1973

In 1973, the Endangered Species Act was passed by Congress to "provide a means whereby the ecosystems upon which endangered species and threatened species depend may be conserved." Officially, the act protects the biodiversity of the earth. Biodiversity can be defined as the variety of life on earth—the diversity of genes, species, and ecosystems and the interaction among them. An important outcome of this act was the creation of a formal list of biological organisms in danger of extinction, *regardless of their direct or indirect use to humans.* Originally numbering 109 in 1973, the list of endangered and threatened species in the United States includes nearly 600 species as of 1990. Of these, plants represent over half the number, fish account for the second largest group, and all other types of species such as mammals, reptiles, insects, and crustaceans are numbered among the remainder. Reportedly, over 3,000 species are candidates for the official listing that would give them U.S. protection, with some 600 in need of immediate government action.

Since its original passage over 20 years ago, the Endangered Species Act has undergone the scrutiny of reauthorization on six separate occasions, with the most recent having been the most tenuous in the act's history. At the heart of the controversy surrounding this act are the benefits and costs of biodiversity. To a great extent, the issues that dominate today's discussions about this act and biodiversity in general are the same ones that surfaced when the act was first created. On the benefit side, the relevant question is: Should a species be protected because of the existing or anticipated benefit it provides to humans or should it be saved because it has a right to exist? Notice that this question recognizes and distinguishes between **user value** and **existence value.**

Already a complex issue, the matter is even more complicated when and *if* costs are introduced into the debate. There are opportunity costs to saving an endangered species that go well beyond the explicit costs of implementing a national program to protect the earth's ecology. Industry objectives may have to be compromised to save an animal or plant nearing extinction. For example, if as a nation we stand firm to protect the northern spotted owl, the forestry industry and its workers will incur economic costs. At the very least, the prosperity of the northwestern United States and literally thousands of jobs are at stake. Should these costs be part of the consideration to save the ecology, and if so, would they outweigh the benefits? In part, the answer depends upon whether existence value is considered along with user value in the benefit evaluation.

When the Endangered Species Act was originally proposed, some arguments were made to justify its passage on economic grounds. The basic argument was that species were to be protected because they may serve a direct benefit to mankind that scientific study had not yet discovered. One justification for this view is the recent discovery that a compound called taxol found in the bark of Pacific yew trees holds promise for the treatment of certain cancers. Approximately 60 pounds of yew bark are needed to produce enough taxol to treat one cancer patient, and the Pacific yew is a slow-growing species being harvested by timber companies at a rapid rate. Notice that this discourse attempts to focus on the **user value** of environmental resources. Just as strong in their position were those who asserted that environmental resources offer significant benefits to society that span a much broader range than their direct or indirect value in human consumption. These proponents of the act argued that its objective ought to be to protect species based upon a presumed right of survival—clear evidence of the role of **existence value** in benefit assessment.

There is not now, nor is there likely to be, a consensus about whether user value is relevant to the benefit assessment of legislative initiatives to promote biodiversity and protect the earth's ecological systems. What *is* clear is that society recognizes and appreciates environmental benefits because of their existence value—an issue that continues to emerge in the ongoing deliberation about biodiversity and economic development.

Sources: Jerry Adler and Mary Hager, "How Much Is a Species Worth?" *National Wildlife,* April/May 1992, pp. 4–14; Council on Environmental Quality, *Environmental Quality: 23rd Annual Report* (Washington, D.C.: U.S. Government Printing Office, January 1993), pp. 17–28.

financially support the work of environmental groups, such as the National Wildlife Federation, the Sierra Club, and the National Audubon Society—groups whose agendas focus on preserving resources that many of their benefactors never expect to use or even see firsthand. Apparently, natural resources have a measure of value that extends beyond the benefits of direct consumption.

One of the earlier discussions of existence value in the literature is presented by Krutilla (1967), who asserts the following:

> When the existence of a grand scenic wonder or a unique and fragile ecosystem is involved, its preservation and continued availability are a significant part of the real income of many individuals.[8]

vicarious consumption
The utility associated with knowing that others derive benefits from an environmental good.

Since the early work of Krutilla, economists have been studying various theories about the motivations of existence value. In a recent text about valuing public goods, Mitchell and Carson (1989) classify the motives for existence value as **vicarious consumption** and **stewardship,** among others.

Vicarious consumption refers to the notion that individuals value a public good for the benefit it provides to others whether or not these ''others'' are known personally. From an economic perspective, this suggests that the utility derived is *interdependent*—that an individual can and does receive benefits from the knowledge that others are enjoying the public good. **Stewardship** arises both from a sense of obligation to preserve the environment for future generations *and* from the recognition of the intrinsic value of natural resources, regardless of whether they are ever actually used. In sum, we can express the total valuation of environmental quality as:

stewardship
The sense of obligation to preserve the environment for future generations.

Total value =	**User value**	+	**Existence value**
=	(Direct and indirect user value)	+	(Vicarious consumption and stewardship value)

Recognizing the sources of society's valuation of an environmental resource is important for identifying the social benefits of a policy proposal. It also helps economists anticipate which of the available estimation methods might be most effective in quantifying those benefits. Yet the question still remains—how do economists assign dollar values to nonmarketed environmental goods like clean water, human health, and the spotted owl? Remember that the objective is to *monetize* or find the **WTP** for changes in user and existence value arising from a policy-driven increase in environmental quality.

To face the issue head-on, consider the following question. What is the monetized value of the incremental benefit of saving one human life? Not only

---

[8]Krutilla attributes the birth of conservation economics to A. C. Pigou, an English economist who wrote: ''It is the clear duty of government, which is the trustee for unborn generations as well as for its present citizens, to watch over, and if need be, by legislative enactment, to defend, the exhaustible natural resources of the country from rash and reckless spoliation.'' (Pigou 1952)

is the answer difficult to determine, but the question itself is one that some find offensive. Nonetheless, if a benefit-cost analysis is to be undertaken, *all* of the benefits accruing to society, including the value of saving a human life, must be considered in the analysis. There is only one common denominator available—a monetized measure.

Approaches to Measuring Environmental Benefits: An Overview[9]

Economists have made great strides over the past decade in developing better methods to estimate the benefit of environmental quality improvements. For the most part, these methods are aimed at estimating primary benefits, implicitly assuming that secondary benefits are insignificant—likely offset by secondary costs. A review of the extensive literature on the subject shows that there are several methods used in practice. Some are better than others at quantifying the more abstract or intangible benefits of improved environmental quality, including the somewhat elusive concept of existence value.

To organize our discussion of benefit measurement methods, we rely upon a general classification introduced by Smith and Krutilla (1982), which places the various measurement techniques into two broad categories: the **physical linkage approach** and the **behavioral linkage approach.** A summary of selected benefit valuation methods within each approach is presented in Table 8.1. The distinctions among them will become clearer in the following overview of each approach and the subsequent analysis of common estimation methods within each.

Physical Linkage Approach to Environmental Benefit Valuation

physical linkage approach
Estimates environmental benefits based on a technical relationship between an environmental resource and the user of that resource.

Methods within the physical linkage category use some tangible attribute of the environment to make a connection to the individual through which benefits can be observed or inferred and subsequently valued. More formally, the **physical linkage approach** measures benefits based upon the existence of a technical relationship between the environmental resource and the user of that resource. A common estimation procedure that uses this approach is the **damage function method.** This method uses a functional relationship to capture the link between a contaminant and the associated environmental damages. Based on this function, incremental benefits can be measured as the reduction in damages due to a policy-induced decrease in the contaminant. This damage reduction is then monetized to obtain a dollar value of the benefits brought about by the policy.

---

[9]This section is drawn mainly from Mitchell and Carson (1989), particularly pp. 74–78 and Cropper and Oates (1992).

TABLE 8.1 A Synopsis of Benefit Estimation Methods

The Physical Linkage Approach

Damage Function Method

Uses a model of the relationship between levels of a contaminant and observed (or statistically inferred) environmental damage to estimate the damage reduction arising from a policy-induced decline in the contaminant.

The Behavioral Linkage Approach
Direct Methods   .

Political Referendum Method

Uses the *actual* market of a public good by monitoring the voting results from political referenda on proposed changes in environmental quality.

Contingent Valuation Method (CVM)

Employs surveys to inquire about individuals' willingness to pay (WTP) for environmental improvements based on *hypothetical* market conditions.

Indirect Methods

Averting Expenditure Method (AEM)

Assesses changes in an individual's spending on goods and services that are *substitutes* for personal environmental quality to assign value to changes in the overall environment.

Travel Cost Method (TCM)

Values a change in the quality of an environmental resource by assessing the effect of that change on the demand for a *complementary* good.

Hedonic Price Method (HPM)

Uses the theory that a good is valued for the attributes it possesses to estimate the implicit or hedonic price of an environmental attribute and identify its demand as a means to assign value to policy-driven improvements in quality.

Often, applications of the physical linkage approach are used in contexts where market prices can be used to value the damage reduction. For example, if a proposed policy improves the stock of commercially harvested fish, prices could be used to attach a dollar value to the incremental benefits. Likewise, a reduction in cancer risk could be monetized using market prices of medical treatments and hospital care.

behavioral linkage approach
Estimates environmental benefits using observations of behavior in actual markets or survey responses about hypothetical markets.

Behavioral Linkage Approach to Environmental Benefit Valuation

Consumer preferences and responses to changes in environmental quality are critical elements of behavioral linkage methods. In general, the **behavioral linkage approach** to quantifying benefits is based upon observations of behavior in actual markets or consumer responses about hypothetical markets for environmental goods. The specific methods used to establish the linkage and to monitor responses vary considerably. In some procedures, benefits are identified by observing how consumers behave in *actual* market settings. In others, the identification is made by evaluating consumers' responses to *hypothetical* markets or conditions.

Another important difference among behavioral linkage methods is how closely the behavior or responses are linked to the environmental good under study. Techniques that assess responses immediately related to environmental changes are broadly termed **direct methods.** As shown in Table 8.1, two types of direct methods that differ by the market data needed are the **political referendum method**, which relies on *actual* market information, and the **contingent valuation method (CVM),** which uses *hypothetical* market data. **Indirect methods** are those that examine responses, not about the environmental good itself, but about some set of market conditions related to it. Three examples of indirect benefit estimation methods are: the **averting expenditure method (AEM),** the **travel cost method (TCM),** and the **hedonic price method (HPM).**

The published literature on benefit valuation methods is extensive. There are many research papers that present specific empirical findings, and there are numerous texts on the methodology itself. We offer only an overview of the operational issues associated with the more common methods used by researchers.[10] We begin by analyzing the physical linkage approach, the less complex of the two broad categories of benefit estimation methods.

Estimation under the Physical Linkage Approach

damage function method
Models the relationship between an environmental contaminant and observed effects to estimate damage reductions arising from policy.

The Damage Function Method

When using the **damage function method,** the researcher specifies a model of the relationship between an environmental contaminant and some type of observed damage.[11] A generalized damage function is shown in Figure 8.4. The levels of some environmental contaminant (C) are measured horizontally, and the total damages (TD) due to exposure to that contaminant are measured vertically.[12] Once the function is specified, the analyst uses the model to

---

[10]To study any of these methods in detail, the reader should consult the references cited along the way and the list of additional readings given at the end of the chapter.

[11]If the subject of a benefit assessment is the reduction in adverse effects to a *biological organism,* the analyst would conduct the estimation using a **dose-response function.** Essentially, the dose-response function is a particular type of damage function applied in a specific context—when the damages are *biological* in nature. Recall from Chapter 7 that scientists use dose-response functions in the risk assessment process.

[12]The model shown is a cubic relationship, but this is just one possible functional form for a damage function. For more on this issue, see, for example, Halvorsen and Ruby (1981), p. 106.

FIGURE 8.4

Measuring incremental benefits using the damage function method: a physical linkage approach

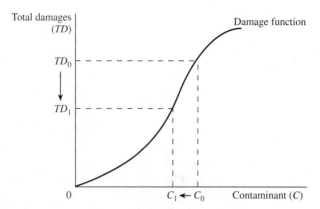

A damage function models the relationship between an environmental contaminant (C) and the total damages (TD) due to exposure to that contaminant. Once the function is specified, the analyst can use the model to estimate the damage reduction from any policy-induced decline in the contaminant. This damage reduction represents the incremental benefits of environmental policy measured in nonmonetary units.

estimate the damage reduction from any policy-induced decline in the contaminant. At this point, the reduction is measured in nonmonetary units—it might be the number of acidified lakes, acres of damaged forests, or number of premature deaths. Ultimately, this reduction must be assigned a monetary value, either by using market prices if available or by employing some estimation technique.

To illustrate the procedure, look at Figure 8.4 and assume that a federal policy initiative is expected to reduce the hypothetical contaminant from C_0 to C_1. Based on the damage function model, this proposal would reduce damage (or equivalently, increase benefits), by the vertical distance between TD_0 and TD_1. If, for example, the damage reduction was diminished injury to wheat crops, this vertical distance might be measured as thousands of bushels of wheat. Having quantified the incremental benefit, a simple way to monetize the change in physical damage would be to multiply the number of bushels by the market-determined price per bushel.

Assessing the Damage Function Method. Although the damage function method is useful, it has limitations. First, by construction it estimates only one aspect of incremental benefits. In our example, the measured benefits are increased wheat crops. In most cases, a contaminant reduction would give rise to other types of gains, perhaps increases in other crops or improvements in human health. Hence, a full assessment of benefits using the damage function approach would require that the same modeling and estimating procedure be performed for *every* type of damage reduction. Second, the procedure is only a first-step approach in that it is not capable of simultaneously monetizing the benefits it quantifies. Therefore, some other technique must be used to perform this latter part of the assessment unless the benefits were marketed commodities.

Applications of the Damage Function Method.   Recognizing the limitations of the damage function method, analysts typically use it for measuring a *specific* type of incremental benefit as opposed to performing a comprehensive benefit assessment. Furthermore, the context is often one where market-determined prices can be used to monetize the measured gain. To illustrate, consider conducting a benefit assessment of those provisions in the U.S. Clean Air Act aimed at reducing ozone in the lower atmosphere or troposphere. According to scientific evidence, one type of damage associated with increased levels of tropospheric ozone is diminished agricultural crop yields. The incremental *agricultural* benefits associated with these provisions could be estimated using the damage function method. To do this, the analyst would develop a model of the relationship between tropospheric ozone and crop loss measured in bushels. The agricultural benefit of the ozone-reducing policy could then be measured as the decrease in bushels of crops damaged by ozone.[13] Application 8.3 presents the actual results of such a benefit estimation conducted as part of a U.S. government study.

Application 8.3

Valuing Agricultural Benefits:
The Case of Tropospheric Ozone Reductions

In 1980, Congress mandated a 10-year scientific, technical, and economic study of the effects of acidic deposition on human health, buildings and materials, forests, fish, and agricultural crops. Termed the National Acid Precipitation Assessment Program (NAPAP), this extensive investigative plan was aimed at gathering information for use in formulating national policy on reducing the risks of acidic deposition. As part of its research effort, NAPAP also studied the effect of tropospheric ozone on health and the ecology, since one of the contributors to acidic deposition, nitrogen oxides (NO_x), also affects ozone levels.

According to NAPAP's 1990 report, scientific research has been unable to find any consistent adverse effect on crop yields caused by acidic deposition in the ambient air. However, there *is* well-documented evidence that elevated levels of tropospheric ozone can diminish crop yields. In fact, estimates of this damage have been shown to range from 2 percent to about 56 percent, depending on such factors as crop species, location, and exposure levels. Consequently, an important part of NAPAP's research on the effects of air pollutants on agriculture dealt with quantifying the incremental benefits that would result from an ozone-reducing policy initiative.

---

[13]The interested reader may wish to consult Kopp and Krupnick (1987) for results of an empirical investigation that estimates the agricultural benefits of ozone reduction.

Application 8.3 (continued)

Conceptually, the agricultural benefits of such a policy can be modeled by assessing the market implications of an increase in crop yields. Defining the relevant market as agricultural crops, the diagram below models the effect of a hypothetical ozone-reducing policy as an increase in market supply from S_0 to S_1.

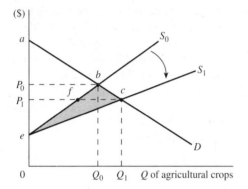

This shift in turn causes a decline in the price of crops from P_0 to P_1.

Since the relevant market is a private good, the incremental benefits can be assessed by measuring the sum of the changes in producer and consumer surpluses. Using the diagram above, consider first the size of these surpluses prior to any policy change, using supply curve, S_0. Consumer surplus is equal to the area below the demand curve and above the market price, or area P_0ab. Producer surplus is the area above the supply curve and below the market price, or area P_0be. Thus, the total sur-

plus at equilibrium *prior* to a policy change is area *eab*. After the ozone-reducing policy is implemented and supply shifts to S_1, consumer surplus becomes area P_1ac, and producer surplus becomes area P_1ce. Thus, the total surplus *after* the policy change is area *eac*. The operative question is whether society is better off as a result. Since the total surplus increased from *eab* to *eac*, the answer is yes, and the incremental benefit can be quantified as area *ebc*, (i.e., *eac* − *eab*).

Notice, however, that the distribution of benefits among society is not as easily determined. Consumers definitely gain, since consumer surplus rises from P_0ab to P_1ac. But the same assertion cannot be made about producers. Some of the original producer surplus, area P_0bfP_1, has been transferred to consumers, but there is also a gain to producers of area *efc*. Whether or not the gain of *efc* exceeds the loss of P_0bfP_1 depends upon the shapes of the supply and demand curves and the magnitude of the shift in market supply. Consequently, to measure the incremental benefits of policy *and* to determine the distribution of these benefits across society, economists must rely on sophisticated models capable of estimating these changes in consumer and producer surpluses.

Modeling techniques to measure environmental benefits were employed in the NAPAP study of ozone's effects on agricultural yields. NAPAP's final report presents the following estimates of changes in consumer and producer surplus for alternative ozone policies:

Changes in Ozone (percent)	Change in Surplus (billions of 1989 dollars)		
	Consumer Surplus	Producer Surplus	Total Surplus
−10	0.785	−0.046	0.739
−25	1.637	0.095	1.732
+10	−1.044	0.215	−0.829
+25	−2.659	0.453	−2.206

Source: NAPAP (November 1991), Table 4.9-6, p. 401.

Application 8.3 (concluded)

Under the first scenario, a 10 percent reduction in ozone concentrations is estimated to increase total surplus by approximately $739 million. Of this amount, consumer surplus would increase by $785 million, while producer surplus is expected to decline by $46 million. Conversely, a more restrictive ozone policy, such as a 25 percent reduction, would increase the benefits to both producers and consumers and elevate the change in total surplus to $1,732 million. These findings have important implications about the distribution of these incremental benefits across buyers and sellers. Notice that consumers and producers do not respond symmetrically to increases in ozone levels. In fact, if ozone levels were to *increase* either by 10 or 25 percent, society as a whole would lose, but producers would actually benefit. According to the

NAPAP report, this gain to producers arises because of farmers' ability to pass on the higher costs of depleted supplies to consumers in the form of higher prices.

Of course, the bottom line is how policy-makers and public officials respond to the kinds of scientific and economic data provided through such comprehensive studies as the NAPAP investigation. While the end result is not always predictable, one thing is certain—advances in scientific knowledge and improvements in benefit estimation techniques have offered the public sector the opportunity to make better and more informed decisions.

Source: National Acid Precipitation Assessment Program, *1990 Integrated Assessment Report* (Washington, D.C.: NAPAP Office of the Director, November 1991), pp. 55, 154–56, 398–401.

Direct Estimation Methods under the Behavioral Linkage Approach

The so-called **direct methods** under the behavioral linkage approach estimate environmental benefits according to responses or observed behaviors directly tied to environmental quality. Although there are a number of direct methods available to researchers, we consider only two representative examples here. These are the **political referendum method** and the **contingent valuation method (CVM)**.

The Political Referendum Method

political referendum method
Uses voter responses to political referenda on environmental issues to make inferences about society's valuation of the associated benefits.

Voter responses to certain **political referenda** convey useful information to researchers about the value of environmental benefits. Of interest are proposals affecting the natural environment, such as the siting of a hazardous waste facility or the establishment of a recycling center. Implicitly, the passage of an environmentally oriented referendum suggests that voters value the incremental benefits more than the incremental costs needed to implement the bill. A defeat suggests the converse. Inferences drawn from a single referendum provide only a *qualitative* assessment about environmental benefits—in this case whether they outweigh the associated costs. Although this is useful information, it is not sufficient to obtain a measure of incremental benefits. To use political referenda to quantify incremental benefits, analysts must monitor voters' reactions to a *series* of proposals that will convey how *changes* in environmental quality are valued. In practice, response data must be collected from a selection of related referenda—either a set of responses from the same jurisdiction to *different* levels of an environmental good or a set of *different* jurisdictional responses to the same level of the good.

Assessing the Political Referendum Method.   Since data on such a series of voter responses are not always available, the applicability of the political referendum method is limited. Nonetheless, the procedure offers several appealing properties, particularly its use of *actual* voting results to overcome the problems of modeling a public goods market. In fact, the political referendum method is often used to confirm the findings of other estimation approaches or to test the predictive power of methods that use *hypothetical* markets.[14]

The Contingent Valuation Method (CVM)

contingent valuation method (CVM)
Employs surveys to elicit responses about willingness to pay for environmental quality based on hypothetical market conditions.

When market data are unavailable or unreliable, economists can use alternative estimation methods that rely on *hypothetical* market conditions. Such methods typically use surveys to inquire about individuals' willingness to pay (WTP) for some environmental policy initiative. This survey approach to benefit estimation is known as the **contingent valuation method (CVM)** because the results are dependent, or *contingent,* upon the hypothetical market devised. The critical assumption is that properly designed surveys can elicit responses comparable to those arising under actual situations.

To approximate real market conditions, economists create a hypothetical market for the good in question to serve as the context for a series of survey questions. In some sense, the model and the survey instrument help to finesse the problem of nonrevelation of preferences that characterizes public goods. Implementing this survey approach involves the following three tasks:[15]

1. The construction of a detailed model of the hypothetical market, including the characteristics of the good and any relevant conditions that affect the market.

2. The design of a survey instrument to obtain an unbiased estimate of individuals' WTP.

3. An assessment of the truthfulness of survey respondents' answers.

---

[14]For more detail on this estimation method, see Mitchell and Carson (1989), pp. 76–78.

[15]For more detail on the specific elements of a CVM analysis, the interested student is referred to Mitchell and Carson (1989), Cummings, Brookshire, and Schultz (1986), and Smith and Desvousges (1986).

Assessing the CVM. The CVM is favored by researchers because of its applicability to a variety of environmental goods and because of its capacity to assess existence value as well as user value. However, because this approach makes inferences about actual markets from a hypothetical model, it is subject to the biases that usually plague a survey-dependent study. In this context, the biases are manifested as differences between survey responses and what these responses would be under actual market conditions. Table 8.2 lists some common sources of bias associated with the CVM. As the table indicates, biases can arise for a variety of reasons, including the design of the survey instrument and the procedures used to conduct the survey.[16]

TABLE 8.2   Classification of Biases Encountered in Contingent Valuation Studies

General Biases

Strategic:	An individual may have an incentive *not* to reveal his or her true preferences about an environmental good when responding to questions about willingness to pay (WTP). This bias may arise from the free-ridership problem typically associated with public goods.
Information:	If there is insufficient information about the commodity being valued, the individual's WTP response may not be equivalent to their actual WTP.
Hypothetical:	Because the market is a hypothetical one, the respondent may view the questions as not believable or unrealistic, and respond with an equally unrealistic estimate of WTP.

Survey Instrument-Related Biases

Starting point:	Some survey instruments use predefined ranges of values to guide responses. The starting points of these ranges can influence the respondent's answers about WTP.
Payment vehicle:	To make the responses more factual, the survey questions about value are often tied to a specific payment vehicle, such as an increase in taxes or an adjustment on a utility bill. The selection of which payment vehicle to employ in the survey may influence how an individual responds to questions about WTP.

Procedural Biases

Sampling:	Not unlike most sampling processes, problems may arise due to the specific sampling procedure used by the researcher.
Interviewer:	The respondent's answers may be influenced by the individual asking the questions.

Source: Adapted from: V. Kerry Smith and William H. Desvousges, *Measuring Water Quality Benefits* (Norwell, Mass.: Kluwer-Nijhoff Publishing, 1986), Figure 4-1, p. 73.

---

[16]Of course, some of these biases are more problematic than others. For example, research shows that the extent of strategic bias, if it exists at all, tends to be minor. Studies that have explicitly examined the issue of strategic bias include Brookshire, Ives, and Schulze (1976) and Rowe, d'Arge, and Brookshire (1980).

Responding to these concerns, economists continue to make improvements to the CVM, most of them aimed at minimizing the potential for biased results. Some researchers add more detail to their models of the hypothetical environmental commodity. Descriptions include information about the quantity, quality, and location of the good, and the timing of its provision. Just as important is the presentation and design of the survey instrument. Supplemental information is often used to more accurately describe the commodity and the conditions under which it would be provided. Some surveys include maps to illustrate the location of the good or photographs of the commodity and the area affected by its provision.[17] Whatever the form, the objective is the same—to make the hypothetical market situation as factual and as close to actual conditions as possible.

Applications of the CVM.   Researchers have used the CVM in a variety of contexts to estimate environmental benefits. One important application is its use in estimating the value of a statistical human life.[18] In a recent review of these findings, these estimates were reported as falling within a range of $1.6 million to $4.0 million ($1986).[19]

Another common focus of CVM studies is to measure society's WTP for water quality improvements. Two examples are a study by Smith and Desvousges (1986), which examines a specific water body—the Monongahela River in Pennsylvania, and an analysis by Carson and Mitchell (1988), which considers a more generalized value measure across all water sites in the United States. To improve survey responses, both studies use a reference for water quality changes devised by Vaughan (1981) called the water quality ladder. This reference measure translates sophisticated indexes of water quality to the types of activities that each index supports. For example, low quality water would support only boating, moderate quality would allow fishing to be done safely, and higher levels would support swimming. By using these simpler representations of water quality, the researchers were better able to communicate with survey respondents.

In terms of specific results, Smith and Desvousges find that the average household in their survey of five counties in western Pennsylvania is willing to pay $25 ($1981) per year to improve the river from boatable to fishable

---

[17]Brookshire and Crocker (1981).

[18]A statistical life saved is related to the concept of environmental risk introduced in Chapter 7. For example, if an environmental policy lowers the risk of death from 2 in 100,000 persons exposed to 1 in 100,000 exposed, the incremental benefit of that policy is one human life saved.

[19]Cropper and Oates (1992), p. 713.

quality. Carson and Mitchell's nationwide survey shows that the average respondent is willing to pay $80 ($1983) per year for water quality improvements. How can the difference be explained? Since the valuation in the national survey is higher than the more localized finding of Smith and Desvouges, the difference may be attributable to existence value. Why? Because the respondents in the more general survey are willing to pay for water quality improvements throughout the United States, even though they do not expect to use these water bodies themselves.[20]

Valuations of incremental benefits from air quality improvements have also been estimated using CVM. In fact, some argue that the CVM is particularly useful for valuing visibility improvements at national parks, where existence value is likely to be significant. One study by Schulze and Brookshire (1983) seems to support this hypothesis. These researchers find that the *user value* of improving visibility at the Grand Canyon from 70 to 100 miles is under $2.00 ($1988) per visitor per day. In contrast, they estimate the comparable *existence value* at $95 ($1988) per household per year to prevent diminished visibility at the Grand Canyon.[21]

Because the CVM is capable of capturing existence value, it has been used to value ecological benefits, such as preserving endangered species. For example, one study estimates that individuals would be willing to pay $22 ($1983) per year to save the whooping crane.[22] Another finds that people would be willing to pay $11 per year to preserve the bald eagle.[23] There is, however, an important caveat regarding CVM studies such as these. While the value of preserving an entire ecosystem is typically what is of interest in policy analysis, many CVM studies focus on a single species. Yet the sum of species-specific valuations is generally lower than the valuation of an entire area. Hence, a simple adding up of individual WTP estimates is not a valid measure of the benefits associated with preserving an entire ecosystem.[24]

Indirect Estimation Methods under the Behavioral Linkage Approach

For some environmental proposals, direct estimation procedures like the CVM might not be viable. In these cases, economists use **indirect methods,** which make inferences about markets or conditions that are somehow linked to the environmental good under investigation. While there are many indirect estimation methods, three dominate the literature on benefit valuation: the

---

[20]Cropper and Oates (1992), pp. 716–17.

[21]Notice that for user value the WTP is appropriately given on a *per visitor* basis, while the existence value is quoted for *households* who may never visit the park.

[22]Bowker and Stoll (1988).

[23]Boyle and Bishop (1987).

[24]Cropper and Oates (1992), pp. 719–20.

averting expenditure method (AEM); the **travel cost method (TCM);** and the **hedonic price method (HPM).** Let's take a look at each of these.

Averting Expenditure Method (AEM): An Indirect Approach Using Substitutes

averting expenditure method (AEM)
Uses changes in an individual's spending on goods that are *substitutes* for a cleaner environment to estimate the value of environmental quality improvements.

To indirectly estimate the WTP for such nonmarketed commodities as cleaner air or water, the **averting expenditure method (AEM)** uses spending on goods that are *substitutes* for environmental quality. The motivation for the approach is quite intuitive. Exposure to pollution causes damages that negatively affect an individual's utility. Consequently, people undertake ''averting'' action to reduce their risk of exposure by purchasing goods and services that improve their *personal* environmental quality. The elements of someone's personal environment include the air inside the home and a private supply of drinking water.[25] These purchases are effectively substitute goods for a cleaner overall environment. If the general environment is improved by some policy initiative, the individual can spend *less* on these substitute goods. It is precisely this decline in averting expenditures that gives an *indirect* estimate of the individual's WTP for the incremental benefits of the policy proposal. Notice that there are two critical assumptions implied by this approach. First, it assumes that a systematic relationship can be identified between the quality of the *overall* environment and that of an individual's *personal* environment. Secondly, it maintains that there are goods that act as *substitutes* for environmental quality.

Table 8.3 gives some common examples of what individuals do to reduce the effects of pollution on their personal environment. Notice that in each case the averting action involves an expenditure on a substitute good or service. For instance, faced with a contaminated drinking water supply, an individual might purchase bottled water or a water-filtering system. If a government policy improves the public drinking water supply, the individual can spend less on these substitute commodities. This reduction in spending identifies the value of the incremental benefits provided by the drinking water policy.

We model the AEM in Figure 8.5, where the relevant market is defined as *personal* environmental quality (X). The demand curve (d) is also the marginal benefit (MB) function, and each supply (s) relationship is modeled as a marginal cost (MC) curve.[26] The critical assumption is that each MC curve represents the averting expenditures on environmental quality substitutes to

---

[25]The reference to an individual's ''personal'' environment was first used by Bartik (1988) to describe the use of the AEM to value nonmarginal improvements in the environment.

[26]Since we are modeling *personal* environmental quality, the marginal benefits and costs accrue to a single individual. To avoid confusion, we use the simple labels of MB and MC so as not to infer a distinction between private and social decisions, which is irrelevant in this unique situation.

TABLE 8.3   Averting Actions to Reduce Risks of Exposure to Pollution

Pollution	Effect	Averting Action
Air pollution	Material soiling	Clean or repaint material surfaces; use protective covers; move to new location.
	Health problems	Install air purifiers and/or air conditioners; schedule more frequent visits for medical examinations; purchase medications to alleviate respiratory symptoms; move to new location.
Water pollution	Material soiling	Install water filtration system; purchase cleaning products and rust removers; move to new location.
	Health problems	Install water filtration system; purchase bottled water; move to new location.
Hazardous waste site	Aesthetic degradation	Install fencing or shrubbery; move to new location.
	Health problems	Test water supply for contamination; install air filtration or air conditioner; move to new location.
Noise pollution	Health problems	Install sound-deadening insulation; purchase medication to aid sleeping; move to new location.

Source: Adapted from Timothy J. Bartik, "Evaluating the Benefits of Non-marginal Reductions in Pollution Using Information on Defensive Expenditures," *Journal of Environmental Economics and Management* 15 (1988), pp. 111–126, Table 1.

---

achieve various levels of *personal* environmental quality (X) based upon a given level of *overall* environmental quality (E). As overall environmental quality improves, the individual spends less (or incurs lower costs) to achieve each level of personal environmental quality, and the MC curve moves downward to the right. In our diagram, MC_o represents the marginal cost of averting expenditures at the existing level of overall environmental quality, E_o. MC_1 is the marginal cost after quality increases to E_1 due to some policy initiative.

At the initial equilibrium point when overall environmental quality is E_o, the individual's personal level of environmental quality is X_o, where MB and MC_o intersect. At this point, total averting expenditures are shown as the area under the MC_o curve up to X_o, or area $0abX_o$. After the policy is implemented to improve overall environmental quality to E_1, the individual's marginal cost

FIGURE 8.5

*Measuring
incremental benefits
using the averting
expenditure method
(AEM): a behavioral
linkage approach*

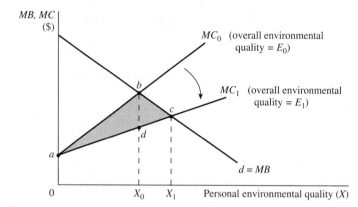

MC_0 represents the individual's averting expenditures at the *existing* level of overall environmental quality, E_0, and MC_1 is based on a higher level E_1 arising from a policy initiative. When overall environmental quality is E_0, personal environmental quality is X_0, and total averting expenditures are area $0abX_0$. After a policy increases overall environmental quality to E_1, personal environmental quality increases to X_1, and averting expenditures change to area $0acX_1$. To achieve X_1 in the absence of the policy change, the individual would be willing to spend an amount equal to the area under the original MC_0 curve up to X_1 and bounded by MB, or area $0abcX_1$. Thus, the individual's WTP for the incremental benefits of the policy is the difference between $0abcX_1$ and $0acX_1$, or the triangular area abc. An alternative benefit valuation could be based on the *original* level of personal environmental quality, X_0. In this case, the incremental benefits would be the difference between $0abX_0$ and $0adX_0$, or area abd.

curve shifts to MC_1. At the new equilibrium where MB and MC_1 intersect, personal environmental quality increases to X_1, and averting expenditures change to area $0acX_1$. Now, we can use this information to monetize the incremental benefits of the improvement in overall environmental quality from E_0 to E_1.

The key is to compare averting expenditure levels before and after the policy change *for the same level of personal environmental quality.* As we determined, postpolicy averting expenditures for X_1 are represented by area $0acX_1$. Let's compare this to what the individual would be willing to spend to achieve X_1 without the influence of the policy change. This is found by calculating the area under the original MC_0 curve up to X_1 and bounded by MB, or area $0abcX_1$. Thus, the individual's WTP for the incremental benefit associated with the policy initiative is the difference between the two areas, $0abcX_1$ and $0acX_1$, or the triangular area abc. An alternative valuation could be based on a constraint that holds personal environmental quality level at its original level, X_0. This approach might be preferred as the calculation is simpler, requiring information only on the two MC curves rather than both the MC curves and the MB curve. Under this scenario, the incremental benefits would be the difference between areas $0abX_0$ and $0adX_0$, or the area abd. This smaller area can be interpreted as a lower bound for the WTP valuation.[27] A summary of these calculations is as follows:

Personal environmental quality held constant at its postpolicy level, X_1:

Prepolicy averting expenditures   = Area $0abcX_1$
Postpolicy averting expenditures   = Area $0acX_1$

Incremental benefits of policy $= \dfrac{\text{Area}}{0abcX_1} - \dfrac{\text{Area}}{0acX_1} = \dfrac{\text{Area}}{abc}$

Personal environmental quality held constant at its prepolicy level, X_0:

Prepolicy averting expenditures   = Area $0abX_0$
Postpolicy averting expenditures   = Area $0adX_0$

Incremental benefits of policy $= \dfrac{\text{Area}}{0abX_0} - \dfrac{\text{Area}}{0adX_0} = \dfrac{\text{Area}}{abd}$

Assessing the AEM. One potential drawback of the AEM arises from the phenomenon known as *jointness of production.* This refers to the fact that some averting expenditures yield benefits beyond those associated with a cleaner environment. Consider, for example, the averting expenditures on an air-conditioning system. While the system does reduce certain health risks of air pollution, it also provides comfort. Hence, the savings in expenditures arising from an environmental policy initiative cannot be attributed solely to the incremental benefits of that policy.

Applications of the AEM. While there are some disadvantages to using the AEM, a number of studies have used this approach to value a statistical life. One is a research paper by Blomquist (1979) that focuses on the averting action of wearing seat belts in automobiles to reduce mortality risk. This study estimates the incremental benefit of a life saved as ranging between $380,000 and $1.4 million ($1986). Another study by Dardis (1980) conducts the same sort of analysis using expenditures on smoke detectors, and monetizes the value of a statistical life at $460,000 ($1986).[28] Notice how these estimates are lower than those derived using the CVM. One explanation is that the use of seat belts and smoke detectors is not a decision of *degree* but rather one of use versus nonuse. In such instances, the decision to engage in the activity is based upon whether the individual believes doing so is *worthwhile.* Consequently, individuals answer affirmatively as long as the marginal benefit exceeds marginal cost, causing the resulting estimate to be generally undervalued.[29]

---

[27]Bartik (1988).
[28]These estimates are reported in Fisher, Violette, and Chestnut (1989).
[29]Cropper and Oates (1992), pp. 713–14.

Travel Cost Method (TCM):
An Indirect Approach Using Complements

travel cost method (TCM)
Values environmental benefits by using the *complementary* relationship between the quality of a natural resource and its recreational use value.

An alternative approach to valuing environmental benefits is the **travel cost method (TCM),** which uses the *complementary* relationship between the quality of a natural resource and its recreational use value. Simple observation suggests that the demand for the recreational use of an environmental resource, such as a lake or a national forest, increases as its quality improves. This recreational demand function can be modeled using visitation rates[30] as the quantity variable and the cost of traveling to the recreational site as a proxy for price. Then, as this demand function shifts with a change in environmental quality, the resulting change in consumer surplus can be used to assess the associated incremental benefits.

We model the travel cost method in Figure 8.6, assuming recreational demand has been properly identified. Two demand curves for the recreational use of a lake are shown in the diagram labeled D_0 and D_1. D_0 is the relevant demand at some preexisting environmental quality level, E_0. D_1 is the new demand curve after the implementation of some public policy that improves the lake's quality to some level E_1. A price line is drawn at P_0 to represent the admission fee to use the lake. Before the policy is implemented, the number of visits to the site is V_0, where visitors enjoy a consumer surplus equal to area abP_0. After the policy is put into effect, the total number of visits increases to V_1, and consumer surplus increases to area cdP_0. The resulting *change* in consumer surplus, shown as area $acdb$ (i.e., area cdP_0 minus area abP_0), represents an estimate of the monetized value of the incremental benefits to visitors associated with improving the lake's quality.[31]

One technique used to identify a recreational demand curve is called the Clawson-Knetch method.[32] This method can best be explained as a series of steps that show how travel costs to a recreational site, visitation rates, and other socioeconomic data are used to estimate recreational demand.[33] While there are several variants of the Clawson and Knetch approach, its major elements are summarized in Table 8.4.

---

[30]Notice that a visitation rate, if defined as visitor days per capita, captures increased recreational activity either from more persons engaging in the activity or from increased use by a single individual.

[31]The use of a nonzero admission fee does not affect the result. Notice that if there were no entry fee to use the lake, the model would be the same except that consumer surplus would be the entire area under each demand curve. In such an instance, the resulting change in consumer surplus would extend to the horizontal axis.

[32]Clawson and Knetch (1966).

[33]For detail on this estimation procedure, the reader should consult the original source, Clawson and Knetch (1966). Others have made revisions to the original method. Smith and Desvousges (1986) provide an excellent review of this evolution along with an application of the approach.

FIGURE 8.6

Measuring incremental benefits using the travel cost method (TCM): a behavioral linkage approach

Two demand curves for the recreational use of a lake are D_0 and D_1. D_0 is the relevant demand at some preexisting environmental quality level, E_0. D_1 is the new demand curve after a public policy improves the lake's quality to E_1. The demand shift is based on the assumption that a complementary relationship exists between the recreational use of the lake and its environmental quality. The price line at P_0 represents the admission fee to use the lake. Before the policy is implemented, the number of visits to the site is V_0, and consumer surplus is area abP_0. After the policy is put into effect, the number of visits increases to V_1, and consumer surplus increases to area cdP_0. The *change* in consumer surplus, area $acdb$, represents the monetized incremental benefits to visitors of improving the lake's quality from E_0 to E_1.

Assessing the TCM.   A disadvantage of the TCM is that it is capable of estimating only user value and not existence value—an omission likely to create serious bias. Furthermore, the method focuses on recreational use, making it ineffective for estimating any incremental benefits that might accrue to commercial users of a resource. Finally, the TCM has been found to generate estimates that are biased downward if access to a site is deterred by congestion.[34]

Applications of the TCM.   Because of its limitations, the TCM is commonly used to estimate the value of improvements to water bodies used mainly for recreational activity. For example, a study by Mullen and Menz (1985) uses the TCM to value acid rain damages to the Adirondack, New York, lake region. Other studies have used the procedure to value the benefits of improving water quality from boatable to fishable conditions. The findings tend to vary considerably. Consider the following results from three independent analyses, all measured as WTP per person per day in 1982 dollars:

---

[34]Smith and Desvousges (1986), p. 220.

TABLE 8.4   **The Clawson-Knetch Method of Estimating Recreational Demand**

Steps to Identify Recreational Demand

1. Construct distance zones as concentric circles emanating from the recreation site.
2. From a sample of visitors at the recreation site, determine their zones of origin.
3. Calculate the visitation rates for each zone of origin.
4. Construct a travel cost measure that reflects the round-trip cost of travel from the zone of origin to the recreation site.
5. Collect relevant socioeconomic data, such as income and educational data for each distance zone.
6. Use regression analysis to determine the relationship between visitation rates and per unit travel costs (costs per visit), controlling for socioeconomic differences.
7. Locate one point on the demand curve by using the observed total number of visits to the site from all travel cost zones as the quantity variable and the existing entry fee for the price variable.
8. Find other points on the demand curve by using the estimated equation that relates visitation rates to per unit travel costs, assuming that individuals respond to a $1 increase in the entry fee in exactly the same way as they would to a $1 increase in per unit travel costs. That is, find the various visitation rates and total number of visits that correspond to a series of hypothetical increases in the entry fee added to existing travel costs. The series of entry fee–visitation rate pairs plots out the demand for recreational use of the resource.

Source: The step-by-step summary is adapted from Myrick A. Freeman III, ''A Survey of the Techniques for Measuring the Benefits of Water Quality Improvement,'' in Henry M. Peskin and Eugene P. Seskin, eds., *Cost Benefit Analysis and Water Pollution Policy* (Washington, D.C.: The Urban Institute, 1975), pp. 67–104, which in turn describes the method developed in Clawson and Knetch (1966).

Vaughan and Russell (1982):   Between $4.68 and $9.37;
Smith and Desvousges (1985):   Between $0.06 and $29.92; and
Smith, Desvousges, and McGivney (1983):   Between $1.04 and $2.15.[35]

Part of the reason for the inconsistent valuations is that TCM estimates tend to be sensitive to the site under study. While demographic variables across regions can be controlled for, there are other site differences, such as general aesthetics, access to major highways, substitute recreational opportunities, and weather conditions, that are difficult to quantify and control for. Consequently, it is unlikely that the TCM is capable of determining a *generalized* value of the incremental benefits of improved water quality.[36]

---

[35]These comparisons are discussed in Smith and Desvousges (1985).

[36]For more detail on the TCM, the reader should consult Cropper and Oates (1992) or Mitchell and Carson (1989), Chapter 3.

Hedonic Price Method (HPM):
An Indirect Approach Using Product Attributes

hedonic price method (HPM)
Uses the estimated hedonic or implicit price of an environmental attribute to assign value to policy-driven improvements in the environment.

The **hedonic price method (HPM)** is based on the theory that a good or service is valued for the attributes or characteristics it possesses.[37] This perception of value suggests that *implicit or hedonic prices* exist for individual product attributes, and these can be determined from the explicit price of the product. There is a fairly extensive literature of hedonic empirical studies. Many of these estimate the prices of product characteristics for some policy evaluation. In environmental economics, researchers use this technique to value the environmental attributes of certain commodities.

Housing markets have been a classic context for hedonic environmental pricing studies. Such analyses assume that the market price of a home is determined by the implicit value of its many characteristics, such as location, number of baths, lot size, public services, and the environmental quality of the community. Hence, changes in any of those characteristics are reflected in or capitalized into the market price of the property. The conventional model specifies the market price of a house, *P*, as a function of its attributes. A simplified version of such a model is:

$$P = f(X_1, X_2, \ldots X_n, E),$$

where each *X* variable represents some housing attribute, like lot size and number of baths, and the *E* variable signifies the level of environmental quality associated with the property.[38] As one of these characteristics increases in magnitude, *c.p.,* the price of the property, *P,* increases.[39] This *marginal* price is the implicit value of that attribute. Thus, as environmental quality improves, the resulting increase in property values can be used to estimate the associated incremental benefits.

Another common context for the HPM is wage analysis. Here, the method is used to explain wage differentials that might be associated with occupational risks, including those of environmental origin. Similar to hedonic studies of housing prices, hedonic wage (*w*) models generally are specified as:

$$w = g(Z_1, Z_2, \ldots Z_n, E).$$

The *Z* variables would include such attributes as the age, gender, education, and experience of the worker. The *E* variable would be some measure of occupational-specific environmental risk, such as the dangers faced by hazardous waste handlers or by engineers in a nuclear power plant. These workers are expected to receive a higher wage than those not so exposed to compensate

---

[37]Lancaster (1966).

[38]There may of course be a *set* of environmental variables, one for water quality, another for air quality, etc.

[39]This assumes that each attribute is specified as a favorable property characteristic.

them for the added risk exposure. This environmentally oriented wage differential is used to value the incremental benefits to workers of reducing occupational environmental risk.

The HPM uses a statistical procedure known as regression analysis to determine the implicit price of any environmental variable. In simple terms, the idea is to decompose an *explicit* price, [such as the price of a house (P) or the wage rate (w)], into its *implicit* price components, one of which is the price of environmental quality (E). Once the implicit price of E is determined, the demand for environmental quality can be estimated. This in turn can be used to measure changes in consumer surplus arising from policy-driven improvements in environmental quality.

Assessing the HPM.   The appeal of the HPM is that it is highly intuitive. It approaches the problem of monetizing incremental benefits in a logical way, directly using market prices. Its major disadvantage is that it requires a fairly complicated empirical model. Furthermore, the method calls for extensive data on product characteristics, which are often unavailable or incomplete. If an important product attribute is missing from the model, it will not be possible to determine the connection between a change in an explicit price and a change in environmental quality. The only way this link can be made with some measure of confidence is if all major attributes are specified and therefore held constant when conducting the empirical estimation.

Researchers attempt to satisfy these empirical requirements in various ways depending on the context of the model. As a result, findings across independent studies are not always consistent. So, while the theory of the HPM is intuitive, its application to practical investigations is not straightforward. Economists are continuing to search for better statistical techniques to improve the results.

Applications of the HPM.   Economists have used the HPM to estimate a variety of pollution control benefits. One application of this approach is in measuring how the siting of hazardous waste facilities affects the prices of nearby properties.[40] Hedonic wage differential studies have been used to estimate the value of a statistical life saved as a result of reducing occupational risk. For example, Thaler and Rosen (1976) estimate that society's WTP for saving one additional life is between $440,000 and $840,000 ($1986). A more recent finding is presented by Moore and Viscusi (1988), who estimate the value at approximately $5.4 million.[41] As discussed, the complex specification

---

[40]For a recent study that looks at the impact of hazardous waste sites on property values, see Kohlhase (1991). Examples of hedonic price models that attempt to value air quality include a study by Harrison and Rubinfeld (1978) and an analysis done by Freeman (1979). Freeman's paper also provides an excellent survey of the major issues surrounding the HPM.

[41]These results are reported in Fisher, Violette, and Chestnut (1989).

and data requirements of the HPM are partly responsible for the varying results across studies.

Of all the available benefit valuation techniques, there is no clear consensus about which of these is consistently superior. The fact that there are so many approaches speaks to the inherent difficulty of estimating environmental benefits *and* the recognition of how important this work is to policy evaluation. We next investigate how environmental costs are identified and measured where the valuation process is simpler and more direct.

Defining and Valuing Environmental Costs: Conceptual Issues

In the cost estimation process of risk management, the objective is to monetize the value of *all* economic resources allocated to reducing environmental risk. Unlike the benefit side of the analysis, the challenge here is not in assigning a monetary value to costs, since most are already expressed in money terms. Instead, the more critical issue is in identifying *all* the resources used to design, implement, and execute the policy prescription.

Few would debate that identifying environmental costs is a monumental undertaking. Think about the enormous amount of government spending needed to support the scientific research, the network of administrative agencies, and the labor force needed to put a major environmental policy initiative into action. Add to that the billions of dollars spent by private businesses on abatement equipment and labor to comply with environmental regulations. Identifying these expenses on such a massive scale is by itself a tremendous task. But there is another element of cost analysis that adds to the difficulty—the premise that *economic* costs, and not simply *accounting* costs, are to be determined.

explicit or monetary costs
Administrative, monitoring, and enforcement expenses paid by the public sector plus compliance costs incurred by all economic sectors.

implicit costs
The value of any nonmonetary effects arising from environmental policy that influence the well-being of society.

As discussed in Chapter 2, economic costs are a more accurate measure of resource utilization than are accounting costs, since they include both **explicit or monetary costs** and **implicit costs.** The **explicit costs** of implementing an environmental policy include all the administrative, monitoring, and enforcement expenses paid by the public sector as well as the compliance costs incurred by virtually all sectors of the economy. **Implicit costs** are the value of any associated nonmonetary impacts that negatively affect the well-being of society. These might include the value of diminished product variety arising from a ban on certain materials, the time costs of searching for substitutes, and the reduced convenience that control policies might impose. While implicit costs are arguably an important element of the analysis, identifying and measuring these in practice is another issue entirely. In fact, most analyses fail to fully capture these values, ignoring effects that represent real costs to society. The result? Many environmental cost assessments are seriously understated—a problem that has yet to be fully resolved.

Since these conceptual issues are so important, they are the focus of our initial discussion—a much needed preliminary step to addressing the procedural aspects of cost estimation. While the discussion will not resolve all the problems, it will illustrate the significance of the underlying issues and their implications for environmental risk management.

Defining Incremental Costs

incremental costs
The change in explicit and implicit costs arising from an environmental policy initiative.

Starting with the basics, we know that the relevant measure of costs must be defined in incremental terms, just as is the case for environmental benefits. In fact, the motivation is identical—the analyst must estimate the *increase* in costs associated with the *changes* in environmental quality brought about by policy. **Incremental costs** are calculated by first identifying the existing level of environmental expenditures, then estimating the costs after the policy is implemented, and finally finding the difference between the two. Technically, incremental costs include both explicit and implicit costs. However, since the latter are not readily identifiable, analysts often derive incremental cost values based solely on explicit or monetary expenditures.

Explicit Environmental Costs: Major Classifications

As part of the cost assessment process, analysts are interested in determining the *composition* of environmental control costs. In some analyses, the motivation may be that some component of costs, such as spending on water quality control or the abatement costs incurred by private industry, has particular relevance to a policy decision. More importantly, information about the composition of control costs gives policy-makers a clearer sense of how resources are being allocated to achieve environmental objectives—critical information for evaluating policy on the basis of allocative efficiency. Similarly, adjustments to correct for environmental inequities require knowledge about how the cost burden is distributed across sectors of the economy. Because of the diversity of objectives in cost assessment, there are different cost classifications used to obtain different kinds of information. An overview of the more relevant of these classifications follows.

Capital and Operating Costs. Explicit costs and their components are easier to identify than their benefit counterparts, since most of the resources used to implement pollution control policies are traded in private markets. Those associated with the use of economic resources—land, labor, and capital, are rents, wages, and interest, respectively. Since these resources are traded on the open market, expenditures are based on per unit market-determined input prices. However, expenditures on these inputs are not made simultaneously, and some are less controllable than others in the short run. Recognizing this, economists generally classify costs into two components: **fixed costs,** which are not controllable in the short run and do not depend on production

capital costs
Fixed expenditures
for plant, equipment,
construction in
progress, and the
costs of production
process changes
associated with
pollution abatement.

operating costs
Variable expenditures
incurred in the
operation and
maintenance of
pollution abatement
processes, such as
costs of labor,
materials, and fuel.

levels, and **variable costs,** which have the opposite characteristics. In the context of environmental policy implementation and compliance, the accounting equivalents of these are **capital costs** and **operating costs,** respectively. According to U.S. government guidelines provided by the Department of Commerce and used by the EPA, these costs classifications have very specific meanings. **Capital costs** are expenditures for plant and equipment (including both replacement and expansion), and construction in progress, as well as the costs of changes in production processes that reduce or eliminate pollution generation. **Operating costs** are those incurred in the operation and maintenance of pollution abatement processes, including spending for materials, equipment leasing, parts and supplies, direct labor, fuel and power, services provided by private contractors, and research and development.[42]

The distinction between these two categories is in the relationship between the level of costs and the quantity of pollution abatement. A **capital cost** is incurred regardless of the amount of pollution abated, analogous to the economic definition of fixed cost. Examples include the installed price of a scrubber system to control air pollution, construction costs of a wastewater facility, and the purchase of acreage to use as a landfill. Notice that these capital costs are incurred prior to making any of the investments operational and are independent of whether the capital is ever used to abate pollution. Conversely, **operating costs** are directly related to the quantity of pollution abatement, comparable to the economic definition of variable production costs. Examples include costs of labor and fuel to run an abatement facility.

Cost Classifications by Economic Sector.   Policy analysts are often concerned with how environmental costs are distributed across the various public and private sectors of the economy. For instance, the costs of policy revisions that strengthen monitoring and enforcement programs are going to shift a higher cost burden to the public sector, perhaps at all levels of government. Conversely, tighter abatement requirements will change the cost distribution toward private industry. To illustrate, consider the U.S. trend data for 1972 to 1990 classified by economic sector in Table 8.5. The expenditures are broken down by major function—abatement, regulation and monitoring, and research and development.

As the data indicate, the aggregate level of real spending on environmental issues has grown fairly steadily in the United States, up to $81.8 billion ($1987) in 1990. Furthermore, spending by each sector has also shown a similar growth pattern, so much so that the relative proportions of total costs borne

[42]U.S. EPA, Office of Policy, Planning, and Evaluation (December 1990), pp. 1-2, 1-3, in accordance with U.S. Department of Commerce, Bureau of the Census, *Government Finances,* various years and U.S. Department of Commerce, Bureau of Economic Analysis, ''Pollution Abatement and Control Expenditures,'' published periodically in *Survey of Current Business.*

TABLE 8.5   U.S. Pollution Abatement and Control Expenditures
by Sector, 1972–1990
(in billions of 1987 dollars)

| | Pollution Abatement | | | | | Regulation and Monitoring | | Research and Development | | | |
| | Private | | Government | | | | | | | | |
Year	Personal	Business	Federal	State	Other	Federal	State	Private	Federal	State	Total
1972	3.45	30.53	0.40	3.67	5.03	0.48	0.48	1.44	0.55	0.27	46.3
1973	4.54	32.14	0.54	3.69	5.34	0.63	0.56	1.49	0.68	0.17	49.8
1974	4.95	32.63	0.69	3.62	6.81	0.74	0.60	1.42	0.78	0.09	52.3
1975	6.17	33.11	0.94	3.74	9.72	0.74	0.61	1.28	0.93	0.10	57.3
1976	6.73	34.88	0.95	3.71	10.33	0.74	0.67	1.39	1.02	0.09	60.5
1977	7.15	37.10	0.92	3.73	8.90	0.74	0.78	1.56	1.04	0.10	62.0
1978	7.41	38.15	0.81	3.89	10.03	0.99	0.80	1.69	0.99	0.10	64.9
1979	7.16	40.22	0.84	3.93	10.27	0.91	0.72	1.76	0.87	0.12	66.8
1980	7.31	40.15	0.68	4.05	10.82	1.11	0.76	1.50	0.82	0.10	67.3
1981	8.49	40.47	0.63	3.98	8.98	1.04	0.77	1.33	0.81	0.04	66.5
1982	8.52	37.79	0.65	4.07	8.43	0.98	0.73	1.32	0.70	0.04	63.2
1983	10.02	38.04	0.91	4.20	7.70	0.92	0.69	1.82	0.71	0.04	65.1
1984	10.97	41.18	1.05	4.38	8.42	0.81	0.69	1.81	0.63	0.04	70.0
1985	11.78	42.41	1.30	4.65	8.67	0.61	0.75	1.86	0.62	0.02	72.7
1986	12.69	43.80	1.40	4.99	9.29	0.74	0.85	1.93	0.67	0.03	76.4
1987	10.88	44.50	1.24	5.36	10.54	0.70	0.82	1.99	0.63	0.03	76.7
1988	11.83	45.96	1.34	5.88	9.78	0.81	0.83	1.99	0.64	0.03	79.1
1989	10.15	47.76	1.27	6.50	10.04	0.78	0.88	1.99	0.72	0.03	80.1
1990	8.67	49.69	1.23	6.99	10.89	0.77	0.87	2.01	0.68	0.04	81.8

Notes:
Some totals may not agree due to independent rounding.
All of personal spending is used to purchase and operate motor vehicle emission abatement devices.
State government spending includes expenditures by local authorities.
Other government spending refers to government enterprise fixed capital for publicly owned electric utilities and public sewer systems.
Source: G. L. Rutledge and M. L. Leonard, "Pollution Abatement and Control Expenditures, 1972–90," *Survey of Current Business* (Washington, D.C.: Department of Commerce, Bureau of Economic Analysis, June 1992), Table 9, pp. 35–38.

by each have remained fairly constant. However, the cost burden is not at all shared equally across the economy. Private business spending has represented about 60 to 65 percent of the total, public sector spending has accounted for about 20 to 25 percent of the total, with the personal private sector responsible for the remainder.

These data also show that for all economic sectors, the greatest proportion of spending is allocated to pollution abatement, although private business absorbs the highest absolute dollar amount. To see this distribution more clearly, look at Table 8.6, which gives a complete breakdown of the 1990 cost data. Notice that aggregate spending on abatement was 94.7 percent of the total,

---

TABLE 8.6   Decomposition of U.S. Pollution Abatement and Control Expenditures by Sector for 1990

	Constant (1987) Dollars in Billions (percentages given in parentheses)	
	Allocation by Sector	*Subtotal by Category*
Pollution Abatement		
Personal consumption	8.67 (10.6%)	
Durable goods 8.47		
Nondurable goods 0.20		
Business	49.69 (60.7%)	
Capital 16.45		
Operating 33.24		
Government	19.11 (23.3%)	
Federal 1.23		
State/local 6.99		
Other 10.89		
Subtotal pollution abatement		77.47 (94.7%)
Regulation and Monitoring		
Government	1.64 (2.0%)	
Federal 0.77		
State and local 0.87		
Subtotal regulation and monitoring		1.64 (2.0%)
Research and Development		
Private	2.01 (2.5%)	
Government	0.72 (1.0%)	
Federal 0.68		
State and local 0.04		
Subtotal research and development		2.73 (3.3%)
Grand total		81.84 (100%)

Notes:
Some totals may not agree due to independent rounding.
All of personal spending is used to purchase and operate motor vehicle emission abatement devices.
State government spending includes expenditures by local authorities.
Other government spending refers to government enterprise fixed capital for publicly owned electric utilities and public sewer systems.
Source: G. L. Rutledge and M. L. Leonard, "Pollution Abatement and Control Expenditures, 1972–90," *Survey of Current Business* (Washington, D.C.: Department of Commerce, Bureau of Economic Analysis, June 1992), Table 9, p. 38.

---

with most of it borne by the private business sector, primarily for operating expenses. In fact, business operating expenses for abatement were more than twice the level of capital outlays. For the personal private sector, all of the spending is for the purchase and operation of abatement equipment for motor vehicles. Notice that the bulk of the spending was on durable goods at $8.47 billion. Application 8.4 takes a closer look at how this category of spending has been affected by tougher regulations on emissions from motor vehicles.

Application 8.4

Abatement Control Costs on Motor Vehicles

Virtually all cars on the road today are equipped with some type of pollution abatement equipment. In response to tougher federal air quality legislation, automobile manufacturers have shifted from using so-called "low-tech" equipment, such as engine timing devices, to more sophisticated "high-tech" equipment, like catalytic converters and computerized emission control systems. As this technological transition has evolved, analysts have been interested in examining how this trend has affected personal private spending on abatement control and how it has altered the composition of that spending. Such information is helpful in analyzing current environmental policy and in pre-

dicting the cost implications of proposed legislative initiatives.

To investigate the incremental costs of motor vehicle abatement policies, extensive data must be collected and analyzed. Using a variety of sources, analysts present such data in the *Survey of Current Business*. The table below presents some of the cost data given in this document, specifically the expenditures for motor vehicle emission abatement devices by the personal private sector. Durable goods expenditures refer to capital costs, and nondurable goods expenditures refer to operating and maintenance costs.

Personal Expenditures on Air Pollution Abatement and Control 1972–1990 (millions of 1987 dollars)

Year	Durable Goods	Nondurable Goods	Total Personal Consumption
1972	994	2,455	3,449
1973	1,425	3,117	4,541
1974	1,395	3,553	4,948
1975	2,528	3,637	6,165
1976	3,199	3,526	6,725
1977	3,606	3,541	7,147
1978	3,804	3,608	7,412
1979	3,999	3,157	7,156
1980	4,620	2,691	7,311
1981	5,913	2,581	8,494
1982	5,854	2,664	8,518
1983	7,119	2,898	10,016
1984	8,119	2,848	10,967
1985	8,832	2,948	11,780
1986	9,604	3,081	12,685
1987	8,642	2,233	10,875
1988	9,832	1,999	11,831
1989	9,213	934	10,147
1990	8,469	197	8,665

Application 8.4 (concluded)

These data show how total expenditures have changed over time with strengthening U.S. air quality policy initiatives. Notice, for example, that these expenditures grew by about 151 percent between 1972 and 1990 and reached a high in 1986 of $12.7 billion. In 1990, real expenditures were approximately $8.7 billion, reflecting a decline of 32 percent from the peak 1986 level. Much of this decline is attributed to a fall in unit sales of automobiles over the period.

While changes in total expenditures are important, analysts are also interested in examining how the trend toward more capital-intensive regulations influenced the *composition* of these costs. In general, the changes in durable goods expenditures over time reflect the introduction of major technological advances in automobile pollution abatement equipment. For example, spending on catalytic converters began with the 1975 model year, which explains the increase in durable goods spending from $1,395 million in 1974 to $2,528 million in 1975. Similarly, rising spending throughout most of the 1980s reflects the costs of more sophisticated high-tech capital equipment introduced during that period. In sum, changes in durable goods expenditures are coincident with the more demanding capital-intensive changes called for in U.S. clean air regulations.

The nondurable goods component of expenditures shows relatively little movement over much of the 1972 to 1990 period. Yet there were major shifts taking place in the *composition* of these operating costs. Researchers have identified three major types of nondurable goods expenditures: fuel consumption penalties, maintenance costs, and fuel price penalties. Fuel consumption penalties refer to the costs of increased fuel usage associated with the installation of abatement control equipment. Maintenance costs are the additional upkeep expenses for vehicles so equipped. Finally, fuel price penalties reflect the difference in the per gallon price between leaded and unleaded gasoline. As technology changed, there was a transformation in the relative size of these various types of operating costs—a change that is not apparent in the aggregate operating cost data. In the pre-1975 model years, most of the operating expenses were attributable to fuel consumption penalties and increased maintenance costs. In later-model cars, fuel price penalties became the more important component of nondurable expenditures. Hence, over time, there was a distinct shift in the composition of pollution abatement operating costs—a direct result of technological advance.

While catalytic converters and computer controls have fairly high purchase costs, these devices tend to lower operating costs. They improve fuel economy, decreasing the fuel consumption penalty, and extend the life of vehicles' exhaust systems, reducing maintenance costs. This explains the dominance of fuel price penalties in modern-day nondurable abatement costs. However, since the 1980s, this component of operating costs also has begun to show signs of decline. Again, the primary explanation is technology. Improvements in the production of nonlead octane boosters as well as scale economies have caused a reduction in the price differential between leaded and unleaded fuel.

Such an in-depth analysis of pollution abatement costs is precisely what is required in an assessment of the incremental costs of environmental policy. Through such data studies, policy-makers can more accurately evaluate existing policy provisions and improve the reliability of cost estimates for proposed policy mandates.

Source: G. L. Rutledge and M. L. Leonard, "Pollution Abatement and Control Expenditures, 1972–1990," *Survey of Current Business* (Washington, D.C.: Department of Commerce, Bureau of Economic Analysis, June 1992), pp. 26–38.

TABLE 8.7   **U.S. Pollution Abatement and Control Expenditures Disaggregated by Environmental Media for 1981–1990**
(billions of 1987 dollars)

Year	Air	Water	Solid Waste
1981	28.5	25.2	13.4
1982	27.2	24.2	12.1
1983	28.5	24.7	12.0
1984	31.0	26.2	13.2
1985	32.0	27.4	13.7
1986	33.3	28.7	14.8
1987	30.7	30.6	15.9
1988	31.9	30.1	17.9
1989	29.2	31.6	19.8
1990	27.3	34.4	20.9

Source: G. L. Rutledge and M. L. Leonard, "Pollution Abatement and Control Expenditures, 1972–90," *Survey of Current Business* (Washington, D.C.: Department of Commerce, Bureau of Economic Analysis, June 1992), Table 9, pp. 35–38.

Cost Classifications by Environmental Media.   Another important policy consideration is the distribution of expenditures by environmental media, that is, air, water, and solid waste. Table 8.7 shows U.S. pollution abatement and control expenditures for 1981 through 1990 disaggregated by environmental media. Such information is useful for policy-makers to examine how resources are allocated across environmental problems at any point in time and how this allocation changes from period to period. Notice, for example, that a rough estimate of the incremental costs of clean water regulations during the 1989 to 1990 period is $2.8 billion ($1987). Of course, a more accurate assessment would require a more complex series of calculations. For one thing, analysts are usually interested in assessing the costs of a policy once it has been fully implemented. So, the appropriate analysis would extend over a period of years, and annual expenditure data would have to be adjusted to account for overlap with other regulations. We will pursue the cost implications of major U.S. policies for water, air, and solid waste in upcoming chapters.

Implicit Environmental Costs

Although the explicit costs of pollution abatement presented thus far appear to be comprehensive, it turns out that these data convey only part of the story. Ideally, the economist wants to determine the *social costs* of environmental policy, which include not only the **explicit** expenditures on compliance, monitoring, and enforcing, but also the **implicit or nonmonetary costs** of those activities.

    In theory, the social costs of any policy initiative are the expenditures needed to compensate society for the resources used so that its utility level is maintained. This compensation would have to account for all the price, output, and income effects that arise from a given regulation.[43] One example is the increased price of automobiles caused by the cost of abatement equipment like catalytic converters. Another is the higher price of household products arising from the use of more recyclable packaging and the costs of more highly regulated labeling. There are also real income changes, such as those caused by higher taxes needed to support regulatory expenses. Beyond these effects are **implicit or nonmonetary costs,** which also have to be identified and monetized. An example of an implicit cost is the inconvenience of using public transportation or car pools in response to new urban air quality policies.

To capture these effects and obtain a comprehensive measure of environmental social costs, the analyst would have to measure changes in social welfare, perhaps by estimating changes in consumer and producer surplus. This is a complex undertaking, but there is some evidence that doing so improves the accuracy of cost assessments. A study conducted by Hazilla and Kopp (1990) estimates the social costs of U.S. air and water quality control policies. According to this study, there is a significant divergence between social costs and the explicit cost estimates typically used in practice. In fact, the researchers recommend that policy-makers adjust their procedures to consider more of a general equilibrium approach to cost analysis than is currently in place.[44] However, it appears that available methods to execute this more comprehensive cost assessment are too cumbersome and unreliable to be employed as a regular practice. Hence, at least for the present, cost analysis continues to be based solely upon explicit expenditures, although it is generally acknowledged that such an approach understates the true social costs.

While this compromise might appear to imply that cost assessment is a straightforward exercise, such an inference would be naive. Even setting aside the dilemma of measuring implicit costs, estimating environmental expenditures is neither an exact science nor a simple task. In fact, while there are established procedures for estimating these values, none are without flaws and some degree of difficulty.

Estimation Methods for Measuring Explicit Costs

Two major approaches are used by economists to estimate incremental environmental costs. These are known as the **engineering approach** and the **survey approach.** The **engineering approach** estimates abatement expenditures based on the least-cost available technology needed to achieve some given level of pollution abatement. The **survey approach** derives estimated abatement expenditures directly from polluting sources.

---

[43]Recall from earlier chapters that one of these effects might be the forgone profits caused by firms' reducing production levels to lower pollution releases.

[44]We will have more to say about these research findings in upcoming chapters.

While each of these is quite distinct, a common practice is to use a combination approach that draws from both. First, the survey approach is used to solicit information about available technologies and existing market conditions. Then, the engineering approach is employed to estimate dollar values based on the collected data. What follows is a brief discussion of each approach with some mention of their respective shortcomings.

The Engineering Approach

engineering approach
Estimates abatement expenditures based on the least-cost available technology needed to achieve a given level of pollution abatement.

The **engineering approach** to expenditure estimation relies upon the knowledge base of experts in abatement technology. Based on the state of the art in pollution abatement, engineers and scientists are called upon to identify combinations of equipment, labor, and materials needed by polluting sources to comply with a policy mandate. Then, capital and operating costs for all feasible abatement designs are estimated. Finally, the analyst selects the least-cost model from among these technology-based designs and uses the result to estimate the *aggregate* incremental cost for all affected polluting sources.

While theoretically reasonable, the engineering approach to cost estimation is not without problems. For one thing, the procedure is difficult to implement for *proposed* environmental controls, since there is uncertainty about price movements, availability of raw materials, and energy costs in future time periods. Even absent these forecasting problems, there are inherent difficulties with any aggregation procedure of this magnitude. Most comprehensive environmental policy initiatives affect a wide range of industries and public facilities. To account for these, the engineering approach would have to be customized to suit each type of production setting. If ignored, the results would likely suffer from the averaging process. Even if industry-specific values were derived, the heterogeneity of firms and the unique market conditions that each faces could not be captured in such a generalized estimate. Finally, because the approach is based on the least-cost abatement design, it explicitly assumes that all firms operate as cost-effective or technically efficient entities—an assumption that likely understates the true costs incurred.

The Survey Approach

survey approach
Polls a sample of firms and public facilities to obtain estimated abatement expenditures.

In contrast to the engineering approach, the **survey approach** relies upon polluting sources instead of external experts to provide data for the estimation. Similar to the contingent valuation method for estimating benefits, the survey approach polls a sample of firms and public facilities to inquire about existing or projected environmental expenditures. To illustrate the general usage of this approach, Table 8.8 lists the surveys used to gather U.S. cost data in 1990 (some of which we used in earlier tables). Also given are the various government sources responsible for administering each survey. Approximately 63

TABLE 8.8   Survey Approach to Pollution Abatement and Control Expenditures for 1990

Title of Survey	Source	Proportion of Cost Data Determined by the Survey
Pollution Abatement Costs and Expenditure (MA-200)	Bureau of Census	23
Government Finances*	Bureau of Census	19
Value of New Construction Put in Place	Bureau of Census	12
Federal Funding for Pollution Control	Bureau of Economic Analysis	4
Structures and Equipment Survey	Bureau of Census	2
Steam-Electric Plant Operation and Design	Department of Energy	3

Note:
*This line item is not the title of one particular survey. Rather, several sources make up the survey of government finance data. For example, the Bureau of Economic Analysis gathers information from Energy Information Agency reports and the EPA.

Source: Drawn from G. L. Rutledge and M. L. Leonard, "Pollution Abatement and Control Expenditures, 1972–90," *Survey of Current Business* (Washington, D.C.: Department of Commerce, Bureau of Economic Analysis, June 1992), Table 8, p. 33.

percent of the information used for 1990 cost reporting was obtained from some type of survey. Notice that these surveys target both private and public sector costs of abatement and control.[45]

On the plus side, the survey method is a more direct means to obtain abatement cost information than the engineering approach. However, there are also disadvantages. First, it implicitly assumes that polluting sources are sufficiently well-informed to provide reasonable estimates. Second, there is an inherent tendency for bias. Polluting sources have an incentive to offer inflated values to government officials, since they recognize that higher costs will increase the probability that the proposed regulation will be rejected.

Just as in benefit assessment, no cost estimation method is perfect. In fact, this realization is what has motivated researchers to use a combination of the engineering and survey methods. The objective is to attempt to have the best of both worlds and minimize potential bias. Given the growing emphasis on benefits and costs in environmental policy decisions, efforts are ongoing to improve the accuracy of environmental cost estimation.

[45]For the remaining 37 percent of the needed cost information, the Bureau of Economic Analysis uses various *indirect* costing methods, most of which also use some type of survey information. See Rutledge and Leonard (1992), pp. 32–34.

Conclusions

As a risk management strategy, benefit-cost analysis can be used to set policy objectives and to select the "best available" control instrument to achieve those objectives. However, its success in guiding these important decisions hinges on the accuracy of benefit and cost measurements. To that end, economists are working to derive more reliable estimates of the incremental benefits and costs linked to environmental policy initiatives. This ongoing search for better results has led to the development of a variety of estimation methods. The diversity of approaches reflects both the complexity of the task and a recognition of its importance in public policy decision-making.

In this chapter, we have explored some common estimation approaches used in environmental economics. For each method, we examined the underlying theory and the mechanical procedure, assessed the effectiveness of the approach, and surveyed a selection of empirical results. From a general perspective, our investigation uncovered some of the difficulties inherent in any social benefit or cost estimation—difficulties that often are magnified in an environmental context. On the benefit side, the primary challenge is in monetizing gains that involve many intangibles not traded in the marketplace. Hence, economists have had to devise methods to quantify these intangibles using something other than explicit prices. On the cost side, the major obstacle is finding a way to capture *implicit* costs. As economists search for a practical solution to this problem, they also look for ways to improve their estimates of explicit costs.

On balance, research efforts in measuring social benefits and costs have been fruitful. Progress has been made in fine-tuning estimation procedures, in recognizing which methods are most useful for which contexts, and in interpreting the results. Although no one expects to achieve perfection, researchers continue to seek improvements in benefit-cost assessment and measurement. The motivation is simple. Policy-makers are having to make important decisions based on the results of this research. In the next chapter, we will explain precisely how these decisions are influenced by benefit and cost estimates when they are systematically considered in a formal benefit-cost analysis.

Summary

- To assess the incremental benefits attributable to environmental policy, policy-makers must determine how health, ecological, and property damages *change* as a result of that policy initiative.
- Within the broad category of incremental benefits are two types of damage-reducing effects, primary and secondary environmental benefits. A primary environmental benefit arises as a *direct* consequence of implementing environmental policy, while a secondary environmental benefit is an *indirect* gain arising either from the primary benefits or some demand-induced effect.

- Since there is no explicit market for environmental quality, a benefit valuation cannot be obtained from observing market-determined prices. Instead, inferences must be made about *how* society derives value or utility from the good. It is generally recognized that society derives utility from environmental quality based on its user value and its existence value. User value refers to the benefit received from physical utilization or access to an environmental resource. Existence value is the benefit received from the continuance of the resource based on motives of vicarious consumption and stewardship.

- There are two major types of benefit measurement techniques: the physical linkage approach and the behavioral linkage approach. The physical linkage approach measures incremental benefits based on the assumption that a technical relationship exists between the environmental resource and the user of that resource. The behavioral linkage approach uses observations of consumer behavior in actual markets or responses to inquiries about hypothetical markets to measure incremental benefits.

- The damage function method is based on a technical model between levels of some contaminant and damages due to exposure to that contaminant. Once the function is specified, nonmonetary incremental benefits can be estimated as the reduction in damages achieved from any policy-induced decline in the contaminant.

- Using the political referendum method, analysts monitor voters' reactions to a *series* of proposals that convey how *changes* in environmental quality are valued.

- The contingent valuation method (CVM) is a survey approach that uses direct inquiry of individuals to determine their willingness to pay (WTP) for some environmental improvement based on hypothetical market conditions.

- The averting expenditure method (AEM) uses expenditures on goods that are substitutes for environmental quality to indirectly determine the WTP for a cleaner environment. The underlying premise is that spending on these substitutes will decline if policy improves overall environmental quality. This decline in spending acts as an indirect estimate of the incremental benefits associated with that policy.

- The travel cost method (TCM) relies on identifying the demand for the recreational use of an environmental resource, which is a complementary good to environmental quality. As environmental quality is improved, recreational demand will increase. Thus, the associated incremental benefits to visitors can be estimated as the resulting change in consumer surplus.

- The hedonic price method (HPM) is based on the theory that a good or service is valued for the attributes it possesses. This perception of value suggests that implicit or hedonic prices exist for individual product attributes, including those related to environmental quality. Economists can empirically estimate the implicit price of an environmental quality characteristic and use this result to identify demand for that attribute. In so doing, changes in consumer surplus associated with environmental improvements can be measured.

- Environmental cost analysis is concerned with incremental costs, that is, the change in explicit and implicit costs to society incurred as a result of government policy. Since most analyses fail to capture implicit costs, their assessments of incremental costs may be seriously understated.

- Because of the diversity of objectives in environmental cost assessment, there are different cost classifications used to obtain different kinds of information. One classification distinguishes capital costs from operating costs. Capital costs are expenditures for plant and equipment used to reduce or eliminate pollution generation. Operating costs are those incurred in the operation and maintenance of pollution abatement processes. Costs are also classified by economic sector and by environmental media.

- Two approaches used by economists to estimate incremental environmental costs are the engineering approach and the survey approach. The engineering approach estimates abatement expenditures based on the least-cost available technology needed to achieve a given level of abatement. The survey approach requests estimated abatement expenditures directly from polluting sources. In practice, a combination of both approaches is often used.

Key Concepts

incremental benefits	damage function method
primary environmental benefits	political referendum method
secondary environmental benefits	contingent valuation method (CVM)
willingness to pay (WTP)	averting expenditure method (AEM)
user value	travel cost method (TCM)
direct user value	hedonic price method (HPM)
indirect user value	explicit or monetary costs
existence value	implicit costs
vicarious consumption	incremental costs
stewardship	capital or fixed costs
physical linkage approach	operating or variable costs
behavioral linkage approach	engineering approach
direct methods	survey approach
indirect methods	

Review Questions

1. Is it possible for an *individual's* valuation of an environmental commodity to include both user and existence value? Explain briefly.

2. Contrast the averting expenditure method with the travel cost method and discuss the relative strengths and weaknesses of each.

3. Refer back to Application 8.3 and the estimated changes in consumer and producer surplus reported by the NAPAP for various ozone policies. Graphically model the result of a 25 percent *increase* in tropospheric ozone to *qualitatively* show the distribution of benefits reported by the NAPAP. (Note: Do not attempt to arrive at the numerical values for the changes in surplus values. Show only how the consumer, producer, and total surpluses *change* in accordance with the reported findings.)

4. One of the strengths of the contingent valuation method is its ability to capture existence value. How can the researcher take advantage of this, yet avoid some of the biases associated with such a survey-based approach?

5. *a.* Suppose you are part of a research team evaluating a proposal to clean up a hazardous waste site. You are in charge of assessing the incremental benefits of the proposal. Which method would you choose to derive the benefit estimation? Explain briefly.

   b. Based on your selection, outline your research plan for this specific estimation problem. Be sure to identify the following in your outline: a general description of your model, the relevant market for your model, the primary variables of interest; the data requirements; and any potential bias in your results.

6. Consider a policy proposal to impose more stringent controls on automobile tailpipe exhausts. Distinguish between the explicit and implicit costs of this proposal and support your discussion with several specific examples of each.

7. Of the two approaches to cost estimation, which in your view likely produces the most reliable estimates? Explain.

Additional Readings

Abdalla, Charles W., Brian Roach, and Donald J. Epp. ''Valuing Environmental Quality Changes Using Averting Expenditures: An Application to Groundwater Contamination.'' *Land Economics* 68, no. 2 (May 1992), pp. 163–69.

Bockstael, Nancy E., Michael W. Hanemann, and Catherine L. Kling. ''Estimating the Value of Water Quality Improvements in a Recreational Demand Framework.'' *Water Resources Research* 23, no. 5 (May 1987), pp. 951–60.

Brookshire, D. S., M. A. Thayer, W. D. Schulze, and R. C. d'Arge. ''Valuing Public Goods: A Comparison of Survey and Hedonic Approaches.'' *American Economic Review* 72 (1982), pp. 165–76.

Clawson, Marion. *Methods for Measuring the Demand for and Value of Outdoor Recreation.* Washington, D.C.: Resources for the Future, 1959.

Kneese, Allen V. *Measuring the Benefits of Clean Air and Water.* Washington, D.C.: Resources for the Future, 1984.

Mendelsohn, Robert. ''Modeling the Demand for Outdoor Recreation.'' *Water Resources Research* 23, no. 5 (May 1987), pp. 961–67.

Mjelde, James, Richard M. Adams, Bruce L. Dixon, and Philip Garcia. ''Using Farmers' Actions to Measure Crop Loss Due to Air Pollution.'' *Journal of Air Pollution Control Association* 34, no. 4 (April 1984), pp. 360–64.

Smith, V. Kerry. ''Can We Measure the Economic Value of Environmental Amenities?'' *Southern Economic Journal* 56, no. 4 (April 1990), pp. 865–78.

Smith, V. Kerry and William H. Desvousges. ''Averting Behavior: Does it Exist?'' *Economics Letters* 20, no. 3 (1986), pp. 291–96.

BENEFIT-COST ANALYSIS IN ENVIRONMENTAL DECISION-MAKING

Should the national limit on sulfur dioxide emissions be tightened? Would society be better off if a tradeable permit system were used instead of technology-based standards to control water pollution? These are the kinds of questions dealt with by environmental decision-makers. Analytical tools like benefit-cost analysis can help them find answers. Benefit-cost analysis begins with identifying and monetizing environmental benefits and costs—the subject of the previous chapter. From this point, these preliminary estimates must be adjusted and then systematically compared to arrive at a decision. These critical steps that link benefit and cost estimates to a decision rule complete the strategic process of benefit-cost analysis.

Adjustments to estimated values are necessary because incremental costs and benefits from a given policy initiative are not realized immediately. Instead, they accrue to society over a period of years. Think about the implementation of major policy initiatives like the Clean Air Act or the Superfund Amendments. Such legislation takes years to put into effect. While some policy costs are incurred right away, others accrue at various points in time in the future. Similarly, the benefits are not realized in a single period. It takes time before the gains from an environmental policy are achieved. In the first place, there is a lag between risk reduction and realized improvements in human health and welfare. Furthermore, even if the effects were immediate, government-mandated reductions in contamination typically are phased in over a period of years.

How do these time differences affect the result? There are two considerations. One is that costs and benefits realized in some future period are not valued as highly as those achieved immediately. Thus, future costs and benefits have to be adjusted downward to be comparable to those incurred in the present. A second adjustment is needed to account for expected changes in the price level over time. For example, the value of costs and benefits measured in today's dollars will be much higher in future dollars during periods of inflation. Without adjusting for these time-oriented differences, the benefit-cost analysis would yield biased results, and any policy decision based upon them would be misguided.

Once benefit and cost estimates are adjusted for time differences, they then must be compared to one another. But on what basis is the comparison made? Is it sufficient for the benefits to outweigh the costs, or must the numerical difference between the two be at a particular level? What if the law precludes the analysis by predetermining the benefit level to be achieved? The answers to these questions are found in understanding the decision rules that guide benefit-cost analysis. Of particular interest are the implications of those rules for meeting economic criteria—an important issue in policy evaluation.

The growing prominence of benefit-cost analysis as a risk management strategy is an important reason for understanding how it is undertaken, what it implies from an economic perspective, and how it has come to be required by the U.S. government in major policy decisions. To that end, this chapter presents and analyzes these aspects of benefit-cost analysis. We begin by giving a thorough exposition of the procedures used to adjust preliminary benefit and cost estimates for time differences. Next, we explore the policy evaluation process and the decision rules used in practice to guide that process. Once done, we consider how the role of benefit-cost analysis in U.S. policy-making has evolved into a major tool for guiding legislative decisions. We conclude with an inside look at how benefit-cost analysis was used in the U.S. decision to tighten the lead standard for gasoline.

Adjusting for the Time Dimension of Environmental Benefits and Costs

Critical to any environmental benefit-cost analysis is to reconcile the timing of benefits and costs. First, benefits and costs do not necessarily accrue at the same time. Furthermore, even if they did, they are not realized immediately. Although an environmental policy evaluation is made in the current period, the effects of that policy typically extend well into the future. Consequently, decision-makers must be forward thinking in their evaluation of a policy proposal and must make projections about its future implications. To support these forecasts, benefit and cost estimates must be adjusted to account for the fact that the value of a dollar is not constant over time. Two types of time-oriented modifications are necessary. One is **present value determination,** which accounts for the opportunity cost of money. The second is **inflation correction,** to adjust for changes in the general price level. We examine each of these procedures in turn.

Present Value Determination

Opportunity cost is one of the most pervasive concepts in economic thinking. It means that the highest-valued alternative of any decision represents the full cost of that decision, whether it arises in production, consumption, or even purely financial transactions. To understand the concept in this latter context, consider the following simple scenario. Assume a friend asks to borrow $200 today, promising to pay back the loan one year from today. What amount of money would the payback have to be to maintain your well-being or utility level? (To keep things simple, assume there is no inflation.) Economically, the answer depends upon the opportunity cost of money—its highest valued alternative use.[1] If the $200 could be invested to yield a 5 percent return, then the opportunity cost of the loan is $10. Therefore, the appropriate payback should be $210, or [$200 + ($200 × 0.05)]. Technically, this calculation represents the conversion of the loan value in the *present period* into its value in the *future period.* Mathematically, the conversion for a one-year period is achieved using the following simple formula:

$$FV = PV + (r \cdot PV) = PV\,(1 + r),$$

where:

$$FV = \text{Future value}$$
$$PV = \text{Present value}$$
$$\text{and } r = \text{Rate of return.}$$

This equation shows that the future value (FV) of a dollar is equal to its present value (PV) plus the opportunity cost of not using the dollar in the present period ($r \cdot PV$). If the future valuation is to account for more than one time period (t), the above formula becomes:

$$FV = PV\,(1 + r)^t,$$

where:

$$t = 0, 1, 2, \ldots \; T \text{ is the number of periods.}$$

present value determination
A procedure that discounts a future value (*FV*) into its present value (*PV*) by accounting for the opportunity cost of money.

Inverting the problem, we can argue that $210 received one year from now is equivalent to having $200 today, or [$210/(1 + 0.05)]. This conversion procedure is called **present value determination** because it involves **discounting** a future value (FV) into its present value (PV). Mathematically, the calculation is performed using a rearrangement of the formula given above, as follows:

$$PV = FV[1/(1 + r)]$$

---

[1] Implicitly, individual preferences about present versus future consumption are revealed by the answer.

discount factor
The term,
$1/(1 + r)^t$, where r is
called the discount
rate and t is the
number of periods.

In this form of the equation, r is called the **discount rate,** and the term $1/(1 + r)$ is called the **discount factor.** If the discounting involves more than one time period (t), the formula is written as:

$$PV = FV[1/(1 + r)^t],$$

where:

$[1/(1 + r)^t]$ is the discount factor.

Discounting is the procedure economists use to adjust the value of environmental benefits and costs accruing in the future.

Notice that the discount rate (r) is the one variable element in present value determination. As this rate is elevated, the PV is decreased, and of course the converse is true. Since the magnitude of the discount rate affects the conversion, its selection is critically important to benefit-cost analysis. In the context of environmental policy development, this rate can directly affect which proposals meet a given criterion and which are rejected out of hand. Because of the implications, discount rate selection is one of the more commonly debated points in the literature on present value analysis.

How *is* the discount rate selected for public policy decision-making? While there are many considerations, one important position is that this rate should reflect the **social opportunity cost** of funds allocated to the provision of a public good. Why? Because monies used to support public policy initiatives are perceived as a *transfer* from the private sector. Therefore, it is argued that the discount rate used for public policy—called the **social discount rate**— should reflect the rate of return that *could* be realized through private spending on consumption and investment, assuming the same level of risk.[2]

social discount rate
The discount rate
used for public policy
initiatives based on
the social opportunity
cost of funds, which
is the rate of return
that could be realized
through private
spending, assuming
the same risk level.

Since 1972, the U.S. government has maintained a policy that its agencies use a social discount rate of 10 percent in their benefit-cost analyses.[3] The operative issue is whether this 10 percent rate reflects the social opportunity cost of public expenditures. Since this rate is stated in **real** terms, that is, net of inflationary effects, the **nominal** rate is roughly equivalent to the sum of the inflation rate and the 10 percent rate. Inflation over the last several years has been about 4 percent, which means that the nominal social discount rate is about 14 percent. If this rate is meant to capture the social opportunity cost of funds, it must be the case that society could earn a 14 percent return through private investment. By today's standards, this is highly unlikely. Thus, *if* social opportunity cost is the relevant criterion, the 10 percent rate is inappropriate. Beyond this issue, there are other conceptual arguments about the appropriate

---

[2]For an excellent discussion of the social discount rate and the opportunity cost of public funding, see Sassone and Schaffer (1978), Chapter 6.

[3]U.S. Office of Management and Budget (March 27, 1972).

determinants of this rate. However, there is no consensus on the matter, which may explain why the U.S. government's 1972 decision has not been amended.[4]

inflation correction
An adjustment procedure that accounts for movements in the general price level over time.

Inflation Correction

Preliminary cost and benefit estimates must also be modified to account for movements in the general price level over time. To adjust a dollar amount in the present period for expected inflation in the *next* future period, the value must be converted to its nominal value for that period. The conversion uses a measure of price such as the consumer price index (CPI) as shown below:

real value
A magnitude adjusted for the effects of inflation.

$$\text{Nominal value}_{\text{period } x+1} = \text{Real value}_{\text{period } x} \cdot (\text{CPI}_{\text{period } x+1}/\text{CPI}_{\text{period } x}) \text{ or}$$

$$\text{Nominal value}_{\text{period } x+1} = \text{Real value}_{\text{period } x} \cdot (1 + p),$$

nominal value
A magnitude stated in terms of the current period.

where p is the rate of inflation between period x and $x+1$. The more generalized formula for any number of (t) periods is as follows:

$$\text{Nominal value}_{\text{period } x+t} = \text{Real value}_{\text{period } x} \cdot (1 + p)^t$$

Consider, for example, annual abatement costs of $50 million expressed in 1995 dollars. If the inflation rate (p) for 1996 is expected to be 6 percent, then this annual expenditure would have to be adjusted to account for the anticipated price rise. Using the formula given above, the 1996 annual costs would be $50(1 + 0.06) or $53 million in nominal terms.

Inverting the formula allows for the conversion of a nominal value to its real value, as follows:[5]

$$\text{Real value}_{\text{period } x} = \text{Nominal value}_{\text{period } x+t}/(1 + p)^t$$

deflating
The procedure to convert a nominal value into its real value.

This conversion procedure, sometimes called **deflating,** is used to assess changes over a period during which there has been inflation. To illustrate, look back at the cost data presented in Table 8.5 of the last chapter. Notice that all of the annual dollar values are expressed in 1987 dollars. This is done to avoid confounding changes in control costs over time with changes in the general price level. For example, the *Survey of Current Business* reports that the *nominal* value of abatement costs rose from $76.7 billion in 1987 to $81.1 billion in 1988.[6] Although these values imply a $4.4 billion increase in abatement expenditures, part of the increase is due to a 2.5 percent inflation rate over the period. To correct for the price effect, the $81.1 billion measured in 1988 dollars must be deflated to 1987 dollars. Using the formula given above, the result is $79.1 billion [i.e., $81.1 billion/$(1 + (0.025)^1)$], which is exactly the

---

[4]For further reading on this important public policy matter, see a series of articles in the March 1990 issue of the *Journal of Environmental Economics and Management* as well as Quirk and Terasawa (1991).

[5]Notice that the deflating formula is identical in form to the present value formula, except that the inflation rate, *p,* is substituted for the discount rate, *r.*

[6]Rutledge and Leonard (1992).

value reported in Table 8.5 for 1988. Thus, the real increase in abatement costs over the 1987 to 1988 period is ($79.1 − $76.7) billion, or $2.4 billion measured in 1987 dollars.

A Summary of Deriving Time-Adjusted Benefits and Costs[7]

present value of benefits (PVB)
The time-adjusted magnitude of incremental benefits associated with an environmental policy change.

The time-adjusted magnitudes for incremental benefits and costs are referred to as the **present value of benefits (PVB)** and the **present value of costs (PVC),** respectively. The steps to measuring the **present value of benefits (PVB)** in *nominal* terms are:

1. Monetize all present and future incremental benefits in real terms (b_t) where t refers to the appropriate time period $(t = 0, 1, 2, \ldots T)$.
2. Adjust each of the b_t for inflation, converting to nominal dollars (B_t), as follows:
$$B_t = b_t \cdot (1 + p)^t.$$
3. Select the appropriate nominal social discount rate, (r_s).
4. Discount the B_t for each period as $B_t/(1 + r_s)^t$.
5. Sum the discounted B_t values over all t periods to find the **present value of benefits** in nominal dollars as $PVB = \Sigma(B_t/(1 + r_s)^t)$.

present value of costs (PVC)
The time-adjusted magnitude of incremental costs associated with some environmental policy change.

Analogous steps yield a measure for the **present value of costs (PVC)** in *nominal* terms:

1. Monetize all present and future incremental costs in real terms (c_t) where t refers to the appropriate time period $(t = 0, 1, 2, \ldots T)$.
2. Adjust each of the c_t for inflation, converting to nominal dollars (C_t):
$$C_t = c_t \cdot (1 + p)^t.$$
3. Maintain the same nominal social discount rate (r_s) used in discounting future benefits.
4. Discount the C_t for each period as $C_t/(1 + r_s)^t$.
5. Sum the discounted C_t values over all t periods to find the **present value of costs** in nominal dollars as $PVC = \Sigma(C_t/(1 + r_s)^t)$.

An Example: Time-Adjusted Incremental Benefits

To illustrate how these steps might be carried out in practice, consider a hypothetical benefit assessment. Suppose an analyst is using the averting expenditure method (AEM) to monetize the incremental benefits of improved water quality. As part of the assessment, the analyst must estimate an individual's averting expenditures on a water-filtering system.[8] Assume the system has an

---

[7]The following presentation derives the time-adjusted values in *nominal* terms. The procedure is analogous for finding *real* values, as long as all magnitudes including the discount rate are properly deflated.

[8]For an actual study of this type of analysis, see Abdalla (1990).

TABLE 9.1   Assessing the Value of Future Operating Costs of a Water Filtering System

Adjustments for Inflation
(assuming an annual inflation rate of 5%)

$$\text{Nominal value}_{\text{period } x+t} = \text{Real value}_{\text{period } x} \cdot (1 + p)^t$$

Year	Expenditure in Real Terms	Future Expenditure in Nominal Dollars
1	$30.00	$31.50 = $30(1.05)^1$
2	$30.00	$33.08 = $30(1.05)^2$
3	$30.00	$34.73 = $30(1.05)^3$
4	$30.00	$36.47 = $30(1.05)^4$
5	$30.00	$38.29 = $30(1.05)^5$

Adjustments for Opportunity Cost
(assuming a nominal annual discount rate (*r*) of 10%)

$$PV = FV[1/(1 + r)^t]$$

Year	Future Value (FV)	Discount Factor $[1/(1 + r)^t]$	Present Value (PV)
0	$200.00	$1.0000 = 1/(1.10)^0$	$200.00
1	$ 31.50	$0.9090 = 1/(1.10)^1$	$ 28.63
2	$ 33.08	$0.8264 = 1/(1.10)^2$	$ 27.34
3	$ 34.73	$0.7513 = 1/(1.10)^3$	$ 26.09
4	$ 36.47	$0.6830 = 1/(1.10)^4$	$ 24.91
5	$ 38.29	$0.6209 = 1/(1.10)^5$	$ 23.78
Total present value in nominal terms:			$330.75

initial capital cost (i.e., purchase and installation) of $200 and a useful economic life of five years. Further assume that annual operating costs for general maintenance and filters are quoted as $30 in real terms due at the end of each year.[9] Part of the objective of the AEM is to determine the overall cost to the individual of purchasing, installing, and maintaining this filtration system, accounting for both the opportunity cost of money and expected inflation.

Assuming for simplicity that prices are expected to rise on average 5 percent each year, the annual operating costs have to be adjusted upward to account for this anticipated inflation. Using the conversion formula defined earlier, the nominal value of the operating costs at the end of the first year will be: $30.00(1.05)^1 = 31.50$. At the end of the second year, the nominal costs will be $30.00(1.05)^2 = 33.08$, and so forth. Table 9.1 presents these calculations for each year of the system's economic life.

---

[9]The timing of the annual expenditures is a critical element of the discounting process. For illustrative purposes, assume that all annual costs are incurred at the *end* of each year. For more detail on this or any other discounting issue, see any public finance text, such as Rosen (1995).

A further adjustment is necessary to find the present value of these future expenditures based on the opportunity cost of money. Assuming the proper discount rate (r) is 10 percent in nominal terms,[10] the present value (PV) of each year's inflation-adjusted expenditures is found using the discounting formula. For example, the PV of the first year's operating costs is $28.63 = $31.50 $[1/(1.10)^1]$. For the second year, the PV of the $33.08 nominal expenditure is $27.34 = 33.08[1/(1.10)^2]$, and so forth. These calculations are given along with the price adjustments in Table 9.1.

To complete the analysis, all of the time-adjusted annual operating costs are added to the initial capital outlay of $200. Notice that the $200 is unaffected by the conversion procedures, since it is incurred in the present period. Overall, the PV of the filtering system expressed in nominal dollars is $330.75.

The Final Analysis:
Comparing Environmental Benefits and Costs

The final phase of any benefit-cost analysis is to compare the time-adjusted values of incremental benefits and costs and arrive at a decision based on their relative magnitudes. In the context of environmental policy, remember that the subject of the analysis is either the setting of a policy objective or the selection of a control instrument. During policy formulation, the analysis is carried out over a series of possible options and used to identify the "best" solution among them.[11] The first step of this comparative evaluation is to determine if an option is *feasible* from a benefit-cost perspective. This step is essentially a zero-one decision made for every option under consideration— to accept or to reject. All of the "acceptable" options are then evaluated in a second step, where they are assessed *relative* to one another on the basis of a decision rule. At this point, a single "best" solution can be identified.

benefit-cost ratio
The ratio of *PVB* to *PVC* used to determine the feasibility of a public policy option if its magnitude exceeds unity.

Step One: Determining Feasibility

To distinguish feasible options from infeasible ones, the analyst must compare the time-adjusted values of incremental benefits and incremental costs for each option under study. A common way to do this is to form a **benefit-cost ratio** of (*PVB/PVC*) and compare the result to unity. If the ratio for a policy option exceeds one, it is counted among the feasible solutions; if not, it is rejected.

---

[10]Since the annual costs have been converted to their nominal values, the discount rate must also be expressed in nominal terms to account for the effect of inflation on the rate of return. Alternatively, one can express all the cost values in real terms and use the real discount rate.

[11]Benefit-cost analysis is also used in the policy appraisal phase to evaluate an *existing* policy initiative. In later chapters, we will examine the findings of such evaluative analyses of various U.S. environmental policies.

If (*PVB/PVC*) for a given option > 1, the option is considered feasible.

present value of net benefits (*PVNB*)
The differential of (*PVB* − *PVC*) used to determine the feasibility of a public policy option if its magnitude exceeds zero.

An equivalent test for feasibility is to find the **present value of net benefits (*PVNB*)** as (*PVB* − *PVC*) and compare the result to zero. If this differential is greater than 0, the policy option is feasible; if not, it is rejected.

If (*PVB* − *PVC*) for a given option > 0, the option is considered feasible.

What both rules communicate is that feasibility is implied if the benefits associated with a policy proposal *outweigh* the costs incurred.

Although any policy option satisfying the (*PVB/PVC*) > 1 condition necessarily meets the requirement that (*PVB* − *PVC*) > 0, the equivalency ends there. First, the magnitudes of the two expressions have different interpretations. The numerical value of the (*PVB/PVC*) ratio conveys the benefits of a policy option *per dollar of costs incurred.* For example, a ratio of 4.2 means that for every dollar of costs imposed on society, there are \$4.20 in realized benefits. The value of (*PVB* − *PVC*) measures the dollar value of *excess benefits.* So, it directly communicates a monetized measure of net gain to society. Secondly, although it might be tempting to think that either measure could be used to rank feasible projects and arrive at the same ''best'' solution, such a hypothesis is incorrect. In fact, of the two measures, only the benefit-cost differential is useful in establishing such a ranking—a point we will return to later. For now, we need to explore the unreliability of the benefit-cost ratio in comparing feasible policy proposals.

Attempts to use the benefit-cost ratio for any kind of ranking among options will lead to ambiguous results. The problem arises because of the inherent uncertainty about whether to consider an event as an increase in costs or a reduction in benefits. Suppose, for example, that a policy option is expected to create some amount of unemployment. Should the value of that unemployment be counted as a negative benefit or a positive cost? Intuitively, it should be apparent that either approach is correct and should not affect the outcome. However, although the choice would not affect the value of the *PVNB,* it would change the benefit-cost ratio. A simple example will illustrate.

Assume that this hypothetical policy option is expected to cause unemployment valued at \$2 million after discounting and adjusting for inflation. Excluding this effect, suppose also that the *PVB* is \$18 million and the *PVC* is \$10 million. If the \$2 million is counted as a negative benefit, the benefit-cost ratio would have a value of 1.6. If instead the \$2 million is counted as a cost, the ratio would be 1.5. Try the same experiment with the *PVNB* to see that in either case the result is consistent at \$6 million. What this example implies is that in the second step of evaluation, only the *PVNB* is useful in guiding the decision to select among feasible projects.

Step Two: Decision Rules to Select among Feasible Options

In practice, the decision-making process used to evaluate feasible options is guided by one of the following economic criteria: **allocative efficiency** or

cost-effectiveness. Adding the dimension of time to these criteria, the decision rules are as follows:

For **allocative efficiency:**   Maximize the present value of net benefits (*PVNB*).

For **cost-effectiveness:**   Minimize the present value of costs (*PVC*) based upon a preestablished benefit objective.

In the United States, the determination about which decision rule to employ generally is dictated by the legislation or by presidential executive order—an issue we will explore later in the chapter. For now, notice that both rules involve some type of optimization to guide the selection of the "best" available option.

maximize the present value of net benefits (*PVNB*)
A decision rule to achieve allocative efficiency by selecting the public policy option that yields the highest amount of excess benefits after adjusting for time effects.

DECISION RULE: Maximize the Present Value of Net Benefits (*PVNB*). As noted earlier, the **present value of net benefits (*PVNB*)** is a benefit-cost differential found as the difference between the **present value of benefits (*PVB*)** and the **present value of costs (*PVC*).** Thus, this decision rule calls for choosing the option that yields to society the highest amount of excess benefits after adjusting for time effects. Recall that according to basic microeconomic theory, the point at which benefits exceed costs by the greatest amount corresponds to where $MB = MC$ or where resources are efficiently allocated. Hence, we can summarize this decision rule in the following way:

To achieve allocative efficiency, maximize $PVNB = (PVB - PVC) = \Sigma[B_t/(1 + r_s)^t] - \Sigma[C_t/(1 + r_s)^t] = \Sigma[(B_t - C_t)/(1 + r_s)^t]$
for all t periods ($t = 0, 1, 2, \ldots T$) among all feasible alternatives.

An important caveat is that the efficiency criterion will be assured only if *all* feasible options are considered. In practice, only a subset of possibilities is ever evaluated. If the efficient solution does not happen to be in this subset, the decision rule will identify the most efficient option of those considered, but the efficiency criterion will not be satisfied in a strict sense.

minimize the present value of costs (*PVC*)
A decision rule to achieve cost-effectiveness by selecting the least-cost public policy option that achieves a preestablished objective.

DECISION RULE: Minimize the Present Value of Costs (*PVC*).   The decision rule to minimize the present value of costs (*PVC*) guides the policy-maker to select the least-cost option among those capable of achieving some preestablished objective. This is an explicit directive to set policy based on the criterion of cost-effectiveness. Of the two economically based decision rules, this one is the more common. The reason is that the law often predetermines the level of environmental benefits to be achieved through its definition of an environmental quality objective. When this is the case, the *PVB* is essentially fixed, leaving only *PVC* as a decision variable.

Before the cost comparison is done, the analyst has to first eliminate any options that do not achieve the requisite benefit level. Once done, the *PVC* is calculated for the remaining possibilities, and the option that incurs the lowest costs is selected. This decision rule can be summarized as follows:

To achieve cost-effectiveness, minimize $PVC = \Sigma[C_t/(1 + r_s)^t]$ for all t periods ($t = 0, 1, 2, \ldots T$)
among all feasible alternatives that achieve a predetermined benefit level.

Just as with the efficiency-based decision rule, the cost-effectiveness solution will be obtained only if it is among the feasible options being considered. Since it is not practical for decision-makers to consider more than a small number of possibilities, it is likely that the selected option will not be the true cost-minimizing solution, though it will be the least-cost alternative among those evaluated.

Reservations about the Use of Benefit-Cost Analysis

While benefit-cost analysis is a viable risk management strategy, it is not without flaws. In fact, as a tool of environmental decision-making, it has been the object of a fair amount of scrutiny. Critics of benefit-cost analysis generally point to two sources of concern. The first is the inherent problem of accurately measuring and monetizing environmental costs and benefits. The second refers to potential equity problems not addressed by this approach.

Measurement Problems

Attempting to measure and assign a dollar value to environmental benefits and costs is unquestionably a major challenge of using benefit-cost analysis to guide policy decisions. While economists have made great strides in developing methods to estimate these oftentimes elusive concepts, the methods are nonetheless imperfect. As we indicated in the last chapter, estimation is particularly problematic on the benefit side, where many intangibles are involved. Not only is it difficult to identify all the health and ecological benefits of a policy proposal, but assigning a dollar value to these gains is difficult at best. In fact, this measurement problem is often used to support the use of cost-effectiveness as an alternative criterion to allocative efficiency. On the opposite side of the analysis, capturing implicit costs is the primary source of difficulty. Solving this problem continues to be the objective of ongoing research. Finally, the selection of the social discount rate, which affects the present value of both benefit and cost estimates, is the subject of much debate—even among proponents of the benefit-cost approach.

Equity Issues

In an objective assessment of benefit-cost analysis, equity concerns are not unfounded. The decision rules in benefit-cost analysis do not consider *how* the benefits and costs are distributed across various segments of society. Yet it is possible that the distribution of incremental benefits might be highly skewed, so that some group of consumers or some industrial sector receives less than its fair share. Similarly, the distribution of costs might be such that some economic sector bears an inequitable share of the burden. Of course, either problem is less troublesome if the same inequity occurs on both the benefit and the cost side, such as lower benefits matched by lower costs. However, there is no assurance that this will be the case.

Even proponents of benefit-cost analysis do not dismiss the measurement problems or potential inequities associated with benefit-cost analysis. So, it is important that policy-makers understand the implications and make adjustments for any noted shortcomings. In the interim, economists are continuing to research better estimation techniques. And many researchers and government officials are working to analyze and correct inequities associated with environmental policy decisions. We will see instances of these efforts in upcoming chapters. Finding ways to improve the results is worth the effort. As a risk management strategy, benefit-cost analysis adds vital information to a very difficult undertaking. Furthermore, in the United States, benefit-cost analysis is required of all major policy proposals—a decision that has a long history behind it.

U.S. Government Support of Benefit-Cost Analysis[12]

Most policy analysts point to the Flood Control Act of 1936 as the first U.S. federal legislation that explicitly acknowledged benefits and costs in a public policy initiative. According to this mandate, federal funds could be allocated to water projects only if the associated benefits were found to exceed the costs. Notice that this is precisely the feasibility rule based on $(PVB - PVC) > 0$ that we discussed earlier. Since this historic first, the use of economic theory as a decision-making tool has been promoted in many public policy settings—a practice that continues into present-day rule making. In fact, in 1993 a bill was introduced before the Senate as the Environmental Risk Reduction Act. The proposed legislation sought to strengthen the role of risk assessment and benefit-cost analysis in environmental policy decisions. See Application 9.1 for more detail.

---

[12]Much of this discussion is drawn from the following: Andrews (1984), pp. 43–85; and U.S. EPA, Office of Policy Analysis, Office of Policy, Planning, and Evaluation (August 1987), pp. 2-1–2-6.

The Environmental Risk Reduction Act of 1993

Recognizing the importance of risk assessment and risk management in environmental policy decisions, Senator Daniel Patrick Moynihan (D-N.Y.) introduced into Congress Senate Bill 110 as the Environmental Risk Reduction Act of 1993. One of the bill's objectives was to make the major findings of the EPA's 1990 report called *Reducing Risk* part of federal law. This report summarizes an EPA Science Advisory Board study of how the United States could improve its efforts to reduce environmental risk.

According to the proposal, the Environmental Risk Reduction Act would advance the integration of risk assessment and benefit-cost analysis in the environmental decision-making process. As Senator Moynihan stated in a recent article,

> I am convinced that risk ranking and cost-benefit analysis are valuable tools for making environmental decisions. They are not our only tools, but they do offer the means to set priorities and to measure success.

As part of its proposed requirements, the Senate bill called for quantitative estimates of risk exposure, an understanding of the alternatives available to reduce this exposure, and accurate estimates of the benefits and costs associated with these alternatives. Notice that these requirements would effectively legislate the tasks of risk assessment and risk management.

To make these requirements operational, the bill proposed that two new advisory committees be created. One of these, the Committee on Relative Risk, would have been charged with the responsibility of providing expert advice about ranking environmental risks of exposure to humans and the ecology. The second committee, the Committee on Environmental Benefits, would have been responsible for providing advice on quantifying the benefits associated with risk reduction. A financial allocation of $3 million per year was proposed to support the activities of these committees.

Long-term programs also were outlined in the bill, one aimed at supporting research in environmental risk assessment and another at developing better methods to monitor environmental quality. A graduated budget for these programs was proposed, starting at $80 million in 1994 and rising to $200 million by 1996.

To consider and evaluate the new act, the bill was sent to the Senate's Committee on Environmental and Public Works, chaired by Senator Moynihan. Reservations were voiced by some of the committee's membership, most notably Senator David Durenberger (R-Minn.). Senator Durenberger expressed concern about the use of risk assessment in policy decisions, a practice he characterized as still in its infancy. The Minnesota senator also argued that equity should be a factor in environmental decision-making, a comment that reflects the common criticism of benefit-cost analysis based solely on economic criteria.

Senator Moynihan continued to be aggressive about the bill's intent. Referring to U.S. annual spending of 2.2 percent of its GNP on environmental protection, he argued:

> While this may not be too much money to spend on environmental protection, it is too much to spend unwisely.

Despite Moynihan's efforts, the proposed legislation was not passed by the 103rd Congress. However, proponents of risk-based initiatives are hopeful that the new Republican Congress will assume a different position toward such reform bills and advance policy efforts to reduce environmental risk.

Sources: Senator Daniel Patrick Moynihan, "A Legislative Proposal: Why Not Enact a Law That Would Help Us Set Up Sensible Priorities," *EPA Journal*, January/February/March, 1993, pp. 46–47; Jenifer Heath, "Moynihan Bill Sets Goals," *Water Environment and Technology*, July 1993, pp. 28–30; U.S. Environmental Protection Agency, Science Advisory Board, *Reducing Risk: Setting Priorities and Strategies for Environmental Protection* (Washington, D.C., September 1990); Terry Davies, "Congress Discovers Risk Analysis," *Resources*, Winter 1995, pp. 5–8.

TABLE 9.2   A Recent History of U.S. Regulation Using Economic Analysis

Act/Executive Order	Year	Title of Analysis	Type of Analysis
OMB October 1971 Memo	1971	Quality of Life (QOL) Review	Costs, benefits
Executive Order 11821	1974	Inflation Impact Statement (IIS)	Cost, benefits, inflationary impacts
Executive Order 11949	1976	Economic Impact Statement (EIS)	Costs, benefits, economic impacts
Executive Order 12044	1978	Regulatory Analysis	Costs, economic consequences
Regulatory Flexibility Act	1980	Regulatory Flexibility Analysis	Impacts on small businesses
Executive Order 12291	1981	Regulatory Impact Analysis (RIA)	Costs, benefits, net benefits

Source: U.S. Environmental Protection Agency, Office of Policy Analysis, Office of Policy, Planning, and Evaluation, *EPA's Use of Benefit-Cost Analysis: 1981–1986* (Washington, D.C., August 1987), Table 2–1, p. 2-2.

Over the last 25 years, U.S. presidents have used the power of the office to require economic analysis in federal regulatory decision-making. Table 9.2 lists some of the presidential executive orders and other directives that specifically call for the consideration of benefits and/or costs in policy decisions. To understand the evolution of economic thinking in policy decisions, we consider a few of the instruments called for in certain of these directives, namely the **Quality of Life (QOL) Review,** the **Inflation Impact Statement (IIS),** and the **Regulatory Impact Analysis (RIA).**

OMB October 1971 Memo: Quality of Life (QOL) Reviews

In 1971, the Office of Management and Budget (OMB) under President Nixon instituted a procedure known as a Quality of Life (QOL) review. The QOL review was to be conducted for all proposed regulations that would affect environmental quality, consumer protection, or occupational and public health and safety. It was to include: (1) the principal objectives of the regulation; (2) alternatives to the proposed regulation; (3) a *comparison of the benefits and costs* associated with each alternative; and (4) the reason or reasons for choosing the proposed regulation.

On face value, the QOL review seemed as if it would have strengthened the decision-making process, particularly its mandate to compare benefits and costs. However, the review process stopped short of achieving an allocatively efficient solution, since the guidelines failed to call for a *maximization* of the present value of net benefits (*PVNB*). Some even argue that Nixon's QOL review was little more than a political mechanism to allow businesses to influence regulatory proposals before they were made public.[13]

Executive Order 11821: Inflation Impact Statements (IIS)

In an attempt to slow the inflationary effects caused primarily by the OPEC energy crisis, President Ford signed Executive Order 11821 on November 27, 1974. It was through this executive order that an Inflation Impact Statement (IIS) was required as part of the regulatory decision-making process for any *major* federal legislative proposal. According to the OMB, these statements were to include: (1) a review of alternatives to the proposal along with their expected costs, benefits, risks, and inflationary impacts; (2) the costs associated with the recommended alternative along with the inflationary effects of the action; and (3) a comparison of the benefits to be derived from the proposal with the estimated costs and inflationary impacts. Costs, benefits, and economic impacts were to be quantified as much as possible.[14] Charged with implementing the new mandate, the OMB established the guideline that any proposal involving impacts of over $100 million per year was to be considered a *major* regulation subject to the IIS requirement. This time, the office delegated the responsibility of establishing IIS criteria to each administrative government agency. The criteria were in turn subject to the approval of the OMB and a newly created Council on Wage and Price Stability (COWPS).

Like the QOL review, the IIS positioned economic considerations among those important to national policy initiatives. However, the IIS criteria were not published in the *Federal Register* nor were they made subject to commentary or review by the judiciary or the general public. Only the OMB and the COWPS were required to comment on any new proposal and its accompanying IIS, but neither was obligated to decide if the proposal should be rejected on the basis of its economic impact. Furthermore, the definitions and procedures used for the concepts of benefits, costs, and risks were never made part of the public record. Consequently, it is argued that the review process was used as a means to align federal agencies' proposals with the administration's economic platform rather than to achieve any objective criterion. In fact, it was never explicitly mandated that a policy proposal should achieve the efficiency criterion of maximizing net benefits. Despite these weaknesses, the review process was extended through 1977 by a subsequent executive order, except that the IIS was referred to thereafter as an Economic Impact Statement (EIS).[15]

---

[13]Andrews (1984), p. 63.

[14]U.S. EPA, Office of Policy Analysis, Office of Policy, Planning, and Evaluation (August 1987), p. 2-3.

[15]Andrews (1984), p. 66.

Executive Order 12291: Regulatory Impact Analysis (RIA)[16]

While the framework for considering the benefits and costs of regulatory proposals had been present in the mandates of previous administrations, it was not until President Reagan's first term in office that the *efficiency criterion* was explicitly made a part of the regulatory review process.[17] In 1981, Reagan signed Executive Order 12291, which outlined specific requirements that federal agencies had to follow in proposing or reviewing any major rule or regulation. Under Section 1 of this executive order, a ''major rule'' referred to any regulation likely to result in one of the following:

(1) an annual effect on the U.S. economy of $100 million or more; (2) a major increase in costs or prices for consumers, individual industries, Federal, State, or local government agencies, or geographic regions; or (3) significant adverse effects on competition, employment, investment, productivity, innovation, or on the ability of United States–based enterprises to compete with foreign-based enterprises in domestic or export markets.

Section 2 outlined the requirements that all agencies had to follow in developing new regulatory actions or assessing existing ones. Specifically, it called for the following:

In promulgating new regulations, reviewing existing regulations, and developing legislative proposals concerning regulations, all agencies, to the extent permitted by law, shall adhere to the following requirements:

(a) Administrative decisions shall be based on adequate information concerning the need for and consequences of proposed government action;

(b) Regulatory action shall not be undertaken unless the potential benefits to society for the regulation outweigh the potential costs to society;

(c) Regulatory objectives shall be chosen to maximize the net benefits to society;

(d) Among alternative approaches to any regulatory objective, the alternative involving the least net cost to society shall be chosen; and

(e) Agencies shall set regulatory priorities with the aim of maximizing the aggregate net benefits to society, taking into account the condition of the particular industries affected by regulations, the conditions of the national economy, and other regulatory actions contemplated for the future.

Notice that, unlike prior references to economic considerations, this set of requirements *explicitly* called for the achievement of economic criteria in adopting regulatory actions. **Allocative efficiency** is referenced in paragraphs

---

[16]For more detail concerning this executive order, see *Federal Register* 46, February 17, 1981: 13193-98.

[17]Similar to President Ford's 1974 Executive Order, President Carter's 1978 executive order also required policy-makers to explicitly consider the economic implications of legislative proposals. In Carter's mandate, the official document conveying this information was referred to as a Regulatory Analysis. Carter's Executive Order called for more explicit procedures and allowed for more public scrutiny than what the IIS review process required. However, Carter's Regulatory Analysis, like Ford's IIS, did *not* employ economic efficiency as a criterion for evaluating policy proposals.

(c) and (e), which called for maximizing net benefits. The criterion of **cost-effectiveness** is referenced in paragraph (d), which required that the selection from among alternatives fulfilling a given objective be made on the basis of least net cost to society.

Taken out of context, paragraphs (c) and (d) suggest that these economic criteria were to have been met by every new policy proposal. However, there is an important caveat in the first sentence of Section 2, given in the phrase "to the extent permitted by law." Because of this wording, many major environmental laws precluded the EPA from using either allocative efficiency or cost-effectiveness in establishing and implementing policy. Look at the list of EPA regulations given in Table 9.3. Notice that some rulings, such as the primary and secondary air quality standards established by the Clean Air Act, do not consider economic costs at all.[18] Hence, the level of environmental quality under these provisions is set to achieve some objective other than maximizing net benefits or cost-effectiveness.

Although the law was to prevail over the requirements of the executive order, all major regulations nonetheless had to be accompanied by what is called a **Regulatory Impact Analysis (RIA)** described in Sec.3(d) of the executive order:

Regulatory Impact Analysis (RIA)
A document required under Executive Order 12291, which called for specific information about the potential benefits and costs associated with a "major" federal regulation.

> To permit each proposed major rule to be analyzed in light of the requirements stated in Section 2 of this Order, each preliminary and final Regulatory Impact Analysis shall contain the following information:
>
> (1) A description of the potential benefits of the rule, including any beneficial effects that cannot be quantified in monetary terms, and the identification of those likely to receive the benefits;
>
> (2) A description of the potential costs of the rule, including any adverse effects that cannot be quantified in monetary terms, and the identification of those likely to bear the costs;
>
> (3) A determination of the potential net benefits of the rule, including an evaluation of effects that cannot be quantified in monetary terms;
>
> (4) A description of alternative approaches that could substantially achieve the same regulatory goal at lower cost, together with an analysis of this potential benefit and costs and a brief explanation of the legal reasons why such alternatives, if proposed, could not be adopted; and
>
> (5) Unless covered by the description required under paragraph (4) of this subsection, an explanation of any legal reasons why the rule cannot be based on the requirements set forth in Section 2 of this Order.

The guidelines of Sec.3(d) left little doubt about the importance of identifying and monetizing the potential costs and benefits of any policy proposal or regulatory review process.[19] In that sense, the RIA was an uncompromising

---

[18]In subsequent chapters, we will investigate the implications of certain of these provisions in more detail. For now, recognize that some environmental laws explicitly disallow the use of economic criteria in devising policy solutions.

[19]This process continues to be required as part of President Clinton's Executive Order 12866 dealing with regulatory planning and review.

TABLE 9.3   Type of Analysis Specified in Selected U.S. Environmental Legislation

Act/Regulation	Benefits			Costs		
	Pollution Reduction	Health	Welfare/ Environment	Compliance Costs	Cost-Effectiveness	Economic Impacts
Clean Air Act						
Primary standards	X					
Secondary standards			X			
Hazardous air pollutants		X				
New-source standards	X	*	*	†	†	†
Motor vehicle standards‡	X	X	X	X	X	X
Aircraft emissions	X	X	X	X		X
Fuel standards‡	X	X	X	X		
Clean Water Act						
Private treatment works	X		§	X	X	X
Public treatment works	X					
Safe Drinking Water Act						
Maximum contaminant level goals		X				
Maximum contaminant levels				X		X
Toxic Substance Control Act	X	X	X	X	X	X
Resource Conservation and Recovery Act		X	X			
Comprehensive Environmental Response, Compensation and Liability Act						
Reportable quantities		X	X			
National contingency plan	X				X	
Federal Insecticide, Fungicide and Rodenticide Act						
Data requirements			X			
Minor uses	X	X	X	X	X	X
Atomic Energy Act						
Radioactive wastes	X	X	X			
Uranium mill tailings	X	X	X	X	X	X

* Includes non-air-quality health and environmental impacts only.
† Statute refers only to "cost."
‡ Type of analysis depends on grounds for control.
§ Includes non-water-quality environment impacts only.

Source: U.S. Environmental Protection Agency, Office of Policy Analysis, Office of Policy, Planning, and Evaluation, *EPA's Use of Benefit-Cost Analysis: 1981–1986* (Washington, D.C., August 1987), Table 3–1, p. 3-2.

work assignment for economists engaged in policy formulation. What was *not* outlined in the executive order was exactly *how* this formidable task was to be implemented in practice. To better understand the issues involved, we next investigate how the EPA used the net benefits decision rule in its 1984 RIA for the phasedown of lead in gasoline.

A Regulatory Impact Analysis (RIA): Reducing Lead in Gasoline[20]

Petroleum refiners have been using lead additives as an inexpensive source of octane since the 1920s. By adding lead to gasoline, refiners were able to reduce engine knock and increase engine performance. However, these gains were not without consequence. Coincident with the increased use of lead additives over time, research scientists began to observe a link between lead exposure and adverse health effects such as mental and cardiovascular disorders. Acting on this growing body of scientific evidence, the EPA was charged with the responsibility of achieving a reduction in the lead content of gasoline.

In 1985, the existing U.S. lead standard was 1.1 grams per leaded gallon (gplg). As part of its plan to reduce society's exposure to lead, the EPA proposed a tightening of this standard to 0.1 gplg effective January 1, 1986. Since such a policy change came under the legal definition of a "major" rule, the EPA had to conduct a Regulatory Impact Analysis (RIA). As stated in this directive, the agency was required to examine the costs, benefits, and net benefits of approaches that could be used to meet the more stringent lead standard.

Estimating the Incremental Benefits of the Lead Standard Proposal

An important element of the benefit assessment for the RIA was an evaluation of the predicted health improvements associated with the lead standard proposal. Based on the findings of existing scientific studies, the EPA conducted tests to determine the relationship between human blood lead levels and leaded gasoline usage. Figure 9.1 shows the correlation between these two variables.

As part of the risk assessment process, the EPA also analyzed available scientific findings to find out if any population groups were more susceptible to the health risks of lead exposure. Even then, there was already an abundance of scientific evidence about the effects of lead exposure on children. According to the final report of the RIA, "These effects range from relatively subtle changes in biochemical measurements at low doses to severe retardation and even death at very high levels." Based upon the evidence, it was clear that an important incremental benefit of tightening the lead standard would be improvements in the health of children. To monetize children's incremental health benefits, the EPA used two measures: (1) savings in medical care expenditures, and (2) savings in compensatory educational expenditures. These measures attempted to capture the benefits of improving both physiological health and cognitive development. Using these predefined measures, the EPA estimated that the value of incremental health benefits for children would be approximately $600 million in 1986—the first full year of the revised lead

---

[20]The following is drawn from U.S. EPA, Office of Policy Analysis (February 1985).

FIGURE 9.1

Correlation between lead in gasoline and average blood lead levels

Source: Lily Whiteman, "Trades to Remember: The Lead Phasedown," *EPA Journal* 18, no. 2 (May/June 1992), p. 38.

standard. (This value and all others given in the RIA report are expressed in 1983 dollars.)

Another element of the EPA's study of lead-related health effects was an examination of the evidence linking lead exposure to blood pressure levels in adult males. Much of the agency's analysis was based on the findings of two very recent scientific studies. Because of this, the EPA stated that their findings on this health issue were to be viewed as preliminary and *not* to be considered for the subject rule making. Hence, results were presented in the RIA for informational use only.

Using statistical models, the EPA estimated the relationship between blood lead levels in adult males and blood pressure levels. Based upon the results, models were constructed to estimate the associated incremental benefits of reductions in cardiovascular-related death and various disorders delineated as follows: (1) hypertension; (2) myocardial infarctions; (3) strokes; and (4) deaths. To monetize the benefits of reducing *nonfatal* health effects, the EPA used the dollar value of medical care costs, expenditures on medications, and lost wages. For *fatal* cases, the EPA used the findings of existing studies that estimate the value of a statistical life and selected a magnitude of $1 million per life saved. Taken together, the monetized values of the incremental benefits per case were reported in the RIA as follows: $220 per case of hypertension; $60,000 per heart attack; $44,000 per stroke; and $1 million per life saved. In the aggregate, the incremental benefits of the lead ruling associated with adult male health were reported over a six-year period and ranged from $5.897 billion in 1986 to $4.692 billion in 1992.

Three types of nonhealth benefits were analyzed in the RIA: (1) reducing harmful emissions caused by misfueling (i.e., the use of leaded gasoline in vehicles requiring unleaded gasoline); (2) lowering maintenance costs; and

(3) increasing fuel economy. Misfueling causes harmful emissions because leaded gasoline damages a car's catalytic converter, which is designed to abate such pollutants as hydrocarbons (HC), carbon monoxide (CO), and nitrogen oxides (NO_x). Thus, the lower lead content was expected to slow the rate at which catalytic converters are damaged, which in turn would reduce these various pollutant emissions. Furthermore, the new standard was expected to reduce misfueling because it would increase production costs of leaded gasoline, thus reducing the price differential between leaded and unleaded fuel.

To estimate the incremental benefits of reducing misfueling damage, the EPA assumed that the new lead standard would eliminate about 80 percent of the misfueling. Accounting for all the associated damage reductions, the EPA estimated that the resulting decrease in emissions of HC, CO, and NO_x would yield incremental benefits of approximately $222 million in 1986. In addition, the values for reduced maintenance expenditures and for increased fuel economy for 1986 were estimated to be $914 million and $187 million, respectively.

Estimating the Incremental Costs of the Lead Standard Proposal

On the cost side of the analysis, the EPA had to define, quantify, and monetize the social costs of the proposed lead ruling. The RIA defines real social costs as ''the costs of real resources that are used to comply with the rule (i.e., the extra energy, capital, labor, etc. that are needed to meet the tighter lead standard).'' To approximate these costs, the EPA used estimates of the change in manufacturing costs of gasoline and other petroleum products arising from the new lead ruling. The agency used an engineering cost model of the refinery industry, which was originally developed for the Department of Energy. First, the model was specified under the existing or baseline lead content standard. Then, it was reestimated, using the new standard. The difference between the two yielded the incremental cost estimate.

In general, real manufacturing costs were found to decrease over the seven-year period under study, due primarily to the expected decline in the demand for leaded gasoline. Year-to-year cost estimates suggested a relatively small impact on refiners. For example, tightening the standard from 1.1 gplg to the proposed rule of 0.1 gplg yielded an incremental cost estimate of $608 million in 1986, the first full year of the proposed rule, and $441 million in 1992.

Putting It All Together: Benefit-Cost Analysis

Table 9.4 summarizes the EPA's estimates of the *real* incremental benefits and costs associated with tightening the lead standard from 1.1 gplg to 0.1 gplg. Notice that the magnitudes show that the net incremental benefits of the proposed rule are positive and quite substantial. Including the benefits of reducing adverse effects on adult blood pressure, the magnitudes range from

TABLE 9.4   The Regulatory Impact Analysis (RIA) for Reducing Lead in Gasoline: The EPA's Estimates of Incremental Benefits and Costs

	Monetized Benefits and Costs of Reducing Lead in Gasoline (millions of 1983 dollars)							
	1985	*1986*	*1987*	*1988*	*1989*	*1990*	*1991*	*1992*
Monetized benefits:								
Children's health effects	223	600	547	502	453	414	369	358
Adult blood pressure	1,724	5,897	5,675	5,447	5,187	4,966	4,682	4,692
Conventional pollutants	0	222	222	224	226	230	239	248
Vehicle maintenance	102	914	859	818	788	767	754	749
Fuel economy	35	187	170	113	134	139	172	164
Total monetized benefits	2,084	7,821	7,474	7,105	6,788	6,517	6,216	6,211
Monetized costs:								
Total refining costs	96	608	558	532	504	471	444	441
Net benefits	1,988	7,213	6,916	6,573	6,284	6,045	5,772	5,770
Net benefits excluding adult blood pressure	264	1,316	1,241	1,125	1,096	1,079	1,090	1,079

Notes: The above estimates are reported under the assumption of partial misfueling.
Sums may not equal totals shown due to rounding.
Source: U.S. Environmental Protection Agency, Office of Policy Analysis, *Costs and Benefits of Reducing Lead in Gasoline, Final Regulatory Impact Analysis.* Report No. EPA-230-05-85-006, Washington, D.C., February 1985, p. E-12.

$7,213 million in 1986 to $5,770 million in 1992. Since the evidence for the adult blood pressure benefits was not well established, the EPA chose to rely upon the net benefit estimates *excluding* these benefits to defend the economic feasibility of the proposed rule change. Using this more conservative estimate, net benefits still were found to be positive for each forecasted year. In fact, the estimates are above $1 billion for each of the seven full years affected by the proposed ruling.

Finally, to adjust for time differences over the period, the EPA conducted a present value analysis of their net benefit estimates. Using the conservative estimate that excludes blood pressure effects and selecting a *real* social discount rate of 10 percent, the present value of net benefits (*PVNB*) over the period was estimated to be $5.9 billion ($1983).

The Final Decision

Following the estimation of incremental benefits and costs required in the RIA, the EPA officially announced a low-lead standard of 0.1 gplg effective January 1, 1986. The decision was supported by the economic evidence that the more stringent lead standard would be beneficial to society.

Conclusions

In its most fundamental form, environmental policy is aimed at minimizing society's risk of exposure to environmental hazards. For a litany of reasons, this objective is at once one of the greatest challenges faced by society today and one of its more important responsibilities. While all of society is involved in public policy development, most of the detail of formulating, evaluating, implementing, and monitoring regulatory provisions falls in the hands of public officials. The enormity of these tasks is nearly incomprehensible. By itself, this fact supports the need for analytical tools such as benefit-cost analysis to guide the decisions that define environmental policy.

While not without flaws, benefit-cost analysis is a useful strategic approach to environmental decision-making. Its objectivity is its primary strength in helping officials evaluate the social gains and the opportunity costs of their decisions. Choosing between a policy that reduces mortality risk to save one more life in a million exposed or a regulation that will reduce the risk of birth defects by 10 times that amount is a tough decision by any measure. Yet, these kinds of decisions are precisely what environmental policy development is all about. Every resource allocated to save a national forest is one less resource available to clean rivers and streams. Every dollar spent to clean a hazardous waste site is one less dollar available to save an endangered species. Such is the dilemma that confronts every society as it makes decisions about how to allocate scarce resources, and such is the fundamental premise of economic thought.

Guiding decision-making is the purpose of benefit-cost analysis. Explaining what this analytical tool can accomplish, how it is implemented, and what it fails to achieve have been the primary objectives of this chapter. Since benefit-cost analysis is becoming a more dominant force in public policy decisions, it is critical that we comprehend how it influences environmental regulations and how, in so doing, it affects the quality of our lives.

Summary

- In benefit-cost analysis, two types of time-oriented adjustments are necessary. One is present value determination, which accounts for the opportunity cost of money, and the second is inflation correction to adjust for changes in the general price level.
- To discount a future value (FV) into its present value (PV), the proper conversion formula is $PV = FV[1/(1 + r)^t]$, where $t = 0, 1, 2, \ldots T$ is the number of periods, and $[1/(1 + r)^t]$ is the discount factor. An important consideration in selecting the discount rate for public policy decision-making is that it should reflect the social opportunity cost of funds allocated to a public good. Since 1972, the U.S. government has required its agencies to use a real social discount rate of 10 percent in their benefit-cost analyses.

- To adjust a dollar amount in the present period for expected inflation in the future period, the value must be converted to its nominal value for that period. The generalized formula for any number of (t) periods is: Nominal value$_{\text{period } x+t}$ = Real value$_{\text{period } x}$ · $(1 + p)^t$, where p is the rate of inflation and $t = 0, 1, 2, \ldots T$ is the number of periods.

- The time-adjusted magnitudes for incremental benefits and costs are referred to as the present value of benefits $(PVB) = \Sigma[B_t/(1 + r_s)^t]$ and the present value of costs $(PVC) = \Sigma[C_t/(1 + r_s)^t]$, respectively, where $t = 0, 1, 2, \ldots T$ is the number of periods.

- After the benefits and costs of an environmental proposal have been adjusted for time-oriented effects, the magnitudes are compared and evaluated. The first step of this procedure deals with identifying which options are feasible. A policy option is considered feasible if the (PVB/PVC) for that option > 1 or if $(PVB - PVC) > 0$. The second step evaluates all "acceptable" options *relative* to one another on the basis of a decision rule.

- One decision rule is to maximize $PVNB = \Sigma[B_t/(1 + r_s)^t] - \Sigma[C_t/(1 + r_s)^t]$ among all feasible alternatives to achieve allocative efficiency. Another is to minimize $PVC = \Sigma[C_t/(1 + r_s)^t]$ among all feasible alternatives that attain a predetermined benefit level to achieve cost-effectiveness.

- Measurement difficulties are among the primary concerns of using benefit-cost analysis. Examples include measuring and monetizing intangibles, the selection of the social discount rate, and capturing implicit costs. Another problem is the potential for an inequitable distribution of costs and benefits across various groups in society.

- Over the last 25 years, U.S. presidents have used the power of the office to require economic analysis in federal regulatory decision-making. Three instruments that call for some type of benefit and/or cost considerations in public policy decisions are the Quality of Life (QOL) Review, the Inflation Impact Statement (IIS) called for in Executive Order 11821, and the Regulatory Impact Analysis (RIA) required by Executive Order 12291.

- Section 2 of President Reagan's Executive Order 12291 explicitly called for the achievement of economic criteria in adopting regulatory actions. Allocative efficiency is referenced by calling for objectives that "maximize net benefits." Cost-effectiveness is required by a mandate to select an alternative on the basis of "least net cost to society."

- In the RIA for evaluating a proposal to tighten the lead standard, the EPA estimated that the present value of the net benefits $(PVNB)$ was $5.9 billion ($1983). The EPA officially announced a low-lead standard of 0.1 gplg effective January 1, 1986.

Key Concepts

present value determination	social opportunity cost
discounting	social discount rate
discount rate	inflation correction
discount factor	real value

nominal value
deflating
present value of benefits (*PVB*)
present value of costs (*PVC*)
benefit-cost ratio
present value of net benefits (*PVNB*)

maximize *PVNB*
minimize *PVC*
Quality of Life Review (QOL)
Inflation Impact Statement (IIS)
Regulatory Impact Analysis (RIA)
Executive Order 12291

Review Questions

1. Suppose industry abatement costs rise from $850 million in 1990 to $1,000 million in 1991 in nominal terms, and that the CPI is 100 in 1990 and 106 in 1991.
   a. Evaluate the change in costs over the period in real terms, first in 1990 dollars, and then in 1991 dollars.
   b. Are your answers the same? Explain why or why not.

2. To examine the implications of selecting various discount rates, reconsider the water filtration system example in the text, but change the discount rate from 10 percent to 5 percent.
   a. Find the present value of the system.
   b. Now compare this present value with the one calculated under the assumption of a 10 percent rate. Explain the difference intuitively.

3. Refer to the RIA for the revised lead ruling discussed in the chapter.
   a. Mathematically confirm that the estimate of the present value of net benefits (*PVNB*) is approximately $5.9 billion as stated.
   b. Discuss how the *PVNB* would have changed if the EPA had used a social discount rate of 8 percent.

Additional Readings

Baumol, William J. "On the Social Rate of Discount." *American Economic Review,* September 1968, pp. 788–802.

Cropper, Maureen L. and Wallace E. Oates. "Environmental Economics: A Survey." *Journal of Economic Literature* 30 (June 1992), pp. 675–740.

Dorfman, Robert. "An Introduction to Benefit-Cost Analysis." In Robert Dorfman and Nancy Dorfman, eds. *Economics of the Environment: Selected Readings.* New York: W.W. Norton & Company, 1993.

Halvorsen, Robert and Michael G. Ruby. *Benefit-Cost Analysis of Air-Pollution Control.* Lexington, Mass.: D.C. Heath and Company, 1981.

Krupnick, Alan J. and Paul R. Portney. "Controlling Urban Air Pollution: A Benefit-Cost Assessment." *Science* 252 (April 26, 1991), pp. 522–28.

Peskin, Henry M. and Eugene P. Seskin. *Cost Benefit Analysis and Water Pollution Policy.* Washington, D.C.: The Urban Institute, 1973.

THE CASE OF AIR

Technically, there has been some form of air pollution as long as the earth has supported life. Decaying plant material, salt from the spray of ocean surf, and even the simple act of breathing alters the delicate chemical composition of the atmosphere. Yet air pollution did not begin to be a pervasive problem until the Industrial Revolution. The combination of population growth, motorized transportation, and manufacturing activity that characterized the 19th century also marks the period in our history when air quality became a real concern. As industrial growth proceeded on its course, so too did air pollution, though few realized the severity of the problem in those early days of industrial development.

In the United States, as urban smog became more and more apparent in cities like Los Angeles and Philadelphia, pressure began to mount for public officials to take action. Local communities and some state governments began to enact air quality laws. But it was literally decades before the federal government took an active role in what was fast becoming a worldwide problem. By then, air pollution had advanced considerably, and industry had become quite accustomed to the lack of restraint on their polluting activities. There was little doubt that public officials would face some of the toughest challenges in legislative history.

Over the last four decades, U.S. air quality control policy has evolved into a comprehensive body of laws, with the most recent revisions embodied in the 1990 Clean Air Act Amendments. These extensive provisions are supported by an equally sophisticated infrastructure to implement controls and monitor compliance. In addition, international conferences have begun to address worldwide air pollution problems such as global warming and depletion of the earth's protective layer of ozone.

Overall, there has been a good deal of progress. We have a much better sense of the implications of air pollution, thanks in part to medical and scientific research. As our knowledge base has advanced, we have become better able to find solutions. Recently, there has been a trend toward integrating market-based instruments into domestic and international policy initiatives. Economic incentives are displacing some of the former command-and-control approaches to regulating air quality. Understanding the extent of this progress and analyzing what has been accomplished thus far requires a fairly thorough examination of the facts and some sense of the evolution of policy.

To that end, this module provides a multistep approach to learning about air quality problems and policy solutions, using economics as an analytical tool. We begin in Chapter 10 with a broad-based exposition and analysis of U.S. air quality control policy and the standard-setting process that defines clean air for the nation. In Chapter 11, we investigate how U.S. standards are implemented through various control instruments aimed at mobile and stationary sources. A particular focus is an analysis of how well these initiatives address the problems of urban air pollution and acidic deposition. Finally, in Chapter 12, global air pollution is explored with an in-depth discussion of international policy initiatives and various proposals aimed at the problems of ozone depletion and global warming.

10

DEFINING AIR QUALITY

The Standard-Setting Process

One of the most important elements of clean air policy development is determining the target level of air quality that legislative initiatives are to achieve. In simpler terms, policy-makers have to decide how clean is clean air. In the United States, standards or emissions limits are used to define a national level of air quality that will protect human health and the ecology. Many factors enter into the standard-setting process that ultimately guides U.S. policy. Among them are such determinants as technological feasibility, energy requirements, and economic considerations. But more fundamentally, a determination has to be made about which substances in the atmosphere present an environmental risk to society and the extent to which these substances *can* and *should* be controlled.

This important determination proceeds from the basic premise that the earth's atmosphere comprises a specific combination of various gases. Nitrogen and oxygen account for 99 percent, and other gases such as carbon dioxide and helium make up the remainder—a composition critical to supporting life on earth. Any substances that contaminate or disrupt this natural composition pose an environmental risk and are therefore potential targets for clean air policy. Identifying these atmospheric contaminants is critical, but it is only part of the story. Ultimately, a decision must be made about *how much* of any of these contaminants society is willing and able to tolerate—an issue of considerable debate. What *is* clear is that we cannot entirely avoid the risks of air pollution without incurring unreasonable opportunity costs.

To understand this assertion, consider the following. Some contaminants in the atmosphere are **natural pollutants,** such as pollen, airborne dust particles from volcanic disturbances, gases from decaying animals and plants, even salt from the oceans' waters. Because these pollutants occur naturally, they are virtually beyond human control. Other contaminants are **anthropogenic,** meaning they are caused by human activity. These include such

natural pollutants
Those contaminants that come about through nonartificial processes in nature.

anthropogenic pollutants
Those contaminants associated with human activity.

substances as carbon monoxide from automobile tailpipe exhausts, sulfur dioxide emissions arising from electricity generation, and toxic chemicals released from manufacturing plants. Although these types of pollutants *are* controllable and generally present a much greater environmental risk than natural contaminants, they cannot be avoided completely without incurring the unrealistic opportunity cost of the absence of all industrial activity. Consequently, we must accept the reality that our national level of air quality will *not* be synonymous with a zero pollution level. But just what level of pollution is "acceptable," and how should it be determined?

Based on economic theory, we know that an *efficient* level of air quality is identified as the point where the marginal social benefits of cleaner air are balanced with the marginal social costs incurred to achieve it. Furthermore, we recognize that market-based instruments can be employed to reduce the negative externalities from pollution-generating production and consumption activities and to encourage the positive externalities associated with pollution abatement. These theories can and sometimes do guide policy decisions. However, as is often the case, the real-world complexities of the democratic process, scientific uncertainty, and political pressures tend to delay or even prohibit the realization of this economic policy approach.

Our goal in this chapter is to explore the realities of clean air policy development by studying how the process has evolved in the United States. Of particular interest is to examine how the U.S. government uses standards to define air quality for the nation and to critically evaluate the implications of using a standards-based approach. To organize the presentation, we begin by discussing the following aspects of U.S. air quality policy: (1) its evolution and development; (2) its primary objectives; (3) its standards-based definition of air quality; and (4) the infrastructure it establishes for implementation. Once done, we conduct a two-part benefit-cost analysis—the first as an overall appraisal of the Clean Air Act and its amendments and the second as an evaluation of the standard-setting process. An appendix at the end of the chapter provides a reference of the acronyms we use in our discussions.

An Overview of Air Quality Legislation in the United States

On November 15, 1990, President Bush signed into law extensive changes in U.S. air quality policy in the form of the 1990 Clean Air Act Amendments. This legislation received strong congressional support measured by an 89 to 11 vote in the Senate and a 401 to 21 vote in the House. Its hallmark is the integration of market-based policy instruments, which use incentives in place of standards and allow firms some flexibility in deciding how best to comply with the law. Such a precedence-setting policy shift is an indication that government is starting to recognize the potential effectiveness of market mechanisms in achieving environmental objectives. This legislative landmark came only after years of political battles, false starts, and a chronicle of events that underscores the importance of environmental issues and the complexity of drafting policy to deal with them.

In the Beginning

Prior to the 1950s, all air quality legislation in the United States had been enacted by state and local governments, most of which have a rather extensive history of laws aimed at cleaner air. Logically, the earliest of these were passed during the Industrial Revolution. Chicago and Cincinnati share the historical distinction of having passed the first air pollution laws in 1881 to deal with emissions from furnaces and locomotives.[1] Even in contemporary times, state and local governments typically have taken the lead. The most notable example is California, whose often pathbreaking legislation has been in direct response to the smog problem in Los Angeles.[2] In 1961, California passed the first state-level air pollution law to control motor vehicle emissions. This legislation followed many years of struggle between California officials and the American automobile industry, the subject of Application 10.1. In fact, a decade had passed since a 1951 study by Dr. A. J. Haagen-Smit of the California Institute of Technology scientifically confirmed that automobile emissions were a major contributor to the formation of smog.

Application 10.1

California Smog and the Automobile Industry

California's severe smog problem motivated its early attempts in the 1950s to gain the support of the automobile industry in solving its dilemma. Despite the evidence connecting motor vehicle emissions to smog production revealed in Dr. A. J. Haagen-Smit's 1951 study, the automobile industry denied that auto emissions were a major contributor to the problem and argued that the source of urban smog required further investigation.

The result was a volley between the industry and the state government that accomplished little throughout the 1950s. California officials naively continued to await a resolve from the industry despite their own unwillingness to allocate the substantial dollars needed to research the problem. For their part, the profit-maximizing manufacturers argued that the problem was complex and required more time for further research.

---

[1] See Stern (1982), p. 44. This article provides a thorough historical perspective on U.S. air quality laws.

[2] In the next chapter, we will discuss some of the factors responsible for this continuing urban air problem.

Application 10.1 (concluded)

In 1959, manufacturers acknowledged that the engine's design was an important source of the emissions problem. In 1961 automakers began to install engine ventilation devices on all new cars sold in California to control these emissions, a technology change that was eventually mandated under California law. However, this technology was not new. In fact, it had been developed back in the 1930s. The California government, apparently weary of the lack of progress, attempted to force the issue. Legislation was passed calling for the installation of equipment to control vehicle exhausts as soon as it was developed either by the major automakers or by any three independent manufacturers. The automobile producers asserted that such technology simply did not exist. Yet, in June 1964, the state confirmed that the requisite number of independent parts manufacturers could provide the needed add-on equipment at a reasonable cost and mandated its installation on all new vehicles starting with the 1966 model year. Predictably, the automakers announced in August 1964 that they had the capability to install their own devices on 1966 models, despite the fact that in March they had claimed that 1967 was the earliest model year by which they could accommodate the change.

Not only were the major auto producers using delay tactics, but the measure of their innovative effort was something less than impressive. Ford and General Motors developed only a simple air pump, while Chrysler's solution, marketed as a "clean air package," involved only minor alterations to its fuel and carburetion system. It was later discovered that Chrysler's "solution" contributed significantly to nitrogen oxide emissions.

Why were there such significant delays? Part of the answer is based on economic theory. If there had been a demand for cleaner-running cars, competitive firms would have recognized the advantage of being the first to satisfy that demand as well as the threat to their survival of being left behind in what is often a race to innovate. However, it is not at all clear that such a demand existed, and even if it had, market incentives were thwarted by the market power possessed by the "Big Three"—General Motors, Ford, and Chrysler. The giant automakers enjoyed a comfortable position of market strength that was protected by entry barriers from the threat of any innovative entering firms. This collusive environment was exacerbated in 1953 when the three firms formally pooled their efforts by forming a committee to jointly investigate the pollution problem. Later, in 1955, they executed a cross-licensing agreement to share access to any patents on emission controls. In so doing, they effectively removed the incentive for any one of them to find an innovative solution. (It turns out that in 1969 the Department of Justice filed suit against the Big Three, charging them with collusive attempts at hindering the advancement of pollution control technology. The suit was settled by a consent decree that ended the cross-licensing agreement.)

Economic theory explains the futility of the California government's approach. Simply urging an imperfectly competitive industry to find a solution to the emissions problem was not likely to be successful without some market incentive. Not only were the Big Three reluctant to incur the associated research costs, but they had no motivation to develop emissions control equipment that they knew would adversely affect engine performance.

Sources: Lawrence White, *The Regulation of Air Pollutant Emissions from Motor Vehicles* (Washington: American Enterprise Institute for Public Policy Research, 1982), Ch. 3; U.S. Senate, Staff of the Subcommittee on Air and Water Pollution of the Committee on Public Works, *The Impact of Auto Emission Standards* (Washington, D.C.: U.S. Government Printing Office, October 1973); Eugene P. Seskin, "Automobile Air Pollution Policy," in Paul R. Portney, ed., *Current Issues in U.S. Environmental Policy* (Baltimore: The Johns Hopkins University Press, 1978), pp. 68–104.

TABLE 10.1   A Brief Retrospective of U.S. Air Quality Legislation

---

Air Pollution Control Act of 1955	This was the first federal legislation on air pollution. Its focus was very limited, aimed primarily at providing federal appropriations to state governments in support of research and training on air quality.
Clean Air Act of 1963	This was the first comprehensive federal air quality legislation, though it continued to place the onus of air quality control on state governments. Emissions regulations for stationary sources were established, and the secretary of the Department of Health, Education and Welfare (HEW) was empowered to set up a liaison committee with the auto industry to study the effects of motor vehicle emissions.
Motor Vehicle Air Pollution Control Act of 1965	The HEW secretary was authorized to set emission standards on new motor vehicles, but there was no statutory deadline by which this was to be accomplished.
1965 Clean Air Act Amendments	The HEW was authorized to establish the first federally mandated mobile emissions standards. Maximum emissions of carbon monoxide and hydrocarbons were set for new motor vehicles, starting with the 1968 model year.
Air Quality Control Act of 1967	Air quality control regions (AQCR) were to be established across the country. The HEW was to determine air quality criteria for common air pollutants and was to identify available control technologies. States were to set and implement ambient air quality standards for their designated regions based on results of federal research on the effects of air pollution. The federal government could intervene if it did not approve of the states' decisions.
1970 Clean Air Act Amendments	National Ambient Air Quality Standards (NAAQS) were established for stationary sources, and emissions limits were set for mobile sources. Both were to be implemented through formalized State Implementation Plans (SIPs). New source performance standards (NSPS) were established at more stringent levels than for existing sources.
1977 Clean Air Act Amendments	Previously set deadlines for meeting air quality objectives were modified. AQCRs were reclassified into attainment and nonattainment regions. The objective was to protect regions that were "cleaner" than what was required by the NAAQS. These regions were termed "PSD" areas to indicate "prevention of significant deterioration."

Sources: Arthur C. Stern, "History of Air Pollution Legislation in the United States," *Journal of the Air Pollution Control Association* 32, no. 1, January 1982, pp. 44–61; Edwin S. Mills, *The Economics of Environmental Quality,* New York: W.W. Norton and Company, Inc., 1978, pp. 189–94; Paul R. Portney, "Air Pollution Policy," in Paul R. Portney, ed., *Public Policies for Environmental Protection,* Washington, D.C.: Resources for the Future, 1990a, pp. 27–96; Sidney M. Wolf, *Pollution Law Handbook: A Guide to Federal Environmental Laws,* New York: Quorum Books, 1988, Chapter 2.

At the federal level, the legislative history of air pollution initiatives is much shorter. In fact, there were no *national* air quality laws until the Air Pollution Control Act of 1955 was passed, and there was no truly comprehensive legislation until the Clean Air Act of 1963 was enacted—nearly a century after state and local governments had begun to take action. From that point on, there were a series of revisions and new initiatives that helped form U.S. policy as it is now defined. Look at Table 10.1 for a synopsis of the major federal laws that map out this important legislative evolution.

Notice in the table that during the 1960s there were many policy revisions, many of which gradually shifted authority away from the states and toward the federal level. However, it was the decade of the 1970s that marked the turning point in the history of U.S. air quality legislation. Through the 1970 Clean Air Act Amendments, Congress established national standards for air quality and authorized the newly created Environmental Protection Agency (EPA) to administer and implement its policy.

Much of the impetus for these major changes started at the grassroots level. Chronicles of environmental degradation, some with ominous predictions, had begun to appear on bookstore shelves.[3] In 1970, the first Earth Day was celebrated, exemplifying society's growing interest in environmental issues. In 1972, the Stockholm Conference on the Human Environment was held, the largest international symposium on the environment to date. Throughout the decade, membership in environmental groups grew at a record-setting pace. Society was sending a strong signal to public officials and political hopefuls that government should be more responsive to environmental problems. There was no doubt that environmental issues would play a considerable role in national policy decisions and global politics in the future.

Recognizing the need for further policy reform, Congress passed still more amendments to the Clean Air Act in 1977. Among its many provisions, the 1977 Amendments strengthened the law to protect areas in the country that already met national air quality standards. Meanwhile, the EPA developed new programs to give state governments viable alternatives through which they could satisfy federal requirements. Although some of these had a market orientation, there was no question that the command-and-control policy framework was well entrenched in U.S. air quality policy. It was clear that the use of standards as well as federally controlled procedures to implement them would continue to be the fundamental basis of air quality legislation.

Current U.S. Policy

With this chronicle of policy reform behind it, Congress passed into law some of the most comprehensive legislation in its history—the 1990 Clean Air Act Amendments. These map out national directives for reducing the risks associated with air pollution. The 1990 Amendments are extensive. Eleven major sections comprising new and revised statutes describe complex changes to U.S. air quality control policy. Table 10.2 itemizes these titled sections and gives a brief summary of what each entails.

Notice from the table how the collective provisions are all-inclusive, which to a large extent reflects the long history that preceded them. Also, take note of the fact that certain of the titled sections use market-based approaches, such as Title IV and Title VI. Yet despite this integration of incentive-based instruments in the 1990 Amendments, the underlying structure continues to

---

[3]The classic example of such writings is *Silent Spring* by Rachel Carson, published in 1962.

TABLE 10.2   An Overview of the Clean Air Act Amendments of 1990

Title I. Provisions for Attainment and Maintenance of National Ambient Air Quality Standards

Summary: This section amends and extends provisions for achieving the National Ambient Air Quality
              Standards, (NAAQS), and regulates changes in State Implementation Plans (SIPs) for
              nonattainment areas. Special sets of provisions are written for ozone, carbon monoxide, and
              particulate matter.

Title II. Provisions Relating to Mobile Sources

Summary: More stringent emissions controls are established, and the vehicle useful life for most emissions
              standards is extended to 10 years or 100,000 miles. New provisions address the use of reformulated
              gasoline, oxygenated fuels, and alternative fuels in certain nonattainment areas. Leaded gasoline is
              prohibited after December 31, 1995. A pilot test program is authorized for California to show the
              effectiveness of clean-fuel vehicles in ozone nonattainment areas. Vehicle inspection and
              maintenance programs are to be enhanced in the worst smog and carbon monoxide areas.

Title III. Hazardous Air Pollutants

Summary: 189 toxic pollutants are listed in the law as the basis for setting emissions controls. Maximum
              Achievable Control Technology (MACT) standards are to be established for all listed source
              categories within a 10-year period. Firms are allowed to postpone installation of MACT if they
              voluntarily and permanently reduce toxic emissions in advance of the deadline. A Chemical Safety
              Board is established to study accidental releases of hazardous substances.

Title IV. Acid Deposition Control

Summary: A market-based allowance program is established to achieve a permanent 10-million-ton reduction in
              sulfur dioxide emissions by January 1, 2000. A national cap on sulfur dioxide emissions of 8.9
              million tons from utilities is established beginning January 1, 2000. A 2-million-ton reduction in
              nitrogen oxide emissions is mandated.

Title V. Permits

Summary: States are required to establish permit programs to facilitate compliance with the new amendments.
              All major sources of air pollution are required to have federal permits to operate. The permits, to be
              administered by states and supervised by the EPA, will provide a mechanism for enforcement of the
              1990 law.

Title VI. Stratospheric Ozone Protection

Summary: All Class I and II substances contributing to ozone depletion are to be identified and listed by the
              EPA. A phase-out program is outlined for both classifications. Allowances are to be issued by the
              EPA and a procedure established to facilitate trading that will result in a net reduction in
              production and consumption of ozone-depleting substances.

Title VII. Provisions Relating to Enforcement

Summary: Enforcement is strengthened by an increased range of civil and criminal penalties for violations of
              the law and the establishment of new authorities.

Title VIII. Miscellaneous Provisions

Summary: Programs are established to control air pollution from sources on the Outer Continental Shelf.
              Negotiations with Mexico are authorized to improve air quality in border regions. Funds are
              allocated to support studies aimed at evaluating sources of visibility impairment and to assess
              progress in visibility in Class I areas.

Title IX. Clean Air Research

Summary: The EPA is to establish research programs associated with air pollution. The National Acid
              Precipitation Assessment Program (NAPAP) is reauthorized, and its responsibilities are modified
              and expanded. Cost-benefit analysis is specifically mandated as the decision rule to be used by the
              NAPAP in implementing the new amendments, the first such directive in any major environmental
              legislation.

TABLE 10.2   *(concluded)*

Title X. Disadvantaged Business Concerns
Summary: The EPA Administrator is to require that not less than 10 percent of funding for research relating to
                         the 1990 Amendments be made available to disadvantaged firms, that is, those at least 51 percent
                         owned and controlled by the socially and economically disadvantaged.

Title XI. Clean Air Employment Transition Assistance
Summary: A program is established for eligible workers who have been laid off or terminated due to
                         compliance with the 1990 Amendments. The program is to include training, employment services,
                         job-search allowances, relocation allowances, and needs-related payments to eligible persons.

Sources: Council on Environmental Quality, *Environmental Quality, 22nd Annual Report* (Washington, D.C.: U.S. Government Printing
Office, March 1992), pp. 12–17; U.S. Environmental Protection Agency, Office of Air and Radiation, *The Clean Air Act Amendments of
1990 Summary Materials* (Washington, D.C., November 15, 1990); U.S. Environmental Protection Agency, Office of Air and Radiation,
Clean Air Act Amendments of 1990: Detailed Summary of Titles (Washington, D.C., November 30, 1990).

be command-and-control oriented. In particular, the objectives of U.S. policy
are to be met using national air quality standards, which effectively define a
common air quality level for the nation. These standards in turn are implemented through an extensive infrastructure that facilitates federal oversight.
The uniformity of such an approach impedes the achievement of an optimal
solution based on either economic criterion—allocative efficiency or cost-
effectiveness. To verify this assertion, we begin by examining the motivation
for this regulatory approach given by the statutory objectives of the Clean
Air Act.

Defining the Objectives of Air Quality Control

The current objectives of U.S. air quality policy were originally defined in the
first comprehensive federal body of law on air quality control, the Clean Air
Act of 1963. First among these is:

> . . . to protect and enhance the quality of the Nation's air resources so as to promote
> the public health and welfare and the productive capacity of its population.[4]

To achieve the nation's objectives, the government must have a clear understanding of the environmental risks of air pollution and the extent of abatement
necessary to reduce these risks to some acceptable level. This determination

---

[4]The other three statutory objectives are as follows: "(2) to initiate and accelerate a
national research and development program to achieve the prevention and control of air
pollution; (3) to provide technical and financial assistance to state and local governments in
connection with the development and execution of their air pollution prevention and control
programs; and (4) to encourage and assist the development and operation of regional air
pollution control programs" [Sec.101(b)].

must be supported by medical and scientific research on the associated health, welfare, and aesthetic effects. The first step is to identify the primary causes of air pollution and to isolate those contaminants deemed most harmful. The ultimate decisions are critical, since they form the basis for a national level of air quality.

Identifying Major Air Pollutants

Consider the extraordinary responsibility of determining which pollutants are most responsible for air pollution and setting the proper level at which to control them. Such a decision-making process is complex given the wide range of human sensitivity to various pollutants, the uncertainty about health and welfare effects—particularly over the long term—and the enormous task of assessing the effects of various *combinations* of pollutants. Under U.S. law, official reports called **criteria documents** present an evaluation of the available scientific evidence on the properties and effects of any known or suspected pollutant.[5]

criteria documents
Reports that present an evaluation of scientific evidence on the properties and effects of known or suspected pollutants.

criteria pollutants
Identified substances known to be hazardous to health and welfare, so named because they are characterized as harmful by criteria documents.

The evidence summarized in these documents is used to identify common air pollutants known to present a risk to health and the environment. Officially, these **criteria pollutants** are identified substances known to be hazardous to health and welfare. As of 1994, there are six identified criteria pollutants in the United States. These are:

Particulate matter (PM-10)[6]

Sulfur dioxide (SO_2)

Carbon monoxide (CO)

Nitrogen dioxide (NO_2)

Tropospheric ozone (O_3)

Lead (Pb)

hazardous air pollutants
Non-criteria pollutants that may cause or contribute to irreversible illness or increased mortality.

Table 10.3 summarizes the health and welfare effects of exposure to these pollutants, which are critical to the identification process.

A second group of contaminants identified by U.S. legislation are the so-called **hazardous air pollutants** or **air toxics.** These are noncriteria pollutants that may reasonably be expected to cause or contribute to irreversible illness or increased mortality.

---

[5]The documents are so named because the assessment process is to be based on descriptive factors called **criteria.** These criteria are characteristics of pollutants and their potential health and welfare effects. Mandating the establishment of criteria at the federal level was first accomplished through the Air Quality Act of 1967.

[6]PM-10 refers to particles less than 10 micrograms in diameter.

TABLE 10.3   Health and Welfare Effects of the Six Criteria Pollutants

Criteria Pollutant	Major Effects
Particulate matter (PM)	*Health:* Breathing symptoms; aggravation of existing respiratory and cardiovascular disease; impairment of the body's natural defense systems; damage to lung tissue; carcinogenesis; and premature mortality.
	Welfare: Damage to materials; soiling; and visibility impairment.
Sulfur dioxide (SO$_2$)	*Health:* Adverse effects on breathing; respiratory illness; alterations to the lung's defenses; and aggravation of existing respiratory and cardiovascular disease.
	Welfare: Foliar damage on trees and crops; contributes to acidic deposition, which in turn causes acidification of waterways, accelerated corrosion of buildings and monuments, and visibility impairment.
Carbon monoxide (CO)	*Health:* Exposure to elevated levels causes impairment of visual perception, work capacity, manual dexterity, learning ability, and performance of complex tasks; individuals with existing cardiovascular disease are at greater risk.
Nitrogen dioxide (NO$_2$)	*Health:* Lung irritation; reduced resistance to respiratory infection; continued or frequent exposure may cause higher incidence of acute respiratory disease in children.
	Welfare: Contributes to ozone formation and acidic precipitation, which in turn affect terrestrial and aquatic ecosystems.
Ozone (O$_3$)	*Health:* Reduced lung functioning; damage to lung tissue; increased sensitivity of the lung to other irritants.
	Welfare: Reduction in crop yields; foliar damage to crops and trees; damage to ecosystems.
Lead (Pb)	*Health:* Damage to kidneys, liver, nervous system, and blood-forming organs; changes in fundamental enzymatic, energy transfer, and homeostatic mechanisms in the body; particularly susceptible to low doses are fetuses, infants, and children who may suffer damage to the central nervous system; excessive exposure can cause neurological problems such as seizures, mental retardation, and/or behavioral disorders.

Source: U.S. Environmental Protection Agency, Office of Air Quality Planning and Standards, *National Air Quality and Emissions Trends Report, 1992* (Washington, D.C., October 1993).

What distinguishes these substances from the criteria pollutants is that the risk of exposure is much greater, although typically a much smaller segment of society is affected. The 1990 Clean Air Act Amendments include an initial list of 189 identified hazardous air pollutants, which is to be periodically revised as needed. Prior to 1990, only eight such substances had been identified and placed under the EPA's control.[7] It was precisely because of

---

[7]The 1970 Amendments originally called for a published listing of identified hazardous pollutants within 90 days of its enactment and required that the list be revised on a regular basis. Yet, by March 31, 1971, only three substances had been listed—asbestos, beryllium, and mercury—and it was not until 1975 that a fourth substance, vinyl chloride, was identified. Until the 1990 Amendments, the only other additions were for benzene, added in 1977, radionuclides in 1979, inorganic arsenic in 1980, and coke oven emissions in 1984.

this lack of regulatory action that a more aggressive policy was enacted in the 1990 Amendments.

Setting Standards as a National Definition of Air Quality

Once the EPA identifies the major air pollutants, it then establishes **national standards** for these substances. These standards set maximum allowable levels of each identified pollutant, which are applicable to all polluting sources. The two major types of identifiable and potentially controllable sources are stationary sources and mobile sources. A **stationary source** is any building or structure that emits pollution, such as a coal-burning power plant. A **mobile source** refers to any transport vehicle that generates polluting emissions, such as an automobile or truck.

By establishing national standards, the federal government implicitly defines air quality for the entire country—a practice that is not exclusive to the United States. For example, Japan and some European countries also use a standard-setting approach to communicate an acceptable level of air quality for society. While the specifics vary across countries, in almost every case the list of identified air pollutants coincides with those named as criteria pollutants in the United States.

stationary source
A fixed-site producer of pollution, such as a building or manufacturing plant.

mobile source
Any nonstationary polluting source including all transport vehicles.

Standards for Criteria Air Pollutants

For the six criteria pollutants, the U.S. standards are referred to as **National Ambient Air Quality Standards (NAAQS).** These are maximum allowable concentrations of criteria air pollutants that may be emitted into the outside air from stationary or mobile sources. Within this broad classification are two subcategories, primary and secondary NAAQS:

National Ambient Air Quality Standards (NAAQS)
Maximum allowable concentrations of criteria air pollutants emitted from stationary or mobile sources into the outside air.

primary NAAQS
NAAQS set to protect public health from air pollution, with some margin of safety.

secondary NAAQS
NAAQS set to protect public welfare from any adverse, non-health effects of air pollution.

- **Primary NAAQS** are standards set to protect public health, with some margin of safety.
- **Secondary NAAQS** are standards intended to protect public welfare.

Originally established under the 1970 Clean Air Act Amendments, these standards have been revised from time to time. In fact, the law requires that the criteria and the NAAQS be reviewed by the EPA every five years. The primary and secondary NAAQS in effect as of 1993 are given in Table 10.4. Notice that none of the standards are set at a zero concentration level. Thus, if we accept these standards as the nation's definition of air quality, then we must conclude that acceptable air quality does not mean the absence of all criteria pollutants.

TABLE 10.4   National Ambient Air Quality Standards (NAAQS) in Effect in 1993

| Pollutant | Primary Standard | | Secondary Standard | |
	Averaging Time	Concentration	Averaging Time	Concentration
Particulate matter (PM-10)	Annual arithmetic mean	50 µg/m^3		Same as primary
	24-hour	150 µg/m^3		Same as primary
Sulfur dioxide (SO$_2$)	Annual arithmetic mean	80 µg/m^3 (0.03 ppm)	3-hour	1300 µg/m^3 (0.50 ppm)
	24-hour	365 µg/m^3 (0.14 ppm)		
Carbon monoxide (CO)	8-hour	9.0 ppm (10 mg/m^3)		No secondary standard
	1-hour	35 ppm (40 mg/m^3)		No secondary standard
Nitrogen dioxide (NO$_2$)	Annual arithmetic mean	0.053 ppm (100 µg/m^3)		Same as primary
Ozone (O$_3$)	Maximum daily 1-hour average	0.12 ppm (235 µg/m^3)		Same as primary
Lead (Pb)	Maximum quarterly average	1.5 µg/m^3		Same as primary

Notes: For some criteria pollutants, both a long-term and a short-term standard are given. The long-term standards give either a quarterly or annual mean level that may not be exceeded. The short-term standards are the upper-bound for 1-, 3-, 8-, or 24-hour averages that may not be exceeded more than once per year. The standard for O$_3$ limits the expected number of days per calendar year with daily maximum concentrations over 0.12 ppm to be less than or equal to one.

pm = parts per million.
µg/m^3 = micrograms per cubic meter mg/m^3 = milligrams per cubic meter.

Values given in parentheses are approximately equivalent concentrations.

Source: U.S. Environmental Protection Agency, Office of Air Quality Planning and Standards, *National Air Quality and Emissions Trends Report, 1992* (Research Triangle Park, N.C., October 1993), Table 2-1, p. 2-1.

National Emission Standards for Hazardous Air Pollutants (NESHAP) Standards set to protect public health and the environment that are applicable to every major source of any identified hazardous air pollutant.

Standards for Hazardous Air Pollutants

U.S. law also calls for the establishment of **National Emission Standards for Hazardous Air Pollutants (NESHAPs)** to be achieved by all identified polluting sources. These are established for every major source of one or more of the listed hazardous air pollutants. They are intended to protect public health and the environment, taking into account the costs to attain the standards, any nonair-quality health and environmental impacts, and energy requirements.

The NESHAP are to attain the maximum degree of reduction for each air toxic achievable, referred to as **maximum achievable control technology (MACT).** Where possible, this reduction is to achieve complete prohibition

maximum achievable control technology (MACT)
The control technology that achieves the maximum degree of reduction to be achieved by the NESHAP.

of the substance. Polluters can employ various methods to meet the standards such as substituting less harmful inputs or completely enclosing production processes to eliminate hazardous emissions.

Establishing an Infrastructure to Implement the Standards

To implement U.S. national standards, an infrastructure has been established that involves both federal and state governments. This infrastructure is defined through two components: (1) State Implementation Plans (SIPs); and (2) Air Quality Control Regions (AQCRs).

State Implementation Plans

State Implementation Plan (SIP)
A detailed procedure outlining how a state intends to implement, monitor, and enforce the NAAQS and the NESHAP.

Coordination between the two major levels of government is achieved through the use of **State Implementation Plans (SIP)** established by the 1970 Clean Air Act Amendments. A **State Implementation Plan (SIP)** is an EPA-approved, detailed procedure of how a state intends to implement, monitor, and enforce the NAAQS and the NESHAP.[8]

Because the law is dynamic, the SIPs must be amended periodically to incorporate new provisions in the law. Determining reasonable deadlines for states to update their SIPs has been a sore point. In fact, when the concept of an SIP was initially established, each state was given only nine months to prepare and submit to the EPA its proposed SIP. In retrospect, most agree that this nine-month deadline was unrealistic at best. In fact, by as late as 1976, only 23 of the 55 SIPs submitted to the EPA had received the agency's full approval.

The SIP system follows a federalist format by delegating certain air pollution control tasks to different jurisdictions. The standard-setting is assigned mainly to the federal level to standardize air quality across the country. State governments are responsible for implementing the standards and monitoring polluting sources within their jurisdictions, since their proximity to these sources and their knowledge of the immediate region gives them an advantage in doing so.

air quality control regions (AQCRs)
Geographical areas designated by the federal government within which common air pollution problems are shared by several communities.

Air Quality Control Regions

To facilitate the coordination of states' responsibilities, **Air Quality Control Regions (AQCRs)** are defined within each state's respective jurisdictions, a mandate instituted by the Air Quality Act of 1967. These regions are geographical areas designated by the federal government within which common air pollution problems are shared by several communities.

---

[8]The NAAQS represent the *minimum* requirements to be attained by every state. However, at its discretion, a state can submit a plan to achieve more stringent standards.

TABLE 10.5   **Number of Nonattainment Areas for the NAAQS Pollutants as of 1993**

Pollutant	*Number of Nonattainment Areas**
Particulate matter (PM-10)	70
Sulfur dioxide (SO_2)	46
Carbon monoxide (CO)	41
Nitrogen dioxide (NO_2)	1
Ozone (O_3)	94
Lead (Pb)	13

*Unclassified areas are not included in the totals.

Source: U.S. Environmental Protection Agency, Office of Air Quality Planning and Standards, *National Air Quality and Emissions Trends Report, 1992* (Research Triangle Park, N.C., October 1993), Table 5-1, p. 5-1.

As of 1994, 247 AQCRs have been designated across the United States. These well-defined geographical areas are monitored to determine compliance with the national air quality standards. Today, a number of AQCRs still have not met the current NAAQS for one or more of the six criteria pollutants. Table 10.5 provides information on these nonattainment areas as of 1993. As these data indicate, regions have the greatest difficulty achieving the ozone standard, with 94 regions still classified as nonattainment for this major contributor of urban smog.

Reclassification of AQCRs to Protect "Clean Air Areas"

In 1972, the Sierra Club filed suit against the EPA for failing to protect areas that were "cleaner" than what was required by law.[9] The environmental group argued that the existing NAAQS were aimed solely at improving air quality in areas that did not meet the standards. The concern was that nondegradation areas, as they are called, would be allowed to deteriorate to the existing national standards. The Sierra Club claimed that the lack of protection for nondegradation areas was a violation of the law, since one of the statutory purposes of the Clean Air Act is to *protect* as well as to *enhance* the quality of the nation's air resources. Ultimately, the group won the suit, and in 1974 a new program was established to protect these already "clean" areas.

The new "clean air areas" program redefined the structure of federal air pollution control and played a significant role in directing future policy decisions. States had to reassess their AQCRs so that they could identify the following three groups: (1) regions that met the standards; (2) regions that did not meet the standards; and (3) regions with insufficient data to confirm a classification. Regions meeting or exceeding national standards were redesignated

---

[9]See *Sierra Club* v. *Ruckelshaus*, D.D.C.1972.

prevention of significant deterioration (PSD) areas
Air quality control regions (AQCRs) meeting or exceeding national ambient air quality standards (NAAQS).

nonattainment areas
Air quality control regions (AQCRs) not in compliance with national ambient air quality standards (NAAQS).

as areas targeted for **prevention of significant deterioration,** or **PSD areas.** Those that did not were designated as **nonattainment areas.**

Once determined, every PSD area was to be designated as Class I, II, or III—a progressive classification based on the maximum allowable concentrations of criteria pollutants for each area. Class I areas, the most stringently controlled, include wilderness areas and national parks. The law specifically prohibits a redesignation of these initially established Class I areas.[10] There is also a declaration in the law that enhancing and protecting visibility in these Class I areas was to be a new national goal. One outcome of these new classifications is the nation's ongoing effort to improve visibility in the Grand Canyon National Park—the first use of the visibility protection law.

1990 Reclassification of Nonattainment Areas by Criteria Pollutant

In response to the nation's pervasive and persistent problem of urban air pollution, the 1990 Amendments reclassify all nonattainment areas for the pollutants most responsible for the problem—ozone, carbon monoxide, and particulate matter—into new progressive categories based upon existing pollutant concentrations. For example, ozone nonattainment areas are reclassified into five groups: marginal, moderate, serious, severe, and extreme. These new categories not only identify the severity of pollution across nonattainment areas but also provide the means to set more stringent regulations in those areas with higher pollution levels.

Monitoring Air Quality across Regions

Determining the compliance status of each region and the overall assessment of air quality for the nation depends upon a systematic measurement of the six criteria pollutants. In general, this is accomplished either by estimating the emissions level of each pollutant or by measuring the ambient concentration of each in some volume of air.

Estimating Pollutant Emissions Levels.   It is not feasible to measure actual pollutant emissions levels on a national scale, so instead they are *estimated.* In the United States, best available engineering methods are used to derive annual emissions estimates for over 450 source categories, which include almost all anthropogenic sources. These are then aggregated to determine regional and national emissions trends. Table 10.6 presents data on emissions estimates for the six criteria pollutants over the 1970 to 1991 period. According to these estimates, there have been reductions in emissions of all criteria pollutants over the long run, with the most substantial declines observed for lead emissions. This dramatic reduction is a direct result of the EPA's lead phaseout program, a market-based plan discussed in Application 10.2.

---

[10]Other than these initially classified Class I areas and certain other exceptions, States can redesignate classifications for PSD areas in accordance with very specific rules.

TABLE 10.6   National Emissions Estimates of Six Criteria Air Pollutants
(teragrams per year)*

Year	Particulate Matter (PM)	(PM-10)†	Sulfur Oxides (SO$_x$)	Carbon Monoxide (CO)	Nitrogen Oxides (NO$_x$)	Volatile Organic Compounds‡ (VOCs)	Lead (Pb)
1970	19.0	N/A	28.4	123.6	19.0	27.4	199.1
1975	11.0	N/A	25.5	104.8	20.3	22.5	143.8
1980	9.1	N/A	23.8	100.0	23.6	21.8	68.0
1985	7.9	5.6	21.7	83.1	19.4	19.8	18.3
1990	7.4	5.4	21.1	67.7	19.4	17.6	5.1
1991	7.4	5.5	20.7	62.1	18.8	16.9	5.0
Percentage Changes							
1970–1991	−61	N/A	−27	−50	− 1	−38	−97
1980–1991	−19	N/A	−13	−38	−20	−22	−93
1985–1991	− 6	−2	− 5	−25	− 3	−15	−73
1990–1991	0	−2	− 2	− 8	− 3	− 4	− 2

*A teragram is equal to one million metric tons, or about 1.1 million short tons (2,000 lbs.).
†PM-10 refers to particles less than 10 micrograms in diameter [which replaced the former standard of total suspended particles (TSP) in 1987], excluding particles from fugitive dust sources.
‡VOCs are used to measure the formation of ozone (O$_3$).
Sources: U.S. Environmental Protection Agency, Office of Air Quality Planning and Standards, *National Air Quality and Emissions Trends Report, 1991* (Research Triangle Park, N.C., October 1992); Council on Environmental Quality, *Environmental Quality, 23rd Annual Report* (Washington, D.C.: U.S. Government Printing Office, January 1993), Table 37.

Application 10.2

Market Incentives to Phase Out Lead Emissions

Even skeptics of market solutions to environmental problems are hard-pressed to deny the success story of lead banking and trading. Touted by economists and environmentalists alike, the use of market instruments in reducing lead emissions was undeniably a victory.

Lead is a toxic heavy metal that poses a serious health hazard if ingested or inhaled. Unfortunately it is ubiquitous, showing up in paints, plastics, lead-acid batteries, plumbing compounds, and gasoline. Its use in gasoline began in the 1920s, when refineries recognized it as the cheapest available source of octane. But by the 1960s and 1970s, evidence had begun to accumulate that linked lead exposure to mental disorders and cardiovascular disease. Research also showed that lead levels in the bloodstream were directly and immediately associated with changes in the lead content of

gasoline. In addition to the health threat, lead was also found to adversely affect the performance of catalytic converters being installed in new cars to meet tougher standards on tailpipe emissions.

In 1973, the EPA responded by requiring that unleaded gasoline be made available by 1974 and by establishing a limit on the average lead concentration of *all* gasoline (both leaded and unleaded) sold by a given refiner. Nonetheless, lead concentrations remained high, averaging about 2.0 grams per gallon in 1975, in part because of misfueling (i.e., using leaded fuels in vehicles designed to use only unleaded gasoline). Meanwhile, researchers continued to study the health effects of lead exposure. During the 1980s, new evidence revealed that the health threat was even more serious than originally believed. On every front, the consumption of leaded gasoline generated serious negative externalities, and existing policy was not tough enough or effective enough to solve the problem.

There was little question that consumption of the apparently hazardous substance had to be cut dramatically. Yet the most obvious solution—to place an immediate ban on the production and consumption of leaded gasoline—was not economically feasible. Such drastic regulatory decisions, however well intended, typically have adverse economic ramifications, and this one was no exception. While newer refineries had begun to adjust production to incorporate alternative octane boosters, such was not the case for older refineries, which had to confront costly retrofitting to accommodate the change. Obviously, such conversions would take a lot of time and money. The knee-jerk reaction might have been to simply shut down these older facilities, but this would have had serious consequences. A decision to abruptly close down a major segment of the nation's oil industry would be entirely benefit-based, ignoring the enormous social costs of such an extreme stratagem. Consider how such a massive shutdown would threaten national fuel supplies and bring about a price increase that could be disastrous to industry and pose a financial burden to private citizens. The sudden loss of jobs for refinery workers would add to the dilemma, leaving society the added costs of financially supporting these displaced workers and their families.

The EPA's ultimate policy response was to tighten the lead standard and use market incentives to achieve it. In 1982, the EPA established a new standard based only on leaded gasoline—1.1 grams per leaded gallon (gplg) effective July 1, 1985. Subsequently, the standard was made progressively more stringent through a series of steps, calling for a concentration of 0.5 gplg after July 1, 1985, 0.1 gplg after January 1, 1986, and a complete ban by 1996. To accomplish this phasedown, the agency introduced a program of **credits** issued to refineries for reductions that surpassed those required by law. These credits could then be *banked* for use during a subsequent stage of the phasedown or *traded* with older refineries unable to meet the reductions by the statutory deadlines.

As a result of this trading, or "constructive averaging" as it is also called, older refineries were allowed to produce gasoline with higher lead levels as long as they purchased credits from other refineries that were producing fuel with lower than required lead concentrations. Similarly, any refinery able to reduce beyond a given standard could bank its awarded credits and save them to meet the more stringent standards of a subsequent phasedown. In fact, this practice was very likely to occur given the physical properties of lead. It turns out that lead's octane power increases as its concentration decreases. This means that as concentration levels are reduced, the costs of further removal in terms of diminished gas performance increases. Under the banking plan, refineries were legally allowed to exploit this property by reducing more lead content when it was easier and less costly to do so, banking the earned credits for use against a later requirement when the costs of removal were much higher. Notice that, regardless of whether the reductions are achieved from a more concentrated or more diluted gasoline composition, the benefits to society are the same.

The end result was that the refineries best able to meet the required standards did so, compensating for their less efficient counterparts who were effectively given more time to retrofit their production processes. Such an outcome is cost-effective as long as the allocation of abatement levels across polluting sources occurs where the marginal abatement costs for each source are equal.

According to EPA reports, 73 percent of all refiners participated in the trading program in the second quarter of 1984. Ultimately, the plan cost the nation $220 million *less* than what it would have under a strict command-and-control approach of standard-setting, and this savings came about with no change in the benefits of lead reduction. Since 1970, airborne lead emissions have fallen by a remarkable 98 percent. The difference is only that the method used to achieve the reductions minimized costs.

Sources: Lily Whiteman, "Trades to Remember: The Lead Phasedown," *EPA Journal* 18, no. 2 (May/June 1992), pp. 38–39; U.S. Environmental Protection Agency, Office of Policy, Planning, and Evaluation, *The United States Experience with Economic Incentives to Control Environmental Pollution* (Washington, D.C., July 1992), pp. 5-7, 5-8; U.S. Environmental Protection Agency, Office of Policy Analysis, *Costs and Benefits of Reducing Lead in Gasoline: Final Regulatory Impact Analysis* (Washington, D.C., February 1985).

TABLE 10.7   **Number of Air Quality Monitoring Sites for Criteria Pollutants**

Pollutant	Number of Sites Reporting in 1992	Number of Trend Sites 1983–92
Particulate matter (PM-10)	1,471	652*
Sulfur dioxide (SO_2)	722	476
Carbon monoxide (CO)	507	308
Nitrogen dioxide (NO_2)	332	183
Ozone (O_3)	853	509
Lead (Pb)	437	203
Total	4,322	2,331

*Number of trend sites in 1988–92.

Source: U.S. Environmental Protection Agency, Office of Air Quality Planning and Standards, *National Air Quality and Emissions Trends Report, 1992* (Research Triangle Park, N.C., October 1993), Table 2-2, p. 2-2.

TABLE 10.8   **National Ambient Concentrations of the Six Criteria Pollutants, 1975–1991**

Year	Particulate Matter (TSP) ($\mu g/m^3$)	Sulfur Dioxide (SO_2) (ppm)	Carbon Monoxide (CO) (ppm)	Nitrogen Dioxide (NO_2) (ppm)	Ozone (O_3) (ppm)	Lead (Pb) ($\mu g/m^3$)
1975	61.9	0.015	11.96	0.029	0.153	1.04
1980	64.2	0.011	8.52	0.025	0.136	0.61
1985	47.7	0.009	6.99	0.024	0.123	0.26
1990	47.3	0.008	5.89	0.022	0.114	0.07
1991	47.3	0.008	5.60	0.022	0.115	0.06

Notes:
TSP = total suspended particulates.
$\mu g/m^3$ = micrograms per cubic meter.
ppm = parts per million.
All data are composite averages based on all sites in the national monitoring network.

Sources: U.S. Environmental Protection Agency, Office of Air Quality Planning and Standards, *National Air Quality and Emissions Trends Report, 1991* (Research Triangle Park, N.C., October 1992) and earlier reports in the series as cited in Council on Environmental Quality, *Environmental Quality, 23rd Annual Report* (Washington, D.C.: U.S. Government Printing Office, January 1993), Table 40, p. 337.

Measuring Pollutant Concentrations.   Pollutant concentration levels are actually *measured* at air monitoring station sites located throughout the country. Most of these sites are in urban regions characterized by relatively high pollutant concentrations and greater population exposure. All sites report their data to the EPA via an air-monitoring network. Table 10.7 shows the number of monitoring sites for the criteria pollutants in 1992 as compared to those operating over the 1983 to 1992 period. This latter group represents sites used to generate 10-year trend statistics. Table 10.8 presents trend data of ambient concentrations for the six criteria pollutants from 1975 to 1991.

Economic Analysis of U.S. Air Quality Policy

If we consider the evolution of U.S. air quality legislation that began in 1955, it is clear that the nation's control policy has become more comprehensive over time. There is now a vast infrastructure to implement and monitor national air quality objectives. This includes the establishment of AQCRs, an intergovernmental system of SIPs, and a network of monitoring sites. But is it reasonable to assess the nation's accomplishments by the greater number of provisions that now define air quality legislation or by the more elaborate implementation and monitoring systems that have been established? These may be *indicators* that the United States is attempting to strengthen policy, but do they suggest that policy is any more effective?

It seems simple enough to argue that the bottom line in assessing regulatory policy is whether or not any headway has been made in achieving cleaner air. However, such an argument is a gross oversimplification of what is in fact a much more complex problem. Look back at the trend data shown in Tables 10.6 and 10.8. Collectively, these data suggest that U.S. air quality is improving and that much has been achieved over the last several decades. Although this is likely true to a point, there are many factors that must be considered before any conclusions can be drawn. Among these are the accuracy of the emissions estimates and the determination of what part of any observed improvement is actually attributable to effective policy. Even if these factors are accounted for, there is the challenge of converting any policy-driven air improvements to monetized values of social benefits, such as reduced health risks, increased visibility, and the preservation of the ecology. Finally, one must consider the full extent of the costs borne by society to achieve whatever progress has been made. These costs should include not only explicit expenditures for compliance, monitoring, and enforcement, but also implicit costs due to shifts in production technology, substitution of fuels and other inputs, and changes in available marketed goods and services.

Collectively, these are the tasks that comprise an economic analysis of environmental policy. By systematically estimating and evaluating the costs and benefits associated with the Clean Air Act, it can be determined whether U.S. air control policy is **allocatively efficient.** Recall from previous chapters that the decision rule assuring an efficient outcome is the **maximization of net benefits**—the point where the associated **marginal social costs** and **marginal social benefits** are equal. To illustrate this approach, we present a two-part benefit-cost investigation of U.S. air policy. The first part assesses the overall efficiency of the Clean Air Act. The second considers the efficiency of the standard-setting process itself.[11]

---

[11]In the next chapter, more detailed analyses will be done, some of which employ cost-effectiveness as the relevant economic criterion.

TABLE 10.9   **Annualized Control Costs for Air**
(in millions of 1986 dollars)

Target	1972	1980	1987	1995	2000
Stationary sources	6,230	13,298	18,960	25,188	29,725
Mobile sources	1,345	4,010	7,469	11,097	14,140
Undesignated sources	341	327	250	207	184
Air pollution total	7,916	17,635	26,679	36,493	44,049

Source: U.S. Environmental Protection Agency, Office of Policy, Planning, and Evaluation, *Environmental Investments: The Cost of a Clean Environment* (Washington D.C., December 1990), p. 3-2.

A Benefit-Cost Analysis of the Clean Air Act

A Benefit-Cost Analysis of the Pre-1990 Clean Air Act

There is a fair amount of research that evaluates the efficiency of *specific* air quality control provisions. Far less prevalent are comprehensive analyses assessing the Clean Air Act in its entirety. Drawn from the work of other researchers, one such investigation was conducted by Paul Portney (1990a), an economist and researcher at Resources for the Future in Washington, D.C. With careful reservations, Portney offers a very telling comparison of the social benefits and costs associated with U.S. policy *prior to* the enactment of the 1990 Clean Air Act Amendments. Beyond the implications of the results, the study illustrates the practical value of benefit-cost analysis and the inherent difficulties of using this decision-making strategy to evaluate policy on a comprehensive scale.

Total Social Costs.   Any cost analysis of environmental policy involves the challenge of estimating the total costs to society from having to adapt to legislated provisions. These include both explicit and implicit costs. In the United States, explicit or out-of-pocket expenditure data are collected mainly by the Department of Commerce. These are the actual compliance and operating costs associated with air quality controls. Cost data for selected years are shown in Table 10.9.[12] Although important, these explicit cost data are insufficient for an economic benefit-cost analysis. Why? Because they do not account for implicit costs to society, such as higher-priced products, loss of employment from production and technology conversions, and restrictions on consumers' choice sets.

Portney's analysis derives social cost estimates of the Clean Air Act primarily from the work of two other researchers, Michael Hazilla and Raymond

---

[12]These costs are deflated to remove any inflationary effects and broken down by year (to present annualized data), by sector of the economy (i.e., EPA, non-EPA federal, state government, local government, and private sector), and by type (i.e., capital versus operating costs).

J. Kopp (1990). These researchers use a model of the U.S. economy to estimate how prices and income change with the implementation of U.S. policy aimed at both air quality and water quality. Ultimately, their measure of social costs is based upon an assessment of how social welfare changed as a result of the environmental legislation. Portney then approximates what proportion of these social costs were attributable to *just* the air quality regulations. Three annual social cost estimates are derived: $4.5 billion for 1975, $13.7 billion for 1981, and $33.0 billion in 1985—all stated in 1984 dollars. Each of these magnitudes is an estimate of both the explicit *and* the implicit costs of the pre-1990 U.S. clean air laws at different points in time, and each can be interpreted as the value of resources given up by society to implement air quality control legislation.

Total Social Benefits.   Estimating the total social benefits of the Clean Air Act involves a systematic process comprised of a series of steps:

1. Analyze the data that measure the trend in air quality over time.
2. Control for external influences on air quality to determine the amount of improvement due solely to public policy initiatives.
3. Determine the benefits gained by society from the air quality improvement and monetize them so that they can be compared to the associated costs.

Given the availability of air quality trend data, it might seem that the only difficulty in executing the first step is in choosing which of these data to employ. While there is some truth to this assertion, it is nonetheless short-sighted. It turns out that most of the available air quality data is not totally reliable or at least is limited in some way. This is not to say that these data are not useful, rather that they have limitations that must be acknowledged in order for the analysis to have validity.

A case in point is U.S. emissions data. Recall that these data are not actual measurements, but rather are estimates determined by the EPA. Thus, it is important to understand how these estimates are calculated, to know exactly what information the data are conveying, and to be aware of the limitations imposed by the estimation procedure. Likewise, ambient concentration data are also imperfect measures of U.S. air quality. Although these data are based on actual measurements, the monitoring system in the United States, while improving, is currently less than adequate.

Another important consideration is that all national statistics, by construction, disguise regional and local differences. Even when national data suggest that the ambient air is improving, there are some parts of the country such as urban areas that continue to face serious air pollution problems. Such localized variations are hidden by the averaging process. Finally, it is necessary to recognize that not all observed changes in air quality are attributable to policy. In truth, there are many factors other than regulatory controls that influence air pollution, many of which are simply beyond our control. For instance, Application 10.3 discusses the effect of weather and temperature on air quality.

Application 10.3

Exogenous Influences on Pollution Emission Levels

The 1989 to 1991 period was an impressive one for realizing improvements in U.S. air quality. According to the EPA, 41 urban areas had achieved compliance with federal smog standards for the first time. In addition, 13 cities that had never met the federal standards for carbon monoxide had finally done so during this period.

While the improvement in urban air quality is encouraging, it is important to assess the progress realistically and with a discerning eye. It is critical that we understand how much of any measured improvement in air quality is the result of policy initiatives and how much is simply the result of exogenous influences. A case in point is the role that weather can play in affecting air pollution, particularly the formation of urban smog. Since sunlight or heat is necessary to smog formation, the problem becomes more severe during the summer months. Moreover, inordinately warm weather exacerbates the problem, while a cooler summer season mitigates the effect. An awareness of these issues is necessary to give an accurate assessment of the nation's progress in controlling air pollution.

An unusually hot summer such as what was experienced in the United States in 1988 will elevate the nation's measures and estimates of air pollution. In contrast, the summer of 1991 was a relatively mild one. Bill Becker, executive director of an association of state and local pollution control administrators, was quoted as saying that the announced improvements in urban air quality for the 1989 to 1991 period were expected, partly because of the relatively cool weather in 1991.

Acknowledging that weather conditions have an effect on air quality, the fact remains that weather cannot be strategically controlled. However, it *is* possible to alter its effects on air quality, particularly in metropolitan areas where the problem is typically more severe. By definition, urban centers are home to major businesses. Consequently, they are characterized by a maze of black asphalt roadways, the congestion of automobiles, and a host of industrial machines, leaving little room for shade-providing trees. These symbols of industrial activity translate to higher temperatures for urban areas as compared to their suburban and rural counterparts. This observation has come to be known as the "urban island heat effect." As illustrated in the diagram below, late afternoon temperatures can be as much as 6 degrees higher in downtown areas than those in the rural countryside.

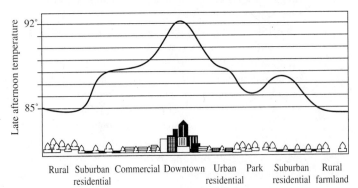

Source: U.S. Department of Energy, *Saving Energy by Managing Urban Heat Islands: Something We Can Do About the Weather* (Washington, DC: DOE, 1991).

Application 10.3 (concluded)

Even in the evening hours, the problem of elevated temperatures continues to plague urban areas. Asphalt streets and massive buildings continue to radiate heat even after sundown, holding evening city temperatures some 10 to 15 degrees higher than their levels in the countryside. Studies show that this "urban heat island effect" aggravates air pollution and increases peak energy demand. Higher demand for energy forces power plants to step up production, adding to the release of air pollutants.

It is little wonder that U.S. officials direct a number of policy initiatives squarely at the problem of urban air pollution. For its part, the U.S. Department of Energy offers a number of strategies that can be undertaken to mitigate the environmental impact of the "urban heat island effect." Some of these are as follows.

- Choose light colors for building exteriors and roofs to reflect rather than absorb sunlight.

- Use concrete or light-colored aggregate in asphalt for roads.
- Plant trees and shrubs to provide needed shade to parking lots and buildings.
- Provide some type of sun-shielding protection for exterior central air-conditioning units to improve efficiency.
- Incorporate natural shading in building energy codes.

Sources: H. Josef Hebert, "EPA Says Air is Improving; Cool Weather Plays Key Role," *Boston Globe,* October 20, 1992; Council on Environmental Quality, *Environmental Quality, 23rd Annual Report* (Washington, D.C.: U.S. Government Printing Office, January 1993); U.S. Department of Energy (DOE), *Saving Energy by Managing Urban Heat Islands: Something We Can Do About the Weather* (Washington, D.C.: DOE, 1991).

Acknowledging these issues, Portney's estimate of social benefits for the pre-1990 clean air laws relies upon a comprehensive survey and synthesis report conducted by another noted economist, A. Myrick Freeman (1982). Using ambient air concentration data from 1970 to 1978, Freeman translates improvements in pollution levels for the period into several benefit categories, using links established in existing research studies. These categories are: (1) improvements in human health; (2) decrease in damage to vegetation; (3) decrease in materials damage; (4) lower cleaning costs; and (5) enhanced aesthetics and visibility. Monetized values for each are derived, resulting in the following estimates expressed in 1984 dollars:

Health impacts:	$27.2 billion
Vegetation:	0.5 billion
Materials:	1.1 billion
Cleaning:	4.8 billion
Property values:	3.7 billion

Aggregating these values, Portney estimates the total value of social benefits as of 1978 at $37.3 billion. While only an approximation, the estimate suggests that society ought to be willing to pay $37.3 billion for the improvements to health, property, and the environment brought about by the clean air laws in effect at that time.[13]

Benefit-Cost Comparison.   The final step in the analysis is to compare the estimates of social costs and social benefits and interpret the result. Notice, however, that in the context of the Portney study, the two independently estimated components are valued for different periods. The relevant social cost estimate is as of 1981, but the comparable estimate of social benefits is as of 1978. Making one final concession, Portney suggests that the social benefits are likely to be higher in 1981 than their estimated value in 1978. He justifies this by observed improvements in air quality through the period as well as increases in the general population, meaning that more people would gain from the improvements. Thus, the $37.3 billion magnitude is treated as a viable, albeit conservative, benefit estimate for 1981. Comparing this value with the 1981 social cost estimate of $13.7 billion, Portney offers a qualified conclusion that the total social benefits (*TSB*) of pre-1990 clean air legislation outweigh the total social costs (*TSC*), at least for 1981.

While Portney suggests that this assessment is likely a reasonable one for 1981, he is adamant that the conclusion cannot be made without a number of reservations. For example, Freeman attributes all of the observed changes in air quality to the Clean Air Act, an assumption that biases the benefit estimates upward. Further, Portney cautions that even if the estimates are reasonable, they cannot be generalized beyond 1981. For instance, he points out that estimated social costs rise sharply in 1985 to $33.0 billion, an increase that is not likely to be matched by higher social benefits. Moreover, the benefit and cost magnitudes are estimated as *total* rather than *marginal* values, which does not convey sufficient information to draw any conclusion about allocative efficiency. Even though the *TSB* of clean air policy exceed *TSC,* there is no reason to assume that abatement controls are at their efficient level. Such an evaluation can be made only by finding out whether the *marginal* social benefit equals the *marginal* social cost at that point. In fact, only through a marginal analysis can the implications of subsequent legislative changes be assessed.

To illustrate this latter point, consider three hypothetical depictions of the 1981 social benefit and cost estimates shown in Figure 10.1(a) through 10.1(c). Costs and benefits in billions of dollars are measured on the vertical axis, and pollution abatement (*A*) associated with air control policy is measured on the horizontal axis. Notice that in all three cases, at the 1981 level of abatement, A_{1981}, *TSB* of $37.3 billion is higher than *TSC* of $13.7 billion. What differs across the three diagrams is the location of A_{1981} relative to the efficient level of abatement, A_e.

In Figure 10.1(a), A_{1981} is shown as equivalent to the efficient level, A_e, precisely at the point where the vertical distance between *TSB* and *TSC* is

---

[13]For a complete analysis of Freeman's work, see Portney (1990a), pp. 54–60. The interested reader may also wish to consult the original source, Freeman (1982).

FIGURE 10.1

A benefit-cost analysis of U.S. air quality controls as of 1981

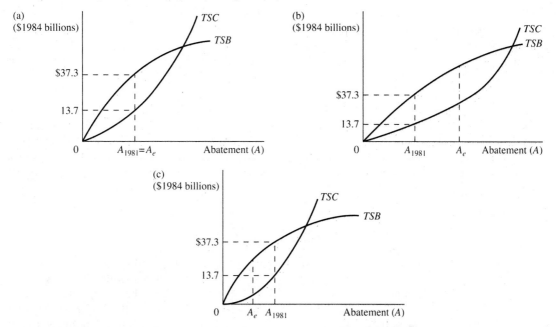

In all three depictions of U.S. policy, the *TSB* of $37.3 billion at the 1981 abatement level, A_{1981}, is higher than the *TSC* of $13.7 billion. What differs is the location of A_{1981} relative to the efficient level of abatement, A_e. In Figure 10.1(a), A_{1981} is equal to A_e, since at this point the slope of *TSB* is equal to the slope of *TSC,* meaning that the vertical distance between *TSB* and *TSC* is maximized. In Figure 10.1(b), A_{1981} is to the *left* of A_e, indicating that *too little* abatement has been legislated. Just the opposite case is depicted in Figure 10.1(c), where *too much* abatement is imposed by law. Without specific *marginal* benefit and cost data, there is no way to know whether the 1981 controls corresponded to an efficient abatement level.

Values drawn from Paul R. Portney, "Air Pollution Policy," in Paul R. Portney, ed., *Public Policies for Environmental Protection* (Washington, D.C.: Resources for the Future, 1990a), pp. 27–96; Michael Hazilla and Raymond J. Kopp, "Social Cost of Environmental Quality Regulations: A General Equilibrium Analysis," *Journal of Political Economy* 98, no. 4 (1990), pp. 853–73; A. Myrick Freeman III, *Air and Water Pollution Control: A Benefit-Cost Assessment* (New York: John Wiley & Sons, Inc., 1982).

maximized or where the slopes of the two functions are equal. This corresponds to the abatement level that maximizes net benefits to society, or put another way, the point where marginal social cost (*MSC*) and marginal social benefit (*MSB*) of abatement are equal. However, it is quite possible that A_{1981} is to the *left* of A_e, as is shown in Figure 10.1(b). Such a result would indicate that *too little* abatement has been legislated. Just the opposite case is also possible where *too much* abatement is imposed by law. This alternative is shown in Figure 10.1(c). The point is, without specific *marginal* benefit and cost data, there is no way to know whether the regulatory controls in place in 1981 corresponded to an efficient level of abatement.

TABLE 10.10   **Estimated Annual Marginal Costs and Benefits of the 1990 Clean Air Act Amendments**

Stated in billions of 1990 dollars
(1984 dollars given in parentheses)

	Acidic Deposition	*Urban Air Quality*	*Hazardous Air Pollutants*	*Aggregate Range*	*Aggregate Point Estimate*
Marginal costs	$4 ($3.2)	$19–$22 ($15.1–$17.5)	$6–$10 ($4.8–$7.9)	$29–$36 ($23.1–$28.6)	$32 ($25.4)
Marginal benefits	$2–$9 ($1.6–$7.2)	$4–$12 ($3.2–$9.5)	$0–$4 ($0–$3.2)	$6–$25 ($4.8–$19.9)	$14 ($11.1)

Source: Drawn from Paul R. Portney, "Economics and the Clean Air Act," *Journal of Economic Perspectives* 4, no. 4, Fall 1990b, pp. 173–81.

Benefit-Cost Analysis of the 1990 Amendments

In an excellent and very readable article, Portney (1990b) extends and updates his benefit-cost analysis to assess the 1990 Amendments. In particular, he assigns estimated benefits and costs to each of the three major sets of provisions of the 1990 law, those for acidic deposition (Title IV), those for urban air pollution (Titles II and V), and those for hazardous air pollutants (Title III). There are two major differences between this analysis and the one Portney conducted for the earlier period. First, in this study *marginal* costs and benefits are examined, whereas the analysis of pre-1990 policy uses *total* costs and benefits. This use of marginal values allows for a determination of whether the *additional* controls imposed by the new amendments are allocatively efficient. Secondly, this study is a "seat-of-the-pants" evaluation, as Portney puts it, because only *explicit* private costs are considered. His defense is simply that such nonrigorous analyses are typically what are used in practice.

Marginal Costs and Benefits.   To facilitate the discussion, we present Portney's estimates in Table 10.10, which we assume are points lying on the true marginal social benefit (*MSB*) and marginal social cost (*MSC*) curves.[14] The table lists the reported values in 1990 dollars for the three sets of provisions as well as for the aggregate of all three. For ease of comparison to the values Portney derived for the pre-1990 period, the magnitudes also are stated in 1984 dollars in parentheses. Notice that most of the estimates are reported as a range of values, since there is some amount of guesswork involved.

---

[14]Recall from Chapter 8 that technically these values are *incremental* as opposed to *marginal,* since the magnitudes represent a discrete change from one policy initiative to another.

Overall, Portney suggests that the abatement associated with the 1990 Amendments should yield a marginal social benefit (*MSB*) of somewhere in the range of $6 to $25 billion annually, with most of it due to improvements in urban air quality. Portney also offers a rough point estimate for *MSB* of $14 billion, which is $11.1 billion in 1984 dollars. The comparable estimate for marginal social cost (*MSC*) is $29 to $36 billion annually, or $23.1 to $28.6 billion in 1984 dollars. Again, the majority of costs are attributable to urban air quality controls. A point estimate for *MSC* to correspond to the benefit side is $32 billion, or $25.4 billion in 1984 dollars. From a relative perspective, the $25.4 billion cost estimate suggests that the 1990 Amendments are expected to be very costly, particularly in light of the fact that the *total* social costs of U.S. policy as of 1981 were estimated to be only $13.7 billion.

Benefit-Cost Comparison.   Based on these estimates, one possible conclusion is that the 1990 Amendments overregulate society, since *MSC* far outweighs *MSB*.[15] This relationship holds even if we conservatively compare the low end of the range for *MSC* ($29 billion) with the upper end of the range for *MSB* ($25 billion), giving an excess of $4 billion in nominal terms. On the other hand, the excess could be as much as $30 billion, if we use the high end of the range for *MSC* ($36 billion) with the low end of the range for *MSB* ($6 billion).

To further illustrate this important result, Figure 10.2 presents two graphical models of these estimates expressed in 1984 dollars. The first in panel (a) depicts the relationship between *MSC* and *MSB*. Notice that the hypothetical abatement level corresponding to the 1990 Amendments, A_{1990}, is located to the *right* of the efficient abatement level, A_e. It follows, therefore, that society would be better off with less regulation, which translates to a movement on the graph from A_{1990} to A_e.

The model in panel (b) illustrates these same results using an approximation of the *TSC* and *TSB* as of 1990. To obtain the estimate for *TSC*, we add the estimated *MSC* for the 1990 law in 1984 dollars, $25.4 billion, to Portney's earlier estimate of *TSC* for 1981 measured in 1984 dollars, $13.7 billion. This yields an estimate for the 1990 *TSC* of $39.1 billion.

TSC effective 1981:	$13.7 billion
+ *MSC* for 1990 Amendments:	+25.4 billion
TSC effective 1990:	$39.1 billion

---

[15]There is, however, an important caveat. If, for example, Portney's marginal cost estimates are *not* reflective of least-cost decisions, meaning they lie *above* the true *MSC* curve, then the appropriate conclusion is that the 1990 Amendments are not being implemented in a cost-effective manner. If this is the case, the efficiency of the abatement level being achieved by the 1990 law is indeterminate.

320

FIGURE 10.2

(a) Analyzing the marginal social cost and marginal social benefit associated with the 1990 Clean Air Act Amendments

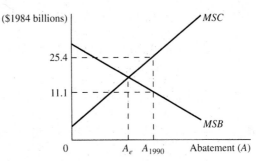

According to Portney's estimates, the *MSC* associated with the 1990 Amendments outweighs the *MSB*. Thus, the *MSC* is above the *MSB* at A_{1990}. Notice that A_{1990} is higher than the efficient abatement level, A_e, where *MSB* intersects with *MSC*. This implies that society would be better off with less regulation, which translates to a movement from A_{1990} to A_e.

(b) Analyzing the total social costs and total social benefits associated with the 1990 Clean Air Act Amendments

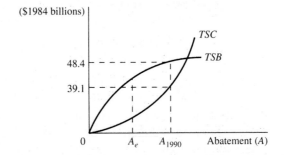

This model shows the estimated values of *TSB* and *TSC* associated with the hypothetical abatement level established by the 1990 Amendments, A_{1990}. Although *TSB* exceeds *TSC* at this point, A_{1990} is higher than the efficient abatement level, A_e. Just as in the upper diagram, this model implies that the 1990 Amendments overregulate the private sector to achieve cleaner air.

Source: Values derived from Paul R. Portney, ''Economics and the Clean Air Act,'' *Journal of Economic Perspectives* 4, no. 4 (Fall 1990b), pp. 173–81; Paul R. Portney, ''Air Pollution Policy,'' in Paul R. Portney, ed. *Public Policies for Environmental Protection* (Washington, D.C.: Resources for the Future, 1990a), pp. 27–96.

Similarly, to derive an approximation of *TSB* from all air quality controls in effect as of 1990, the estimated *MSB* for the 1990 Amendments, $11.1 billion, is added to Freeman's estimate of *TSB*, $37.3 billion, to get an approximation for the *TSB* as of 1990 at $48.4 billion:

TSB effective 1978:	$37.3 billion
+ *MSB* for 1990 Amendments:	+11.1 billion
TSB effective 1990:	$48.4 billion

These values for *TSB* and *TSC* are shown in the diagram corresponding to A_{1990}. Notice that while *TSB* exceeds *TSC,* the associated abatement level is nonetheless in excess of the efficient level, A_e.

The implication of these findings is that by implementing the 1990 Amendments, the U.S. government has overregulated the private sector to achieve cleaner air. Overallocation of resources to implement this legislation means that resources are being underallocated toward other uses. There are many who agree with this conclusion, arguing, for example, that the allocation of government spending among environmental problems is disproportionate to the associated risks. A common outcry is aimed at the relatively small amount of federal monies devoted to reducing the risks of such hazards as radon and tobacco smoke, which are known health hazards. Citing EPA statistics, a recent article in the business press points out that while radon is responsible for some 5,000 to 20,000 deaths per year, only about $100 million is spent annually to fight the problem. These statistics are troubling when compared to the $1.2 billion being spent on global warming, to which zero deaths are attributed.[16] But as we stated at the outset, benefit-cost analysis of environmental issues is *not* an exact science. These values are just estimates, and the scientific evidence on most if not all environmental problems is incomplete.

Taken in this context, Portney's research should be recognized for what it is, *and* for what it is not. While it is validated by some existing data as well as the work of other researchers, it is nonetheless a series of estimates and guesses, albeit educated ones. There are no hard-and-fast conclusions that can be drawn from such preliminary results. Rather, more advanced research, using new data as it becomes available, is necessary to make a more concrete determination about the efficiency implications of the 1990 Amendments.

A Benefit-Cost Analysis of the Air Quality Standards

Perhaps the most important contribution of Portney's findings is that they motivate the need for further investigation of the Clean Air Act. To that end, we conduct a benefit-cost analysis of the standards established through this legislation, focusing on the *efficiency* implications of two specific issues: (1) the *absence of cost considerations* in setting the standards; and (2) the *uniformity* of the standards. The *equity* implications of the Clean Air Act are discussed in Application 10.4. Although equity considerations are not the mainstay of economic analysis, they have taken on increasing importance in U.S. environmental policy-making.

---

[16]See Main (May 20, 1991).

Application 10.4

The Inequities of Air Pollution—Who Suffers More?

While efficiency criteria are the mainstay of economic analyses, an evaluation of any public policy should also consider issues of equity or fairness. Does the policy correct for any preexisting inequities across population groups? Does its implementation affect all segments of society in the same way? These sorts of questions are particularly relevant to an assessment of national air quality policy. As soon as the implications for society are assessed on something less than an aggregated level, the differences become obvious. A case in point is the vast difference in air quality between rural and urban communities or between attainment and nonattainment areas. The fact is, the risks of living with air pollution are far greater for some segments of society than

for others. And while these differences seem to be strictly regional in orientation, it turns out that they translate to inequities across income, ethnic, and racial population groups. Hence, the problem becomes a much more sensitive one that has begun to capture national attention.

The linkage is simple—likely what makes finding a solution to the problem so difficult. Much of the racial- and ethnic-based differences in air pollution exposure arise because a higher proportion of minorities live in urban centers, where the ambient air is significantly dirtier than in suburban and rural areas. In fact, some 63 percent of the nation's air-polluting facilities are located in urban areas. Take a look at the facts.

Racial Ethnic Group	Proportion Living in Urban Areas	Proportion Living in Rural Areas	
		Farm	Non Farm
White	70.3%	2.3%	27.0%
African Americans	86.1	0.3	13.6
Hispanic	91.2	0.7	8.1
Other	86.5	0.4	12.5

Source: U.S. Department of Commerce, Bureau of the Census, *Statistical Abstract of the United States* (Washington, D.C., 1990).

Given these residential differences, it is not surprising that certain minority groups are at greater risk than the rest of the population to the health hazards associated with exposure to urban air pollution.

A recent study conducted at the Argonne National Laboratory examined the proportion of whites, African Americans, and Hispanics living in nonattainment areas for certain of the criteria pollutants. A summary table of the findings is given below:

Proportion of Population Groups Living in Nonattainment Areas			
Air Pollutant	White	African Americans	Hispanics
Particulate matter	14.7%	16.5%	34.0%
Carbon monoxide	33.6	46.0	57.1
Ozone	52.5	62.2	71.2
Sulfur dioxide	7.0	12.1	5.7
Lead	6.0	9.2	18.5

Source: D. Wernette and L. Nieves, "Minorities and Air Pollution: A Preliminary Geo-Demographic Analysis," unpublished conference presentation, 1991.

Application 10.4 (concluded)

These differences in exposure measured on a national scale are also apparent for each of the four U.S. Census regions. For example, in the Northeast census region, 50 percent of whites live in nonattainment carbon monoxide areas, but the percentage is considerably higher for African Americans and Hispanics at 85 percent and 88 percent, respectively. Even at the county level, the findings are qualitatively the same. In 1990, of the 3,109 counties across the country, there were 437 that exceeded the national ambient standards for at least one criteria pollutant. Statistics show that 57 percent of whites, 80 percent of Hispanics, and 65 percent of African Americans live in these counties. This disproportion among population groups is consistently found for more severely affected counties as well, that is, those with progressively higher numbers of pollutants for which the standards are not achieved. Interestingly, while there is also a large percentage of poor families living in these counties, this income-based proportion is lower than for any of the minority groups. This means that income differences alone do not explain the higher exposure rate of minority populations.

Other independent analyses find similar evidence of these environmental inequities. For example, one research study by Brajer and Hall (1992) examines the distribution of income, ethnic, and racial groups affected by exposure to ozone and fine particulate matter in the South Coast Air Basin of California. The results show a positive correlation between particulate matter exposure and the percentage of lower income families as well as with the percentage of African Americans and Hispanics. Similar results are found for ozone exposure, although some of the correlations are statistically weaker.

Consider these findings in the context of benefit-cost analysis, and the dilemma is apparent. The benefits of industrialized activity such as electricity generation, advanced transportation systems, and the availability of manufactured products accrue to people living all over the world. But the costs of the associated air pollution from this productive activity are apparently borne more by some groups than others.

So what is being done about the problem? In the United States, the EPA is very concerned about the disproportionate risk across segments of society and is committed to addressing the issue of environmental equity. In 1990, the agency formed an Environmental Equity Workgroup to assess the evidence about risk to minority and low-income groups and to consider appropriate responses to any inequities it identifies. (Its findings are given in a formal report entitled *Environmental Equity: Reducing Risk for All Communities,* June 1992.) The provisions of the 1990 Clean Air Act Amendments aimed at urban and nonattainment areas will inherently bring the greatest measure of benefit to minority and low-income groups living in those areas. But these anticipated improvements will take time. In the interim, it is important for the United States to recognize and respond to the unequal distribution of the risks of air pollution.

Sources: U.S. Environmental Protection Agency, Office of Policy, Planning, and Evaluation, *Environmental Equity: Reducing Risk for All Communities* (Washington, D.C., June 1992); D. R. Wernette and L. A. Nieves, ''Breathing Polluted Air,'' *EPA Journal* 18, no 1 (March/April 1992), pp. 16–17; Victor Brajer and Jane V. Hall, ''Recent Evidence on the Distribution of Air Pollution Effects,'' *Contemporary Policy Issues,* April 1992, pp. 63–71.

Absence of Cost Considerations in the Standard-Setting Process

Setting the National Ambient Air Quality Standards (NAAQS).

From an efficiency perspective, a common criticism of both the primary and secondary NAAQS is that they are motivated solely by the anticipated benefits from protecting public health and welfare with no mention of the economic feasibility of doing so. Effectively, this means that costs, including implicit costs, are not to be explicitly considered. Such an omission is particularly problematic for the primary standards for health, which are to include a "margin of safety." This wording suggests that there is some level of pollution that will not cause any harm to public health. But is there a pollution level that does not harm at least one individual? Probably not. So, without the balance of cost considerations, the law seems to suggest setting the primary standards for criteria pollutants at zero. Although such an extreme was not Congress's intent, the law does not provide appropriate guidelines to set the NAAQS at an efficient level.[17]

Setting the National Emission Standards for Hazardous Air Pollutants (NESHAP).   An analogous argument has been made about the NESHAP as originally defined in the Clean Air Act. Recall from our prior discussion that the United States had made little progress in controlling air toxics prior to the changes made in the 1990 Amendments. To a great extent, this lack of progress was the result of using a **benefit-based decision rule** to control these substances. Specifically, for any identified air toxic the EPA was required to set a standard that ". . . provides an ample margin of safety to protect the public health."[18] It is difficult to conceptualize what an "ample margin of safety" might be for substances like carcinogens, which pose a threat even at low emission levels. Again, since the law did not allow for any consideration of costs, taken literally the law seemed to be calling for the setting of the NESHAP at zero emission levels. Such a radical decision would have had serious consequences for American industry, since many of these substances are critical to industrial processes. Recognizing the problem, the EPA was reluctant to identify a substance as a hazardous air pollutant, and little was done to control these dangerous toxics for many years.[19]

Through the 1980s, there was some controversy about the identification and subsequent standard-setting for air toxics, particularly for carcinogens. One suggestion was to allow for economic feasibility in the standard-setting process, a solution supported by then EPA administrator, William Ruckelshaus. Opponents argued that such an objective approach was inappropriate for dealing with matters as delicate as human health.

Attempting to settle the debate, researchers tried to assess the efficiency implications of air toxic controls. One such investigation presents a collection of case studies that uses benefit-cost analysis to assess proposed uniform standards known as "Best Available Technology (BAT) standards" to control air toxics.[20] Three substances form the basis of the investigation: benzene, coke

benefit-based decision rule
A guideline to improve society's well-being with no allowance for a balancing of the associated costs.

---

[17]This discussion is elaborated in Burtraw and Portney (1991) and Portney (1990a).
[18]See Clean Air Act, Sec. 112.(b)(1)(B).
[19]National Commission on Air Quality (March 1981), pp. 76–77.
[20]See Haigh, Harrison, and Nichols (1984).

oven emissions, and acrylonitrile.[21] For benzene, the study cites an annual control cost of $2.6 million to achieve a benefit of 0.4 lives saved per year from reduced exposure. These findings imply that for the BAT controls on benzene to be efficient, the value of a statistical life would have to be $6.5 million (i.e., $2.6/0.4). For coke oven emissions and acrylonitrile emissions the comparable values would have to be $2.3 million and $145 million, respectively. Hence, the researchers show that, based on a generally accepted value of $1 million for a statistical life saved, all three control policies would fail a customary benefit-cost test.

Today, U.S. regulation of hazardous air pollutants is better defined, thanks to the 1990 Amendments. All air toxics subject to federal controls are identified explicitly in the law, and the EPA has been charged with the responsibility of setting emission standards for these within a 10-year time frame. Furthermore, although the Clean Air Act continues to require that the standards protect public health and the environment, it also allows for the costs of achieving these standards to be considered—an important step toward efficiency in the setting of the NESHAP.

Uniformity of the National Ambient Air Quality Standards (NAAQS)

A critical observation to make about the NAAQS is that, since they are nationally based, they ignore any regional-specific cost or benefit differences associated with meeting them. All nonattainment regions must meet the same uniform standards regardless of such differences as existing pollution levels, access to technology, demographics, and traffic patterns. Yet the marginal costs and benefits of reducing pollution to the same level across these highly diverse regions likely will be quite dissimilar. This likely explains why some regions met the legislated deadlines with relative ease, while others continue to struggle with compliance. Thus, while the shift to federally mandated standards was intended to strengthen U.S. policy, it nonetheless contributed to the inefficiency that typically arises with a command-and-control approach.

One legislative change that allowed for some regional-specific differences is the recognition of PSD areas and the use of existing air quality in those regions as the relevant standard. This policy reform effectively elevates the standard for PSD areas above the NAAQS applicable to nonattainment areas. The relevant issue is whether this particular use of differentiated standards represents an efficient allocation of resources across both types of regions.[22] Some economists question the wisdom of assigning more resources to already

---

[21]Acrylonitrile is a feedstock used in chemical production to produce such commodities as clothing, automobile hoses, and plastic pipe.

[22]In order for the differentiated abatement levels to be efficient, it must be the case that the efficient level of abatement in a PSD area is higher than that in a nonattainment area.

FIGURE 10.3

Economic modeling of higher air quality standards in PSD areas relative to nonattainment areas

The graphs show three possible scenarios under which the use of higher standards in PSD areas relative to nonattainment areas would be efficient. In panel (a), $MSB_{PSD} = MSB_{NON}$. In this case, the efficient abatement level in the PSD area, A_{PSD}, would be higher than the efficient level in a nonattainment area, A_{NON}, only if MSC_{PSD} is *lower* than MSC_{NON}. In panel (b), $MSC_{NON} = MSC_{PSD}$. Here, efficiency holds only if MSB_{PSD} is *above* MSB_{NON}. Finally, in panel (c), both the MSC and MSB curves are unique to each area. Under this assumption, one way efficiency results is if the following conditions hold: (1) MSB_{PSD} is *below* MSB_{NON}; (2) MSC_{PSD} is *below* MSC_{NON}; and (3) the vertical distance between the MSC curves is sufficiently *greater* than that between the MSB functions to support A_{PSD} being greater than A_{NON}.

clean areas in order to achieve a higher standard of air quality.[23] To investigate this issue, we use benefit-cost analysis in a simple economic model.

Benefit-Cost Analysis of Higher PSD Standards.   To economically justify the relatively higher standards in PSD areas, the associated MSC and MSB of abatement for these regions must intersect at a higher level of abatement than the comparable intersection for nonattainment areas. For this to occur, there must be certain differences in either or both of the MSC and MSB across the two types of regions. In Figure 10.3, we analyze three possible scenarios under which the use of different standards across PSD and nonattainment areas

---

[23]See Portney (1990a), pp. 78–79.

would be efficient. The marginal cost and benefit curves for a representative PSD area are labeled as MSC_{PSD} and MSB_{PSD}, and those for a nonattainment area as MSC_{NON} and MSB_{NON}.

In panel (a), the MSB functions are identical across the two types of areas, that is, $MSB_{PSD} = MSB_{NON}$ at all abatement levels (A). If this relationship holds, the efficient abatement level in the PSD area, A_{PSD}, would be higher than the efficient level in a nonattainment area, A_{NON}, only if MSC_{PSD} is *lower* than MSC_{NON}. In panel (b), the opposite set of conditions is modeled with the MSC functions drawn as identical curves. Here, efficiency holds only if MSB_{PSD} is *above* MSB_{NON}. Finally, in panel (c), both the MSC and MSB curves are allowed to be unique to each area. Under this latter assumption, one way that efficiency results is if the following three conditions hold: (1) MSB_{PSD} is *below* MSB_{NON}; (2) MSC_{PSD} is *below* MSC_{NON}; and (3) the vertical distance between the MSC curves is sufficiently *greater* than that between the MSB functions to support the relative positions of A_{PSD} and A_{NON}.[24]

So far, what we have illustrated is that the use of relatively higher standards for PSD areas *can* be efficient, but only under certain conditions. Now, we need to consider the logic of each scenario based upon the expected relationship between the respective marginal costs and benefits for the two areas. For context, think of the differences between nonattainment areas and the most stringently controlled PSD areas, which are Class I. Recall that these include national parks and wilderness regions. One reason these areas have cleaner air is that they are less populated and less industrialized than their nonattainment counterparts. How might these conditions affect the MSB and MSC?

On the cost side, it is reasonable to expect that MSC_{PSD} is lower than MSC_{NON}, since there are fewer polluting sources to control in PSD regions. By itself, this assertion suggests that the model in panel (b) of Figure 10.3 is not a likely representation of actual conditions. Now consider the benefit side. The primary benefits of maintaining higher air quality in PSD areas are non-health gains, such as enhanced recreational uses, aesthetic improvements, and protection of the ecology. In contrast, the major benefits of cleaning up the more populated nonattainment areas are improvements in human health. Since health improvements are generally valued more at the margin than nonhealth gains, MSB_{NON} is likely higher at all abatement levels than is MSB_{PSD}. Based on this hypothesis, the model shown in panel (a) appears to be inaccurate. Taking these assumed benefit differences into account along with the expected cost differences, the model in panel (c) appears to be more accurate than either (a) or (b). But recall that for this model to support the efficiency criterion, several conditions have to hold. Hence, all we can conclude is that the higher standards in the cleaner PSD areas *may* be justifiable on efficiency grounds under certain economic circumstances.

---

[24]Other scenarios are possible under which both the MSC and MSB curves are allowed to be unique and the A_{PSD} is higher than A_{NON}. To see this, try modeling a case different from the one shown in panel (c).

Another reform that acknowledges regional-specific differences was the reclassification of nonattainment areas for ozone, carbon monoxide, and particulate matter enacted within the 1990 Amendments. By imposing progressively more stringent controls on the dirtiest of these areas, these revisions may have improved efficiency. Again, this issue can be examined through benefit-cost analysis.

Benefit-Cost Analysis of Progressively Regulated Nonattainment Areas.   To give our analysis context, we consider two of the new classifications for nonattainment ozone areas—''marginal'' at the cleaner end of the continuum and ''extreme'' at the other. Now, we can apply benefit-cost analysis to examine the efficiency of strengthening regulatory controls in extreme ozone areas.

Since the United States is imposing more stringent regulations on extreme ozone regions, the *MSC* in extreme regions will necessarily be higher than the *MSC* in marginal ozone regions at all levels of abatement. Hence, in order for the use of different control methods to make sense from an economic perspective, it must be the case that the *MSB* at the existing level of abatement in extreme regions must be greater than the *MSB* at the current abatement level in marginal regions.[25] As long as this is correct, we can argue that the higher incremental costs of more stringent regulations are at least to some extent justified by higher incremental benefits.

Conclusions

U.S. air quality policy has evolved considerably over the last several decades. Legislative initiatives and the infrastructure to implement them have become more extensive and more complex. Indeed, the 1990 Clean Air Act Amendments are far more comprehensive than any U.S. environmental legislation enacted to date. Today, there is a massive network of agencies and interagencies working toward the important objective of improving national air quality. In some sense, such an evolution is not surprising. Air pollution is a difficult problem, and the sheer size of the United States means that air quality controls must accommodate a variety of meteorological, geographical, and economic conditions.

Having said all of this, the most pressing question is to ask what tangible progress has been made over the last several decades as a result of this legislative evolution. Available trend data *do* suggest that U.S. air quality is improving. But even if we assume that at least some of the improvement is

---

[25]If the *MSB* curves are the same for both regions, this relative difference will necessarily hold, since the abatement level in extreme regions is by definition lower than that in marginal regions. If the two curves are distinct, then it must be the case that the *MSB* in extreme regions lies everywhere above the *MSB* in marginal regions.

attributable to policy reform, we also must consider whether the observed progress has been achieved in an economically sound manner.

Despite the numerous revisions and new initiatives, U.S. legislation continues to be based primarily on a command-and-control approach evidenced largely by the use of uniform standards to define national air quality. The problem is that such an approach is not likely to achieve an efficient solution to the nation's air pollution problems. In fact, benefit-cost analysis suggests that clean air policy initiatives have been more costly to society than necessary. Similar conclusions follow from a qualitative evaluation of the standard-setting process. From an economic perspective, uniform standards are a troubling element of U.S. air legislation. Likewise, the absence of cost considerations in establishing these standards defies time-tested economic theory.

Of course, there are no simple answers, nor can there be any sweeping conclusions without careful reservations. Air quality issues involve many intangibles that are difficult to quantify. Moreover, many of the nation's new clean air policies have not been fully implemented, so part of the assessment must rely on estimated projections. Nonetheless, the analytical process guided by economic theory provides a way to better understand the motivation and economic implications of the Clean Air Act and to set more realistic expectations about achieving the nation's air quality objectives.

Summary

- There were no federal air pollution laws until 1955 when the Air Pollution Control Act was passed, and there was no comprehensive legislation until the Clean Air Act of 1963. The 1970 Clean Air Act Amendments marked dramatic policy changes in the United States, followed by still more amendments in 1977.

- On November 15, 1990, President Bush signed into law extensive changes in U.S. air quality control policy in the form of the 1990 Clean Air Act Amendments.

- To meet U.S. air quality objectives, officials must determine which pollutants are most responsible for air pollution and must establish the level at which to control them. Two groups of air pollutants have been identified as those causing the greatest damage to outdoor air quality, criteria pollutants and hazardous air pollutants.

- Criteria pollutants are identified by scientific evidence summarized in official reports called criteria documents. The six criteria pollutants are particulate matter, sulfur dioxide, carbon monoxide, nitrogen dioxide, tropospheric ozone, and lead. The 1990 Amendments identify an initial list of 189 hazardous air pollutants.

- For the six criteria pollutants, National Ambient Air Quality Standards (NAAQS) are established by the EPA. These are maximum allowable concentrations of criteria air pollutants emitted from stationary or mobile sources into the outside air. Primary NAAQS are standards set to protect public health, with some margin of safety. Secondary NAAQS are intended to protect public welfare.

- For the hazardous air pollutants, National Emission Standards for Hazardous Air Pollutants (NESHAPs) are established for every major source of one or more of the listed hazardous air pollutants.

- Coordination of air quality control policy between federal and state governments is formalized through the State Implementation Plan (SIP). An SIP is an EPA-approved procedure outlining how a state intends to implement, monitor, and enforce the NAAQS and the NESHAP.

- There are currently 247 air quality control regions (AQCRs) defined in the United States. These are classified into nonattainment areas and PSD areas. In the 1990 Clean Air Act Amendments, new classifications are established for certain of the nonattainment areas, namely those for ozone, carbon monoxide, and particulate matter.

- The research of Paul Portney suggests that the total social benefits of U.S. clean air legislation as of 1981 outweigh the total social costs. In a more current study, Portney finds that the 1990 Amendments may abate pollution beyond the efficient level.

- The NAAQS ignore regional-specific cost or benefit differences associated with meeting them. This uniformity suggests an inefficient allocation of resources across the AQCRs.

- The primary and secondary NAAQS are motivated solely by anticipated benefits from protecting public health and welfare, meaning that costs are not explicitly considered.

- The historical lack of progress in setting the NESHAP was the result of using a benefit-based decision rule. The 1990 Amendments have improved air toxics regulation by identifying substances to be controlled within the law and by revising the standard-setting to allow for costs to be considered.

- The higher standards in the cleaner PSD areas *may* be justifiable on efficiency grounds under certain economic conditions.

- The use of progressively more stringent controls on the dirtiest nonattainment regions may have improved resource allocation, if the marginal benefit of abatement in these regions is higher than in cleaner nonattainment areas.

Key Concepts

criteria documents
criteria pollutants
hazardous air pollutants
stationary source
mobile source
National Ambient Air Quality Standards (NAAQS)
primary NAAQS
secondary NAAQS

National Emission Standards for Hazardous Air Pollutants (NESHAPs)
maximum achievable control technology (MACT)
State Implementation Plan (SIP)
Air Quality Control Regions (AQCR)
prevention of significant deterioration (PSD) areas
nonattainment areas

APPENDIX
A REFERENCE TO ACRONYMS AND CHEMICAL FORMULAS IN AIR QUALITY CONTROL POLICY

Environmental Economics Acronyms

TSB	Total social benefits
TSC	Total social costs
MSB	Marginal social benefit
MSC	Marginal social cost
MSC_{PSD}	Marginal social cost of abatement in a PSD area
MSB_{PSD}	Marginal social benefit of abatement in a PSD area
MSC_{NON}	Marginal social cost of abatement in a nonattainment area
MSB_{NON}	Marginal social benefit of abatement in a nonattainment area

Environmental Science Acronyms

CO	Carbon monoxide
CO_2	Carbon dioxide
$\mu g/m^3$	Micrograms per cubic meter
mg/m^3	Milligrams per cubic meter
NO_x	Nitrogen oxides
NO_2	Nitrogen dioxide
O_3	Ozone
Pb	Lead
PM	Particulate matter
PM-10	Particulate matter of less than 10 micrograms in diameter
ppm	Parts per million
SO_2	Sulfur dioxide
SO_x	Sulfur oxides
TSP	Total suspended particulates
VOC	Volatile organic compound

Environmental Policy Acronyms

AQCR	Air Quality Control Region
BAT	Best Available Technology
MACT	Maximum Achievable Control Technology
NAAQS	National Ambient Air Quality Standards
NAPAP	National Acidic Precipitation Assessment Program
NESHAP	National Emission Standards for Hazardous Air Pollutants
PSD	Prevention of Significant Deterioration
SIP	State Implementation Plan

Review Questions

1. If you were responsible for setting the NAAQS for lead, what key determinants would you consider if the standard were established to meet the efficiency criterion. Be sure to itemize separately the benefits and costs associated with your decision.

2. Using the efficiency criterion, carefully analyze the problem faced by the EPA in identifying hazardous air pollutants prior to the 1990 Amendments.

3. *a.* Briefly explain the significance of Prevention of Significant Deterioration (PSD) areas to the setting of air quality standards.

   b. From an economic perspective, explain the paradox associated with setting higher standards in PSD areas relative to nonattainment areas. Show how an inefficient result may arise using an *MSB-MSC* model.

4. Briefly summarize Portney's overall assessment of the 1990 Clean Air Act Amendments and discuss the major implications of these findings for society.

5. Refer back to Table 10.10 of the marginal benefit and cost estimates for the 1990 Clean Air Act Amendments. Conduct an individual benefit-cost analysis for each of the three major components of the amendments, namely acidic deposition, urban air quality, and hazardous air pollutants. What do you conclude?

Additional Readings

Aeppel, Timothy. "Clean Air Act Triggers Backlash as Its Focus Shifts to Driving Habits." *The Wall Street Journal,* January 25, 1995, pp. A1, A10.

Brannigan, Martha. "CAT Scan May Soon 'Map' Air Pollution." *The Wall Street Journal,* November 10, 1994, p. B7.

EPA Journal 18, no. 1. "Environmental Protection—Has It Been Fair?" March/April 1992.

Freeman, A. Myrick III. "Air and Water Pollution Policy." In Paul R. Portney, ed. *Current Issues in U.S. Environmental Policy.* Baltimore: The Johns Hopkins University Press, 1978.

Halberstam, David. *The Reckoning.* New York: William Morrow and Company, Inc. 1986.

Koch, Gayle S. and Paul R. Ammann. "Current Trends in Federal and State Regulation of Hazardous Air Pollutants." *Journal of Environmental Regulation* 4 no. 1 (Autumn 1994), pp. 25–41.

Solomon, Caleb and Oscar Suris. "Hot Weather Hurts Efforts to Clean Up Air." *The Wall Street Journal,* July 7, 1994, pp. B1, B6.

Tietenberg, T. H. *Emissions Trading: An Exercise in Reforming Pollution Policy.* Washington D.C.: Resources for the Future, Inc., 1985.

11

ACHIEVING AIR QUALITY

Controlling Mobile and Stationary Sources

Of the two major classes of air pollutants identified by the Clean Air Act, the criteria pollutants are more common. Because they are so pervasive, these substances are responsible for most of the air pollution in the world even though they are less dangerous than hazardous air pollutants. The relevant point is that all of society is exposed to the risks of criteria pollutants, which explains why the Clean Air Act places such a strong emphasis on them and why Congress elected to legislate federally mandated control strategies to implement the National Ambient Air Quality Standards (NAAQS). Although the motivation for this decision may be well placed, it turns out that this top-down policy approach has had some adverse consequences—an assertion that will be supported with economic analysis in this chapter.

Starting from a general perspective, we know that the Clean Air Act establishes stringent regulations on both stationary and mobile sources, since both contribute significantly to the release of all six criteria pollutants. This is clear from the emissions data shown in Table 11.1. Although the control instruments applicable to each source group are different, some of these are commonly motivated. A case in point is the problem of urban air pollution, which is caused by the combination and concentration of essentially all the criteria pollutants released from both types of sources.

On the other hand, some air quality problems are more closely linked to certain types of polluting sources, and these require more specific policy strategies. Look again at Table 11.1, and notice, for example, how mobile sources contribute more to the level of carbon monoxide (CO) emissions, while stationary sources are bigger emitters of sulfur oxides (SO_x). Consequently, some control instruments *are* uniquely motivated by specific emissions and their associated environmental risks.

TABLE 11.1   Annual Criteria Pollutant Emissions for Mobile and Stationary Sources

	Particulate Matter (PM-10)	Sulfur Oxides (SO$_x$)	Carbon Monoxide (CO)	Nitrogen Oxides (NO$_x$)	Volatile Organic Compounds (VOCs)[b]	Lead (Pb)
1988 Annual Emissions (millions of short tons except lead measured in thousands of short tons)[a]						
Stationary sources[c]	3.73	22.13	14.22	12.70	14.12	3.57
Mobile sources	1.67	0.95	80.52	10.81	10.31	2.91
Miscellaneous[d]	1.06	0.00	4.33	0.13	0.59	0.00
Total[e]	6.44	23.09	99.07	23.63	25.02	6.46
1990 Annual Emissions (millions of short tons except lead measured in thousands of short tons)[a]						
Stationary sources[c]	3.37	21.81	13.68	12.77	14.00	3.75
Mobile sources	1.76	1.01	74.44	10.66	9.10	1.89
Miscellaneous[d]	0.96	0.00	4.27	0.13	0.58	0.00
Total[e]	6.08	22.82	92.38	23.56	23.67	5.63
1992 Annual Emissions (millions of short tons except lead measured in thousands of short tons)[a]						
Stationary sources[c]	3.29	21.68	12.93	12.67	13.92	3.59
Mobile sources	1.83	1.06	69.97	10.33	8.23	1.59
Miscellaneous[d]	0.81	0.00	4.27	0.13	0.58	0.00
Total[e]	5.93	22.73	87.18	23.15	22.73	5.18

Notes:

[a]Beginning with the EPA's 1992 emissions report, all emissions data are reported in short tons (2,000 lbs.) versus the metric ton (2,205 lbs.), used previously.

[b]VOC emissions are used to measure the formation of ozone, O$_3$.

[c]Includes emissions from waste disposal and recycling.

[d]Includes forest fires, agricultural burning, structure fires, etc.

[e]Sums of categories may not equal total shown due to rounding.

Source: U.S. Environmental Protection Agency, Office of Air Quality Planning and Standards, *National Air Quality and Emissions Trends Report, 1992* (Research Triangle Park, N.C., October 1993), Tables 3–1 through 3–7.

There are also practical distinctions that must be addressed in designing effective regulatory instruments. For instance, controls on stationary sources can be tied to physical geography, such as limiting the number of fossil-fuel-fired power plants operating in a particular region. However, such a policy is more difficult to implement for motor vehicles, which by definition are mobile. There are also technological differences among polluting sources that influence which control devices and abatement strategies can be employed in practice. In any case, controlling mobile and stationary sources of criteria pollutants is the means by which the NAAQS are implemented. Hence, the nation's opportunity to achieve the legislated definition of air quality depends critically on the effectiveness of all federally mandated control instruments—an issue that merits careful investigation and analysis.

To motivate our study of mobile and stationary controls, we begin by discussing urban air pollution, since it is linked to both types of sources. Understanding this widespread problem will help explain the rationale for many U.S. policy initiatives. Once done, we begin our two-part analysis with mobile source controls. In addition to investigating current policy based on the 1990 Clean Air Act Amendments, we also conduct a brief retrospective of what has transpired over the last several decades between the government and the American automobile industry. The subsequent economic analysis examines the efficiency and cost-effectiveness of U.S. mobile source initiatives. An analogous study follows for stationary sources. Here, an important context will be an environmental problem tied primarily to stationary sources—acidic deposition, more commonly known as acid rain. Of particular interest is an economic evaluation of the market-based program aimed at this problem initiated by Title IV of the 1990 Amendments. An appendix of commonly used acronyms is provided for reference at the end of the chapter.

Urban Air Pollution:
An Important Policy Motivation

Environmentalists as well as policy-makers are concerned about the air pollution that characterizes urban centers. In metropolitan areas, the high concentration of human population, traffic and industrial activity intensifies the concentration of criteria pollutants and hence increases the environmental risks of exposure. Much of the concern is rooted in the fact that so many people live and work in urban centers, which means that a large proportion of the population is exposed to the associated health hazards. Consequently, increased abatement efforts in cities should yield a higher level of marginal benefit than in rural communities.

Measuring U.S. Urban Air Quality

Pollutant Standards Index (PSI)
An index number that signifies the worst daily air quality in an urban area over some time period.

To develop a better sense of the magnitude of the problem in the United States, the EPA monitors urban air quality with a particular focus on 23 major urban centers.[1] Over the past several years, the agency has been reporting part of its findings using a **Pollutant Standards Index (PSI).** The PSI value uses daily maximum statistics obtained from a monitoring network on particulate matter (PM-10), sulfur dioxide (SO_2), carbon monoxide (CO), ozone (O_3), and nitrogen dioxide (NO_2) to form a single index number based on the short-term national standards for each substance.[2] The resulting value, ranging from 0 to 500, signifies the worst daily air quality in an urban area over a given time

[1]The 23 cities include the 10 in which the EPA has regional offices (Boston, New York, Philadelphia, Atlanta, Chicago, Dallas, Kansas City, Denver, San Francisco, and Seattle), plus 13 other cities (Baltimore, Cleveland, Detroit, El Paso, Houston, Los Angeles, Miami, Minneapolis–St. Paul, Phoenix, Pittsburgh, San Diego, St. Louis, and Washington, D.C.).
[2]The only criteria pollutant omitted from the index is lead, since there are no short-term NAAQS for this substance.

TABLE 11.2   **Trend Data for Major Urban Areas**
Number of PSI Days Greater Than 100 at Trend Sites

MSA	1983	1984	1985	1986	1987	1988	1989	1990	1991	1992
Atlanta	23	8	9	17	19	15	3	16	5	4
Baltimore	60	46	21	24	28	41	7	12	20	4
Boston	37	28	9	9	10	17	5	3	7	4
Chicago	23	18	16	15	21	30	6	7	15	8
Cleveland	17	4	1	2	10	18	8	1	5	3
Dallas	20	18	19	10	10	6	4	7	7	4
Denver	69	62	39	47	37	19	12	7	7	7
Detroit	18	7	2	5	9	18	10	3	7	0
El Paso	16	20	24	34	27	13	29	20	8	11
Houston	70	49	48	45	54	48	32	48	40	29
Kansas City	4	12	3	4	3	3	2	2	1	1
Los Angeles	194	225	205	218	199	240	231	180	177	183
Miami	3	2	5	4	4	4	4	1	2	0
Minn.–St.Paul	36	21	21	13	7	1	6	1	0	0
New York	89	140	88	72	64	58	27	24	30	10
Philadelphia	58	39	29	24	37	43	22	17	32	8
Phoenix	72	107	82	85	40	22	30	8	4	8
Pittsburgh	27	15	9	8	13	23	9	11	3	1
San Diego	60	51	54	45	41	49	61	39	25	19
San Francisco	26	33	31	16	15	11	17	7	12	2
Seattle	11	4	27	11	13	6	4	3	0	0
St. Louis	33	22	10	14	16	17	12	8	6	2
Washington, D.C.	53	30	15	12	25	35	7	5	16	2
Total	1019	961	767	734	702	737	548	430	429	310

Notes: PSI is the Pollutant Standards Index, a dimensionless number ranging from 0 to 500 converted from daily monitoring data for PM-10, SO_2, CO, O_3, and NO_2 based upon their short-term NAAQS, Federal Episode Criteria, and Significant Harm Levels. (Lead is excluded because it has no short-term NAAQS.) MSA is a Metropolitan Statistical Area.
Data are reported from trend sites, that is, those for which there is sufficient historical data to be used for trends.
Source: U.S. Environmental Protection Agency, Office of Air Quality Planning and Standards, *National Air Quality and Emissions Trends Report, 1992* (Research Triangle Park, N.C., October 1993), Table 6-2, p. 6-4.

period. The descriptor words that identify the health effects associated with various ranges of the PSI are as follows:

0 to 50:	Good
51 to 100:	Moderate
101 to 199:	Unhealthful
200 to 299:	Very unhealthful
300 and above:	Hazardous.

The PSI and its descriptor are often used by local media to communicate air quality conditions to the general public.

Table 11.2 presents PSI trend data over a 10-year period. The table shows the number of days in a year each city experienced an air quality level that was unhealthful or worse, signified by a PSI of over 100. Notice, for example, that these data show that Baltimore, Boston, Chicago, New York, Philadelphia, and Washington, D.C., recorded more PSI days over 100 in 1991 than they did over the prior two-year period. The data also indicate that the air quality in Los Angeles is far worse than any other major urban area in the sample—a distinction that has persisted for several decades. As early as the 1940s, Los Angeles residents began to notice frequent episodes of a brownish haze on the horizon—an awareness that eventually led to nationwide concern about urban air pollution. Today, we know that the brownish haze in Los Angeles and many other metropolitan areas is **urban smog.**

Urban Smog

Coined from the words *smoke* and *fog,* the word *smog* originally referred to the overall air quality first observed in London at the turn of the century. Used in this context, it refers primarily to the presence of particulate matter and other emissions such as sulfur oxides in the air.[3] Because of Los Angeles's history and its dubious distinction as America's "king of smog," many people erroneously think of this city as the only one facing a severe smog problem. It *is* true that the dense traffic there and the meteorological conditions (technically, persistent low-level inversion[4]), make this region particularly vulnerable to smog formation. However, most major cities suffer from the effects of smog. The problem is more pervasive in highly industrialized and heavily populated parts of the world, such as Japan and countries in North America and Europe.

In urban areas, another type of smog can form from a chemical reaction involving several of the criteria pollutants. Scientists refer to this type of smog as **photochemical smog** to distinguish it from the more conventional "smoke and fog" variety. Photochemical smog is formed from certain air pollutants that chemically react in the presence of sunlight, (thus the prefix *photo*), to form entirely new substances. Its principal component is tropospheric ozone (O_3), referred to as "ground level ozone." Along with over 100 different compounds, ground level ozone is produced by a chemical reaction of nitrogen oxides (NO_x), volatile organic compounds (VOCs, primarily hydrocarbons), and sunlight. Since the chemical reaction is stimulated by sun and temperature, peak ozone levels are observed in the warmer seasons of the year. In most parts of the United States, the ozone season is from May to October. In warmer regions such as the South and Southwest, ozone levels might be elevated for the entire year.

photochemical smog
A phenomenon caused by a variety of air pollutants that chemically react in sunlight to form new substances; its principal component is ozone (O_3).

---

[3]Pryde (1973), p. 147.

[4]Inversion refers to the reversal of the normal temperature profile of the air above the earth's surface, whereby a layer of warm air prevents the rise of cooling air beneath it, trapping pollutants that might otherwise be dissipated.

TABLE 11.3   NO$_x$ and VOC Emissions by Source for Selected Countries in 1985

Country	NO$_x$ Emissions (000 metric tons)*		VOC Emissions (000 metric tons)*	
	Mobile Sources	*Stationary Sources*	*Mobile Sources*	*Stationary Sources*
Canada	1,245	695	855	885
United States	8,800	11,000	6,700	13,600
Austria	149	69	103	147
France	1,130	570	N/A	N/A
Germany	1,718	1,206	1,196	1,175
Italy	793	762†	644	93†
Netherlands	329	219	203	269
Norway	189	35	74	101
Portugal	116	187	56	5†
U.K.	952	1,166	613	1,665

*1 metric ton = 2,205 pounds
†Data exclude emissions from industrial processes.
N/A means data are not available.

Source: Organisation for Economic Co-operation and Development, *OECD Environmental Data Compendium 1989* (Paris: OECD, 1989b), Table 2.1E, p. 25, and Table 2.1G, p. 29. Reprinted with permission of OECD.

Both mobile and stationary sources contribute to photochemical smog formation, since both emit NO$_x$ and VOCs. To see the relative contribution of mobile and stationary sources to these causes of smog, see Table 11.3, which gives emissions levels of VOCs and NO$_x$ aggregated by source group for selected countries. The transportation sources emitting the largest amounts of these substances are ordinary highway vehicles, particularly those fueled by gasoline. Among stationary sources, fossil-fueled power stations are the primary emitters of NO$_x$, while oil refineries, gas stations, and chemical manufacturing plants are important sources of VOCs.

It is important to recognize that in urban centers, officials are more concerned with emissions from transportation sources because of the traffic congestion found in most major metropolitan areas. In Mexico City, for example, local officials are implementing drastic controls on mobile sources, including a program that prohibits the use of every automobile for one day per week. Application 11.1 discusses the air quality conditions faced by Mexico's smoggy capital city and officials' attempts to find a solution. In the United States, mobile source controls are less dramatic, but they have become more comprehensive over time. This particular aspect of U.S. environmental law took an inordinately long time to develop and, according to some, still has a long way to go.

Application 11.1

Mexico City's Serious Smog Problem

Mexico City is attempting to reduce its air pollution problem, said to be the worst in the world. At points in time, its ozone and carbon monoxide levels have been measured at almost four times the stated acceptable level by U.S. standards. The smog in this famous capital city is so severe that the future of many of its historic buildings, statues, and monuments is seriously threatened. Workers are unable to keep up with the continual degradation of the city's buildings, some of them centuries old. The city's historian, Jorge Hernandez, laments the lost detail on Mexico City's treasured statues that can never be replaced.

Officials are pulling out all the stops in an attempt to reverse at least some of the damage. A primary target is the automobile, allegedly responsible for two-thirds of the smog problem. Such a statistic is not surprising given that some 3 million drivers operate vehicles averaging 10 years of age. In an attempt to rid the city of the aging automobile population, new car buyers must turn in an old one—a requirement started in 1993. To mitigate the problem in the future, automobile manufacturers in Mexico made a commitment to begin installing catalytic converters on their new vehicles, but residents demanded more immediate action.

In response, Mexico City officials ordered the installation of pollution abatement devices on all taxicabs and small buses. This mandate may extend to private citizens as part of the license renewal process. Needless to say, this official stance has sparked the entrepreneurial spirit in literally hundreds of firms, submitting prototypes of pollution devices for the city's approval. In another bold move that began in 1990, every car in the city is prohibited from the streets one day each week. Each automobile is assigned a colored sticker corresponding to the particular day of the week on which driving is banned. The city's billboards herald which color corresponds to which day, and teams of enforcers work the intersections to make certain the mandate is followed. Violators are fined 30 days of minimum wages, about $120.

Whether officials will be successful in their fight to clean the city's air remains to be seen. In any case, some experts, including former EPA administrator William Reilly, have suggested that Mexico's pollution problems will diminish as the country grows and develops economically. As it gains economic strength, it should be better equipped to develop technology, fund regulation programs, and shift its industrial base away from heavy industry and toward more labor-intensive markets such as textiles and agriculture.

Sources: William Cormier, "Smog Eats Mexico City's Monuments," *The Brockton Enterprise* (November 23, 1992); Stephen Baker, "Mexico's Motorists Meet the Smog Patrol," *Business Week* (June 25, 1990), p. 100; Jonathan Marshall, "How Ecology Is Tied to Mexico Trade Pact," *San Francisco Chronicle* (February 25, 1992), p. A8.

Controlling Mobile Sources

Of all the transportation vehicles, the primary focus of U.S. policy is highway vehicles such as passenger cars and trucks.[5] As the trend data in Table 11.4

---

[5]The EPA has begun to control other mobile sources of smog such as gasoline-powered lawn mowers and other motorized garden tools. In May 1994, the agency announced new standards for these pollution sources, which are scheduled to take effect in 1996 (Associated Press, May 5, 1994).

TABLE 11.4   National Emissions Estimates for Mobile Sources by Major Category

(Teragrams per Year except Lead in Gigagrams)

	PM^a	SO_x	CO	NO_x	$VOCs^b$	Pb
Gasoline-powered highway vehicles						
1970	0.77	0.16	65.03	5.21	8.96	156.0[c]
1975	0.87	0.18	56.76	5.93	7.41	118.1[c]
1980	0.80	0.20	48.11	5.48	7.52	56.4[c]
1985	0.76	0.24	39.89	4.44	6.18	14.5[c]
1990	0.89	0.29	29.55	3.36	4.96	2.0[c]
Diesel-powered highway vehicles						
1970	0.13	0.10	0.30	1.13	0.01	
1975	0.18	0.14	0.39	1.64	0.13	
1980	0.26	0.21	0.62	2.38	0.21	
1985	0.36	0.28	0.79	2.59	0.22	
1990	0.38	0.30	0.73	2.24	0.17	
Other mobile sources[d]						
1970	0.27	0.35	9.07	1.65	1.26	7.6[e]
1975	0.25	0.33	7.83	1.75	1.24	4.5[e]
1980	0.26	0.48	7.35	1.97	1.24	3.0[e]
1985	0.27	0.36	7.21	1.89	1.22	0.2[e]
1990	0.25	0.36	7.33	1.90	1.27	0.2[e]

Notes:
1 teragram = 1 million metric tons; 1 gigagram = 1 thousand metric tons; 1 metric ton = 2,205 pounds. Data are based on MOBILE4 model. Beginning in 1991, these data were recalculated using a new model, MOBILE4.1, but only the total for all transportation sources was available.

[a]Data for particulate matter are for *all* total suspended particles, since PM-10 data are available only for 1985 and beyond.
[b]VOC emissions are used to measure the formation of ozone, O_3.
[c]Data shown for Pb are for *all* highway vehicles.
[d]Other mobile sources are aircraft, railroads, vessels, and other off-highway vehicles.
[e]Data shown for Pb are for *all* off-highway vehicles.

Source: U.S. Environmental Protection Agency, Office of Air Quality Planning and Standards, *National Air Pollutant Emissions Estimates 1940–1990* (Research Triangle Park, N.C., November 1991).

show, these polluting sources, particularly those that are gasoline powered, emit the largest quantity of nearly every criteria pollutant.[6] These data ex plain the policy focus on the manufacture of these vehicles and the increasing number of initiatives aimed at developing alternative fuels. For its part, the American automobile industry has begun to take a more aggressive position toward reducing motor vehicle pollution, not only because of government controls, but also to accommodate environmentally conscious consumers.

---

[6]As noted in the table, the emissions of volatile organic compounds (VOCs) are used as a proxy measure of ground-level ozone formation.

Recently, the ''Big Three'' formed a research consortium to develop cleaner-running automobiles, a cooperative effort discussed in Application 11.2.

Such public and private initiatives were unheard of as recently as 20 years ago. The evolution of U.S. controls on motor vehicles underscores the inherent problems associated with government regulation of a major industrial sector—in this case, the U.S. automobile industry. Scientific evidence tying the automobile to the formation of smog had existed since the early 1950s, but no federal mandate to control auto emissions was legislated until 1965. And it was not until 1970 that emission limits appeared within the federal law itself.

Application 11.2

The ''Big Three'' Form a Research Consortium in the 1990s

Stiffer requirements for auto emissions in the 1990 Clean Air Act Amendments and under current California law are partly responsible for the formation of a 1990s version of an emissions control research consortium comprising the three largest U.S. automakers—General Motors, Ford, and Chrysler. A similar arrangement formed in 1953 and a related cross-licensing agreement ultimately were dissolved by a 1969 antitrust suit settled through a consent decree. Interestingly, the provisions of that consent decree, which prohibited cooperation for any technological research in emissions controls, expired in 1987.

Of course, times have changed from the 1950s when General Motors, Ford, and Chrysler enjoyed unquestionable dominance of the automobile industry. Their control of the market in that era was in large part responsible for the legal action against the former research consortium. Government officials had reason to believe that this earlier research effort was another delay tactic made possible through implicit collusion. Now, in the 1990s, the so-called ''Big Three'' face pressure from foreign producers and as a result control a much less commanding market share. Imports currently account for some 30 percent of all U.S. new car sales, rocketing from a 0.4 percent share in the post–World War II period. That fact, coupled with a pro-business political atmosphere, makes the 1990s

consortium an unlikely target for antitrust officials. In fact, the U.S. government is now supporting collaborative research efforts, validating that support through legislation passed in 1984 by Congress. For their part, GM, Ford, and Chrysler argue that their cooperative effort not only will help achieve environmental policy objectives but also will strengthen their position against foreign competition.

The research effort, one of eight such agreements among the automakers, is aimed at investigating a variety of technologies to develop cleaner-running automobiles as well as cleaner fuels. It will be interesting to observe their progress vis-à-vis past performance. Not only has the industry been generally unresponsive to environmental issues in the past, they have also marred their technological track record with their use of the catalytic converter, a technology viewed by the National Academy of Sciences as a poor solution in terms of cost, serviceability, and fuel economy. Time will tell whether the results of this 1990s effort will contribute to environmental quality or if it is another case of history repeating itself.

Sources: Krystal Miller, ''Big 3 to Cooperate on Efforts to Meet Clean-Air Rules,'' *The Wall Street Journal* (June 9, 1992); Walter Adams and James W. Brock, ''The Automobile Industry,'' in Walter Adams, ed., *The Structure of American Industry* (New York: Macmillan Publishing Company, 1990).

A Brief Retrospective on Motor Vehicle Emission Controls

By most accounts, national legislation on motor vehicle emissions was slow to start in this country. In 1963, the United States passed into law the Clean Air Act, the first extensive set of air quality controls. Yet, notably absent from its provisions was any direct regulation of automobile emissions. This was a startling omission given that the state of California had passed new laws that same year to do exactly that. In contrast to California's activism, the Clean Air Act of 1963 took a much more cautious approach, giving virtually no power to federal officials to act directly in controlling mobile sources. It was not until 1965 when the Clean Air Act was amended for the first time that federal controls on mobile sources were strengthened, calling for the establishment of uniform emission standards. Somewhat ironically, this legislative transition was motivated in large part by the historically uncooperative automobile industry. The reason was an economic one. Automakers had an incentive to lobby for *national* controls, since they wanted to avoid the costly alternative of having to meet state-specific standards for new production lines. The 1965 law set maximum emissions for new automobiles starting with the 1968 model year, but only for two of the major pollutants—carbon monoxide and hydrocarbons.[7]

Mobile source controls in the 1970 Amendments were precedent setting in that new car emission standards were explicitly stated in the statutes themselves, and these newly defined standards were extremely stringent. In retrospect, most argue that achieving them was not feasible given available technology. Emissions of carbon monoxide and hydrocarbons were to be reduced by 90 percent by the 1975 model year from their 1970 levels, with comparable reductions for nitrogen oxide emissions by the 1976 model year from their 1971 level. These standards were to be applicable over the entire useful life of the vehicle—a requirement that placed even more pressure on the automobile industry. Manufacturers had to guarantee their emission control systems for this entire period, not only to the initial buyer, but to every subsequent purchaser as well. Predictably, Detroit's automakers sought extensions to the legislated deadlines and adjustments to the targeted emission levels. Ultimately, the compliance dates originally set for 1975 and 1976 were postponed for five years.

All told, the early years of mobile source controls were marked by a series of such extensions and a chronicle of delays. As the power struggle between

---

[7]It is important to note that the 1965 laws did not limit nitrogen oxide emissions, even though scientific evidence existed that these emissions contributed significantly to the presence of smog. Moreover, the emission standards applied only to cars produced in 1968 or beyond and only for the year in which they were produced. There was no provision for cars produced prior to 1968 and no law to govern emissions on used cars, even if they were originally manufactured to meet a given standard when new (Mills 1978, pp. 190–91). Effectively, the law ignored the durability of motor vehicles and did not control emissions over an automobile's economic useful life.

Washington and Detroit continued, society grew increasingly impatient with the lack of progress. Washington officials knew that federal policy on motor vehicle emissions was in need of major revision.

Current U.S. Controls on Motor Vehicles and Fuels

Attempting to correct the errors of the past, the 1990 Clean Air Act Amendments strengthen U.S. controls over motor vehicle emissions and fuels. In addition to more stringent command-and-control regulations, the new laws also incorporate several market-based incentives to encourage technological development of cleaner-running vehicles and cleaner alternative fuels. Among the more salient features of the new law are: (1) emission reductions for cars and trucks; (2) onboard pollution control systems for conventional motor vehicles; (3) fuel quality controls; and (4) initiatives to develop clean fuel vehicles. A brief summary of each of these initiatives follows.

Emission Reductions for Motor Vehicles.   The 1990 Amendments impose tougher regulations on tailpipe emissions from all types of highway vehicles. More refined than under existing law, the new standards have two tiers. The first refers to the initial 5 years, or 50,000 miles of use, and the second establishes less stringent standards for the remainder of the vehicle's useful life redefined at 10 years, or 100,000 miles. Beyond this extension of a car's economic life, the new emissions limits are implemented much as they have been in the past—uniformly applicable to every new model car.

Onboard Pollution Control Systems for Light-Duty Vehicles.   To control refueling emissions, the 1990 law requires the installation of onboard vapor recovery systems on new light-duty vehicles. Other provisions call for the installation of emission control diagnostic systems on all light-duty vehicles and trucks starting with the 1994 model year. At minimum, these systems must be capable of accurately identifying a failure in the vehicle's catalytic converter and oxygen sensor over its useful life. To assure compliance, states must revise their State Implementation Plans (SIPs) to make certain that their vehicle inspection and maintenance programs can properly test these new diagnostic systems. In fact, the 1990 law requires that more metropolitan areas establish at least a basic inspection and maintenance program, and that 82 of the nation's dirtiest cities set up high-tech or enhanced inspection programs.

reformulated gasoline
Newly-developed fuel formulations that emit less hydrocarbons, carbon monoxide, and toxics than gasoline currently in use.

Fuel Quality Controls.   Just as vehicles are more stringently regulated under the 1990 law, so too are fuels and fuel additives. For example, effective October 1, 1993, it is unlawful to manufacture, sell, or transport any diesel fuel containing a sulfur content above 0.05 percent. Similarly, any fuel containing lead or lead additives is prohibited for highway use after December 31, 1995. Other provisions require the use of newly developed cleaner fuels in certain of the nonattainment areas. For instance, **reformulated gasoline** must be used

oxygenated fuel
Fuel formulations containing an enhanced amount of oxygen to allow for more complete combustion and hence a reduction in carbon monoxide emissions.

in some ozone nonattainment regions and **oxygenated fuel** in designated carbon monoxide nonattainment areas. **Reformulated gasoline** refers to new formulations that emit less hydrocarbons, carbon monoxide, and toxics than gasoline currently in use. **Oxygenated fuel** contains an enhanced proportion of oxygen to allow for more complete combustion and a reduction in carbon monoxide emissions.

To encourage compliance with these new fuel laws, market-based incentives are used. Credits are issued for fuels that exceed legal requirements such as those with lower hydrocarbon levels or a higher oxygen content. These marketable credits can be used by the recipient or may be transferred to another individual in the same nonattainment area.

Clean Fuel Vehicles.   Responding further to the nation's urban air quality problems, the 1990 legislation establishes a **clean fuel vehicles** program. According to law, a **clean fuel vehicle** is one that has been certified to meet stringent emission standards for substances such as CO, NO_x, PM, and formaldehyde over prescribed time periods. For designated ozone and carbon monoxide nonattainment areas, states must set up programs for the adoption of clean fuel vehicles by owners or operators of fleets of more than 10 vehicles. These programs must be phased in starting with the 1998 model year. At this point, a fixed percentage of all new fleet vehicles bought in each area must be clean fuel vehicles and must use what are called **clean alternative fuels.** These are any fuels, including methanol, ethanol, or other alcohols, or any power sources, including electricity, used in a clean fuel vehicle. There are also provisions for converting existing and new conventional vehicles to clean fuel vehicles. Application 11.3 analyzes the pros and cons of using clean fuels to reduce air pollution.

clean fuel vehicle
A motor vehicle certified to meet stringent emission standards.

clean alternative fuels
Fuels, such as methanol, ethanol, or other alcohols, or power sources, such as electricity, used in a clean fuel vehicle.

Application 11.3

Changing Fuels for America's Automobiles: The Pros and Cons

The gas-powered automobile has long been known as a major source of harmful emissions into the earth's atmosphere. Historically, most air quality legislation has been aimed at the vehicle itself, calling for better emission controls and high-tech diagnostic systems. More recently, regulation also has been directed toward the development of cleaner fuels as substitutes for petroleum-based products.

Two characteristics of petroleum-based fuels are linked to air pollution—its *burning efficiency* and its *volatility.* When fuels burn inefficiently, carbon monoxide (CO) emissions are produced as a by-product of combustion. This problem is more prevalent in cold weather and is exacerbated when fuels are burned in poorly maintained engines. As efficiency improves, carbon dioxide (CO_2) emissions are formed instead. A fuel's volatility, or its

Application 11.3 (continued)

capacity to evaporate, is also important to air pollution, since evaporation releases toxic vapors into the air. Fuel volatility arises from the presence of volatile organic compounds (VOCs), which are added to enhance a fuel's octane rating or antiknock properties. The higher the volatility of gasoline, the more VOC emissions are released into the atmosphere. Recall that VOCs are major contributors to the formation of urban smog.

The 1990 Clean Air Act Amendments explicitly call for the use of several types of "cleaner fuels" under certain well-defined conditions. These cleaner fuels are broadly classified into three groups: **oxygenated fuels, reformulated gasoline,** and **clean alternative fuels.** On the plus side, each group possesses certain attributes that lessen air pollution. However, based on current technology, none of these is a cure-all. In fact, there are disadvantages of using these fuels that policy-makers must consider in mandating their use by consumers.

Oxygenated Fuels.   The U.S. oxygenated fuels program is aimed at reducing carbon monoxide (CO) emissions and therefore is scheduled for use in CO nonattainment areas. Fuel additives provide the oxygen content needed to enhance fuel efficiency and allow for more complete combustion. Currently, the additives used are corn-based ethanol or methyl tertiary butyl ether (MTBE), which is a petroleum-based methanol derivative. Fuel prices are expected to increase by a few cents per gallon as a result.

Reformulated Gasoline.   Launched in 1995, the reformulated gasoline program is applicable to

regions facing severe ozone problems. Aimed specifically at fuel volatility and toxicity, reformulated fuel must contain at minimum 2 percent oxygen and at maximum 1 percent benzene. Standards for this fuel require specific reductions in hydrocarbon and toxic emissions. Based on estimates, fuel prices have risen by a few pennies per gallon.

Clean Alternative Fuels.   In addition to requiring changes in the chemical mixture of gasoline, the 1990 Amendments also call for the use of clean alternative fuels in clean fuel vehicles. For example, such requirements are imposed for fleets of 10 or more vehicles in certain CO and ozone nonattainment areas. According to law, clean alternative fuels may include reformulated gasoline or other alternatives in place of the more conventional petroleum-based products. These alternatives include ethanol ("grain alcohol"), methanol ("wood alcohol"), compressed natural gas, propane (liquified petroleum gas), and electricity. The table below summarizes the major advantages and disadvantages of these fuels based on information provided by the EPA.

Sources: U.S. Environmental Protection Agency, Office of Mobile Sources, "Clean Fuels: An Overview." Fact Sheet OMS-6 (Ann Arbor, Mich., January 1993a); U.S. Environmental Protection Agency, Office of Mobile Sources, "Vehicle Fuels and the 1990 Clean Air Act," Fact Sheet OMS-13 (Ann Arbor, Mich.. January 1993b); Art Kinsman, "Fueling the Future," *AAA World* (April 1992); Joseph D. Younger, "Cleaner, 'Greener' Gasoline?" *AAA World* (November/December 1992).

Fuel	*Advantages*	*Disadvantages*
Ethanol	Excellent automotive fuel. Very low emissions of ozone-forming hydrocarbons and toxics. Made from renewable sources. Can be domestically produced.	High fuel cost. Somewhat lower vehicle range.

Application 11.3 (concluded)

Methanol	Excellent automotive fuel. Very low emissions of ozone-forming hydrocarbons and toxics. Can be made from a variety of feedstocks, including renewables.	Fuel initially would be imported. Somewhat lower vehicle range. Possible increase in NO_x. Lower cold-weather performance. High levels of formaldehyde emissions.
Natural gas	Very low emissions of ozone-forming hydrocarbons, toxics, and CO. Can be made from a variety of feedstocks, including renewables. Excellent fuel especially for fleet vehicles.	Higher vehicle cost. Lower vehicle range. Less convenient refueling.
Propane	Cheaper than gasoline today. Most widely available clean fuel today. Somewhat lower emissions of ozone-forming hydrocarbons and toxics. Excellent fuel, especially for fleet vehicles.	Cost will rise with demand. Limited supply. No energy security or trade balance benefits.
Reformulated gasoline	Can be used in all cars without changing the fuel distribution system. Somewhat lower emissions of ozone-forming hydrocarbons and toxics.	Somewhat higher fuel cost.
Electricity	Potential for zero vehicle emissions. Power plant emissions easier to control. Can recharge at night when power demand is low.	Current technology is limited. Higher vehicle cost. Lower vehicle performance. Lower vehicle range. Less convenient refueling.

Again, market incentives are integrated into the new provisions. In this case, credits are to be issued to fleet operators or owners who surpass the requirements in the law. They might do this by purchasing clean fuel vehicles in advance of the deadline or by buying more of these vehicles than the law requires. The awarded credits can be held, banked for future use, or traded. The marketable credits are to be weighted by the emission reduction achieved by each vehicle, which gives the fleet owner a further incentive to go beyond what the law requires. Those for whom such an option is most lucrative will do so, while those who are unable to meet the standards will have to enter the market for fleet emissions credits and purchase the right to pollute.

Economic Analysis of Mobile Source Controls

Historically, U.S. attempts to control emissions from mobile sources have been frustrated by a litany of problems and delays. In a very real sense, many of the difficulties were predictable, even avoidable. In retrospect, much of the problem was that the law failed to consider the dynamics of the marketplace and the importance of benefit-cost analysis. To provide some structure to our evaluation of these and other important issues, we focus our analysis around the following characteristics of mobile source emissions control policy: (1) the absence of benefit-cost analysis in setting standards for tailpipe emissions; (2) the uniformity of auto emissions standards; (3) the bias against new vehicles; and (4) the implications of clean fuel alternatives.

The Absence of Benefit-Cost Analysis: An Inefficient Decision Rule

It is an interesting irony that after years of delay in establishing federal limits on auto emissions, the Clean Air Act Amendments of 1970 imposed controls that by most accounts were extraordinarily stringent. Even at that point in legislative history, there was virtually no argument that the stated objectives for emission reductions were ambitious. In part, the stringent controls were a response to accumulating evidence that motor vehicles were a major source of pollution. However, there was also reason to believe that Washington was attempting to take a strong position against the American automobile industry.

Beyond the motivations for tougher standards, the more critical issue is whether the emissions targets were technologically feasible and, if not, whether they were intentionally set beyond what was possible given the existing knowledge base. Most argue that the standards were not attainable and in fact were meant to be *technology-forcing* by design—that is, specifically set to compel the auto industry to find solutions. Such a strategy may have been in order, given the industry's track record to that point. However, most have questioned the government's wisdom in setting emission reductions so far out of reach that manufacturers had a strong case to seek adjustments and postponements.

Just as important is the fact that the implied decision rule used to establish the emissions controls was not supported by benefit-cost analysis. Rather, the standards were set to protect public health and welfare—a purely benefit-based objective. Decisions that ignore cost implications are destined for economic failure. As it turned out, the 1970 standards were never implemented in their original form. In fact, they were modified considerably. Worse, the haggling over the unrealistic standards between the government and the automobile industry only added to the already long delays. No one can say with certainty how the course of events might have changed had the 1970 standards not been set at such stringent levels. However, the following is not an unreasonable hypothesis given what we now know to be true. Had the standards been set at levels that accounted for the full extent of the associated costs, it is quite possible that the automobile industry would not have had sufficient support for its lobbying efforts to extend the statutory deadlines. Instead, the lack of efficient decision-making left policy-makers unarmed for the assault mounted by the automakers. The result? The ultimate burden was borne by society, and the ill-defined decisions of that era accomplished little more than to postpone the provision of cleaner-running vehicles to the marketplace.

Uniformity of Auto Emissions Standards

An ongoing problem with U.S. mobile source controls is that with few exceptions the national emission standards for automobiles are applicable ''across the board'' on every model produced and without regard to where the vehicle will be driven. Another uniform requirement calls for all cars and light-duty trucks starting with 1984 models to meet high-altitude standards, despite the fact that only about 3.5 percent of cars sold in the United States are purchased in high-altitude areas.[8] Ultimately, such uniformity needlessly increases the costs of reducing pollution with no offsetting benefit to society.

Analysts argue that the disregard for the geographical area in which a vehicle is operated overcontrols vehicles sold in relatively clean areas and undercontrols those sold in more polluted areas. An alternative suggestion is to have two sets of standards to be administered at the state level based on the degree of pollution in that area. Proponents of this more federalistic approach believe this would yield important cost savings. A 1974 study conducted by the National Academy of Science estimates the costs of a uniform 0.4 grams per mile (gpm) standard for NO_x relative to the costs of a two-tiered standard, calling for a 0.4 gpm standard in seriously polluted areas (about 37 percent of motor vehicles), and a 3.1 gpm standard in all other areas.[9] The study predicts that a $23 billion savings over the 1975 to 1985 period would have resulted if the two-tiered system had been used.

Similarly, it is argued that the emission controls need not be applicable to every model produced by an automobile manufacturer. Substantial savings could be achieved by allowing producers to meet the legislated targets based on *average* emissions of all new cars produced. The benefits based on overall emission reductions would be unchanged, but the costs of compliance would be much lower.[10] The forgone savings help to explain the growth rate of mobile source control costs since the 1970 Amendments, from $1.3 billion ($1986) in 1972 to $7.5 billion ($1986) in 1987.[11]

Current law *does* allow some exceptions to uniform emissions standards. Perhaps the most notable example is the use of more stringent mobile source standards for vehicles in the state of California. More recently, other states

---

[8]Council of Economic Advisers (1982), pp. 145–46; Seskin (1978), p. 91; and White (1982), pp. 67–68. White reports that, according to General Motors, the per unit cost in current dollars of this high-altitude standard is approximately $65 for a gas-powered automobile and $230 for a diesel-powered car.

[9]See National Academy of Sciences and National Academy of Engineering (1974).

[10]This proposal is discussed in the economic analysis of mobile source emissions in Council of Economics Advisers (1982), p. 146, which asserts that such an averaging plan could save millions of dollars.

[11]U.S. EPA, Office of Policy, Planning, and Evaluation (December 1990).

have followed suit. In December 1994, the EPA approved a plan submitted by clean air officials in 12 eastern states and the District of Columbia (members of the Ozone Transport Commission), to require cars manufactured for their regions to meet California-style emissions standards by 1999. California law also calls for 2 percent of vehicle sales in the state to be zero-emission vehicles (i.e., electric cars), by 1998, phasing in toward a 10 percent level by 2003. Massachusetts and New York have enacted similar requirements.

These regional variances from national requirements have set off a round of debates. The auto industry points to the increased manufacturing costs of complying with several sets of emissions standards. Others question the wisdom of moving to electric vehicles that have to be fueled by power plants. In some regions like the Northeast, electric power plants are more important contributors to smog than are mobile sources, so the net gain in air quality may not be worth the effort. Furthermore, the technology of electric car engineering is still in its infancy, particularly in addressing the harsher conditions of cold-weather climates.[12] What these arguments suggest is that alternatives to uniform emission standards must be well thought out to achieve any significant gain.

Inherent Bias against New versus Used Automobiles

One of the more troubling dilemmas in environmental law is the inherent bias caused by more stringent controls imposed on new polluting sources. This partiality is particularly problematic for motor vehicles, since engine performance as well as sticker price are at issue. As long as there are differences between the regulation of new and used vehicles, there will be price and performance impacts that can create market distortions.

To fully understand how the law influences market decisions, consider the following. The automobile is a durable good, meaning it has an economic life that extends beyond a single time period. Because of this, new and used automobiles are substitutes for one another with the usual relationship between their relative prices. The imposition of government regulations on new car emissions naturally adds to the production costs of those vehicles—costs which are passed on, at least in part, to consumers. Faced with higher relative prices for new automobiles, some consumers will purchase a used car or opt to keep a deteriorating one, either of which is likely to be a relatively high emitter of pollutants. Hence, because the regulation encourages consumers to substitute in favor of used cars, it effectively extends the economic life of cars

---

[12]Even stronger opposition comes from University of Denver Professor Don Stedman, who argues that all emission standards for automobiles are costly and ineffective. Stedman claims that most automobile emissions come from a relatively small proportion of cars with faulty emissions systems or badly tuned engines. These culprits, he claims, can be singled out using his invention called a remote-sensor. According to Stedman, his idea is a better and cheaper control approach than across-the-board rules on tailpipe emissions and fuels (Monaghan, March 10, 1993).

already on the road. There is also the issue that emission control devices negatively affect a new car's acceleration and gas mileage. Thus, the legislation confounds the signaling mechanism of price by diminishing the performance of a relatively higher priced vehicle. In sum, the regulations bias consumers' decisions against new cars by influencing two important determinants of demand—relative price and performance.

The implication of these observations is a very real and paradoxical problem. The regulations implicitly encourage consumers to purchase used cars or keep their old cars, which emit more pollution into the atmosphere than new, cleaner-running vehicles. Thus, laws designed to reduce pollution may actually *increase* it temporarily if purchasing decisions are affected by the resulting price distortions. Some evidence of this phenomenon is presented in a 1982 empirical study that examines the effect of the tougher 1981 vehicle emissions standards on actual emissions.[13] This research finds that short-run aggregate emissions through 1984 actually would have been lower without the more stringent standards.

There have been some policy changes, and still others on the drawing board, that address this dilemma. For example, the 1990 Amendments extend the economic life of the automobile over which emission standards are mandated by increasing the relevant regulatory period from its former 5 years or 50,000 miles to 10 years or 100,000 miles. Although the standards for the second half of the period are less stringent, the extension to a longer and more realistic time period helps to reduce the bias against future new vehicles, since most cars on the road ultimately will be subject to at least some degree of emissions control. An alternative idea, still in the experimental stage, is a program called "Cash for Clunkers." This incentive-based proposal, discussed in Application 11.4, would allow firms to earn pollution credits in return for buying older, vintage cars and scrapping them to get these high emitters off the road.

Implications of Clean Fuel Alternatives

Clean fuel provisions in the 1990 Amendments provide a much-needed extension of technology-based standards, which were formerly directed almost entirely toward vehicle engines and emission control systems. Beyond this explicit advantage, it is also the case that the new clean fuel laws are being implemented in regions where they can yield the most benefit to society. Although the controls on sulfur and lead content are being imposed uniformly, the use of more advanced fuel compositions is required only in the dirtier regions of the country. Targeting these specific areas makes good sense from an economic perspective. The development and use of these alternative fuels is associated with higher marginal costs, which aligns with the higher expected marginal benefits that will accrue in the designated nonattainment regions.

---

[13]Gruenspecht (1982).

Application 11.4

The "Cash for Clunkers" Program

In March 1992, the United States announced an innovative proposal aimed at encouraging the scrapping of older-model, high-emitting automobiles. This so-called "Cash for Clunkers" program promotes the issuance of emission reduction credits to firms that purchase and scrap old cars. As in other emissions trading programs, these credits can be applied against legislated reductions imposed on the firm as a stationary source. While not fully developed, the plan ties together the controls on stationary sources with those imposed on mobile sources. In fact, President Bush called it "mobile-stationary source trading and emissions control."

To some extent, the national proposal is based upon a prototype experiment put into place in Los Angeles. In 1990, an oil company called Unocal Corp. purchased some 8,400 pre-1971 cars for $700 each over a one-year period and scrapped them. The oil firm estimates that the plan reduced hydrocarbon emissions at an average cost of $7,000 per ton removed. Based on these estimates, it has been suggested that Unocal's approach is cost-effective in a severely polluted area like Los Angeles. Of course, this begs the question whether the company's estimates were accurate *and* whether such a plan would be worthwhile in other regions of the country.

Beyond these fundamental questions, there are others issues to be resolved before the "Cash for Clunkers" program could be implemented nationwide. For one thing, some argue that $700 is not likely to be a sufficient inducement for an individual to give up his or her used automobile and face the expense of buying a newer car. Responding

to this objection, a Unocal official cited a survey it conducted that showed that 360 of the 800 individuals surveyed did in fact use the $700 to purchase newer and presumably cleaner-running cars. Another problem is in determining the price to be paid for these old cars. Related to this issue is controlling the migration of older vehicles from one region to another to seek out the best available price. Compounding these problems is the matter of how to calculate credits for the purchased vehicles. Should the credits be uniform across all vehicles or should they reflect the expected reduction in pollution per mile over the remaining economic life of the car?

Whatever the ultimate approach, there is a powerful incentive for policy-makers to find some way to pull high-emitting vehicles off American highways. According to former acting assistant EPA director Richard Morgenstern, 38 percent of all cars on the road in 1992 were built prior to 1980. These vehicles generated 86 percent of the hydrocarbons and carbon dioxide released by mobile sources into the atmosphere. Appealing to the effectiveness of contrasts, Mr. Morgenstern said:

> The dirtiest 6 percent of the cars on the road today emit 50 percent of the hydrocarbons. The cleanest 50 percent of cars emit only 3 percent of these hydrocarbons.

Sources: *EPA Journal,* " 'Cash for Clunkers' to Cut Pollution," *EPA Journal* 18, no 2 (May/June 1992), p. 2; U.S. Environmental Protection Agency, Office of Policy, Planning, and Evaluation, *The United States Experience With Economic Incentives to Control Environmental Pollution* (Washington, D.C., July 1992), p. 7–2, 7–3.

Hence, this selective legislation follows the fundamental decision rule of benefit-cost analysis, which may approach an efficient solution.

A separate issue is whether the fuel-switching program is a cost-effective approach to reducing mobile source emissions. Some of the cleaner fuels, such as reformulated gasoline, are already available in certain markets. In fact, reformulated gasoline has been on sale in Southern California since 1990 and does not require any engine retooling. Some blends have been developed specifically for high-emitting older cars and have been shown to reduce their emissions by at least 20 percent. However, providing reformulated fuel on a mass scale to comply with the 1990 Amendments will require extensive production changes and plant expansion by oil companies, which is expected to cost billions of dollars. ARCO, the oil company that pioneered the development of reformulated fuel, estimates that it can produce a reformulated gasoline to satisfy the 1990 laws that will cost consumers 15 cents more per gallon.[14] But is this a cost-effective solution? This is precisely the issue discussed in Application 11.5, which presents new research evidence on the costs of using oxygenated fuel and methanol.

Application 11.5

Are Fuel-Based Control Strategies Cost-Effective Solutions?

The 1990 Clean Air Act Amendments call for the use of cleaner fuels to help achieve national air quality objectives. Oxygenated fuels are recommended for use in carbon monoxide (CO) nonattainment areas, particularly in high-altitude regions such as Denver. Clean alternative fuels like methanol are targeted for high-ozone areas such as Los Angeles. Despite this national commitment, there is debate about the **cost-effectiveness** of such fuel-based strategies. Still in its embryonic stage, research on this issue is far from conclusive as are the associated projections. Nonetheless, the research results offer insight about the cost implications of using new fuels—vital information for policy-makers.

Using Oxygenated Fuels

A recent research paper (Rowe et al., 1990) investigates the use of oxygenated fuels in Denver, an area where the cold temperatures and high altitude make it particularly vulnerable to CO pollution. Faced with the possibility of disapproval of its implementation plan, Colorado introduced new legislation in 1987 requiring the use of fuel with a minimum oxygen content of $1\frac{1}{2}$ percent for all CO nonattainment areas—the first such program in the nation. As a pilot program for other CO problem areas, the cost implications are worth investigating.

Rowe and his colleagues form a baseline for their research by estimating the cost per ton of CO reduction in the Denver area from using either of two oxygenated additives, methyl tertiary butyl ether (MTBE) and ethanol. The estimates are based primarily on the incremental costs of blending and distribution, net of the offsetting effect of added octane provided by oxy-additives. Ultimately, they arrive at a statewide total cost for the program's first year of $1 million in 1988 dollars with an effective incremental cost per gallon of fuel of 0.45 cents. Based on an estimated reduction of 10,250 tons of CO for the first year, the program's cost is approximated at $100 per ton of CO reduction. The researchers then modify this regional estimate to be applicable to a national program, adjusting for different prices and market conditions. The result is approximately $300 per ton for the MTBE program and about $590 per ton for ethanol.

---

[14]Dickerson (January/February 1991).

Application 11.5 (continued)

With these estimates as a baseline, Rowe and his colleagues consider how these costs per ton compare with three other control alternatives: (1) an enhanced inspection and maintenance program; (2) Denver's Better Air Campaign, which includes a ''no drive day'' plan in the high CO season; and (3) a trip reduction ordinance which requires large employers to provide a plan for their workers to reduce the use of single-occupant vehicles. The comparison based on cost per ton of CO removed is shown in the table at the bottom of this box.

Using as a major argument the quantifiable costs of the inspection and maintenance program, the study concludes that the use of oxygenated fuel in the Denver area is cost-effective. A similar argument is viable using the other plans as comparisons but with less confidence given the less-than-satisfactory data. While the results are not directly applicable to low-altitude regions, they do offer important support to laws on oxygenated fuel for climates similar to Denver's.

Using Methanol

A similar study by Thomas J. Lareau (1990) investigates the cost-effectiveness of using methanol in high-ozone areas of the nation. This study argues that the use of methanol suffers from two major disadvantages. First, it has about half the energy content of regular gasoline, which reduces the driving range of vehicles. Secondly, there is uncertainty about methanol's price per gallon. In fact, the author presents several long-run, domestic and imported cost scenarios based on different types of

production facilities and various projected costs of feedstocks used to produce methanol. The result is a range of domestic retail price estimates from $0.88 to $1.65 per gallon in 1988 dollars and a range of imported fuel price estimates from $0.69 to $1.15 per gallon.

On the benefit side, improvements from using methanol also are difficult to predict. The resulting emissions are primarily methanol, which are less likely to contribute to ozone formation than those associated with gasoline use. However, these emissions also contain formaldehyde and volatile organic compounds (VOCs). Formaldehyde is very reactive, which increases the likelihood of ozone formation. A high ambient concentration of VOCs relative to nitrogen oxides (NO_x) lessens the ozone-reducing potential of using methanol. So on net, the benefit of using methanol is not at all certain.

To determine if methanol use is cost-effective, the researcher presents a series of cost estimates based on different scenarios that vary with the VOC emission standard, the existing VOC/NO_x ratio, and the price differential between gasoline and methanol. While the estimates vary considerably, most are in the range of tens of thousands of dollars per ton of VOCs reduced, and some are as high as hundreds of thousands of dollars per ton. The operative question is whether such a high cost is worth it. Existing studies assign a cutoff value at which a methanol substitution plan would be cost-effective. Most estimates fall in the range of $2,000 to $10,000 per ton. Based on this range, few of the scenarios posed by Lareau would be cost-effective, and these assume a very low or even zero price differential between gasoline and methanol. The

Inspection and maintenance program with 1987 enhancements	$785.
Better Air Campaign plan (based only on quantifiable costs)	>$250.*
Trip reduction ordinances	$1,000 to $5,000.†

*The great majority of costs are not quantifiable; thus, this estimate is highly understated.
†No data on Denver's plan were available, so the estimate is based on the costs of a Phoenix, Arizona, plan.

Application 11.5 (concluded)

problem is, no one can predict such a potentially volatile price difference with any certainty.

Lareau concludes that other VOC-reducing strategies ought to be considered instead of methanol substitution. The costs of implementing this fuel strategy are highly sensitive to a number of factors that are unpredictable at best. Such a risky strategy could impose high costs on society, and policy-makers should rethink the issue and consider more predictable alternatives.

Sources: Robert D. Rowe, Michael G. Shelby, Joshua B. Epel, and Ari Michelsen, ''Using Oxygenated Fuels to Mitigate Carbon Monoxide Air Pollution: The Case of Denver,'' *Contemporary Policy Issues* 8 (January 1990), pp. 39–53; Thomas J. Lareau, ''The Economics of Alternative Fuel Use: Substituting Methanol for Gasoline,'' *Contemporary Policy Issues* 8 (October 1990), pp. 138–52.

Controlling Stationary Sources

Stationary sources contribute to the emissions levels of all the criteria pollutants. This source group covers a lot of ground. Within it are electric power plants, chemical plants, steel mills, and even residential furnaces. Obviously certain categories are more important to U.S. control policy than others, and some release more of certain criteria pollutants than others. Look at the trend data reported in Table 11.5. Notice how fuel combustion sources, which include fossil-fueled electric power plants, are major contributors of sulfur oxide emissions—the primary cause of acid rain. On the other hand, industrial sources such as petroleum refineries and chemical manufacturers are responsible for most of the VOC emissions. So these types of stationary sources are important targets for policies aimed at reducing urban smog.

Emissions of all stationary sources are regulated primarily by uniform technology-based standards—indicative of a command-and-control policy approach. In the late 1970s, the EPA did introduce some market-based programs, although these were intended to be subordinate to the ongoing use of standards. For the most part, both the technology-based standards and the market programs are defined and implemented in accordance with two distinguishing features of stationary sources: (1) the age of the facility—whether it is new or existing; and (2) the location of the facility—whether it is within a prevention of significant deterioration (PSD) area or a nonattainment area. These characteristics form the structural basis for our discussion. To serve as a guideline for what is to follow, refer to Table 11.6 for a summary of the various standards and trading programs that evolved based on these factors.

Age-Specific Control Differences: New versus Existing Sources

Defining Technology-Based Emissions Limits.   Age-specific control differences initially were established in the 1970 Clean Air Act Amendments. In general, the rulings require that facilities constructed or modified after 1970

TABLE 11.5   **National Emissions Estimates for Stationary Sources by Major Category**

(Teragrams per Year except Lead in Gigagrams)

	PM*	SO$_x$	CO	NO$_x$	VOCs†	Pb
Fuel combustion						
1970	5.07	21.29	4.21	9.11	0.61	9.60
1975	3.28	20.23	4.03	9.33	0.60	9.39
1980	3.04	19.10	6.59	10.10	0.95	3.90
1985	2.47	17.58	6.29	9.38	0.90	0.47
1990	1.87	16.98	4.30	10.63	0.62	0.46
Industrial processes						
1970	10.54	6.43	8.95	0.70	8.93	23.86
1975	5.19	4.57	6.88	0.68	8.19	10.32
1980	3.31	3.74	6.34	0.68	9.13	3.57
1985	2.70	3.17	4.38	0.56	8.35	2.30
1990	2.53	3.05	4.64	0.59	8.02	2.23
Solid waste disposal						
1970	1.10	0.00	6.40	0.40	1.80	2.00
1975	0.44	0.04	2.93	0.14	0.88	1.45
1980	0.33	0.03	2.09	0.10	0.67	1.10
1985	0.29	0.02	1.85	0.08	0.60	0.79
1990	0.28	0.02	1.70	0.08	0.58	0.73
Miscellaneous						
1970	1.10	0.10	7.20	0.30	3.30	0.00
1975	0.75	0.02	4.77	0.15	2.54	0.00
1980	1.08	0.01	7.57	0.23	2.90	0.00
1985	1.01	0.01	7.09	0.21	2.49	0.00
1990	1.19	0.01	8.62	0.26	2.82	0.00

Note: 1 teragram = 1 million metric tons; 1 gigagram = 1 thousand metric tons; 1 metric ton = 2,205 pounds.

*Data for particulate matter are for *all* total suspended particles, since data on PM-10 are available only for 1985 and beyond.

†VOC emissions are used to measure the formation of ozone, O$_3$.

Sources: U.S. Environmental Protection Agency, Office of Air Quality Planning and Standards, *National Emissions Trend Report, 1991* (Research Triangle Park, N.C., October 1992) as cited in Council on Environmental Quality, *Environmental Quality, 23rd Annual Report* (Washington, D.C.: U.S. Government Printing Office, January 1993), Table 37, pp. 331–34.

are to meet more stringent emissions limits than those already in existence. The reasoning was that new or modified stationary sources presumably could integrate the technology needed to meet stringent standards more easily than their older counterparts. Existing facilities would likely face high retrofitting costs, which could hurt local economies. Furthermore, they eventually would deteriorate to the point of needing to be modified or replaced. Hence, over time, the tougher emissions standards would have to be met by *all* stationary sources.

TABLE 11.6   Technology-Based Standards and Market Programs under the Clean Air Act

	PSD Areas Classification of Stationary Source	
	---	---
Approach	*New or Modified Sources*	*Existing Sources*
Standards	Best available control technology (BACT)	Best available retrofit technology (BART)
Market-based program	Netting	Bubble policy

BACT refers to an emission limitation based upon the maximum degree of pollution reduction that the permitting authority deems achievable on a case-by-case basis, accounting for energy, environmental, and other economic impacts and costs.

BART is applicable only to emissions that might negatively affect visibility in a PSD area and must consider factors such as compliance costs, existing control technology, and the energy and environmental impacts.

Netting refers to the use of emissions trading among points within a given source for the same type of pollutant, such that any increase in emissions from a modified source is *exactly matched* by a reduction in emissions from another point within that same source.

The **bubble policy** allows a plant or plant complex to measure its emissions of a single pollutant, not from each of the single-point-sources within that plant or complex, but rather as an average of all emission points emanating from that plant or complex, as if they were captured within an imaginary bubble.

	Nonattainment Areas Classification of Stationary Source	
	---	---
Approach	*New or Modified Sources*	*Existing Sources*
Standards	Lowest achievable emission rate (LAER)	Reasonably available control technology (RACT)
Market-based program	Offset plan	Bubble policy

LAER refers to an emissions rate that reflects the most stringent emission limitation outlined in a given SIP for the same type of source, or the most stringent limitation achieved in practice for such a source category, whichever is the more stringent.

RACT refers to an emissions standard based upon the use of technology deemed to be practically available, accounting for technological and economic feasibility, and determined on a case-by-case basis.

An **offset plan** provides for any emissions associated with a new or modified major stationary source to be *more than countered* by the overall reductions achieved by existing sources.

New Source Performance Standards (NSPS) Technology-based emissions limits established for new stationary sources.

new or modified stationary source A source for which construction or modification follows the publication of regulations.

Emissions limits applicable to new and modified stationary sources are called **New Source Performance Standards (NSPS).** According to the Clean Air Act, these NSPS are to be technology-based in accordance with the "best system of emission reduction." Such a phrase suggests that the NSPS were meant to be stringent. But in this case, the stringency is tempered somewhat by allowing for costs and energy requirements to be considered as well.[15] Since technological factors are the basis for these limits, the NSPS are allowed to vary across industry categories designated by the EPA. However, each set of industry standards is to be applied *uniformly* across all firms within a given category. Because of the long-term importance of these more stringent

---

[15]However, in practice this cost consideration is meant to imply only that the technology be affordable and *not* to be used as part of a formal benefit-cost analysis in setting the standards (Portney 1990a, p. 38).

existing stationary source
A source already present when regulations have been published.

bubble policy
Allows a plant or complex to measure its emissions as an average of all emission points emanating from that plant or complex.

emissions banking
Allows a source to accumulate emission reduction credits if it reduces emissions more than required by law and "deposit" these through a banking program.

controls, Congress established a **dual-control approach,** placing the responsibility for controlling **new or modified stationary sources** with the EPA, and assigning the comparable duties for **existing stationary sources** to state governments.

The Bubble Policy.   In December 1979, the EPA launched its **bubble policy,** originally conceived as an option for states to use in implementing the national standards for *existing* sources. The essence of this concept was to allow a plant or plant complex to measure its emissions of a given pollutant, not from each of the single release points within the plant or complex, but rather as an *average* of all such points—as if they were captured within an imaginary bubble. The aim of this new policy was to offer firms flexibility in deciding *how* they could achieve the requisite emission limitations at least cost.

In 1980, just a year after the bubble concept was instituted, the EPA introduced another market-based program called **emissions banking.** Designed to complement the bubble concept, this plan allows a source to accumulate **emission reduction credits** if it reduces emissions more than required by law. These credits are then "deposited" through the banking program for future use, establishing the foundation for an emissions market.[16]

Location-Specific Control Differences: PSD versus Nonattainment Areas

Defining Emissions Limits in PSD Areas.   With the official introduction of prevention of significant deterioration (PSD) areas in 1977, U.S. stationary source controls had to be revised to accommodate the change. Since the air quality standard in PSD regions is higher relative to nonattainment areas, controls for sources located in these areas had to be made more stringent across the board. However, new facilities in PSD areas would face relatively tougher standards than existing ones. Implemented through a permit procedure, any new or modified source in a PSD area has to meet emissions limits based on what is called the **best available control technology (BACT).** What this means is that a new source has to meet a standard that aligns with the *maximum* degree of pollution reduction available. The only special contingency for existing facilities is that those who release emissions that might impair visibility are required to install **best available retrofit technology (BART).**

Defining Emissions Limits in Nonattainment Areas.   Overall, standards for nonattainment areas are relatively less stringent. But just like their PSD counterparts, sources face different standards based on their age. Existing sources are required to use **reasonably available control technology (RACT),** which is the least stringent of all the technology-based standards. In

---

[16]For an interesting and comprehensive discussion on emissions banking and the bubble concept, the reader is referred to Liroff (1986).

contrast, new or modified sources in these areas must comply with the **lowest achievable emission rate (LAER),** roughly defined as the most stringent emission limit achieved in practice by the same type of source.[17]

Emissions Trading in PSD Areas.   To facilitate control in PSD areas, a trading program known as **netting** was developed for use by modified sources.[18] A type of bubble policy, netting allows emissions trading to take place among release points within a facility for the same type of pollutant. Its distinguishing feature is that any added emissions associated with a plant modification must be *exactly matched* by a reduction from somewhere else within that same plant. Hence, netting assures that any construction project will have no detrimental effect on the air quality in a PSD area.

Emissions Trading in Nonattainment Areas.   In some sense, implementing pollution controls in nonattainment areas must be more strategic. Obviously, there is concern about the environmental impact of allowing new or modified facilities into an area already not meeting the national ambient standards. Yet, preventing new construction could potentially worsen air quality, since new plants likely operate more efficiently and cleanly than older ones. In an attempt to achieve the best of both worlds, the 1977 Amendments introduced a program known as an **offset plan.** Implemented through a permit procedure, an offset plan assures that emissions from a new or modified stationary source be *more than countered* by the reductions achieved by existing sources in the area. Notice that unlike the bubble policy or netting, the offset plan involves trades between existing and new sources rather than within the same facility or plant complex. In any case, the offset plan simultaneously allows new construction to proceed *and* achieves a reduction in overall emissions. To facilitate firms' obtaining the necessary offsets from other sources, an **emissions bank** of accumulated **emission reduction credits** was set up where all facilities could deposit and access offsets as needed.

Although the collection of technology-based standards can be confusing, the key points to remember about them are: (1) the emissions limits in PSD areas are more stringent than those in nonattainment areas; and (2) the limits for new sources are more stringent than those for existing sources within both types of areas.[19] Another important observation to make about stationary source controls is the way in which market incentives are used in the bubble policy, emissions banking, offsets, and netting. Although these programs were intended to be subordinate to the technology-based standards, they nonetheless

netting
A program developed for PSD areas that allows emissions trading among points within a given source for the same type of pollutant, such that any increase in emissions due to a plant modification is matched by a reduction from another point within that same source.

offset plan
A program developed for nonattainment areas that allows emissions trading between new or modified sources and existing facilities such that releases from the new or modified source are more than countered by reductions achieved by existing sources.

---

[17]Although LAER is more strict than RACT, it is less stringent than BACT defined for new sources in PSD areas.

[18]Although netting was developed for use in PSD areas, it technically can be used in both attainment and nonattainment areas.

[19]Furthermore, although the new source standards for PSD and nonattainment areas (i.e., BACT and LAER, respectively), are supposed to be more stringent than the New Source Performance Standards (NSPS), in practice, the NSPS are generally accepted for either (Portney 1990a, pp. 37–38).

represented a shift toward integrating some economic-based mechanisms into what had been almost exclusively a command-and-control approach. Title IV of the 1990 Clean Air Amendments continues this trend by establishing another type of trading program for stationary sources specifically aimed at the problem of acid rain.

Controlling Acidic Deposition

Acid rain, or more accurately **acidic deposition,** has been the subject of political and media attention in recent years. Research on the problem has intensified, and both public officials and private citizens have grown increasingly cognizant of the health and ecological implications. As the scientific knowledge base has grown, so too has the motivation to enact stronger legislative controls on the major sources of this environmental problem. Effectiveness of policy initiatives is limited by the fact that acid rain is a *regional* air pollution problem, meaning that the source of the contamination is often hundreds of miles away from where the detrimental effects are felt. Consequently, some form of *federal* intervention generally is necessary to control polluters.

The Problem of Acidic Deposition.   **Acidic deposition** occurs when the production of sulfuric and nitric acids mix with other airborne particles and fall to the earth either as dry deposition or as fog, snow, or rain—thus the descriptive phrase, "acid rain." These acidic compounds result from the chemical reaction of sulfur dioxide (SO_2) and nitrogen oxide (NO_x) emissions with water vapors and oxidants in the earth's atmosphere.[20] Table 11.7 gives an overview of the causes, sources, and effects of this important regional problem. Of the two responsible pollutants, the more significant is SO_2. It is formed when the sulfur found naturally in coal or oil is released during combustion and reacts with the oxygen in the atmosphere. Primary generators of SO_2 emissions are fossil-fueled electric power plants, refineries, pulp and paper mills, and any sources that burn sulfur-containing coal or oil. According to 1990 estimates, 70 percent of U.S. annual emissions of SO_2 are generated by electric power plants, and 92 percent of these are coal-burning plants. By itself, utility coal usage accounts for 85 percent of total coal consumption in the United States.

acidic deposition
Arises when sulfuric and nitric acids mix with other airborne particles and fall to the earth as dry or wet deposits.

The Policy Response: Title IV of the 1990 Amendments.   In response to the nation's concern about acid rain, Title IV of the 1990 Clean Air Act Amendments is dedicated to a reduction plan for NO_x emissions and an innovative allowance program to decrease SO_2 emissions. The reduction plan for NO_x is to be achieved through various performance standards set by the

---

[20]An oxidant is any oxidizing agent such as oxygen (O_2) or ozone (O_3) capable of chemically reacting in the atmosphere to form a new substance.

TABLE 11.7   The Problem of Acidic Deposition: A Summary

Causes	Anthropogenic Sources
SO_2	Fossil-fuel burning primarily by electric power plants.
NO_x	Fossil-fuel burning primarily by electric power plants and motor vehicles.

Major Effects

Ecological and Forestry Effects

Acidification of surface waters; localized forest damage.

Health Effects

Direct effects include respiratory and cardiovascular problems; some indirect effects possible from increased lead or methylmercury exposure under extreme conditions.

Aesthetic Effects

Visibility impairment.

Property Effects

Damage to buildings, statues, and monuments.

EPA. Ultimately, emissions are to be reduced by 2 million tons from their 1980 level. For SO_2, the law establishes a national cap of 8.95 million tons of annual emissions for electric power plants—the major sources of SO_2—and a cap of 5.6 million tons for nonutility industrial sources. Both caps are to be met by the year 2000. This is the first time any national limit has been imposed on a single pollutant. These limits should achieve a 10 million ton reduction in SO_2 emissions below their 1980 level.

The SO_2 Emissions Allowance Program.   One of the more significant aspects of Title IV is the innovative control approach used to achieve the SO_2 emissions cap. The 1990 law sets up an emissions market for SO_2 which operates through an allocation and transfer system. At the start of the program, the EPA issues **tradeable SO_2 emission allowances,** or "rights to pollute," to stationary sources, where each allowance permits the release of one ton of SO_2 into the atmosphere. No emissions are permitted unless they are authorized by an allowance. Hence, the aggregate number issued by the EPA effectively sets the national emissions limit.[21]

tradeable SO_2 emission allowances Permits issued to stationary sources, each allowing the release of one ton of SO_2, which can be held or sold through a transfer program.

Once the emissions allowances are distributed, they can either be used by the recipient or sold to other sources through a transfer program designed by

---

[21]In Phase I of the plan for the 1995 to 2000 period, each stationary source is to receive allowances based upon the following formula: the average fuel usage over the 1985 to 1987 period multiplied by an emission rate of 2.5 pounds of SO_2 per million Btu, all divided by 2,000. In Phase II, which covers the period from 2000 to 2009, the allowance formula is similar except that the emission rate is reduced to 1.2 pounds.

the EPA. This program sets up a market through which allowances can be bought and sold. In May 1992, the first allowance trade was announced between the Tennessee Valley Authority (TVA), a utility operating some 59 coal-fired units, and Wisconsin Power and Light Co., touted to be one of the "cleanest" utilities in the country. The transaction involved the purchase of 10,000 allowances by the TVA at a value of about $2.5 to $3 million. The market incentive for this precedence-setting trade is clear once the facts are known. To meet the new federal standards *without* trading, TVA would have had to invest in abatement technology estimated to cost between $750 and $850 million.

An extension of this interfirm emissions market is provided through a Special Allowance Reserve, a bank of allowances available for direct sale by the EPA. Two subaccounts are formed from this reserve. The first, a Direct Sale Subaccount, is to contain allowances for 50,000 tons per year starting in the year 2000. These are to be sold by request in the order received at a price of $1,500 each, (adjusted for inflation), with priority given to independent electric power producers. A second subaccount, called the Auction Subaccount, is to contain allowances for 150,000 tons per year for the 1995 through 2000 period and 250,000 tons per year for every subsequent year. Starting in 1993, prospective buyers submit sealed bids at an annual auction of allowances, and the allowances are sold to the highest bidder.

Because the success of this program depends greatly on external trades, the EPA designated the Chicago Board of Trade (CBOT) to be in charge of operating the auctions. Because of the board's experience, it can facilitate the exchange of allowances and may reduce the usual transactions costs of matching up buyers and sellers. Virtually anyone can enter the market for SO_2 allowances. In fact, the law specifically states that allowances can be "bought, sold and traded by any individual, corporation, or government body." Application 11.6 describes the major events that characterized the first day of official trading on March 31, 1993. A spin-off of the auction is the CBOT's plan to offer "Clean Air Allowance Futures," that is, futures contracts on SO_2 emissions rights. According to CBOT reports, the contracts are expected to involve bundles of 25 credits and are expected to be offered in the near future.

As it turns out, a number of private firms have anticipated the profit opportunities of the newly created pollution market and are competing with the CBOT as allowance brokers. In fact, one of these brokers, called Clean Air Capital Markets, arranged the first $3 million trade between the TVA and Wisconsin Power and Light Co. Thus far, Clean Air Capital has arranged transactions totalling $72 million. Another firm called Cantor Fitzgerald, Inc. has launched a computer-assisted plan to match up long-term exchanges. These entrepreneurial entities are capturing part of CBOT's market, making some question the longevity of CBOT's role in SO_2 allowance trading.[22]

---

[22]Taylor (August 24, 1993) and Hong (July 20, 1992).

Application 11.6

Fighting Acid Rain with Pollution Rights:
The First Annual Auction

In March of 1993, the first annual auction of rights to release sulfur dioxide (SO_2) emissions was held. The event was administered by the largest commodity exchange in the world—the Chicago Board of Trade (CBOT). While most of the available permits are allocated by the EPA directly to the nation's largest polluting sources, a relatively small number—150,000 one-ton permits per year—are set aside in what is identified as an "Auction Subaccount" for direct sale. Selected by the EPA to conduct the one-day auction each year, the CBOT receives no remuneration from the agency and may not charge for its services.

Not surprisingly, most of the bids in the 1993 auction came from the nation's major utilities. A case in point is Illinois Power, a utility responsible for releasing about 240,000 tons of sulfur dioxide emissions each year. This facility is unable to operate on the 171,000 permits issued by the EPA. So it bought some of the 75,000 to 125,000 more it needed from other utilities at about $225 each. It subsequently submitted bids for another 5,000 permits in the 1993 auction. For Illinois Power and others like it, the costs to abate are apparently greater than the expected outlay to purchase permits.

Despite the predominance of utilities in the bidding, there was at least one important exception—a nonprofit, environmental group called National Healthy Air License Exchange. According to the group's president, any permits bought in the auction would be retired and kept off the market. That private citizens can exercise such a tangible influence over environmental policy is one of the advantages of an emissions trading program. National Healthy Air License Exchange submitted bids for 1,100 permits but came away with only one for which it paid $350. Reportedly, the group intends to strengthen its participation in the process and to

eventually purchase enough permits to have a measurable effect on the nation's air quality. In any case, the organization was able to participate in the auction and eliminate some emissions from the atmosphere—all without the help of political lobbyists, lawyers, or public officials.

In an apparently altruistic move, Northeast Utilities of Connecticut donated 10,000 of its permits to the American Lung Association just before the auction. The association retired the permits to keep them out of the bidding process. The utility, which did not need the permits to operate, could have sold them for an estimated value of some $3 million on the open market. However, the gesture was not totally without financial incentive. Northeast was expected to enjoy tax deductions for the contribution that would offset any sacrifice of pollution rights' revenues. Hoping to encourage other such donations, Northeast Utilities and the American Lung Association are establishing a repository for permits donated by other utilities.

How did the bidders fare in the first pollution rights auction? Rights to emit the 150,000 tons of SO_2 were purchased by utilities, environmentalists, and brokers for a total sum of $21 million. Prices ranged from $122 to $450 per one-ton permit. The largest single purchaser was Carolina Power and Light Co., a utility that bid and won over 85,000 permits. In accordance with the law, all proceeds of the auction went to the EPA, which then must allocate the funds to those utilities from which the permits were originally obtained.

Sources: Jeffrey Taylor, "Auction of Rights To Pollute Fetches About $21 Million," *The Wall Street Journal*, March 31, 1992; Jeffrey Taylor and Dave Kansas, "Environmentalists Vie for Right to Pollute," *The Wall Street Journal*, March 26, 1992; Scott Allen, "Rights to Pollute Given Up," *Boston Globe*, March 20, 1993; Jeffrey Taylor and Rose Gutfeld, "CBOT Selected to Run Auction for Polluters," *The Wall Street Journal*, September 25, 1992.

Economic Analysis of Stationary Source Controls

Stationary sources span a broad range of industrial activities that are important to the overall performance of the national economy. Consequently, regulatory controls on these entities are likely to impose high opportunity costs on society. At the same time, because these sources contribute to a variety of air pollution problems, the environmental benefits are expected to be large as well. Whether or not the benefits justify the costs can be determined through a benefit-cost analysis. To structure such an investigation, we focus on four aspects of national policy that are of particular interest from an economic perspective: (1) the cost of command-and-control methods relative to market-based incentives; (2) the uniform technology-based NSPS; (3) the dual-control approach for new versus existing sources; and (4) the emissions trading policy.

The Relative Cost of Using Command-and-Control Instruments

Just as is the case for mobile sources, the United States uses a predominantly command-and-control approach to regulate stationary source emissions. In this case, the primary instruments are technology-based standards. As discussed, because of the absence of benefit-cost balancing in the standard-setting process, it would only be by chance that the resulting regulations would correspond to those that maximize the net benefits to society. But despite the failure of the standards to meet the efficiency criterion, it is still possible to minimize the cost of meeting them—efficient or not. Unfortunately, the lack of flexibility in a standards-based approach adds significantly to society's costs and offers no incentive to low-cost abaters to clean up beyond the statutory level.

Of course, like most issues of this sort, recognizing the potential for excess costs and actually determining the magnitude of the problem are two very different matters. Fortunately, there is a growing body of research that attempts to measure the extent of cost inefficiency associated with command-and-control policy instruments. These studies use computer simulations to model existing conditions in a given region and compare the cost of implementing command-and-control instruments with that of the least-cost alternative.

Table 11.8 summarizes a sample of those studies that specifically examine stationary control costs for meeting the National Ambient Air Quality Standards (NAAQS). Each quantifies the cost of using a command-and-control instrument *relative* to the least-cost method. This comparison is expressed as a ratio shown in the last column of the table. Notice that the range of results is quite dramatic. For example, at the high end, Spofford (1984) found that the costs of using a uniform percentage reduction to meet the particulate matter (PM) standard in the Lower Delaware Valley exceeded the least-cost alternative by a factor of 22. This implies that the costs of employing a

TABLE 11.8   Cost-Effectiveness and Air Quality Regulation: Some Quantitative Studies

Investigators and Year	Command-and-Control Approach	Pollutant Controlled	Geographic Area	Ratio of Command-and-Control Cost to Least Cost
Atkinson and Lewis (1974)	SIP regulations	Particulate matter	St. Louis	6.0
Roach et al. (1981)	SIP regulations	Sulfur dioxide	Four corners: Utah, Colorado, Arizona, and New Mexico	4.25
Hahn and Noll (1982)	California emissions standards	Sulfates	Los Angeles	1.07
McGartland (1984)	SIP regulations	Particulate matter	Baltimore	4.18
Spofford (1984)	Uniform percentage reduction	Sulfur dioxide Particulate matter	Lower Delaware	1.78 22.0
Maloney and Yandle (1984)	Uniform percentage reduction	Hydrocarbons	All domestic Du Pont plants	4.15
Krupnick (1986)	Proposed RACT	Nitrogen dioxide	Baltimore	5.9
Oates et al. (1989)	Equal proportional treatment	Particulate matter	Baltimore	4.0
ICF Resources International (1989)	Uniform emission limit	Sulfur dioxide	United States	5.0

Sources: U.S. Environmental Protection Agency, Office of Policy, Planning, and Evaluation, *The United States Experience with Economic Incentives to Control Environmental Pollution* (Washington, D.C., July 1992), Table 2–1, pp. 2–3 through 2–5; T. H. Tietenberg, *Emissions Trading: An Exercise in Reforming Pollution Policy* (Washington, D.C.: Resources for the Future, 1985); and the original sources cited in the table.

command-and-control approach are 2,200 percent of what they would be if the policy allowed for equal marginal abatement cost (*MAC*) levels across all polluters in that region. At the other end of the spectrum are the findings of Hahn and Noll (1982). The ratio of 1.07 determined by their analysis suggests that the command-and-control approach is not that far away from the least-cost method. In this case, however, the researchers suggest that their unusual finding may be the result of very stringent controls imposed in Los Angeles by the California control authority with the specific intent of achieving cost-effective standards.

Despite the wide range of values for the cost ratio, in nearly every case the magnitude is significantly greater than one. It is difficult to dispute such a consistent finding that points directly to the excess costs of using command-and-control instruments to implement the NAAQS. These results suggest that in most instances society should realize important cost savings from a shift to more flexible policy instruments with no reduction in air quality benefits.

Uniform Technology-Based NSPS

Concern about the effect of economic growth on air quality motivated the establishment of the more stringent New Source Performance Standards (NSPS) for all new or modified stationary sources. A distinct set of NSPS was to be established for each EPA-designated source category to allow for industry-specific variations, such as differences in existing emission levels or production processes. However, once determined, these technology-based emission controls were required of every new source in a given category regardless of the location of that source, the number of people exposed to its emissions, or the compliance costs incurred.[23] Implicitly then, there are two potential problems with the NSPS. First, they are implemented *uniformly* across all firms in a given category. Secondly, because the standards are *technology-based,* firms have no flexibility in selecting *how* to meet the national emission limits. Both of these characteristics suggest that cost-effectiveness is not being achieved.

The intent of using uniform emission standards was to prevent regional differences in regulations from affecting new firms' decisions about where to locate. Nonetheless, just as is the case for the uniform emissions limits for new cars, this particular command-and-control approach generally disallows the achievement of a cost-effective outcome. Why? Because the cost-effective solution calls for pollution abatement up to the point where all firms face the same marginal abatement cost (*MAC*), *not* to the point where all firms abate at the same level.

Using technology-based instead of performance-based standards can also produce a result that is not cost-effective. By dictating the type of abatement technology to be used across the board, firms are prevented from finding and using cheaper alternative methods. The result is a waste of scarce economic resources. To illustrate the potential problem, we consider one set of NSPS for coal-burning electric power plants established through the 1977 Amendments to control sulfur dioxide (SO_2) emissions—perhaps the most scrutinized set of standards in all of U.S. air quality legislation.

Revisions in the 1977 Amendments included a seemingly innocuous change in the wording of the NSPS. Specifically, the new NSPS called for the following:

> A standard of performance shall reflect the degree of emission limitation and the *percentage reduction achievable* through application of the best technological system of continuous emissions reduction [emphasis added].

The change in wording to refer to a "percentage reduction achievable" coupled with the specific reference to "the best technological system of continuous emissions reduction" forced coal-burning power plants to install

---

[23]Of course, the location-specific differences added with the 1977 Amendments allow for some variation between new sources in PSD areas and those in nonattainment regions. But in practice, the relevant guideline is the NSPS for both types of regions.

scrubbers to meet the SO_2 emissions limit rather than switch to cleaner, low-sulfur coal.[24] The result? The new NSPS created an artificial incentive for coal-burning plants to use high-sulfur fuel with scrubbers, even though substituting low-sulfur fuel would have been a more cost-effective way to achieve the same result.

There is some evidence to support the hypothesis that this technology-forcing revision was a costly one. A 1986 Congressional Budget Office report presents estimates that the implicit restriction on fuel switching would increase the cost of an 8-million-ton reduction in SO_2 emissions by $2.7 billion (in discounted 1985 dollars), and a 10-million-ton reduction by $16.3 billion.[25]

Similar findings were obtained in an independent study conducted by two economists, Lewis J. Perl and Frederick C. Dunbar (1982).[26] Their analysis begins with a baseline estimation of the costs and benefits of SO_2 emission reductions based on the former definition of the NSPS under the 1970 Amendments. At that time, power plants had the flexibility of choosing either scrubbers or fuel switching to comply with the law. To achieve the emission reduction of 20.38 million tons called for in the 1970 law, total annual costs would have been $3.3 billion and total benefits would have been $5.4 billion. Hence, had the former NSPS remained in effect, total benefits would have exceeded costs by $2.1 billion.

The researchers then repeat the exercise based on the 1977 NSPS, which called for a reduction of 23.91 million tons of SO_2 emissions to be achieved through the installation of scrubbers. Under this scenario, they estimate that annual costs would rise to $7.05 billion and benefits would rise to $6.22 billion, so that net benefits become a negative value of −$0.83 billion. On an incremental basis, notice that to achieve the additional reduction in emissions of 3.53 million tons, costs would *rise* by $3.75 billion—a unit cost of $1,062 per ton of removed SO_2, and benefits would *rise* by $0.81 billion—a per unit benefit of $229 per ton. Thus, using benefit-cost analysis, these findings show that the 1977 revision in the NSPS was simply not worth it.

Based on these estimates, it is natural to ask why Congress would force such costly controls on firms. The answer is a complex one, involving political battles, obscure legal interpretations, and special-interest groups. Yet, even a brief review of the facts leaves little doubt that the major force behind these legislative changes was successful lobbying by the United Mine Workers union, a labor group consisting primarily of high-sulfur coal miners. It was in

---

[24]The revision elevated the former 1971 standard on SO_2 emissions from 1.2 pounds per million Btus of coal consumed to a tougher standard that varied with the sulfur content of the coal. Specifically, for high-sulfur coal the new standard became 1.2 pounds per million Btus of fuel consumed plus a 90 percent emissions reduction, and for low-sulfur coal the limit was 0.6 pounds per million Btus of fuel consumed plus a 70 percent emissions reduction.

[25]U.S. Congress, Congressional Budget Office (CBO) (June 1986), Chapter II.

[26]All of Perl and Dunbar's estimates are expressed in 1980 dollars for the year 1990, when the mandated reductions were to have been achieved.

their best interest to limit fuel switching toward low-sulfur coal, leaving high-intensity coal users like electric power plants no choice but to install expensive scrubbers.[27] While the miners' success in saving their jobs did not adversely affect air quality, it *did* elevate abatement costs with no comparable increase in benefits—a clear case of inefficient policy-making. (As an interesting post-script, the reference in the law to a ''percentage reduction'' was omitted in the 1990 Amendments.)

The Dual-Control Approach and the New Source Bias

Attempting to make best use of the U.S. federalistic form of government, Congress approved a dual-control approach to regulating stationary sources. Recall that this approach assigns controls over new or modified sources to the EPA and those for existing facilities to state officials. This delegation of authority gives states more direct supervision over those firms upon which their economies have come to depend. Despite its apparent logic, such a dual-control system can generate market distortions.

There is no reason to expect that state-established controls on existing stationary sources will be the same as those set at the federal level for new or modified sources. As long as there are two sets of standards, firms have both the incentive and the opportunity to avoid the more stringent, and therefore the more costly, of the two. This in turn means that firms' decisions about whether to build a new facility or modify an existing one will be influenced by the legislation. In fact, the logical expectation is that state-determined emissions limits will be relatively more lenient, which suggests that firm decision-making will be biased *against* new construction—a true market distortion.

To understand this latter hypothesis, consider that states have an incentive to attract business as a way to create jobs for their constituents and to maintain a healthy tax base to support fiscal spending. States also compete against one another to attract industry. It is generally in a state's best interest to avoid policies that increase firms' operating costs and reduce profits. In this context, states have a political incentive to avoid setting more stringent, and thus more costly, emissions limits that may encourage firms to exit from their jurisdictions and relocate where regulations are more lenient.

In practice, there are some limits as to how permissive state laws can be. Recall that under the State Implementation Plan (SIP) each state's standards must be approved by the EPA, so they must conform to the EPA's range of reasonableness. Furthermore, every state must answer to residents who would have to live near pollution-generating facilities, also preventing it from carrying this scenario to an extreme. Nonetheless, it has been argued that a state

---

[27]For more detail, see Ackerman and Hassler (1981). Further evidence of the mining industry's influence on U.S. law is found in Section 125 of the Clean Air Act. These provisions specifically allow government intervention to force the use of locally or regionally available coal to avoid economic disruption in the area.

FIGURE 11.1

Analyzing the dual-control approach and the new source bias: marginal abatement cost levels for new versus existing sources

The graph depicts the marginal abatement cost of a hypothetical existing source, MAC_E, and the marginal abatement cost of a new stationary source, MAC_N. Abatement level A_{E1} represents the more lenient level of a state-determined standard on existing sources, and A_{N1} represents the more stringent controls imposed by the NSPS. The result is not cost-effective because MAC_{N1} corresponding to A_{N1} is higher than MAC_{E1} corresponding to A_{E1}. To achieve a cost-effective outcome, the state authority could increase the required abatement level for existing sources to A_{E2} so that MAC_{E2} equals MAC_{N1}. Alternatively, the federal control authority could reduce the abatement requirement for new sources until the corresponding marginal abatement cost level equals MAC_{E1}.

might be able to satisfy both elements of its constituency if the pollution caused by its lenient regulations is conveniently carried off by wind currents into a neighboring jurisdiction. While the EPA does have the authority to intervene if a state is "exporting" pollution, its ability to correct such problems is limited.[28] Hence, the possibility for differences between state and federal standards, absent extremes, clearly exists.

What all of this means for firms is that they can avoid meeting the federally established NSPS simply by maintaining their existing facilities, which would be subject to less stringent state limits. The ironic consequence is that the law sets up a disincentive for businesses to build new facilities that would likely operate more efficiently and more cleanly. Hence, the controls on existing stationary sources are to some extent self-defeating because the disincentive to modernize or replace deteriorating facilities can cause short-term pollution to increase.[29]

From a benefit-cost perspective, notice that the variability in controls for new versus existing stationary sources may cause marginal abatement costs to be higher per ton of pollutant removed in new facilities than in existing ones despite the fact that the associated benefits are identical. As a result, total abatement costs are much higher than they need be to accomplish the same objective. This result is modeled graphically in Figure 11.1. The diagram shows two marginal cost curves, the marginal abatement cost of a hypothetical existing source, MAC_E, and the marginal abatement cost of a new stationary

---

[28]See Portney (1990a).

[29]This issue is discussed in Council of Economic Advisers (1982), pp. 144–45.

source, MAC_N. Notice that the MAC_N is lower than the MAC_E at every level of abatement to show the more advanced control technology available to a new, more modern facility. Now, consider the cost implications of two distinct abatement levels—A_{E1}, a more lenient level to represent the state-determined standard on existing sources, and A_{N1} to represent the more stringent controls imposed by the NSPS. Notice that MAC_{N1} corresponding to A_{N1} is higher than MAC_{E1} corresponding to A_{E1}. Hence, the inconsistency in controls on stationary sources has generated a solution that is *not* cost-effective.

Theoretically, by altering the emission standard for either existing sources or for new sources, the control authority can achieve a cost-effective abatement solution. For example, if the state official increases the required abatement level for existing sources to A_{E2}, MAC_{E2} would equal MAC_{N1}. (Alternatively, the federal control authority could reduce the abatement requirement for new sources until the corresponding marginal abatement cost level equals MAC_{E1}.) In so doing, the bias against new construction could be eliminated. The outcome would be difficult to realize, however, since the control authority would need detailed information about the control costs for each and every polluting source in its jurisdiction.[30]

Empirical evidence about the extent of these cost differentials is limited. However, the EPA has supported research on this issue, and some of the results are reported in Table 11.9. Shown in the table are some of the agency's findings on the incremental costs incurred by both existing and new sources to control sulfur dioxide and particulate matter. Note that in almost all of the industries evaluated, the incremental costs for new sources are higher than those incurred by their existing counterparts.

In sum, the predominant use of a command-and-control framework to uphold U.S. air quality legislation implies that a change toward a more flexible control approach would likely lead to cost savings with no loss of benefits. The evidence is difficult to ignore and just as difficult to defend. While setting national standards at their allocatively efficient levels may not be viable, particularly in light of the difficulty in estimating social benefits, the absence of cost-effectiveness in implementing these standards cannot be so readily dismissed. Fortunately, there has been some movement toward integrating market incentives in U.S. policy, which suggests a potential for cost savings.

The Economics of Market-Based Trading Programs

While the legislative effort in the United States up through the 1977 Amendments was primarily a command-and-control approach, there were some indications that national policy was beginning to use more market-based instruments to control stationary sources. Perhaps the best example of this trend was the initiation of the EPA's emissions trading program in the mid-

---

[30]For a more detailed description of the implications concerning alternative abatement levels for new versus existing sources, the reader is referred to Crandall (1984).

TABLE 11.9   **Incremental Cost Estimates for Controlling Various Criteria Pollutants: Existing versus New Stationary Sources**

(1980 Dollars per Metric Ton Removed)

Industry	Existing Source	New Source
Particulate matter		
Electric utilities*	$252	$2,577
Petroleum refining	1	0.50
Iron and steel:		
Raw materials	982	1,759–2,872
Sintering	260–670	470–21,459
Coke ovens	181–6,285	1,356–27,387
Blast furnaces	308–10,429	2,130–16,600
Electric arc furnaces	1,291–2,448	15,589
Asphalt and concrete	22	343–1,030
Feed mills	1,745–20,397	1,525
Grain handling	96–2,388	176
Paper and pulp	0†	92–7,206†
Sulfur dioxide		
Electric utilities	$412	$265–298
Petroleum refining	409	0†
Iron and steel coking	513	184–579
Primary copper	24–28	22
Primary lead	64–356	315
Primary zinc	38	222
Paper (total reduced sulfur)	0–324†	92–12,437†

*Firms that burn eastern coal.
†Existing plants are estimated to have negative control costs; new plants remove both particulates and sulfur dioxide.
Source: U.S. Environmental Protection Agency, Office of Planning and Management, *Incremental Cost Effectiveness of Selective EPA Regulations* (Washington, D.C., January 1981).

1970s implemented through such instruments as offsets, netting, bubbles, and banking. Economists have been strong proponents of such instruments, since they make use of market incentives to meet environmental objectives.

Analysis of Emissions Trading.   To illustrate how the market process operates through these instruments, reconsider the motivations inherent in the offset plan. If Firm A wishes to construct a new plant in a nonattainment area, it might choose to provide the offsetting emissions through one of its own existing plants in the region. Alternatively, it could independently negotiate the "cost" of having some other firm in the region, Firm B, provide the requisite emission reductions in its place. Firm B has an incentive to provide this service if its costs of doing so are less than what Firm A is willing to pay for it. From an economic perspective, Firm A will ''contract out'' the task of emission reductions if it is cheaper than performing the task itself. In the end, those firms controlling most of the pollution in a given region will be the ones that can do so more cheaply. Ultimately, all sources will control pollution to the point where the marginal abatement cost of doing so is equal across firms—a cost-effective solution.

Notice that the emissions trading process is governed by a polluter's internal benefit-cost analysis. The decision process is essentially the same one a firm undertakes when determining whether to commission a set of tasks like advertising to some outside firm or to assign the work to its own employees. It only seems odd in this context because the task of reducing emissions involves implicit pricing of a good for which private markets do not automatically arise. Yet the result is the same. A cost-effective solution obtains, since firms who can more cheaply reduce emissions do so with no compromise to the benefits of cleaner air to society.

The offset plan was enhanced by the introduction of emissions banking, a procedure whereby firms could accumulate credits for abating beyond the legal requirement. These credits could then be held for future use by the ''depositor'' or made available for sale to a new polluting source. Beyond helping new sources access the emission reductions they need, it also provides an added incentive for low-cost abaters to reduce pollution beyond what the law requires.

Attempts to quantify the gains of emissions trading have been done through estimating the associated control cost savings to firms. The major findings of two such studies that examine trading activity through 1985 are presented in Table 11.10. Notice that the activity is delineated according to the four major instruments: offsets, bubbles, netting, and banking. Within each of these categories, the data are further refined to distinguish between trades that are *internal,* that is, between sources within the same plant, and those that are *external,* that is, between sources in different facilities. The cost savings shown are those accumulated up to 1985. Overall, the results show that trading can be lucrative for firms, with cost savings ranging from $135 million for state-approved bubbles to a range of $525 million to $12,000 million for netting transactions. The overwhelming majority of trades are internal in nature, explained by the inherently higher transactions costs associated with interfirm trades. While in theory banking should help to reduce these costs and foster external trades, the data indicate otherwise. It seems that some other type of mechanism is needed to bring firms together to negotiate trades so that the potential savings can be realized. Such an alternative is evident in the 1990 trading program aimed at acid rain—to date the most ambitious of its kind in either U.S. or international legislative history.

Analysis of the 1990 SO₂ Allowance Trading Plan.   Title IV of the 1990 Amendments initiates an ambitious incentive-based program aimed squarely

---

TABLE 11.10   Emissions Trading Activity

Activity	Cost Savings through 1985 (millions)	Number of Trades	
		Internal	*External*
Offsets*	—	1,800	200
Bubbles, EPA approved	$300	40	2
Bubbles, state approved	$135	89	0
Netting†	$525–12,000	5,000–12,000	None
Banking	Very small	< 100	< 20

Notes: *Cost savings are not applicable for offsets, since firms do not avoid any emission reduction under the offset program.
†According to the EPA, 1984 is the only year for which detailed data exist for netting transactions. Thus, some of the estimates are based on an extrapolation done by Hahn and Hester from the year 1974. For more detail, see U.S. Environmental Protection Agency, Office of Policy, Planning, and Evaluation, *The United States Experience with Economic Incentives to Control Environmental Pollution* (Washington, D.C., July 1992).
Sources: Drawn from Robert W. Hahn and Gordon L. Hester, ''Marketable Permits: Lessons for Theory and Practice,'' *Ecology Law Quarterly* 16 (1989), pp. 361–406; and Robert W. Hahn, ''Economic Prescriptions for Environmental Problems: How the Patient Followed the Doctor's Orders,'' *Journal of Economic Perspectives* 3, no. 2 (Spring 1989), pp. 95–114.

at fighting acidic deposition. Let's consider the cost-effectiveness of the allowance trading established by Title IV. Polluting sources who can reduce SO_2 emissions relatively cheaply will do so and sell off their excess allowances. They have an incentive to do so as long as their respective marginal abatement costs (*MAC*s) are below the market price of an allowance. Excess allowances are actually an asset to these firms, who effectively become *suppliers* in the market for SO_2 allowances. The excess can be used either internally to offset emissions at another source within the firm, banked for future use, or sold on the open market. On the other side of the market are buyers of allowances, or *demanders*. These are primarily firms unable to match their emissions level to the number of allowances held. For these polluters, abatement is relatively costly, so they will pay for the right to release excess emissions as long as the market price of an allowance is below their respective marginal abatement cost (*MAC*) levels. Other potential buyers include brokers and environmental organizations, each of whom has different motivations. Brokers are motivated by profit, expecting to resell the allowances for a lucrative rate of return. Environmentalists want to buy up allowances and remove them from the market to effectively reduce the amount of SO_2 emissions that can be discharged into the atmosphere.

On net, buyers and sellers will trade for allowances, and emissions should reach the level where *MAC*s are equal across firms. By creating an ''emissions market'' and allowing the usual incentives to operate freely, abatement can be accomplished in a cost-effective manner with no compromise to social benefits. Notice that the national emissions limit is achieved, since the number of allowances issued determines the maximum amount of SO_2 emissions that may be released. Hence, all of the health and ecological benefits of pollution abatement still accrue to society, but the associated costs are lower.

Using information from the results of the second annual spot auction held in March 1994, we can gain a better perspective of how the allowance market operates. On the supply side, the EPA offered 50,000 allowances to be sold to the highest bidders.[31] In addition, private utilities supplied another 58,001 allowances to the auction. These were to be sold at various offer prices, ranging from $165 to $550. On the demand side, there were 103 bids submitted for 294,354 allowances. The highest per unit bid submitted by a prospective buyer was $400, while the lowest was $24. At the close of the auction, all the 50,000 EPA-issued allowances had been sold to 37 individual demanders who bid from $150 to $400, for an average price of $159. Once the EPA-offered allowances were sold to the highest bidders, the remaining 58,001 allowances were made available for sale at the prices set by each private supplier. However, none of these were sold, since the remaining bidders were not willing to pay the asking prices.[32]

By developing a national market for SO_2 allowances, Congress and the EPA hope that more trading activity takes place to yield greater cost savings to firms. While still in its infancy, the EPA estimates that the cost savings of this program will likely be in the range of $0.7 to $1 billion per year.[33] In addition, there may be further gains as this national program serves as a prototype for similar cost-saving strategies being developed by state environmental officials.

One example is a Massachusetts plan that allows emissions trading for several types of pollutants—sulfur dioxide, ozone, and carbon dioxide. Launched in 1994, this effort is touted as the first state program of its kind in the United States. On the West Coast, California's South Coast Air Quality Management District developed what it calls the Regional Clean Air Incentives Market (RECLAIM) program. Also started in 1994, this program uses a bubble-type approach whereby polluters are issued tradeable permits for releases of sulfur oxides and reactive organic gases. Trading among polluters is to be allowed under prespecified rules. California officials anticipate a savings in annual compliance costs of $437 million.[34]

---

[31]The 50,000 allowances are sold in the spot auction for use in the same year unless banked for future use. There are also 100,000 allowances sold in an advance auction for use in the seventh year after the year of sale unless banked for future use.

[32]U.S. EPA, Office of Communications, Education, and Public Affairs (March 29, 1994).

[33]56 *Federal Register (FR)* 63097, December 3, 1991.

[34]Allen (January 8, 1993); Allen (September 29, 1993); U.S. EPA, Office of Policy, Planning, and Evaluation (July 1992), pp. 7-1–7-2.

Conclusions

Current U.S. air quality policy is ambitious and complex, implemented primarily through a comprehensive set of controls on mobile and stationary sources. There is no doubt that the trend toward integrating more market-based initiatives is a major landmark in U.S. legislative history. Overall, evidence is accumulating that market instruments are a more cost-effective means to achieve air quality than command-and-control policies. Of course, some of the newer programs such as the allowance trading program for sulfur dioxide are still too new to empirically assess. But the anecdotal evidence seems to suggest that these policies will have at least some measure of success.

Other aspects of existing air control policy are less satisfying and continue to be debated. The dual-control approach to setting standards for stationary sources is one example of how government policy can create market distortions. Another is the regulatory bias against new cars inadvertently caused by the nation's policy on mobile source emissions. All of this means that as a nation, we still have much to learn—about air quality and about policy instruments that work effectively to protect it. As we have come to discover, policy development and appraisal are ongoing processes. In the context of air quality controls, the simple truth is that it is extremely difficult to assess exactly what has been accomplished through all the revisions of the last several decades. Even more difficult is to project the success of the 1990 Amendments, which will not be fully implemented until the year 2005. In the interim, the United States must continue to make policy adjustments and respond to the challenge of achieving both its air quality objectives *and* economic prosperity.

Summary

- In metropolitan areas, the high concentration of human population, traffic, and industrial activity intensify the concentration of criteria pollutants and hence increase the environmental risks of exposure. The EPA prepares trend statistics for 23 major urban centers and reports part of its findings using a Pollutant Standards Index (PSI).

- In a general sense, smog refers to the presence of particulate matter and other emissions such as sulfur oxides in the air. In urban areas, photochemical smog can form from a chemical reaction involving several of the criteria pollutants. The principal component of photochemical smog is "ground-level" or tropospheric ozone. Ozone's precursors, NO_x and VOCs, are emitted by both mobile sources and stationary sources.

- The Clean Air Act of 1963 gave virtually no power to federal officials to control mobile source emissions. It was not until the 1970 Clean Air Act Amendments that emission standards for new automobiles were explicitly stated in the law.

- The 1990 Clean Air Act Amendments strengthen federal control over motor vehicle emissions and fuels. The new law also incorporates market-based incentives to encourage technological development of cleaner-running vehicles and alternative fuels.

- The stringent controls on mobile sources established by the Clean Air Act Amendments of 1970 may have been purposefully unrealistic to force technology development by the automobile industry. The implied decision rule used to establish the controls was benefit-based, set to protect public health and welfare.

- National emission standards for automobiles are applicable ''across the board'' on every model produced and without regard to where the vehicle would ultimately be used. Such uniformity inflates the costs of reducing pollution with no added benefit to society.

- Different controls on new versus used motor vehicles affects relative prices and engine performance, which creates market distortions. Since new and used cars are substitutes, tougher regulations on new vehicles can bias buying decisions in favor of used cars, which emit more pollution than new, cleaner-running vehicles.

- Clean fuel laws in the 1990 Amendments provide a needed extension of technology-based controls on motor vehicles. The use of reformulated fuels and oxygenated fuels is being called for in the nation's dirtiest regions, where they can yield the most benefit to society.

- The standards applicable to new stationary sources are called New Source Performance Standards (NSPS). The EPA is in charge of controlling new or modified sources, while states set standards for existing facilities.

- In 1979, the EPA initiated the bubble policy for stationary sources and launched its emissions banking program in 1980.

- In PSD areas, standards for any proposed new or modified source are to be based on the best available control technology (BACT). Existing facilities releasing emissions that might impair visibility in PSD areas are required to install best available retrofit technology (BART).

- In nonattainment areas, existing sources must use at minimum reasonably available control technology (RACT). New or modified sources must comply with the lowest achievable emission rate (LAER).

- To facilitate control in PSD areas, a trading program known as netting was developed for use by modified sources. For nonattainment areas, the permit program includes trading for new or modified sources through an offset plan.

- Acidic deposition is caused by the reaction of SO_2 and NO_x emissions with water vapors and oxidants in the earth's atmosphere. These chemical reactions form sulfuric and nitric acids, which mix with other airborne particles and fall to the earth as either dry or wet deposition.

- Most NO_x and SO_2 emissions originate from the burning of fossil-fuels. The major contributors are electric power plants and motor vehicles.

- To control acidic deposition, Title IV of the 1990 Amendments is dedicated to a reduction plan for NO_x emissions and an allowance program to reduce SO_2 emissions. Once emission allowances for SO_2 are issued, they may be exchanged through an allowance market. Small banks of allowances are available for direct sale by the EPA or through annual auctions supervised by the Chicago Board of Trade.

- Empirical studies consistently show that there are excess costs associated with command-and-control policies in implementing the NAAQS compared to market-based programs.

- The New Source Performance Standards (NSPS) are implemented uniformly across all firms in a given category and are technology-based. As a result, firms have no flexibility to find the least-cost method of achieving them.

- Because of revisions in the 1977 Amendments, the NSPS for controlling SO_2 emissions created an artificial incentive for coal-burning power plants to use high-sulfur fuel with scrubbers, even though substituting low-sulfur fuel would have been a more cost-effective solution.

- The dual-control system of federally mandated standards for new stationary sources and state controls on existing sources can generate a market distortion. Since state-determined limits will likely be more lenient, firms can avoid meeting the NSPS by maintaining existing plants instead of building new ones. This sets up a disincentive to build new facilities that likely would operate more cleanly.

- The EPA's Emissions Trading Program yields a cost-effective solution, since sources abate to the point where the marginal abatement cost of doing so is equal across firms. Polluters who can more cheaply reduce emissions do so, with no compromise to social benefits.

- Title IV of the 1990 Amendments creates an SO_2 emissions market and allows market incentives to operate freely. Abatement is achieved in a cost-effective manner with no compromise to social benefits.

Key Concepts

Pollutant Standards Index (PSI)
urban or photochemical smog
reformulated gasoline
oxygenated fuel
clean fuel vehicles
clean alternative fuels
New Source Performance Standards
  (NSPS)
dual-control approach
new or modified stationary sources
existing stationary sources
bubble policy

emissions banking
emission reduction credits
best available control technology
  (BACT)
best available retrofit technology
  (BART)
reasonably available control technology
  (RACT)
lowest achievable emission rate (LAER)
netting
offset plan
tradeable SO_2 emission allowances

APPENDIX

A REFERENCE TO ACRONYMS AND CHEMICAL FORMULAS IN AIR QUALITY CONTROL POLICY

Environmental Economics Acronyms

MAC	Marginal abatement cost
MAC_E	Marginal abatement cost for an existing stationary source
MAC_N	Marginal abatement cost for a new stationary source

Environmental Science Acronyms

CO	Carbon monoxide
CO_2	Carbon dioxide
gpm	Grams per mile
NO_x	Nitrogen oxides
NO_2	Nitrogen dioxide
O_2	Oxygen
O_3	Ozone
Pb	lead
PM	Particulate matter
PM-10	Particulate matter of less than 10 micrograms in diameter
SO_2	Sulfur dioxide
SO_x	Sulfur oxides
VOC	Volatile organic compound

Environmental Policy Acronyms

BACT	Best available control technology
BART	Best available retrofit technology
CBOT	Chicago Board of Trade
LAER	Lowest achievable emission rate
NAAQS	National Ambient Air Quality Standards
NSPS	New Source Performance Standards
PSD	Prevention of significant deterioration
PSI	Pollutant Standards Index
RACT	Reasonably available control technology
RECLAIM	Regional Clean Air Incentives Market
SIP	State Implementation Plan

Review Questions

1. In the 1990 Clean Air Act Amendments, Congress and the EPA rely on the automobile industry to develop a ''cleaner'' automobile. At the same time, the government imposes a relatively minor federal tax on gasoline.

   a. Do you see any problem with the implicit signals the federal government is sending to the American auto manufacturer and to American car drivers through these policies? Briefly discuss.

    b. Formulate a hypothetical economic policy to motivate automobile manufacturers to advance the technology of cleaner motor vehicles.

2. Refer back to the discussion of a two-tiered system of automobile emissions standards studied by the National Academy of Science. Use a graph to model this system and illustrate how the cost savings are achieved.

3. New source bias may exist for either stationary or mobile sources. Select one of these, and briefly discuss why this bias leads to a solution that is *not* cost-effective. What policies would you implement to eliminate this bias?

4. Distinguish between the technology-based emission standards, RACT and LAER, used to control stationary sources.

5. *a.* Carefully explain how economic theory supports: (i) the bubble policy; and (ii) the emission allowance program for sulfur dioxide.

    b. Other than these two programs, briefly summarize any two U.S. policies that use market incentives to control air pollution.

6. *a.* Using the results presented in Table 11.10 explain why transactions costs are so important in explaining the success or failure of the EPA's bubble program.

    b. How would you devise a program that minimizes the transactions costs of bringing polluters together so that they could effectively equalize the level of their individual marginal abatement costs?

Additional Readings

Carey, John. "We Can Fight Smog Without Breaking the Bank." *Business Week,* October 3, 1994, pp. 128–29.

Krupnick, Alan J. and Paul R. Portney. "Controlling Urban Air Pollution: A Benefit-Cost Assessment." *Science* 252, (April 26, 1991), pp. 522–28.

Lents, James M. "A Forum: The Los Angeles Venture—The Plan." *EPA Journal* 18, no. 2 (May/June 1992), pp. 32–34.

National Acid Precipitation Assessment Program. *1992 Report to Congress.* Washington, D.C.: U.S. Government Printing Office, June 1993.

Port, Otis. "Engines That Run on Water?" *Business Week,* August 8, 1994, p. 47.

Raufer, Roger K. and Stephen L. Feldman. *Acid Rain and Emissions Trading.* Totowa, N.J.: Rowman and Littlefield, 1987.

Taylor, Alex III. "Why Electric Cars Make No Sense." *Fortune,* July 26, 1993, pp. 126–27.

Tietenberg, T. H. *Emissions Trading: An Exercise in Reforming Pollution Policy.* Washington, D.C.: Resources for the Future, 1985.

Toman, Michael A., ed. *Pollution Abatement Strategies in Central and Eastern Europe.* Washington, D.C.: Resources for the Future, 1994.

United Nations Environment Programme and the World Health Organization. "Air Pollution in the World's Megacities." *Environment* 36, no. 2 (March 1994), pp. 4–13, 25–37.

U.S. Environmental Protection Agency. *United States/Canada Air Quality Agreement—Progress Report.* Washington, D.C., March 1992.

Woodruff, David, Larry Armstrong, and John Carey. "Electric Cars: Will They Work and Who Will Buy Them?" *Business Week,* May 30, 1994, pp. 104–14.

12

GLOBAL AIR QUALITY
Policies for Ozone Depletion
and Global Warming

While most air pollutants produce localized effects, others have more far-reaching implications. Such is the case for contaminants that alter atmospheric conditions, posing a risk that is geographically without bound. Of course, the specific effects can vary by degree across different locations. But since the associated damage is widespread, and since the source cannot be linked to a specific site or region, this air quality problem is termed *global* air pollution. Controlling global air pollution is a unique policy challenge, since solutions must be developed not only through domestic initiatives but also through international treaties and programs.

Two global air problems have been the subject of scientific research and debate as well as a source of political contention on both a national and international scale. These are **ozone depletion** and **global warming.** In both instances, the scientific knowledge base is growing but still inadequate. Consequently, policy development has been cautious and tentative. Furthermore, because this development relies in part on international consensus, the process has been that much more difficult.

In this chapter, we investigate the principal issues associated with global air pollution by studying ozone depletion and global warming in turn. In each case, we consider the scientific theories about the causes and sources of the respective atmospheric disturbance and the available evidence to support these theories. Using this as a fundamental basis, we then explore the major policy responses that have been set in motion in the United States and other nations along with proposals for alternative solutions. Ultimately, our objective is to economically evaluate the effectiveness of existing and proposed policy responses given what we know about the origin of the problem and the associated risks to society. As in the last two chapters, there is a reference list of acronyms in an appendix to the chapter.

The Problem of Ozone Depletion

ozone layer
The ozone present in the stratosphere that protects the earth from harmful ultraviolet radiation.

Starting in the 1950s, scientists began measuring the earth's **ozone layer,** specifically the ozone present in the stratosphere. This layer of the atmosphere lies between 7 and 10 miles above the earth's surface. The effort was motivated by more than scientific curiosity. Stratospheric ozone, as it is termed, protects the earth from harmful ultraviolet radiation. Some variability in the depth of the ozone layer was assumed normal, including an observed thinning above Antarctica during the southern spring. This would generally fill back in by November each year. However, in the early 1980s, scientists became concerned when this thinning was found to be increasing in size and persisting into the month of December. In 1985, an "ozone hole" the size of North America was discovered over Antarctica. It was then that world attention was drawn in earnest to the problem of **ozone depletion** and the pollutants responsible for the damage.[1]

ozone depletion
A thinning of the earth's ozone layer originally observed as an "ozone hole" over Antarctica.

While all of the implications are not known with certainty, there are some consequences of increased ultraviolet radiation about which there seems to be some agreement. Scientists tell us that rising levels of ultraviolet radiation can alter delicate ecosystems, diminish human immune systems, and increase the risk of skin cancer. The National Academy of Sciences estimates that 10,000 more cases of skin cancer per year would result for every 1 percent decline in stratospheric ozone. Thus, anthropogenic pollutants that damage this protective shield need to be identified and controlled.

Searching for the Causes of Ozone Depletion

Research scientists debate about the principal cause of the "ozone hole" extending approximately 9 million square miles over the Antarctic.[2] While no one theory has been able to fully explain the extent of ozone depletion, many scientists agree that the presence of **chlorofluorocarbons (CFCs)** in the atmosphere is the most likely explanation—a theory originally advanced in 1974 by Sherwood Rowland and Mario Molina, two University of California researchers.

chlorofluorocarbons (CFCs)
A family of chemicals commonly used in refrigeration and air conditioning that scientists believe contributes to ozone depletion.

CFCs are a family of chemicals commonly used in refrigeration, air-conditioning, packaging, insulation, and as aerosol propellants. These are sometimes referred to by their trade names, Freon and Styrofoam. In fact, the energy crisis in the 1970s was responsible for an even greater usage of CFCs as foaming agents in the production of home insulation. The rise of the fast-food industry was also a contributing factor to intensified CFC use, as polymer foams were utilized in the production of disposable cups and food containers.[3] These long-lived compounds are not destroyed in the lower atmosphere and

---

[1]For the published report, see Farman, Gardiner, and Shanklin (1985).
[2]A smaller hole over the Arctic is also under investigation.
[3]Kemp (1990), pp. 127–28.

TABLE 12.1   Cumulative Release of CFC-11 and CFC-12 for Selected Years (thousands of metric tons)

Year	CFC-11	CFC-12
1935	0.0	0.8
1940	0.3	7.3
1945	1.2	32.6
1950	14.8	148.9
1955	90.6	347.2
1960	254.4	706.3
1965	658.3	1,406.4
1970	1,470.2	2,691.1
1975	2,900.7	4,683.1
1980	4,375.2	6.685.1
1985	5,790.8	8,957.4
1986	6,125.6	9,502.4
1987	6,483.2	10,087.6

Source: Organisation for Economic Co-operation and Development, *OECD Environmental Data Compendium 1989* (Paris: OECD, 1989b), Table 2.4, p. 43. Reprinted with permission.

therefore are able to drift up into the stratosphere, where their chlorine components destroy ozone.

Another major group of pollutants identified as primary ozone depleters are halons, also characterized as having long atmospheric lifetimes. Prior to government controls, these substances were becoming increasingly important in the production of fire extinguishants. While their use is not as widespread as CFCs, halons are known to have a higher potency for ozone depletion than their chlorine-containing counterparts.

Despite the lack of hard evidence at the time, the United States opted to ban the use of CFCs in most aerosol sprays in 1978, and other countries followed suit. However, other uses of these ozone depleters were not controlled, and little effort was aimed at finding substitutes. As a result, domestic and international CFC use continued to grow. Data on *cumulative* CFC releases are given in Table 12.1 to acknowledge the long atmospheric lifetime of these substances. As these data suggest, there was little question in the 1980s that a stronger policy position was needed to respond to scientific data on the factors contributing to ozone depletion.

Controlling Ozone Depletion

As a global air pollution problem, ozone depletion cannot be controlled without an integrated international effort. More formally, think of this environmental problem as an externality with *transboundary* implications. Indeed, the 1990 Clean Air Act Amendments specifically call for the president of the

United States to enter into international agreements that encourage joint research on ozone depletion and to establish regulations consistent with those applicable in the United States. While not without political implications, a number of international agreements and multilateral treaties have been executed or are on the negotiating table. A brief summary of the most significant of these follows.[4]

International Agreements to Control Ozone Depletion

In 1987, 24 countries as well as the European Community Commission signed the Montreal Protocol on Substances that Deplete the Ozone Layer. Among the signatories were the major producers of CFCs. This landmark agreement called for a 50 percent reduction of CFC consumption and production, a target that was to be achieved gradually up through the turn of the century. To achieve this objective, each party to the Protocol was responsible for designing and implementing an effective control program in accordance with the agreed-upon deadlines.

In 1990, some 59 countries executed the London Amendments to the Protocol. These amendments, which strengthened the worldwide commitment to protecting the ozone layer, were in direct response to reports that ozone depletion might be more severe than originally believed. The new agreement outlined a full phaseout plan aimed at eliminating ozone-depleting substances such as methyl chloroform, fully halogenated chlorofluorocarbons, and carbon tetrachloride between 1995 and 2005. Later, at the 1992 Copenhagen Conference, these phaseout deadlines were advanced to 1996. As of 1992, 92 countries have joined in this international effort and have ratified the treaty. Collectively, these nations represent 96 percent of the world's usage of CFCs and 85 percent of the world population.[5] Table 12.2 offers a summary of how these phaseout agreements have evolved over time.

A market approach is also a part of the international effort to protect the ozone layer. Specifically, production and consumption allowances are issued to the Protocol participants, and transfers are permitted under certain guidelines. To assure that the phaseouts are achieved, trading is conditioned upon revision of each country's aggregate production limits to levels that are lower than what would have occurred without the transfers.

Ongoing negotiations are aimed at encouraging more nations to ratify the Protocol's amendments. Some countries have been hesitant to participate because of the high costs of converting production technology to eliminate the use of ozone-depleting substances. This is particularly problematic for developing nations. In response to these real concerns, a three-year Interim Multilateral Fund of $160 million was established in 1990 by the Protocol

---

[4]Much of the subsequent discussion is drawn from Council on Environmental Quality (March 1992, January 1993).

[5]Dumanoski (November 26, 1992).

TABLE 12.2   International Agreements for Phaseout of Ozone Depleters

Substance	*1987* *Montreal Protocol*	*1990* *London Amendments*	*1992* *Copenhagen Conference*
CFCs	50% cut by 2000 (5 types covered)	Phaseout by 2000 (15 types covered)	Phaseout by 1996 (15 types covered)
Carbon tetrachloride (a solvent used in CFC production)	No controls	Phaseout by 2000	Phaseout by 1996.
Halons	Freeze at 1986 levels in 1992	Phaseout by 2000	Phaseout by 1996.
HCFCs (CFC substitutes)	No controls	Phaseout by 2040	Freeze in 1996; phaseout by 2020
Methyl bromide (pesticide)	No controls	No controls	Freeze in 1995 at 1991 levels
Methyl chloroform (solvent)	No controls	Phaseout by 2005	Phaseout by 1996

Sources: Council on Environmental Quality, *Environmental Quality, 23nd Annual Report* (Washington, D.C.: U.S. Government Printing Office, January 1993), p. 139; UN Environment Program cited in Dianne Dumanoski, ''Nations Act to Speed Phaseout of Ozone-depleting Chemicals,'' *Boston Globe,* November 26, 1992.

participants to assist developing countries in transitioning toward the requisite CFC-replacement technologies. There is also a provision to allow a 10-year grace period for these countries.

Support for developing nations, such as China and India, is crucial to the success of the global initiative. As these nations evolve economically, their increased need for refrigeration (and the associated use of ozone-depleting substances), coupled with their large populations have serious implications for the earth's ozone layer. In response, the parties to the Protocol agreed to increase the Interim Fund to $240 million if China and India signed the agreement, committing the incremental amount directly to these two countries.[6] In June 1991, China did agree to sign. Thus, as of 1992 the aggregate voluntary contributions to the Interim Fund reached $200 million, with the United States contributing about 25 percent of that sum.

To better understand the importance of gaining the cooperation of developing nations, consider the following. By 1996, China's use of CFC-containing refrigerators is expected to nearly double from its 1991 level of about 30 million units with an associated rise in production to over 11 million units per year. An even worse scenario is posed by India's expected growth rate, where refrigerator consumption is predicted to rise to nearly 80 million units by the year 2010—a dramatic increase from its 1989 level of only 6

---

[6]To that end, the Clean Air Act, Sec. 617.(b), authorized up to $30 million for U.S. assistance to developing countries over the 1991 to 1993 period and an additional like sum if China and India became parties to the Montreal Protocol.

million.[7] Without cooperation and commitment that extends beyond national borders, the problem of ozone depletion cannot and will not be resolved.

For its part, the United States has charged the EPA with the tasks of formulating and implementing a domestic control policy to meet the Protocol's phaseout schedule. We next investigate the fundamentals of U.S. policy on ozone depletion with a particular emphasis on the market-based instruments that are integral to achieving both national and international objectives.

U.S. Policy to Control Ozone Depletion

The 1990 Clean Air Act Amendments significantly strengthened U.S. policy on ozone-depleting substances. Title VI of these amendments is dedicated solely to protecting the earth's ozone layer. Chief among its rulings are those that define how ozone-depleting substances are to be identified and those that establish a plan to phase them out of usage. These provisions must comply with the United States' commitment to the Protocol.[8]

Congress charged the EPA with the responsibility of publishing a complete list of all ozone-depleting substances, including those already identified in the 1990 Amendments. This listing distinguishes between what are termed Class I and Class II substances, where Class I refers to those having a greater potential for damage. Each listed substance is assigned a numerical value signifying its relative **ozone-depletion potential (ODP)** as compared to chlorofluorocarbon-11 (CFC-11). For each substance class, specific phaseout schedules are outlined, which state the maximum amount that can be produced or consumed each year through the phaseout period. Subsequently, these schedules were accelerated through a unilateral decision by President Bush in February 1992. Other nations subsequently joined the United States in advancing these deadlines at the Copenhagen Conference.

Recognizing the existing dependence of industry on CFCs, the 1990 Amendments include provisions to establish a national recycling program for Class I and II substances, with the intent that recycled refrigerants could be used as substitutes for virgin materials. A related set of provisions calls for federal programs and research aimed at finding safe alternatives to identified ozone depleters.[9] There are also two legislated instruments that explicitly use market incentives to achieve the United States' commitment to eliminate the production and consumption of ozone-depleting substances. These are: (1) an

ozone depletion potential (ODP)
A numerical score that signifies a substance's potential for destroying stratospheric ozone relative to chlorofluorocarbon-11 (CFC-11).

---

[7]World Resources Institute (1992a), pp. 152–53.

[8]Other provisions deal with safety requirements such as the proper handling of refrigerants in servicing motor vehicle air conditioners and the safe use and disposal of listed substances during the servicing or disposal of appliances and refrigeration equipment. Strict labeling regulations are also mandated.

[9]See Sec.608 and Sec.612 of the 1990 Amendments as well as Lee (May/June 1992) for a discussion of these and other provisions in the act related to ozone depletion.

excise tax imposed under the Omnibus Reconciliation Act; and (2) a **marketable allowance system** established in 1988 and subsequently affirmed in the 1990 Amendments. Following is a brief overview of these two important national programs.

An Excise Tax on Ozone Depleters.   One market-based instrument used in the United States to control ozone depletion is an escalating **excise tax** on the production for sale of ozone-depleting substances. This new tax was enacted by Congress in 1990. The tax rate per pound of any ozone-depleting substance is a base dollar amount multiplied by the chemical's ozone depletion potential (ODP), where the base amount is higher for each successive year in the phaseout schedule. From an economic perspective, notice that such a tax elevates the effective price of ozone depleters and thus motivates a reduction in the quantity demanded of these harmful chemicals.[10]

excise tax on ozone depleters
An escalating tax on the production of ozone-depleting substances.

An Allowance Market for Ozone-Depleting Chemicals.   The other major market instrument used under U.S. policy is an allowance system for ozone-depleting substances. The underlying premise is that firms are allowed to produce or import the regulated substances only if they are in possession of an appropriate number of allowances. Each allowance authorizes a one-time release of some amount of a controlled substance based on its ODP.[11] In the aggregate, the number of baseline allowances was set to effectively freeze domestic production of ozone-depleting substances at their 1986 levels. Given the large number of potential buyers for these allowances, the EPA chose to allocate them only to the largest domestic consumers and producers.[12] Over time, the number of available allowances will be gradually reduced and eventually brought to zero.

allowance market for ozone-depleting chemicals
A system that allows firms to produce or import ozone depleters only if they hold an appropriate number of tradeable allowances.

In the interim, market exchanges of allowances are permitted under strict guidelines—even with firms in other signatory nations of the Protocol. Transfers are of two types: (1) trades with other parties; and (2) interpollutant transfers. Interpollutant transfers are exchanges of production of one substance in a given year for production of another in that same year, using a weighting scheme based on the ozone depletion values.[13] The critical proviso for allowance transfers is that trading must result in greater reductions in annual production or consumption than would occur without such transfers.

---

[10]For more information, the reader may consult the Internal Revenue Code, Sections 4681 and 4682.

[11]For example, CFC-11 and CFC-12 each have an ozone depletion potential (ODP) of 1.0, whereas CFC-113 has an ODP of 0.8. Using these ODPs as weights, 100 allowances could be used either to produce 100 tons of CFC-11 or CFC-12 or 125 tons of CFC-113. Notice how this weighting system gives firms more flexibility in terms of how they comply with the law.

[12]For a complete list of the largest producers and consumers, see 40 CFR Parts 82.5 and 82.6.

[13]There is a restriction, however, that limits these exchanges to occur only within EPA-designated substance groups.

Interestingly, the policy move toward the allowance system preceded the 1990 Amendments and followed only after years of study and analysis by U.S. policy officials. Following the 1978 ban of CFCs in all so-called nonessential aerosols, the EPA began investigating the feasibility of further controls on the ozone-depleting substances. In an EPA-commissioned study conducted by the Rand Corporation, three alternative control approaches were analyzed: a technology-based command-and-control approach, a fixed emission charge, and a tradeable emission permit system.[14] Each approach was modeled to achieve a given level of reductions over a 10-year period so that the accumulated costs of each plan could be compared. The study showed that the permit system achieved the desired reductions in the most cost-effective manner. Specifically, the costs for this more flexible market-based approach were estimated to be $94.7 million versus $107.8 million for the fixed emission charge, and $185.3 million for the technology-based controls.

Given the long life of ozone depleters, the EPA considered the regulatory implications over an even longer time period—out to 2075 to be exact. As part of its Regulatory Impact Analysis (RIA), the EPA conducted a benefit-cost study of a formal phaseout plan.[15] The agency's benefit assessment assigned a value to the damages that would be prevented by controlling these substances. These included health effects associated with increased exposure to ultraviolet radiation and nonhealth effects like reduced crop yields, rising sea levels, and property damage.[16] In total, the EPA estimated that accumulated damages would be approximately $6.5 trillion by the year 2075.[17]

On the cost side, a value had to be assigned to all anticipated market disruptions that would arise from a proposed phaseout plan. Some 84 distinct use categories for CFCs had to be analyzed—the two largest being mobile air-conditioning and refrigeration.[18] All told, the EPA's estimate of control costs associated with a phaseout plan was $27 billion through the year 2075. To get a sense of how this dollar amount might be shared among various CFC-dependent products and services, see Table 12.3. Obviously, while these costs are significant, they pale in comparison to the dollar value of damages that would result if the United States took no action at all. Consequently, U.S.

---

[14]Palmer et al. (1980).

[15]For more detail, the interested student is referred to U.S. EPA, Stratospheric Protection Program, Office of Air and Radiation (December 1987).

[16]In addition to destroying stratospheric ozone, CFCs have been identified as so-called "greenhouse gases"—a fact we will address later in the chapter. Hence, some of the effects identified in the RIA are associated with the contribution of CFCs to global warming.

[17]Cogan (1988), p. 88.

[18]To provide some sense of the pervasive use of CFCs at the time, consider the following. In 1985, approximately 90 million cars and light-duty trucks used 120 million pounds of CFCs in their air-conditioning units. Another 95 million pounds of CFCs were used in over 100 million refrigerators, 30 million freezers, 180,000 refrigerated trucks, and hundreds of thousands of food service businesses. In all, approximately 660 million pounds of CFCs were consumed during 1985 (Cogan 1988, p. 15).

TABLE 12.3   Value of CFCs to American Industry

Usage	*Value of Products and Services*
Refrigeration	$ 6.0 billion
Air-conditioning	$ 10.9 billion
Mobile air-conditioning	$ 2.0 billion
Plastic foams	$ 2.0 billion
Cleaning agents	Valued in $ billions
Food freezants	$ 400 million
Sterilants	$ 100 million

Source: Drawn from Alliance for Responsible CFC Policy, *Montreal Protocol: A Briefing Book* (Rosslyn, Va.: Alliance for Responsible CFC Policy, December 1986).

regulations to control ozone-depleting substances were announced in August 1988, less than one year following the official signing of the Montreal Protocol.[19]

An Economic Analysis of U.S. Policy on Ozone Depletion

Critical to U.S. policy on ozone-depleting substances is the market-based allowance system for producers of these chemicals. Starting from a fundamental economic premise, we should expect this program to work toward a cost-effective solution. Since trades are permitted among those firms holding allowances, those best able to find substitutes for the controlled chemicals will do so and sell their allowances to less efficient producers. Because the number of allowances is controlled by the government and in fact scheduled to decline over time, the environmental objective of gradually eliminating the damaging substances is not impeded. Yet, the provision for trading acts as the needed incentive for the development of substitutes by those firms that can do so at least cost.

   Because U.S. policy is implemented through such a market-oriented instrument, we should expect to observe its progress through the price mechanism. The prices of CFCs and other ozone-depleting chemicals should signal the impact of the phaseout and the underlying market adjustments. As the phaseout plan advances, reduced availability of CFCs will elevate their prices, and manufacturers of CFC-dependent products will face higher production costs as a result. These producers will pass at least some of this cost increase on to consumers of their products. Thus, buyers of commodities such as refrigerators and auto air-conditioning units can expect to pay higher prices as

---

[19]See 53 *Federal Register* 30598.

time goes on.[20] Furthermore, as production of CFC-dependent goods and services declines, so too will the demand for workers in these industries. Hence, some loss of jobs may occur as well. These employment effects as well as higher product prices adversely affect society's welfare and add to the social costs of the phaseout.

Of particular interest is exactly how the market will respond to these changes. Because costs and prices are allowed to move naturally, the usual incentives will encourage a market adjustment to the observed industry declines and price changes. Theoretically, two opposing reactions are possible. On the one hand, firms may perceive an important profit advantage in developing ozone-friendly substitute products. Recall that such a market reaction is explicitly supported by U.S. policy on developing safe alternatives. Typically, prices of substitutes will be relatively high at the outset. For example, the 1987 price of CFC-12, commonly used in automobile air-conditioning units, was approximately $0.50 per pound, while a potential substitute, HFC-134a, was estimated to be $3 per pound.[21] However, this price differential should diminish as the prices of ozone depleters continue to rise as a result of regulation and as technological advance brings about production cost declines for substitutes. Application 12–1 illustrates how industry is responding to the market incentives brought about by the changing price of ozone-depleting substances.

Application 12.1

Searching for Alternatives to CFCs: The Corporate Response

Private efforts to respond to the phaseout plan on CFC production and consumption are the subject of much attention from Capitol Hill to Wall Street. Some of the nation's largest corporate entities are having to make major adjustments in the way they do business or suffer the consequences. To gain a better perspective on the corporate attitude toward the laws banning CFCs, consider the recent statement by Edgar Woolard, CEO of Du Pont—the leader in CFC production:

> In my opinion it has not been proven that CFCs are harmful to the ozone, but there is a fairly good probability, and we have to deal with that.

In 1988, Du Pont announced its plans to voluntarily halt all production of CFCs by the year 2000, a

---

[20]Of course, the ultimate change in price depends on the elasticity of demand for these products, which in turn depends upon the availability of substitutes. The more substitutes there are for a given product, the more elastic or responsive consumers will be to changes in the price of that product. Since there are few good substitutes for refrigerators, we would expect demand to be price inelastic. Hence, much of the cost increase from the phaseout plan will likely be passed on to refrigerator buyers.

[21]Putnam, Hayes, and Bartlett, Inc. (1987).

Application 12.1 (concluded)

segment of its business that generates revenues of $750 million per year. As of 1990, the conglomerate had allocated $170 million to research aimed at developing substitutes for ozone depleters and has reportedly committed up to $1 billion to continue that effort. Notwithstanding the importance of these ventures, only the naive would view these actions as corporate altruism. There is no question that firms recognize the value of an environmentally conscious image and the financial retribution that befalls a careless decision. In a speech delivered in London entitled "Corporate Environmentalism," Woolard argued:

> Avoiding environmental incidents remains the single greatest imperative facing industry today.

Beyond aggressive efforts on the production side of the house, industrial consumers of CFCs are also exerting a measure of influence. Most are making dramatic cuts in consumption of CFCs and are pushing hard for the development of viable alternatives to make up the difference. Over a recent two-year period, IBM reduced its CFC consumption by approximately 31 percent and announced a complete halt in usage by 1993. The automobile industry, already a major player in air pollution issues, is in dire need of an alternative to CFCs. Of the 355 to 425 million pounds of CFCs produced in 1991, approximately 20 percent was used as a refrigerant in motor vehicle air-conditioning units.

Fortunately, the market is responding, and with little time to spare. The statutory deadline for phasing out most ozone-depleting substances is the end of 1995. As is almost always the case, there is likely to be a "first-mover advantage." Spurred by the entrepreneurial spirit, the effort of research teams has begun to pay big dividends. Coming

to market are useable and less environmentally harmful alternatives. Many 1993 cars have been equipped with a redesigned air-conditioning unit that uses a hydrofluorocarbon by the trade name of "R-134a." This is the successor to the ozone-depleting refrigerant R-12 also known as Freon. The new compound contains no chlorine, greatly diminishing its adverse effect on the earth's protective ozone layer.

Still more innovative advances have been brought to market, some aimed at replacing aerosol propellants. When faced with the legislated bans on aerosol products, manufacturers replaced the ill-fated propellants with hydrocarbons such as butane and propane. With 20/20 hindsight, it is not surprising that the explosive properties of those substances would have made them poor substitutes according to most consumers. More recent innovations are directed toward new packaging that uses flexible pouches to house the product, surrounded by a mass of compressed air.

There is no doubt that the best and fastest innovators stand to gain substantially in the movement away from ozone-depleting substances. But regardless of the motivation, the end result will be the preservation of the earth's ozone layer. Once again, reacting to government intervention, the corporate sector is pursuing market opportunities that are likely to benefit all of society.

Sources: David Kirkpatrick, "Environmentalism: The New Crusade," *Fortune*, February 12, 1990, pp. 44–52; Emily T. Smith, Vicki Cahan, Naomi Freundlich, James E. Ellis, and Joseph Weber, "The Greening of Corporate America: 'Sometimes You Find That the Public Has Spoken and You Get On With It,' " *Business Week*, April 23, 1990, pp. 96–103; Emily T. Smith, "Developments to Watch: Aerosol Cans That Run on Compressed-Air Power," *Business Week*, June 12, 1989; Consumer Reports, "Greener Cooling," *Consumer Reports*, March 1993, p. 133; AAA World, "CFC-Free A/C," *AAA World*, March/April 1993, p. 23.

A second possibility is that the relatively small number of firms possessing valuable allowances gives those producers some measure of market power and control over price. These firms could enjoy above-normal profits at society's expense and make little if any move toward providing alternative solutions to the marketplace. Hence, opponents of the allowance plan argue that the EPA compromised its intended cost-effective plan by issuing the valuable "rights" only to a select few. One possible solution to this dilemma would be to transfer any excess profit to the government, which in turn could redistribute the windfall in a more effective and equitable manner. Such a safeguard was implemented in 1990 when Congress approved the escalating excise tax on ozone-depleting chemicals. Notice how a redistribution of income is achieved when any fiscal spending is funded by the tax revenues collected from producers of CFCs and other such substances.

In another step to lower the costs associated with the phaseout plan, the 1990 Amendments call for a national recycling program for CFCs used in refrigeration and air conditioners. Consider the economics of this approach. By making recycled substances available in the market, firms will reduce their demand for virgin compounds to produce more ozone-depleting products. Furthermore, firms that depend on these substances can use recycled materials beyond the phaseout deadlines, thus avoiding costly retrofitting until substitutes are developed and made available for sale.[22]

Overall, the use of the tradeable allowance plan along with the excise tax, the recycling program, and the safe alternatives policy should achieve the phaseout objectives in a cost-effective manner. Such a control program can be expected to be less disruptive than an immediate ban on production, which would affect virtually every segment of society with no time to make proper adjustments. It is too soon to predict the success or failure of the program. However, there are already some positive signs. For example, in March 1993, Du Pont Co., the largest producer of CFCs, announced its plan for a complete exit from CFC production one year in advance of the Protocol deadline, in part because of its advances in developing CFC substitutes.

The Problem of Greenhouse Gases and Global Warming

greenhouse gases (GHGs)
Gases that are collectively responsible for the absorption process that naturally warms the earth.

A source of controversy is the predicted climate response to the increasing production of what are termed **greenhouse gases (GHGs).** On the agenda of the 1992 Rio Summit, the issue of accumulating greenhouse gases and the associated predictions of global warming is one that continues to be hotly debated. The scientific community is not at all in agreement about every aspect

---

[22]Lee (May/June 1992).

of this complex phenomenon. Because of the uncertainty, national and international policy responses to this hypothesized global air pollution problem have been tentative at best.

Understanding the Potential Problem

global warming
Also called the "greenhouse effect," a phenomenon caused by sunlight hitting the earth's surface and radiating back into the atmosphere where its absorption by GHGs heats the atmosphere and warms the earth's surface.

The premise of **global warming** is based on the following accepted scientific facts. Sunlight, passing through the atmosphere, hits the surface of the earth and is radiated back into the atmosphere, where it is absorbed by naturally present gases such as carbon dioxide (CO_2). This absorption process heats the atmosphere and thus warms the earth's surface. This is somewhat like a greenhouse that allows sunlight through the glass exterior but prevents the heated air from escaping back outside—thus the phrase, "greenhouse effect." This natural phenomenon is responsible for the existence of life on earth as we know it. Without the so-called greenhouse gases,[23] the earth's temperature would be some 30 to 40 degrees Celsius cooler.

There are about 20 such gases collectively responsible for this warming phenomenon. The primary ones are carbon dioxide (CO_2), methane (CH_4), nitrous oxide (N_2O), tropospheric ozone (O_3), and chlorofluorocarbons (CFCs), all of which arise from a number of different sources. Look at Table 12.4, which itemizes the primary anthropogenic sources of each and gives estimates of their proportionate contribution to global warming. Since the

TABLE 12.4 Greenhouse Gases and Their Contribution to Global Warming

Greenhouse Gas	*Proportionate Effect*	*Major Sources*
Carbon dioxide (CO_2)	61%	Burning of fossil-fuels and deforestation
Methane (CH_4)	15%	Various agricultural and biological activities, including decomposition at landfills
Chlorofluorocarbons (CFCs)	12%	Aerosol propellants, refrigerants, and various industrial activities
Nitrous oxides (N_2O)	4%	Fertilizers, fossil-fuel burning
Other [ozone (O_3), halons, water vapor, particles]	8%	Chemical reactions from combustion

Source: J. T. Houghton; G. J. Jenkins; and J. J. Ephraums, eds. *Climate Change: The IPCC Scientific Assessment.* Report Prepared for the Intergovernmental Panel on Climate Change by Working Group I (Cambridge, England: Cambridge University Press, 1990), as reported in Timothy E. Wirth and John Heinz, *Project 88—Round II Incentives for Action; Designing Market-Based Environmental Strategies* (Washington, D.C.: May 1991), Table 2-1, p. 16.

---

[23]While commonly referred to as "greenhouse gases," the scientific community identifies these as trace gases.

presence of these gases affects the earth's temperature, any significant disruption to their natural levels would have climatological impacts. A study conducted by the National Academy of Sciences in 1979 predicts that a doubling of CO_2 would generate a rise in the earth's temperature of 1.5 to 4.5 degrees Celsius (or 2 to 8 degrees Fahrenheit).[24] Climate changes in turn would alter the distribution and productivity of agricultural regions, weather conditions, and the level of the earth's seas. Although there is a consensus about the linkage between rising levels of CO_2 and temperature change, there is great uncertainty about the timing and magnitude of the outcome.

Although scientists estimate that there have been a number of cooling and warming cycles throughout the earth's history, current concern about a warming trend stems from the rising anthropogenic production of the most prevalent GHG, which is CO_2. CO_2 is a by-product of fossil-fuel combustion, which is basic to the production of energy that supports most industrial activities. Accumulating CO_2 is exacerbated by widespread deforestation such as the burning of tropical rain forests. As plant life is destroyed, there is less photosynthesis taking place—a process that naturally absorbs CO_2 from the atmosphere. On these basic facts, most scientists seem to agree. Many also agree that the magnitude of increased levels of atmospheric CO_2 is likely to be substantial—estimated to grow to twice the level of preindustrial times by the year 2050. Table 12.5 gives an overview of the growth and projected trend of atmospheric concentrations of CO_2 and the other primary GHGs. However, predicting the *effect* of this trend on the environment is wrought with difficulty.

Scientific Uncertainty

While there is consensus that rising amounts of CO_2 will produce some change in the earth's climate, the real dilemma is that no one knows with certainty the timing or the extent of the ultimate outcome, in part because there are so many other factors to consider. Not the least of these is the influence of other GHGs that play a critical role in this complex process. Increasing amounts of methane, nitrous oxides, and CFCs are cause for concern, since they are believed to be more damaging than CO_2, even though they are present in lower amounts.[25]

Even more problematic to scientific predictions are the so-called "feedback effects" that can either mitigate or intensify the warming phenomenon. For example, volcanic dust acts to filter the sun's warming rays, which would counter some of the influence of accumulating GHGs. Similarly, scientists argue that sulfur particles emitted into the air can have a countervailing

---

[24]This estimate was later supported in 1985 by a number of other organizations, namely the World Meteorological Organization, the United Nations Environment Programme, and the International Council of Scientific Unions. See National Research Council (1979) cited in U.S. EPA, Office of Policy, Planning and Evaluation, Office of Research and Development (December 1989).

[25]Kemp (1990), pp. 154–55.

TABLE 12.5   Growth of Greenhouse Gas Concentrations

| | Atmospheric Concentration | | *Projected Concentration* |
Gas	*Pre-1850*	*1987*	*Mid-21st Century*
CO_2	275.00 ppmv	348.00 ppmv	400.00–550.00 ppmv
CH_4	0.70 ppmv	1.70 ppmv	1.80–3.20 ppmv
N_2O	0.29 ppmv	0.34 ppmv	0.35–0.40 ppmv
CFC-11	0	0.22 ppbv*	0.20–0.60 ppbv
CFC-12	0	0.39 ppbv*	0.50–1.10 ppbv
O_3	0% to 25% lower than present day	10.00–100.00 ppbv†	15% to 50% higher than present day

Notes:

ppmv = parts per million by volume; 1 ppmv = 0.0001% of the atmosphere.

ppbv = parts per billion by volume; 1 ppbv = 0.001 ppmv.

*Estimated value given is for 1986.

†Estimated value given is for 1985.

Source: U.S. Environmental Protection Agency, Office of Policy, Planning, and Evaluation, Office of Research and Development, *The Potential Effects of Global Climate Change on the United States* (Washington, D.C., December 1989), Table 2-1, p. 13, citing Ramanathan (1988) and Lashof and Tirpak (1989).

carbon sinks
Natural absorbers of CO_2 such as forests and oceans.

cooling effect on the earth. On the other side of the ledger is the role of the earth's oceans and forests, which are **carbon sinks,** or major absorbers of CO_2. But this capacity likely will be diminished by warmer temperatures, thus intensifying the warming effect. Even cloud cover is a factor to be considered in the net result, although the qualitative impact is itself a source of uncertainty. Clouds contribute directly to the greenhouse effect, but they also are expected to have an even stronger cooling influence because of their ability to reflect sunlight back into space.[26] The nature and amount of cloud cover is itself affected in complex ways by climate changes. So, depending upon *how* the earth's cloud cover changes with climate variations, the net outcome will be different.[27] Since so little is known with certainty, scientific research is ongoing in an attempt to settle at least some of the controversy about the anticipated degree and extent of global warming.

Predicting the Potential Effects of Global Warming

Since the science of global warming is itself the subject of much controversy, it is not surprising that there is a symmetrical lack of substantive information on what the eventual outcome of accumulated GHGs might be. Nonetheless, through the use of computer simulation models and laboratory experimentation, researchers have been able to assimilate some information about the

[26]Ramanathan et al. (1989).

[27]U.S. EPA, Office of Policy, Planning, and Evaluation, Office of Research and Development (December 1989), pp. 17–18.

TABLE 12.6   Predictions of Climate Response according to an Expert Panel

The following summarizes the conclusions of an expert panel convened by the National Academy of Sciences on the possible climate responses to increased levels of greenhouse gases. For detail, the full report should be consulted.

Climate Response	Definition	Prediction
Large stratospheric cooling	Increased levels of CO_2 and other trace gases combined with reduced heating from diminished ozone will cause a significant temperature reduction in the upper stratosphere.	Virtually certain
Global mean surface warming	If the level of CO_2 doubles, global mean surface warming over the long term is predicted to be between 1.5 to 4.5 degrees C.	Very probable
Global mean precipitation increase	The heating of the earth's surface will cause elevated evaporation and, therefore, greater global mean precipitation, although some regions may actually have diminished rainfall.	Very probable
Reduction of sea ice	As the earth's temperature increases, the warmer temperature will cause melting of sea ice.	Very probable
Polar winter surface warming	The air at the polar surface may warm as much as 3 times the global average due to the reduction in sea ice.	Very probable
Summer continental dryness/warming	Several, but not all, studies show that summer continental dryness will result, primarily from earlier termination of winter storms. "Of course, these simulations of long-term equilibrium conditions may not offer a reliable guide to trends over the next few decades of changing atmospheric composition and changing climate."	Likely in the long term
Rise in global mean sea level	An elevated mean sea level is considered probable due to the thermal expansion of the seas and the melting of ice.	Probable

Source: National Research Council, *Current Issues in Atmospheric Change* (Washington, D.C.: National Academy Press, 1987) as cited in U.S. Environmental Protection Agency, Office of Policy, Planning, and Evaluation, Office of Research and Development, *The Potential Effects of Global Climate Change on the United States* (Washington, D.C., December 1989), p. xxvi.

presumed implications. By way of example, Table 12.6 presents a summary of expert predictions assembled by the National Academy of Sciences in 1987 about the estimated climate responses to increased GHGs in the atmosphere. Notice that the predictions span a broad range of expected outcomes.

A more comprehensive study was conducted by the EPA at the request of Congress in 1987. The results of the agency's findings culminated in a December 1989 report.[28] The resulting predictions were based in part upon data generated by atmospheric models called general circulation models. These models attempt to simulate the complex relationships associated with the earth's oceanic and atmospheric systems. The national estimates include predictions about forest ranges, biodiversity, the earth's sea levels, agricultural productivity, water and air quality, and health risks. There are also regional-specific effects estimated by the EPA study.

---

[28]U.S. EPA, Office of Policy, Planning and Evaluation, Office of Research and Development (December 1989).

Rising sea levels are considered to be one of the more probable outcomes of global warming, arising from both thermal expansion of the earth's waters and melting of ice glaciers. Estimated changes range from an increase of 0.5 meters to as much as 2.0 meters, (or 1.5 to 7 feet), by the year 2100. One of the studies conducted as part of the EPA investigation estimates that a one-meter rise could destroy 26 to 66 percent of the 13,145 square miles of U.S. coastal wetlands. Other changes include erosion of coastal regions, flooding, and storm surges.[29]

Agricultural changes are particularly difficult to predict, in large part because of the inherent uncertainty of the complex agricultural system. Even absent the influence of global warming, crop yields are sensitive to weather conditions, insect damage, and soil conditions, none of which can be predicted with certainty. Nonetheless, scientific predictions attempt to identify both gains and losses to the world's agricultural production.

On the plus side, there is some evidence to support the possibility of a beneficial fertilization effect from increased levels of CO_2, as it is a necessary component of photosynthesis. In fact, some believe that present levels of CO_2 are suboptimal, so a rise in temperature could be quite beneficial.[30] Furthermore, certain parts of the world would profit from the northward shift of viable agricultural land predicted to occur with a warming trend. For example, the former Soviet Union and Canada would likely gain valuable agricultural land, and some existing agricultural regions would enjoy extended growing seasons and enhanced productivity. Of course, some areas that currently support grain production may suffer serious losses should this shift occur. Examples include farming regions in the former Soviet Union, the midwestern part of the United States, and wheat-growing sections of Canada.[31] Ultimately, such changes in food productivity could have serious implications for trade patterns among nations and overall food supplies.

Other effects such as changes in ecosystems are also the subject of research. For example, there is concern about the ability of plants and animals to adjust at the same rate as a relatively fast-changing climate. Scientists are concerned that ecosystems may be detrimentally affected and that some species may even die off in the process.

Scientific predictions about the effects of global warming are not at all conclusive. There is disagreement about which of the conjectured events may occur, the degree of environmental impact, and the timing of any associated outcome. Even with sophisticated modeling techniques, forecasts are based

---

[29]The reader should refer to the full 1989 EPA report, in particular Table 2 in the executive summary. The specific estimates for wetlands loss were conducted by Park et al. (1989), participants in a contributing project to the EPA study. Other national studies are also ongoing. For example, research conducted by the Canadian government is presented in an annual report produced by Environment Canada, *Understanding CO_2 and Climate* (Ottawa: Atmospheric Environment Service).

[30]Wittwer (1984).

[31]Kemp (1990), p. 157.

upon many assumptions, the accuracy of which directly affects the precision of the prediction. Thus, scientific research is ongoing in an attempt to settle some of the controversy about global warming. In the interim, policy-makers are faced with the dilemma of deciding how to respond to the fact that CO_2 levels are rising when there is so much uncertainty about the implications.

The Policy Response to Global Warming

Setting policy in response to accumulating GHGs is a difficult problem for two reasons. First, as discussed, the concept of global warming itself is a complex one, and little is known with certainty. Second, because both the source of the problem and the predicted effects are global in scope, any effective policy solution relies on some measure of international agreement. As the country data in Table 12.7 indicate, many nations contribute significantly to the aggregate level of GHG emissions.

The International Response

At the 1992 Rio Summit, global climate change was an important agenda item for the many national representatives that gathered at the 12-day worldwide conference. Among the major agreements produced at the summit was the U.N. Framework Convention on Climate Change, which deals directly with global warming and other air quality issues. Adoption of this convention by over 150 nations, including the United States, signifies the establishment of a baseline foundation for an international response to climate change. Among its major provisions are the following:

- Countries must implement national strategies to limit GHG emissions with the objective of reducing emissions to their 1990 levels by the year 2000.
- The treaty accommodates differences in political and economic conditions among nations by avoiding uniform emission targets and timetables for only one GHG.
- Signatories are encouraged to recognize climate change in the formulation of economic, social, and environmental policies.
- Industrialized nations will assist developing countries in obtaining data and in limiting emissions.
- Countries will elevate public awareness of climate change through education and training.
- Nations will participate in a continuing international research effort.

The Convention was to become effective following the ratification by 50 nations. In October 1992, the United States became the first industrialized

TABLE 12.7   Greenhouse Index Ranking and Percent Share of Global Emissions, 1991*

Rank	Country	Share (%)	Rank	Country	Share (%)
1	United States	19.14%	26	Czechoslovakia	0.70%
2	Former Soviet Union	13.63	27	Malaysia	0.61
3	China	9.92	28	Colombia	0.61
4	Japan	5.05	29	Netherlands	0.59
5	Brazil	4.33	30	Philippines	0.59
6	Germany	3.75	31	Myanmar	0.55
7	India	3.68	32	Argentina	0.54
8	United Kingdom	2.37	33	Turkey	0.53
9	Indonesia	1.89	34	Romania	0.52
10	Italy	1.72	35	Bulgaria	0.51
11	Iraq	1.71	36	Bolivia	0.48
12	France	1.63	37	Pakistan	0.46
13	Canada	1.62	38	Belgium	0.40
14	Mexico	1.43	39	Peru	0.39
15	Poland	1.16	40	Yugoslavia	0.36
16	Australia	1.13	41	Nigeria	0.35
17	South Africa	1.12	42	Egypt	0.34
18	Spain	1.01	43	Vietnam	0.32
19	Venezuela	1.01	44	Greece	0.31
20	Republic of Korea	0.98	45	Ecuador	0.30
21	Zaire	0.93	46	Bangladesh	0.29
22	Thailand	0.88	47	Hungary	0.26
23	Dem. People's Republic of Korea	0.84	48	Austria	0.25
24	Islamic Republic of Iran	0.82	49	Denmark	0.24
25	Saudi Arabia	0.78	50	Algeria	0.23

Note:

*The Greenhouse Index for each country is calculated as the sum of the national emission estimates of each greenhouse gas weighted by a "global warming potential" (GWP) according to the Intergovernmental Program on Climate Change (IPCC). The GWP accounts for the impact of each gas based on its atmospheric lifetime and its potency for absorbing heat.

Sources: The World Resources Institute, *World Resources 1994–1995, A Guide to the Global Environment* (New York: Oxford University Press, 1994b), Table 11.6, p. 201. Reprinted with permission.

National Action Plan (NAP)
A description of a nation's policy prescription to control GHGs and a statement of its target emissions level for the future.

country, and the fourth overall, to do so following a unanimous vote by the U.S. Senate.[32] By the close of 1993, the requisite number of nations had ratified the treaty, and it became legally binding in March 1994. Following ratification, certain of the signatories were required to develop a **National Action Plan (NAP)** for their respective countries. An NAP includes a specific description of a nation's policy prescription to control GHGs and its estimated target level of emissions for the future. NAPs are reviewed by the Conference of Parties—the ruling body of the Framework Convention, and the participants are then bound by specific requirements of the treaty.[33]

[32]Council on Environmental Quality (January 1993), pp. 142–43.
[33]World Resources Institute (1994b), p. 202.

The U.S. Response

Subsequent to the ratification of the U.N. Framework Convention, President Clinton announced his program for reducing national emissions of GHGs to 1990 levels by the year 2000. The Clinton program relies primarily on voluntarism, a cooperative effort between industry and government termed "partnerships for progress." The objectives are to advance technologies aimed at improving energy efficiency and to develop markets for sources of renewable energy. According to President Clinton, the program will cost government $1.9 billion and industry over $65 billion through the year 2000.

Among the voluntary steps of the Clinton proposal are outreach programs to train contractors on how to build more energy-efficient homes and a plan to encourage investment in hydroelectric power plants. Such an approach is not new to U.S. energy-saving efforts. The same sort of cooperative spirit is the fundamental premise of an EPA program called "Green Lights" discussed in Application 12.2. Although voluntarism is the hallmark of Clinton's program, there *are* some regulations included as well. For example, more stringent efficiency standards are called for on household appliances, and tougher limits on methane emissions are being imposed on landfills.[34]

Application 12.2

The EPA's "Green Lights Program"

Cooperation between the public and private sectors is the hallmark of the "Green Lights Program," an energy-saving plan initiated by the EPA in 1991. One of several voluntary programs, this one urges both the corporate sector and lower levels of government to make a formal commitment to investing in energy-efficient lighting, but only if it is profitable to do so *and* if lighting quality is improved or at least maintained at existing levels.

Just how important is the Green Lights Program to a cleaner atmosphere? According to EPA reports, lighting accounts for about 25 percent of U.S. electricity consumption. And every kilowatt-hour of electricity saved prevents the release of 1.5 pounds of carbon dioxide (CO_2) emissions, 5.8 grams of sulfur dioxide (SO_2), and 2.5 grams of nitrogen oxides (NO_x). In fact, if energy-efficient lighting were used wherever it was profitable to do so, U.S. electricity demand would be reduced by over 10 percent, resulting in reductions of these emissions by 4 to 7 percent. An even more impressive statistic is that the decrease in CO_2 emissions would be

---

[34]Associated Press (October 19, 1993a); Beamish (October 18, 1993).

equivalent to reducing the number of cars on the road by 42 million—about one-third of the total.

Organizations that sign a partnership agreement with the EPA, or a *Memorandum of Understanding* as it is called, make a formal commitment to survey and upgrade 90 percent of their domestic facilities within five years. For its part, the EPA agrees to provide technical support services and training to its partners. By September 1992, there were 651 participants in the program, including 296 corporate partners, 195 lighting manufacturers, 42 utilities, and 24 state and local government partners. In the aggregate, these participants have made a commitment involving more than 2.8 billion square feet of facility space—a total that exceeds all the leasable office space in New York City, Los Angeles, Chicago, San Francisco, Washington, D.C., Philadelphia, and Dallas combined.

The anticipated improvements to the environment from the Green Lights Program and other similar plans sponsored by the Department of Energy are shown in the table below.

Programs such as this one operate on the premise that the private sector will cooperate to help improve the environment as long as their market-based objectives are not undermined. The EPA is winning support for its Green Lights Program and other energy-efficient plans by illustrating to potential participants that they can contribute to a cleaner environment and at the same time reduce operating costs and enhance profitability. The EPA argues that using more efficient lighting technologies is expected to yield an internal rate of return of 20 to 30 percent on average.

There are already a number of success stories, including two well-known corporations that signed on early in the program and have already surpassed the maximum expected savings of electricity estimated to be 25 to 54 percent. These include The Gillette Company, reporting energy savings of 61 percent with an internal rate of return of 37 percent, and Whirlpool Corporation with a 54 percent energy savings and a 72 percent rate of return.

Source: U.S. Environmental Protection Agency, Office of Air and Radiation, *The Climate Is Right for Action: Voluntary Programs to Reduce Greenhouse Gas Emissions* (Washington, D.C., October 1992); U.S. Environmental Protection Agency, Office of Air and Radiation, *Green Lights Program: The First Year* (Washington, D.C., February 1992).

	Green Lights	
	Today (1992)	*Tomorrow (2000)*
Commitment	2.8 billion square feet	24 to 60 billion square feet
Expected results:		
Energy savings	12.4 billion kWh/yr	104 to 226 billion kWh/yr
Carbon emissions avoided	2.3 million metric tons	22 to 55 million metric tons
Sulfur dioxide emissions avoided*	0.0675 million metric tons	1.3 million metric tons
Savings in electricity bills†	$870 million	$7 to $15.8 billion

Notes: kWh = kilowatt-hour.

*Due to the trading allowances for sulfur dioxide introduced in the 1990 Amendments, these emission reductions may be in the form of allowance credits, expected to be worth $300 to $1,000 per ton.

†Values based upon a price of 7.0 cents/kWh.

Although climate control policy is being developed both nationally and internationally, the evolution is proceeding cautiously. As long as scientists continue to debate about the effects of accumulating GHGs, it is difficult to justify policy proposals on benefit grounds. Complicating the dilemma are predictions about the enormous social costs of attempting to slow the predicted climate change through reductions in GHG emissions. With so much at stake and so few facts, it is not surprising that governments have been reluctant to formulate stringent policy controls aimed at a moving target. Nonetheless, since the scientific predictions and the possible economic impacts are far from trivial, discussions are ongoing on an international scale to discuss any new information and the feasibility of various policy options.

Investigating Policy Options

Recognizing both the uncertainty about global warming and the potential implications for society, analysts continue to look for policy solutions. The alternatives being proposed vary, depending on how the benefits and costs of controlling climate change are assessed. To illustrate this assertion, we consider the proposals outlined in a recently published article by William Nordhaus, professor of economics at Yale University.[35] Nordhaus outlines three strategic options for responding to the threat of a warming trend.

1. Allow populations, institutions, and the market to adjust naturally to the changes associated with the predicted temperature increase.
2. Use climatic engineering to offset global warming.
3. Initiate market-based policy to slow or prevent global warming.

Notice that these three options run the gamut of possible responses. The first is essentially a "do-nothing" *adaptation* tactic, which allows adjustment to the phenomenon to occur naturally. The second is aimed at *reversing* the rise in temperature. Finally, the third is a middle-ground approach that attempts to *control* the causes of the phenomenon.

The Adaptive Approach.   One strategy proposed by Nordhaus is based upon the premise that government should not intervene at all. Notice that such an option implicitly suggests that the benefits of control policies are not justified by the costs. In large part, this strategy reflects the lack of solid information about the projected damages of climate change. Consequently, the gains to society of controlling a warming trend are unknown. In any case, this option is a risky one, given the inherent uncertainty of assessing environmental benefits in any context.

---

[35]Nordhaus (March/April 1990).

climatic engineering
A process of chemically altering the earth's atmosphere to change climatic conditions.

Climatic Engineering.   Another option suggested by Nordhaus relies on the premise that the earth's atmosphere can be chemically altered to change climatic conditions. In some sense, this concept of **climatic engineering** is not as implausible as it may seem. We now know that human activity and production processes have been changing the composition of the earth's atmosphere for hundreds of years. What is proposed by some as a viable solution to global warming is to scientifically reverse the degradation of the atmosphere and the accompanying rise in temperature. A number of specific proposals have been offered. One suggests that particulate matter can be discharged into the stratosphere to change the reflective capacity of the earth. Still others rely on chemicals capable of countering the effect of accumulating GHGs.

Conceptually, climatic engineering has some appeal, since it attempts to attack the problem directly at its source. But at the same time, opponents dislike the premise of deliberate and discretionary attempts at altering what should be a natural phenomenon. Then, of course, there are significant operational issues that make implementation infeasible in the near future. Nonetheless, research in this field continues, and many believe that the theoretical premise holds promise.

pollution charge
A fee charged to the polluter that varies with the amount of pollutants released.

gasoline tax
A per unit tax levied on each gallon of gasoline consumed.

Btu tax
A per unit charge based on the energy or heat content of fuel measured in British thermal units (Btu).

Policy Proposals: Market-Based Initiatives.   An alternative strategic response to global warming is to formulate market-based policy instruments aimed at reducing the *cause* of the problem—the accumulation of GHGs, primarily CO_2. A variety of such initiatives have been proposed in the economic literature. These are specifically designed to correct the market failure aspect of global warming. Anthropogenic emissions of GHGs are a **negative externality.** The effects of these gases are not captured within the market transaction and therefore are borne by society. To correct the problem, policy instruments must internalize the externality so that the market participants absorb the cost of the damages. Two types of market-based controls that have been proposed both in domestic and international policy forums are: (1) a **pollution charge;** and (2) a **tradeable permit system.**[36]

The use of some type of **pollution charge** to reduce CO_2 emissions has received a fair amount of attention in both domestic and international policy discussions. However, the specific form of the charge has been the subject of debate. In general, three types of product charges have been proposed as possible candidates: a gasoline tax, a Btu tax, and a carbon tax.

- A **gasoline tax** is a per unit tax levied on each gallon of gasoline consumed.
- A **Btu tax** is a per unit charge based on the energy or heat content of fuel measured in British thermal units (Btu).

---

[36]For an excellent discussion of a wide variety of proposals aimed at reducing greenhouse gases, see Wirth and Heinz (1991), Chapter 2.

carbon tax
A per unit charge based on the carbon content of fuel.

corrective tax
A tax aimed at rectifying a market failure and improving resource allocation.

tradeable permit system for CO_2 emissions
A proposed approach to controlling CO_2 based on the issuance of marketable permits to polluting sources, where each permit would allow the release of some amount of CO_2 into the atmosphere.

• A **carbon tax** is a per unit charge based on the carbon content of fuel.

Unlike taxes on income or consumption that generate market distortions, these are referred to as **corrective taxes,** since they are aimed at internalizing a negative externality and hence correcting a market failure. By design, these taxes should *reduce* market inefficiency. In addition, all three are revenue generating, an attribute that is sometimes used to promote this type of policy in the face of rising national deficits.[37] Beyond these common characteristics, these taxes differ in terms of their applicability, ease of implementation, and overall effectiveness in achieving environmental objectives.

An alternative market-based instrument proposed to control global warming is a **tradeable permit system for CO_2 emissions.** The United States has gained experience with such instruments, using domestic trading of sulfur dioxide permits to mitigate acid rain as well as national and international trading of CFC permits to combat ozone depletion. Conceptually, the design of a CO_2 emissions market would follow those already in place. However, the implementation of this permit program on an international scale would be far more difficult to accomplish.

While these and other market-based proposals have appeal, there are also drawbacks that must be considered. Evaluating the pros and cons is facilitated through economic analysis, using the criterion of efficiency and the decision rule of maximizing net benefits.

Economic Analysis of Global Warming Control Policies

Ideally, environmental policy should achieve an efficient allocation of resources—where net benefits are maximized or equivalently where the marginal social benefit from implementing policy is exactly offset by the marginal social cost. While assessing benefits is always the more difficult process, it is particularly so for global warming because of the grey areas that weaken scientific predictions. Hence, before we can analyze specific policy proposals, we need to first consider the dilemma of estimating the potential benefits from *any* initiative designed to control climate change.

Estimating the Benefits of Controlling Global Warming: Two Opposing Views

To illustrate how benefit assessment is at the root of the global warming policy dilemma, we consider the findings of two research efforts—each arriving at very different conclusions. The first estimates short- and long-term expected

---

[37]Interestingly, however, there are those who believe environmental taxes should be revenue neutral, so that the motivation and the outcome are exclusively oriented in favor of environmental quality. See, for example, OECD (1989a), pp. 13–14.

TABLE 12.8   **Estimated Effects of Global Warming on the U.S. Economy**
(billions of dollars, 1990 prices)

Major Damage	Annual Damage to U.S. Economy	
	2.5 Degrees C	10 Degrees C—Very Long-Term Warming
Agriculture	$17.5	$ 95.0
Forest loss	3.3	7.0
Species loss	4.0	16.0
Sea level rise		35.0
Dykes, levees	1.2	
Wetlands losses	4.1	
Drylands losses	1.7	
Electricity requirements	11.7	67.0
Nonelectric heating	−1.3	−4.0
Human morbidity	5.8	33.0
Migration	0.5	2.8
Hurricanes	0.8	6.4
Leisure activities	1.7	4.0
Water supply	7.0	56.0
Urban infrastructure	0.1	0.6
Tropospheric ozone	3.5	19.8
Total	$61.6	$338.6

Source: William R. Cline, "Global Warming: Estimating the Economic Benefits of Abatement," in Organisation for Economic Co-operation and Development, *Global Warming: The Benefits of Emission Abatement* (Paris: OECD, 1992), p. 55, Table 5. Reprinted with permission.

benefits as reported in a recent publication by the Organisation of Economic Cooperation and Development (OECD) in Paris. The second is a published commentary on the *relative* benefits of climate change control policy authored by economist Wilfred Beckerman.

Short- and Long-Term Expected Benefits: A Report from the OECD.   A recent report prepared as part of the activity of the OECD Environment Committee includes some new estimates of the expected benefits from controlling global warming. These are presented as estimated damages associated with climate change.[38] Some of the projections for the U.S. economy are given in Table 12.8. Notice that two columns of dollar values are given. The first gives damage estimates from the more conventional prediction of a temperature rise of 2.5 degrees Celsius, while the second presents estimates based on a temperature rise of 10 degrees Celsius over a very long term. According to this report, the benefits of controlling global warming based on conventional climate change predictions would be $61.6 billion, and as high as $338.6 billion over the very long run of 250 to 300 years.

---

[38]Cline (1992).

An Assessment of Relative Benefits: A Study by Beckerman. In a recently published article, economist Wilfred Beckerman argues that not only are the damages from global warming difficult to assess, but even if the most dire predictions are correct, most are not sufficiently significant to warrant the high costs of avoidance.[39] Beckerman cites a 1988 EPA report that estimates the net effect of global warming on U.S. agriculture to be within a range anywhere from a net gain of $10 billion to a net loss of $10 billion. While the media often focus on the potential for financial loss, a net gain is actually possible, since some parts of the nation will enjoy longer growing seasons, enhanced by increased precipitation and the fertilization of increased carbon dioxide (CO_2) concentrations. At the other extreme, even if the maximum estimated loss of $10 billion is incurred, Beckerman points out that this is only about 0.2 percent of the U.S. gross national product. Furthermore, these estimates ignore the gains from the inevitable progression of agricultural technology advances, genetic engineering, and the like, all of which would likely counter any losses from global warming.

In sum, Beckerman argues that we should be very cautious about proceeding with any policy initiative to significantly reduce CO_2 emissions. He argues strongly that the costs associated with a 50 percent reduction in CO_2 emissions called for by most environmentalists would far outweigh the expected benefits. Such a massive reduction would likely increase energy prices by 400 to 500 percent. To burden society with such a high cost should be undertaken only with a full understanding of what the reduction will ultimately gain. In this case, it is not at all clear that the gain, measured in terms of reduced damages, would offset the expected costs.

The implications of the OECD report and Beckerman's analysis are quite different, even though both share the same perspective—that benefit assessment is critical to developing policy aimed at global warming. Beckerman argues that the associated benefits do not appear to outweigh the costs that society would have to bear. However, the research reported by the OECD suggests that *long-term* benefits might be more relevant to this particular environmental problem. If this time element is considered, policy development might take a very different direction. Taken together, the two analyses suggest the need for more research and analysis—both of which are ongoing. In the interim, studies such as these help to explain the challenge policy-makers face in deciding how to respond to this environmental issue.

Recognizing this challenge, economists strongly promote market-based policies designed to consider both the benefits and costs of government controls. Although there are many types of instruments that use market forces to operate, all of them can be motivated by modeling the cause of global warming, rising GHG emissions, as a market failure.

---

[39]Beckerman (1990).

FIGURE 12.1

Modeling the negative externality of GHG emissions associated with electricity generation.

Panel (a) depicts the marginal private cost of fossil-fuel users (MPC_F) and the associated marginal social cost (MSC_F). The MEC_F is implicitly shown as the vertical distance between MSC_F and MPC_F and represents the cost of damages associated with carbon dioxide (CO_2) emissions. Panel (b) shows the marginal social cost of alternative fuel users (MSC_A). For simplicity, it is assumed that this segment of the market does not generate any negative externalities. Panel (c) presents the aggregate market for electricity, with some hypothetical demand curve (D) measuring the marginal social benefit of electricity usage (MSB), and two distinct supply curves, (S_p) and (S_s). S_p is the private market supply found as the horizontal sum of MPC_F and MPC_A, while S_s is the social market supply found as the horizontal sum of MSC_F and MSC_A.

In the absence of CO_2 emission controls, the competitive equilibrium is determined by the intersection of market demand, D, and *private* market supply, S_p, yielding a market quantity and price of Q_c and P_c respectively. At P_c, fossil-fuel utilities supply Q_{F1}, while alternative fuel users supply a much smaller amount, Q_{A1}. The efficient equilibrium is determined by market demand D and the *social* market supply, S_s. The resulting efficient price, P_e, is higher than P_c because demanders are now paying the full cost of their consumption activity. At P_e, the efficient quantity of electricity is Q_e, which represents the correct mix of production using fossil and alternative fuels. Fossil-fuel based production has declined from Q_{F1} to Q_{F2}, reducing the emissions of CO_2, and alternative fuel based production has increased from Q_{A1} to Q_{A2}.

An Economic Model of the Market Failure

The environmental problem of global warming can be economically illustrated by modeling accumulating GHG emissions as a negative externality. To simplify our analysis and give it context, we focus on the release of CO_2—the most prevalent GHG, arising primarily from the production of electricity.

Figure 12.1 illustrates a hypothetical market for electricity generation, which consists of two groups of electric power plants—one using fossil-fuels that generate CO_2 emissions and the other using alternative fuel technologies such as solar, wind, or nuclear power. Panel (a) depicts the marginal private cost of fossil-fuel users (MPC_F) and the associated marginal social cost (MSC_F). MSC_F, by definition, is the vertical sum of the MPC_F and the marginal external cost (MEC_F) of electricity production. Thus, MEC_F is implicitly shown as the vertical distance between MSC_F and MPC_F and represents the cost of health and property damages associated with CO_2 emissions. Panel (b) shows the marginal social cost of alternative fuel users (MSC_A). For simplicity, it is assumed that this segment of the market does not generate any negative externalities.[40] Thus, MSC_A is exactly equal to MPC_A. Panel (c) presents the aggregate market for electricity shown with a hypothetical demand curve (D) measuring the marginal social benefit of electricity usage (MSB) and two distinct supply curves, (S_p) and (S_s). The S_p is the private market supply of electricity found as the horizontal sum of MPC_F and MPC_A, while S_s is the social market supply found as the horizontal sum of MSC_F and MSC_A.

In the absence of CO_2 emission controls, equilibrium is determined by the intersection of market demand, D, and *private* market supply, S_p. Thus, the competitive equilibrium quantity and price are Q_c and P_c respectively. At P_c, fossil-fuel utilities are willing to supply Q_{F1}, while the alternative fuel users supply a much smaller amount, Q_{A1}.[41] Notice that fossil-fuel users can supply most of the electricity to the market at price P_c because their MPC_F is relatively low. Without policy controls, these utilities do not consider the external costs of their CO_2 emissions, so private market incentives allocate too many resources to their production processes and too few to alternative fuel users. Consequently, P_c is sending a false signal about how to efficiently allocate productive inputs, and the market fails.

To correct the market failure, the external cost of fossil-fuel emissions must be brought into the market transaction. As shown in panel (c), this means that market price must be determined by market demand, D, and the *social* market supply, S_s, which includes both external and private costs. Notice that the efficient equilibrium price, P_e, is higher than what the private market determines because electricity demanders are now paying the full cost of their consumption activity. That is, the per unit price, P_e, paid for electricity is exactly equal to the marginal social cost incurred to produce it.[42] At this higher

---

[40]It could be argued that nuclear power does in fact generate negative environmental externalities, given present technology. For example, the spent nuclear fuel must be disposed of, which may create costs to society outside the market transaction.

[41]While the market segments modeled in Figure 12.1 are hypothetical, it is interesting to note that in 1991 approximately 68 percent of electricity generated in the United States was produced by burning carbon-based fuels. See Council on Environmental Quality (January 1993), Table 19, p. 303.

[42]It is important to note that the socially desirable level of electricity production, Q_e, still includes some fossil-fuel based production, meaning that CO_2 emissions are not totally eliminated. However, they are reduced to the level that society believes is acceptable based on the trade-off between the marginal social benefit of electricity usage and the marginal social cost.

price level, the quantity of electricity has been reduced to its efficient level, Q_e. This new price level corrects the mix of fossil and alternative fuels used to produce electricity. At P_e, fossil-fuel based production appropriately has declined from Q_{F1} to Q_{F2}, effectively reducing the emissions of CO_2. At the same time, the higher price provides an incentive to alternative fuel users to supply more electricity, shown as the increase from Q_{A1} to Q_{A2}.

Although the above discussion is hypothetical, it turns out that some utility regulators are beginning to examine the notion of **externality regulation.** Application 12.3 explains some of these efforts along with a discussion of the pitfalls that may be encountered as utilities are forced to bear the full cost of their production activity. Other policy instruments employ the same pricing mechanism in a more general context, such as a pollution charge and a tradeable permit system, which were introduced earlier. These can now be analyzed in the context of this model.

Application 12.3

Environmental Least-Cost Planning: Utilities Learn the Economics of Pricing Pollution

Until recently, utilities used what is called **least-cost planning** when seeking regulatory approval for a new power source. This approach involves a determination of prospective conventional costs of a proposed power plant to justify its approval by regulators. While seemingly reasonable, such an evaluative assessment is flawed in that it fails to consider the external costs to society of the pollution generated by the new source. Consequently, proposals involving fossil-fuel burning plants would almost always get the nod of approval, since coal and oil are far cheaper than more environmentally friendly, alternative power sources.

Recently, some state regulators have begun to revise this format to use what is being called **environmental least-cost planning,** a procedure aimed at internalizing the negative externality of pollution. How? Exactly the way economic theory suggests—by pricing pollution. Under this revised method, the regulator's cost assessment must include some measure of the external cost associated with the proposed facility's expected emissions. New York was the first state to initiate this form of **externalities regulation,** with Massachusetts second in line. Several other states are considering similar revisions to their regulatory procedures.

Of course, the changeover is not without its share of problems—the main one being *how* to set the price of pollution. In Massachusetts, the regulators assign the following costs to some of the more common emissions:

Emissions	External Cost per Ton
Sulfur dioxide (SO_2)	$1,700
Carbon dioxide (CO_2)	24
Nitrogen oxide (NO_x)	7,200

Some of these "price tags" are based on estimates of the costs of controlling pollution. For example, the external cost per ton of CO_2 emissions is based on the cost of planting enough trees to rid the atmosphere of that amount of CO_2.

These prices have met with some resistance, particularly from the utilities themselves, many of

Application 12.3 (concluded)

which believe the costs are too high. Other opponents argue that the *basis* of the price estimates is faulty. Among this opposing group is Robert Stavins, an economist at Harvard University. He argues that the cost should be based on a collection of factors that define the *effects* of the pollution, such as health damage and degradation of property values, rather than the cost of controlling it.

In any case, these price tags on pollution dramatically increase the relative costs of a power source dependent on fossil-fuels compared to one that uses wind or solar power. If the bottom line shows that proposed plants powered by alternative fuel sources are less costly from society's perspective, despite the higher market prices for these fuels, regulators will force utilities to select these environmentally safer alternatives. Ultimately, these higher fuel costs will be reflected in the prices charged to electricity consumers. Hence, the cost

to reduce pollution will be shared by the utility and the consumer—precisely where it belongs, internal to the market transaction. An added benefit is that the elevated price of electricity should encourage conservation by consumers. Moreover, utilities will have an incentive to implement demand-side policies, such as efficient-lighting programs, to reduce demand and lessen the need for new power sources.

Absent the debate about the appropriate price of pollution, the rest of the changeover to environmental least-cost planning is in keeping with sound economic theory. The net result should be energy conservation and cleaner air, with the burden of achieving better air quality placed on the market participants.

Sources: Scott Allen, ''Polluting Power Plants to Pay Price,'' *Boston Globe*, November 12, 1992; Joan O'C. Hamilton and Geoffrey Smith, ''Making Clean Energy Sweeter to Utilities,'' *Business Week*, July 15, 1991.

Evaluating Market-Based Policies

An Analysis of Pollution Charges.   As discussed, a pollution charge can be implemented in the form of a **gasoline tax,** a **Btu tax,** or a **carbon tax.** All of these instruments attempt to attach a price to the negative externality of anthropogenic GHG emissions, but each uses a different basis for the tax. This in turn suggests that the implications vary as well.

Because gasoline is a carbon-based fuel, its combustion produces CO_2 as a by-product. By levying a tax on gasoline, its effective market price will increase, discouraging consumption and encouraging the use of cleaner alternative fuels. As fewer gallons of gasoline are burned, less CO_2 is emitted into the atmosphere.[43]

In the United States, gasoline taxes are already being collected by state and federal governments, so an increase in the tax rate to bring about a reduction in carbon emissions would be relatively easy to implement. The major drawback from an environmental perspective is that the tax has limited appli-

---

[43]To the extent that the gasoline tax reduces the consumption of gasoline, other harmful emissions such as nitrogen oxides (NO_x) and volatile organic compounds (VOCs) will also be reduced, helping to mitigate other air quality problems such as urban smog.

cability. It targets only polluting sources using gasoline—relatively minor emitters of CO_2, and ignores more significant sources that burn other fossil-fuels like oil and coal. Furthermore, it imposes a disproportionate burden on some segments of the economy, such as rural communities that lack good public transportation systems and certain industries such as interstate trucking firms. Hence, the broader-based carbon tax or the Btu tax is often proposed as a superior alternative. In fact, during the 1990 U.S. presidential campaign, several candidates recommended the use of a Btu tax. Application 12.4 presents an analysis of the Clinton version of the BTU tax proposed in 1993.

Application 12.4

The Btu Tax: A Market-Based Energy Proposal

One economic instrument that can be used to reduce GHGs is the Btu tax. A type of **product charge,** the Btu tax is so named because it taxes the energy content of fuels measured in British thermal units (Btu). If levied on all types of fuels, the Btu tax encourages energy conservation across the board by elevating the prices of all fuels. If levied only on fossil-fuels, the Btu tax acts much like a carbon tax, raising the relative price of fossil-fuels to discourage their use and mitigate the effects of global warming caused by carbon dioxide (CO_2) emissions. Of course, if global warming is the sole motivation for an energy tax, the carbon-based version is much more direct, since it is levied closer to the source of the pollution. Nonetheless, the Btu tax is a viable alternative and, like its carbon-based counterpart, is both a revenue generator and a **corrective tax** aimed at internalizing an externality.

In 1993, the Btu tax became national news when President Clinton introduced it as part of his economic package. The Clinton version of this energy tax was initially proposed as a levy of 25.7 cents per million British thermal units (mmBtu) on natural gas, coal, nuclear power, and crude oil for the first year of implementation, with an *additional* charge on crude oil of 34.2 cents per mmBtu to be phased in thereafter. The motivation of the energy tax was obvious—to encourage conservation and to generate needed revenues to help reduce the budget deficit. On a relative basis, the price differential against crude oil was meant to lessen U.S. dependence on foreign oil supplies.

However well intended, Clinton's energy tax proposal received mixed reviews. Not surprisingly, the sharpest criticism came from utilities and major organizations like the American Petroleum Institute who objected to the price implications and to the government's interference in the marketplace. Beyond this general resistance, there were also objections from certain parts of the country like New England, a region heavily dependent on oil for home heating. Congressmen from that region opposed the elevated tax on crude oil from an equity perspective, asserting that their constituents would bear a higher than average burden from the tax. Indeed, estimates prepared by the U.S. Treasury Department illustrate that, based on the two-tiered rate schedule for crude oil, New England residents would pay $117 in energy taxes for every $100 paid by the average citizen.

Responding to some of these arguments and other lobbying efforts, the proposal was revised to eliminate the additional levy on oil. U.S. Treasury estimates indicate that while this revision would reduce the relatively higher burden for New

Application 12.4 (concluded)

Englanders, it would not eliminate it. Along with this revision, the Treasury Department announced 13 exemptions, among them solar and wind power, ethanol, and methanol. Notice that by *not* taxing these alternative energy sources, their relative prices would be effectively lower, which should shift consumption in favor of these energy sources and away from more conventional fossil-fuels. Similarly motivated is a proposed lower tax rate on hydroelectric and nuclear power.

In sum, the general motivation of the Clinton Btu tax was to elevate energy prices to encourage conservation by Americans. By combining the Btu tax with various exemptions, relative prices among alternative energy sources also would be affected to encourage consumption of less environmentally harmful fuels. To see these price effects more clearly, the estimated change in various fuel prices associated with the Clinton Btu tax proposal are given below:

Energy Source	Tax-Induced Price Increase
Gasoline	7.5 cents per gallon
Natural gas	26.3 cents per 1,000 cubic feet
Home heating oil	3.6 cents per gallon
Coal	$5.57 per ton
Nuclear and hydro power	$2.66 per 1,000 kilowatts

Source: U.S. Treasury Department.

Sources: Michael Kranish, ''Energy Tax Plan Changes Sought,'' *Boston Globe*, February 19, 1993; Rick Wartzman, ''Administration Alters Proposal for Energy Tax,'' *The Wall Street Journal*, April 2, 1993.

While the Btu tax and the carbon tax each use a slightly different tax base, the general purpose of each is the same—to encourage fuel-switching and conservation by elevating fuel prices. Of the two, the carbon tax is more specific, since it targets only carbon-based fuels. In fact, it is considered to be the more relevant form of taxation to mitigate CO_2 emissions, since the carbon content of fuel and carbon emissions are generally proportional to one another. Effectively, the carbon tax changes *relative* fuel prices, and theoretically could elevate the price of fossil-fuel by the marginal cost of the environmental damage caused by its combustion. In the context of Figure 12.1 panel (a), the tax amount should equal the vertical distance between MPC_F and the MSC_F for fossil-fuel users, measured at the efficient output level, Q_{F2}. Such a per unit charge would successfully internalize the external costs associated with the burning of fossil-fuels.

In practice, this particular tax is being used in Finland, the Netherlands, Norway, and Sweden and is being considered by Denmark, Germany, and Japan.[44] In the United States, the EPA has studied the carbon tax as part of its investigation of alternative control options. The agency has estimated that a tax of $5 per ton of carbon would reduce CO_2 emissions by approximately 1

---

[44]For more information on various international pollution charges aimed at greenhouse gases, the reader should consult the following: U.S. Environmental Protection Agency, Office of Policy, Planning, and Evaluation (July 1992) or Organisation for Economic Co-operation and Development (1989a and 1991).

to 4 percent by the year 2000 with revenues of $7 to $10 billion per year. By increasing the tax to $25 per ton, emissions would decline by some 8 to 17 percent, and revenues would be between $38 and $50 billion per year.[45] In addition, a carbon tax would increase the effective price of crude oil, leading to a reduction in oil imports and less dependence on foreign oil sources.

Evaluating a Tradeable Permit System.   One of the more critical aspects of an international CO_2 tradeable permit system is an agreement that specifies a worldwide emissions limit and allocates some predetermined number of permits to each national participant. Each country would be responsible for the initial distribution of permits to sources within its own borders and the oversight of any trading among those sources. Under some proposed scenarios, emission credits would be issued to countries for reforestation or declines in deforestation, recognizing the importance of forests as carbon sinks. Application 12.5 reports on how some U.S. utilities already are using reforestation programs to help offset the accumulation of CO_2 in the atmosphere.

Regardless of the strategy, countries able to reduce emissions below the amount initially allowed by agreement could sell their excess permits to the highest bidding country. Just as in the trading of SO_2 allowances and CFC permits, the trading of CO_2 permits can lead to a cost-effective solution. Nations and individual sources best able to reduce emissions would do so, while those that could not achieve the needed reductions would buy the permits. If the system operates efficiently, the price of the permit should be the dollar value of the external cost associated with the emissions. Again, as shown in Figure 12.1(a), this price should equal the vertical distance between MSC_F and MPC_F.

While conceptually appealing, the tradeable permit system does have a number of operational problems. For one thing, arriving at an international agreement is difficult, since global warming is expected to have varying impacts on different parts of the world. In fact, some nations stand to gain economically. To persuade these countries to agree to an emissions limit is likely to be difficult. Another problem is setting the initial allowance allocations for each of the participating nations. Matters of population, expected economic growth, and existing emission levels are just some of the relevant considerations. For example, if existing emission levels were used as the cap, this would severely limit the growth of developing nations. Some have suggested that industrialized countries could be given fewer permits. This allocation would force them to purchase allowances from less developed countries, which would in turn help finance abatement innovations in these poorer nations. Still another dilemma is how to monitor emissions of the national participants,

---

[45]These estimates are provided in U.S. Environmental Protection Agency, Office of Policy Planning and Evaluation (March 1991), pp. 3–5.

Application 12.5

Electric Power Plants and Nature: Using Natural Sinks to Offset Carbon Dioxide (CO_2) Emissions

In the United States, fossil-fuel burning electric power plants have assumed an active role in contributing to the nation's commitment to voluntarily reduce GHG emissions. In addition to energy conservation programs, some of these facilities have begun to investigate CO_2 **offset strategies,** a new approach to reducing the threat of global warming. In general, offset strategies make use of naturally occurring phenomena that act as absorbers of CO_2, also known as "carbon sinks."

One offset strategy that appears to offer promise is the participation of utilities in reforestation programs. Forests are natural sinks, since trees consume CO_2 as part of their growth process. Currently, there are several innovative reforestation programs that have been initiated by major U.S. power plants. For example, to help achieve its objective of reducing CO_2 emissions by 45 percent by the year 2000, New England Power Company has formed a partnership with a major Malaysian forest products firm. The goal is to save trees by increasing the efficiency of logging operations and by enhancing regeneration of the rain forests. Over the three-year pilot period, New England Power estimates that the program will save enough trees such that the resulting offset effect will be equivalent to removing 300,000 to 600,000 tons of CO_2 emissions. In a similar venture, Allied Energy

Services Inc. of Arlington, Virginia, is hoping that the acres of trees it plants in Guatemala will be enough to offset *all* of the CO_2 emissions released from its Connecticut power plant.

Taking the offset strategy one step further, some utilities are investigating the potential of developing other natural sinks. Oceans and other bodies of water contain organisms that actually consume CO_2. This naturally occurring phenomenon suggests the potential for another offset strategy—to encourage seaweed and algae growth and enhance the carbon-absorbing capacity of ocean sinks. New England Electric System is investigating the potential of "algae farming" as an alternative strategy to the more conventional reforestation approach. To date, research on the potential success of this unusual concept has been confined to the laboratory. Reportedly, however, the preliminary results are encouraging. In fact, a New England Electric official asserts that the laboratory findings suggest algae farming may be even more successful at absorbing CO_2 emissions than the conventional tree-farming approach.

Sources: Council on Environmental Quality, *Environmental Quality, 23rd Annual Report* (Washington, D.C.: U.S. Government Printing Office, January 1993), pp. 121–22; Sunita Wadekar Bhargava, ed., "Growing Clean Air Down on the Algae Farm," *Business Week,* February 24, 1992, p. 72.

particularly if reforestation were allowed as a means to earn emission credits.[46] This type of globally based program unfortunately lends itself to the public goods problem of free-ridership. So, despite the potential for a cost-effective solution, unless these tough issues are resolved, policy-makers will likely opt for more conventional and practical instruments like the carbon or Btu tax.

---

[46]Satellite monitoring likely would have to be implemented if reforestation were part of the program. See Wirth and Heinz (1991), pp. 28–22 and U.S. Environmental Protection Agency, Office of Policy, Planning, and Evaluation (March 1991), pp. 3–7, 3–10.

Conclusions

Formulating sound policy in response to global air pollution is a major undertaking. Scientific knowledge about atmospheric disturbances and the associated implications is still limited, particularly for global warming. As long as the extent of environmental risk is unknown, the benefits of corrective policy initiatives are likewise indeterminate. Consequently, public officials are unable to justify the social costs of policy controls with reliable information about the comparable benefits.

Even when the knowledge base is stronger, such as for ozone depletion, policy development is still complicated by the global nature of the problem. A successful resolution depends critically on international commitment, supported in turn by domestic initiatives. On this front, there have been several achievements. A case in point is the Montreal Protocol and its subsequent amendments and more recently the ratification of the U.N. Framework Convention. Nonetheless, there are still important issues to be worked out, not the least of which is how to gain the cooperation of developing nations. These countries lack the financial resources and the technology to innovate around the causes of global air pollution. Yet, their cooperation is critical given the expected rate of industrial and economic growth in these nations and the associated ramifications for the environment.

Despite the inherent difficulties, there has been progress in recognizing the relevant issues, acknowledging the unknowns, and investigating alternative solutions. Furthermore, scientific research is ongoing in the hope of reaching a general consensus about the implications of global air pollution. That policy development has been tentative—particularly in responding to the threat of global warming—is recognition of how important a balancing of benefits and costs is to that process. Until more is known about the environmental risks of global air pollution, and hence the benefits of regulation, the opportunity costs of major initiatives simply cannot be justified on economic grounds.

Summary

- Ozone depletion refers to damage to the earth's stratospheric ozone layer caused by certain pollutants. Stratospheric ozone protects the earth from damaging ultraviolet radiation.

- Although there are various theories about the cause of ozone depletion, many scientists agree that the presence of chlorofluorocarbons (CFCs) in the atmosphere is the most likely explanation. CFCs are a family of chemicals commonly used in refrigeration, air-conditioning, packaging, insulation, and as aerosol propellants.

- The Montreal Protocol of 1987, subsequently revised through the 1990 London Amendments and the 1992 Copenhagen Conference, is an international agreement aimed specifically at the problem of ozone depletion. The agreements call for a full phaseout plan of CFCs, methyl chloroform, fully halogenated chlorofluorocarbons, and carbon tetrachloride by 1996.

- Title VI of the 1990 Amendments is dedicated solely to protecting the earth's ozone layer. There are also two legislated instruments that use market incentives to achieve the commitment to eliminate the production and consumption of ozone-depleting substances. These are an excise tax and a marketable allowance system.
- Under the marketable allowance system, firms can produce or import ozone depleters only if they hold allowances or ''rights'' to do so. Over time, the number of available allowances will be gradually reduced and eventually brought to zero. In the interim, exchanges of allowances are permitted under strict guidelines.
- Because the allowance system is market oriented, we should expect to observe its progress through the price mechanism. The prices of CFCs and other ozone-depleting chemicals will signal the impact of the phaseout and the underlying market adjustments. The excise tax helps to counter the accumulation of excess profits to firms holding the limited number of allowances.
- Global warming, or the ''greenhouse effect,'' is caused by sunlight hitting the earth's surface and radiating back into the atmosphere, where it is absorbed by naturally present greenhouse gases (GHGs) such as carbon dioxide (CO_2). This process heats the atmosphere and warms the earth's surface. Any significant disruption to the natural levels of GHGs would have climatological impacts.
- The accumulation of CO_2 arises from fossil-fuel combustion and widespread deforestation such as the burning of tropical rain forests. The resulting global warming is predicted to affect forest ranges, biodiversity, sea levels, agricultural productivity, water and air quality, and human health. However, the timing and the magnitude of these effects are highly uncertain.
- One agreement generated at the Rio Summit was the U.N. Climate Change Convention. By the close of 1993, the requisite number of nations had ratified the treaty, and it became legally binding in March 1994.
- Subsequent to the ratification of the U.N. Framework Convention, President Clinton announced his program for reducing national emissions of GHGs to 1990 levels by the year 2000. The program relies primarily on voluntarism.
- Climatic engineering is one proposed strategy to help mitigate the effects of global warming. The concept involves chemically altering the atmosphere to change climatic conditions. Market-based instruments also have been proposed as strategic options, including the use of a pollution charge and a tradeable permit system.
- Benefit assessment is critical to developing policy to control global warming. Economists promote market-based policies designed to consider both the benefits and costs of government controls.
- The environmental problem of global warming can be illustrated by modeling accumulating GHG emissions as a negative externality. To correct the market failure, the external cost must be brought into the market transaction.
- A common type of pollution charge is the gasoline tax. Its applicability is limited, since it targets relatively minor emitters of CO_2. Also, it imposes a disproportionate burden on some segments of the economy. The carbon tax targets only fossil-fuels and more directly taxes the cause of the pollution. The Btu tax is a charge based on the energy content of a fuel. Because it is broader based, it shifts the tax burden more equally across the economy.

- An alternative market-based proposal to combat global warming is the use of an international market for permits to emit CO_2. Under some proposed scenarios, emission credits would be issued to countries for reforestation efforts or declines in deforestation.

Key Concepts

ozone depletion
global warming
ozone depletion potential (ODP)
excise tax on ozone depleters
marketable allowance system for ozone
 depleters
greenhouse gases (GHGs)
carbon sinks
National Action Plan (NAP)

climatic engineering
negative externality
pollution charge
tradeable permit system for CO_2
 emissions
gasoline tax
Btu tax
carbon tax
corrective tax
externality regulation

APPENDIX
A REFERENCE TO ACRONYMS AND CHEMICAL FORMULAS IN AIR QUALITY CONTROL POLICY

Environmental Economics Acronyms

MPC_F	Marginal private cost of fossil-fuel users
MSC_F	Marginal social cost of fossil-fuel users
MEC_F	Marginal external cost of fossil-fuel users
MSC_A	Marginal social cost of alternative fuel users
MPC_A	Marginal private cost of alternative fuel users

Environmental Science Acronyms

Btu	British thermal unit
CFCs	Chlorofluorocarbons
CFC-11	Chlorofluorocarbon-11
CO_2	Carbon dioxide
GHG	Greenhouse gas
GWP	Global warming potential
mmBtu	Million British thermal units
CH_4	Methane
N_2O	Nitrous oxide
NO_x	Nitrogen oxides
O_3	Ozone
ODP	Ozone-depletion potential
ppbv	Parts per billion by volume
ppmv	Parts per million by volume
SO_2	Sulfur dioxide
VOC	Volatile organic compound

Environmental Policy Acronyms

NAP	National Action Plan
RIA	Regulatory Impact Analysis

Review Questions

1. By restricting CFC production, the Montreal Protocol and U.S. regulations have increased the price of CFCs. Assume your employer is a major CFC producer. Present an economic argument either for or against the restrictions.

2. Other than financial assistance, how might industrialized countries help developing countries to control ozone depletion?

3. *a.* Using supply and demand models, graphically illustrate the short-term effect of the phaseout of CFCs on both the market for CFCs and the market for CFC substitutes.

   b. Now, model the longer-term implications of technology advances toward producing CFC substitutes. Use your graphs to explain how price affects market reactions.

4. Consider the distributional effects of agricultural productivity due to global warming. Discuss some of the ramifications of this outcome with regard to regional economies, national economies, and world trade.

5. *a.* Why is it that a carbon tax is preferred to either a Btu tax or the gasoline tax when the objective is to reduce carbon dioxide (CO_2) emissions?

   b. Instead of enacting a carbon tax, assume Congress decides to provide tax incentives to non-carbon-based energy sources, such as solar and wind power. Would this instrument be cost-effective in reducing CO_2 emissions?

   c. Now suppose that the government chooses to initiate tax incentives (e.g., a tax credit) for these energy alternatives along with the carbon tax. Would this be a more socially optimal solution? Explain briefly.

6. During the 1970s, domestic oil prices rose sharply due to supply restrictions initiated by the OPEC nations. As prices rose, Congress instituted tax incentives for homeowners to substitute away from oil as a heating fuel and move toward alternative sources like solar energy. During the 1980s, these incentives were eliminated. What was the underlying motivation of implementing the tax incentives in the first place? Why did Congress remove them?

Additional Readings

Benarde, Melvin A. *Global Warning . . . Global Warming.* New York: John Wiley & Sons, 1992.

Benedick, Richard Elliot. *Ozone Diplomacy: New Directions in Safeguarding the Planet.* Cambridge, Mass.: Harvard University Press, 1991.

Choucri, Nazli, ed. *Global Accord: Environmental Challenges and International Responses.* Cambridge, Mass.: The MIT Press, 1993.

Edgarton, Lynne T. *The Rising Tide: Global Warming and World Sea Levels.* Washington, D.C.: Island Press, 1991.

Energy Journal 12, no. 1; 12, no. 4. *Global Warming,* 1991.

Environment Canada. *Understanding CO_2 and Climate—Annual Report 1986.* Ottawa: Atmospheric Environment Service, 1987.

Hubbard, Harold M. ''The Real Cost of Energy.'' *Scientific American,* April, 1991, pp. 36–42.

Journal of Economic Perspectives 7, no. 4. *Symposia on Global Climate Change,* Fall 1993.

Manne, Alan, and Richard Richels. *Buying Greenhouse Insurance: The Economic Costs of CO_2 Emission Limits.* Cambridge, Mass.: The MIT Press, 1992.

Nordhaus, William D. ''To Slow or Not to Slow: The Economics of the Greenhouse Effect.'' *The Economic Journal* 101 (July 1991), pp. 920–37.

Roberts, Paul Craig. ''What's Flying Out the Ozone Hole? Billions of Dollars.'' *Business Week,* June 13, 1994, p. 22.

Shapiro, Michael, and Ellen Warhit. ''Marketable Permits: The Case of Chlorofluorocarbons.'' *Natural Resources Journal* 23 (July 1983), pp. 577–91.

Stiff, David, and Frank Edward Allen, ''Forecast for Rio: Scientific Cloudiness.'' *The Wall Street Journal,* June 3, 1992.

PART V

THE CASE OF WATER

Water is so much a part of what we are and where we live, it is generally taken for granted. Satellite photographs of earth are convincing evidence of the predominance of water on our planet, covering over 70 percent of its surface. Over half of the three-mile-deep outer layer of the earth is water. All biological organisms depend on water for life—to transport nutrients, to regulate temperature, and to support virtually all biochemical systems that sustain life.[1] Ironically, the abundance of water on Earth disguises the fact that *usable* water is scarce, and as a result, efforts to conserve and protect this natural resource have been less than adequate.

While most of the earth is covered by water, much of it is seawater and hence unusable for drinking and crop irrigation. A recent review of accumulated scientific research puts the estimate of fresh water on the planet at less than 1/30th of the earth's entire supply, and very little of this amount is contained in lakes and streams. Most of our fresh water supply—some 77 percent, according to estimates—is trapped in ice and snow. Another 22 percent lies beneath the earth's surface, and most of this (about two-thirds) is not accessible absent prohibitive costs.[2] Finally, of what fresh water *is* available and accessible, much of it has been damaged by pollution.

Population growth and industrial development have placed competing demands on water resources. Fortunately, nature provides a powerful mechanism that regularly replenishes water supplies. Precipitation restores some of it, which collects on the earth's surface, runs off into lakes, reservoirs, and streams, and percolates into the soil as groundwater. Evaporation returns some of this water back into the atmosphere, where the process begins again. Yet despite this restorative process, our water supply is not unlimited. Some parts

---

[1]Lyklema and van Hylckama (1988).
[2]United Nations (1978) as cited in White (1988).

of the world face severe water shortages, and virtually everywhere on earth, industrial activity, improper waste disposal, and human carelessness have damaged lakes and streams and contaminated accessible groundwater supplies.

The dependence of all forms of life on this precious commodity demands that society understand the risks of water pollution and take appropriate action to minimize those risks. However, since water pollution is an externality, corrective action must come about through government intervention. In the United States, water quality control policy has taken decades to develop, and by most accounts, still has much to accomplish. Most argue that national policy is in need of significant reform, though there is disagreement about what revisions should be made and how to implement them. What *is* clear is that water quality laws have not been consistently effective. Although there have been some successes, there are still water bodies in decline and there are continuing threats to some drinking water supplies. Furthermore, it appears that national policy objectives are not efficient and that many of the control instruments in use are not cost-effective.

In this module, we undertake a collection of important tasks—to understand how water resources are threatened by contamination, to examine policy initiatives aimed at the problem, and to analyze the outcome using economic criteria. We begin our study in Chapter 13, which provides a broad overview of the Clean Water Act, the objectives it sets forth, and the standard-setting process that defines water quality for the nation. Chapter 14 focuses on the primary control instruments used to achieve clean water goals. In Chapter 15, we shift our attention to the Safe Drinking Water Act and the standards used to protect human health.

13

DEFINING WATER QUALITY

The U.S. Clean Water Act

Water is a classic example of a common property resource characterized by the absence of property rights. Unless government intervenes, water supplies likely will be overused and contaminated. In the United States, controls on water quality have a long history dating back to the turn of the century, and remarkably, certain of these early laws are still on the books. Of course, much has happened in water quality legislation over the last 100 years or so, and the evolution continues.

Effective water policy depends on a careful appraisal of existing water quality conditions, the setting of appropriate objectives, and the design of effective instruments to bring the two together. As we have learned in previous chapters, these tasks depend on good risk assessment techniques and sound risk management practices. In the case of water policy formulation, however, many problems have impeded risk analysis. Assessing the extent of water pollution has been hampered by inadequate monitoring systems. National objectives have not always been properly motivated by benefit and cost considerations, and even when they have, reliable estimates have been hard to come by. Furthermore, some policy instruments have been guided more by public and political pressures than by sound environmental management practices. As a consequence, resources have been misallocated, and society has had unrealistic expectations about what federal policy can accomplish.

Beyond these procedural difficulties are the natural complexities of water resources, which present a further challenge to policy-makers. Water supplies are highly heterogeneous with different chemical, biological, and ecological attributes. They also serve different functions—a critically important factor in policy decisions. Consider how quality controls on water used for drinking have to be much more stringent than those applied to waters used only for navigation. Geographical location, including proximity to urban or industrial centers, affects both the usage of water resources and their vulnerability to contamination. These differences suggest that policy objectives and control instruments must be sensitive to the variations caused by nature and by human activity. Adding to the challenge is a complex, natural cycle that links water resources, land, and the atmosphere together. This interdependence suggests the need for an integrated approach that acknowledges these transmedia implications. Taken together, these issues add up to an ambitious policy agenda—one we begin to investigate in this chapter.

As a preface to our study and analysis of water quality policy, we present a general overview of water resources and the sources of contamination that threaten them. This discussion helps to motivate our subsequent investigation of how U.S. policy to protect these resources has evolved to the present day. We then focus in on national policy goals under the Clean Water Act and how standards are used to define water quality for the nation. A two-part policy analysis follows. The first is an evaluation of the standard-setting process. The second is a benefit-cost analysis of U.S. water quality initiatives that uses the economic analytical tools we have developed previously. At the end of the chapter is an appendix of acronyms for reference.

Understanding Water Resources for Policy Development

Identifying Water Resources and Their Interdependence

Most of us are cognizant of the fact that water is a significant component of both the surface of the earth and its underlying geological layers. In fact, policy specifically addresses two major categories of water resources, **surface water** and **groundwater.**

surface water
Bodies of water that are open to the earth's atmosphere, such as rivers, lakes, oceans, and streams, as well as springs, wells, or other collectors directly influenced by surface water.

- **Surface water** refers to all bodies of water that are open to the earth's atmosphere, such as rivers, lakes, oceans, and streams, and also springs, wells, or other collectors that are directly influenced by surface water.
- **Groundwater** refers to the fresh water located beneath the earth's surface, generally in what are called aquifers, underground geological formations that supply wells and springs.

groundwater
The fresh water beneath the earth's surface, generally in aquifers.

Setting policy to protect and maintain these resources is a major undertaking because these water supplies are so vast and because they are remarkably heterogeneous.

Surface waters represent a highly diverse group of water bodies that support distinct ecological systems, serve different uses, and often face dissimilar sources of pollution. Because of these differences, policy-makers in the United States categorize surface waters into the following groups: open ocean waters, ocean coastal waters, estuaries, inland waters, and wetlands, each of which is briefly described in Table 13.1. Although national policy is aimed at protecting

TABLE 13.1   Surface Waters of the Earth

Open ocean waters	Open ocean waters are the deep waters beyond the continental shelf and those waters over the continental shelf that are not measurably affected by the input of freshwater from rivers.
Ocean coastal waters	Ocean coastal waters refer to the saltwaters along ocean shorelines, which are less enclosed and more influenced by oceanic processes than estuaries and generally lie over the continental shelf within the territorial sea.
Estuaries	Estuaries are regions of interaction between rivers and nearshore ocean waters, where tidal action and river flow mix fresh and saltwater together. Estuaries include bays, mouths of rivers, salt marshes, and lagoons.
Inland waters	Inland waters are bodies of fresh water, including rivers, streams, lakes, and reservoirs.
Wetlands	Wetlands refer to areas that are saturated by surface or groundwater with vegetation adapted for life under those soil conditions. These regions are transitional between aquatic and terrestrial ecosystems and include swamps, bogs, fens, marshes, and estuaries.

Sources: U.S. Congress, Office of Technology Assessment, *Wastes in Marine Environments* (Washington, D.C.: U.S. Government Printing Office, 1987), Box A, p. 4; U.S. Environmental Protection Agency, Office of Communications, Education, and Public Affairs, *Terms of Environment, Glossary, Abbreviations and Acronyms* (Washington, D.C., September 1992).

all of these waters, specific policy instruments and programs often are aimed at one of these categories. Groundwater is an enormous resource—by volume over 50 times the annual flow of the earth's surface waters. It is of critical importance, since it is available at virtually every point on earth and because it is the *only* reliable source for many arid and semi-arid regions of the world.[1]

Adding to the complexity of water supplies is the remarkable interdependence of all water resources—a phenomenon explained by what is called the **hydrological cycle.** This cycle models the natural movement of water from the earth's atmosphere to the surface and beneath the ground, and back into the atmosphere through a series of natural processes, including **precipitation, evaporation, transpiration, infiltration, percolation,** and **runoff.**[2]

The model is depicted in Figure 13.1, which shows how the earth's water supply is continuously in motion to replenish itself. Notice that the hydrological cycle illustrates the remarkable natural process that joins together the waters on the earth's surface, those below the ground, and the water vapor in the atmosphere. It also communicates an important message about the ramifications of water contamination. The earth's atmosphere and its water supplies are remarkably interdependent—a fact that underscores the importance of

hydrological cycle
A model explaining the natural movement of water from the atmosphere to the surface, beneath the ground, and back into the atmosphere.

[1]For more detail, see Heath (1988).
[2]For a complete discussion of this important water cycle, see U.S. Congress, Office of Technology Assessment (1988).

FIGURE 13.1

The hydrological cycle

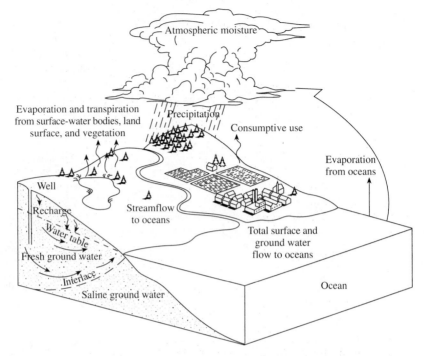

Groundwater and surface water are linked together by the **hydrological cycle.** Water is transported from the atmosphere to the surface of the earth through **precipitation.** Some precipitation never reaches the earth's surface but instead is **evaporated** back up into the atmosphere as water vapor or clouds. Some of it settles on trees and plants where it is absorbed and later returned to the atmosphere through the process of **transpiration.** Water landing on buildings and other man-made structures is also evaporated.

The precipitation that *does* reach the earth's surface can take a number of routes from the point called the **watershed** or the **drainage basin.** It can collect in pools where it is later evaporated. It also might flow over the surface where it is collected in lakes and streams, a process known as **runoff.** From there, it may evaporate, soak into the ground through the process of **infiltration,** or flow into the oceans where some portion of it is evaporated. Finally, precipitation may infiltrate the ground directly and flow into soil and rock formations into the water table where it is collected within an aquifer—a process called **percolation.**

Source: Council on Environmental Quality, *Environmental Trends* (Washington, D.C.: U.S. Government Printing Office, 1989), p. 21.

protecting *all* natural resources from contamination. Pollutants that damage a river or stream can easily be carried to nearby groundwater supplies, and contaminants in the atmosphere can damage surface waters as they are carried to the earth's surface by precipitation.[3] Hence, while surface water and groundwater are in a practical sense distinct water supplies, potential threats to one can have implications for the other because of the hydrological cycle that ties them together.

---

[3]Recall from Chapter 11 that sulfur dioxide (SO_2) and nitrogen oxide (NO_x) emissions contribute to acid rain, which in turn damages lakes and other surface waters.

Targeting Water Quality Policy

point source
Any single identifiable source of pollution such as a fixed location or facility from which contaminants are discharged.

nonpoint source
A source of pollution that cannot be identified accurately and degrades a water body in a diffuse, indirect way over a relatively broad area.

Both surface water and groundwater resources are vulnerable to contamination from a wide variety of sources—some more obvious than others. In fact, most people tend to think only of the discharges from industrial facilities and power plants as the primary sources of water pollution. However, water resources are contaminated by many other sources that are more obscure but nonetheless serious. Conventionally, the source categories of water pollution are characterized as **point sources** and **nonpoint sources.** A **point source** is any single identifiable source of pollution such as a fixed location or facility from which contaminants are discharged. A **nonpoint source** is one that cannot be identified accurately and degrades a water body in a diffuse, indirect way over a relatively broad area.

As a group, point sources cover a lot of ground, so policy instruments often distinguish between the following basic categories: (1) **publicly owned treatment works (POTWs)** that treat wastewaters flowing through sewer systems; (2) **industrial facilities** such as private factories, mills, or other physical plants; and (3) **combined sewer systems** that carry both sewage and storm water runoff to waste treatment plants. Nonpoint sources by definition are difficult to identify, and hence difficult to control. Examples are land runoff (such as from farms, urban areas, construction sites, forests, and mines), septic systems, landfills, spills, and atmospheric deposition. Only recently have government authorities begun to address these less obvious polluting sources. Hence, control efforts are still in the early stages of development. As an example, Application 13.1 discusses how the Chesapeake Bay has been polluted by both nonpoint and point sources and what officials are doing to save this important natural resource.

Setting the Policy Agenda

Recognizing the complexity of water resources and their vulnerability to pollution, policy-makers have a comprehensive agenda of what must be accomplished through specific initiatives. In the United States, there are three general

---

Application 13.1

Deterioration and Restoration of the Chesapeake Bay

For more than 20 years, the Chesapeake Bay has been deteriorating. This popular U.S. estuary—the largest in North America—has suffered serious stress from a barrage of polluting sources. Among them are sewage treatment plants, atmospheric deposition, urban and rural runoff, and industrial dischargers. The vulnerability of this majestic waterbody is explained partly by the large number of major rivers that flow into the bay from Maryland, Virginia, West Virginia, Pennsylvania, and Delaware.

Application 13.1 (continued)

Effects of pollutants in the Chesapeake Bay.

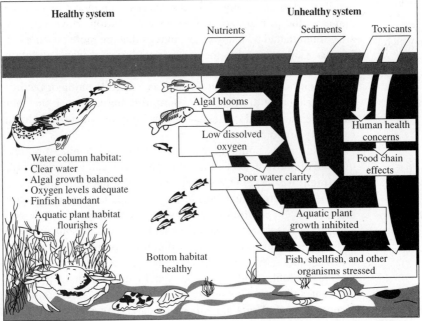

Source: U.S. Environmental Protection Agency, Office of Water, *National Water Quality Inventory: 1992 Report to Congress* (Washington, D.C., March 1994), Figure 11–7, p. 195

Furthermore, its geographical location within the boundaries of Maryland and Virginia is such that it does not benefit from the cleansing forces of the open ocean.

As the graphic suggests, the Chesapeake's decline is obvious by almost any measure. The bay receives an enormous amount of nutrients and suspended solids. Most of these contaminants originate from municipal treatment plants and agricultural runoff, entering both directly and indirectly from upstream sources. The major effects of these pollutants are declines in submerged vegetation and severe eutrophication—the gradual aging process during which a water body evolves into a marsh and eventually disappears. Because the eutrophication is extreme, hypoxia—a serious depletion of dissolved oxygen—is common in the bay. This condi-

tion has been blamed for fish kills that are both ecologically and commercially devastating. Other contaminants such as heavy metals and organic substances are linked to industrial and municipal pipelines as well as urban and rural runoff.

One of the more dramatic consequences of the Chesapeake's contamination is the decline in its once famous productivity. Commercial fishing from this large estuary has always been prolific even when measured on a national scale. In 1985, for example, most of the 815 million pounds of fish caught in Virginia and Maryland came from the bay's waters. For that year, this catch accounted for 13 percent of the national total and was valued at almost $124 million. Hence, national attention was drawn immediately to observations that the bay's bountiful marine life was being threatened by pollution. In the last

Application 13.1 (concluded)

two decades, oyster production has fallen by 99 percent. Severe reductions also have been observed in such species as striped bass, white perch, and the blueback herring.

Official response to the bay's decline began in the 1970s. A seven-year study completed in 1983 reported on the major causes and sources of the deterioration. Later that year, the Chesapeake Bay Agreement was signed by the EPA, Maryland, Virginia, Pennsylvania, the District of Columbia, and the Chesapeake Bay Commission. This historic document authorized the Restoration and Protection Plan—the oldest estuarine program in the United States. It is a cooperative agreement among the signatories to clean up the bay and restore its productivity. In 1987, the program was made a part of the provisions of the Water Quality Act, and a new, more specific agreement was drafted and signed. In 1991, still another in the series of Chesapeake Bay documents was executed—this one aimed at accelerating the restoration efforts to assure progress toward meeting the program's objectives.

Among the program's endeavors is a $100 million cleanup project to reduce nutrients in the central bay waters. Other initiatives include a ban on phosphates in Maryland and the District of Columbia, land use controls in Maryland, point source reductions from municipal sewage treatment plants, and a moratorium on harvesting rockfish. Funding for this comprehensive plan comes from federal and state governments and many private sources, including environmental groups and the Chesapeake Bay Foundation—a nonprofit entity with a $3 million endowment and a $400,000 annual budget. Because of the ecological, commercial, and recreational value of this U.S. estuary, the Chesapeake Bay Program has received more research funding from government than any other of its kind.

These intensive efforts have not gone unrewarded. Since 1985, a 19 percent reduction in the bay's phosphorus levels has been observed along with a 5 percent drop in its nitrogen content. Submerged vegetation has begun to return to the shorelines, and the population of striped bass is showing signs of increase. Of course, the hard work must continue if the goal of restoring the bay to its 1950s condition is to be achieved.

Sources: U.S. Environmental Protection Agency, Office of Communications, Education, and Public Affairs, *Securing Our Legacy: An EPA Progress Report 1989–1991* (Washington, D.C., April, 1992), pp. 32–33; U.S. Congress, Office of Technology Assessment, *Wastes in Marine Environments* (Washington, D.C.: U.S. Government Printing Office, 1987), pp. 21–22, 100–108, 157–64; U.S. Environmental Protection Agency, *Environmental Progress and Challenges: EPA's Update* (Washington, D.C., August 1988), p. 66.

themes that convey what the nation hopes to achieve in formulating and implementing water quality policy. These are:

1. To achieve and maintain drinking water quality through minimizing surface water contamination, preventing groundwater contamination, and instituting proper treatment methods.

2. To prevent the destruction and degradation of critical aquatic habitats, including wetlands, coastal waters, oceans, rivers, and lakes.

3. To reduce the pollution of surface waters and assure protection of their uses.[4]

These themes communicate that water quality is important not only to protect human health but also to protect the ecology and to assure that all uses

---

[4]U.S. EPA (August 1988), p. 45.

of water are maintained. Therefore, we should expect water quality to be defined broadly in the law and pollution controls to be instituted from a wide range of perspectives. Indeed, there are many different laws and special programs aimed at water pollution, although the most comprehensive is the Clean Water Act. To get a sense of how the federal government became involved in clean water legislation and how today's policy position developed, consider the following evolution of U.S. water quality policy.

Water Quality Legislation in the United States: An Overview

Similar to the development of U.S. air policy, government controls on water quality date back to the late 1800s. In the early days, these rulings were aimed solely at protecting human health and were unsophisticated by today's standards. Over time, the legislation evolved into a fairly complex set of laws to protect not only human health, but also the natural condition of the earth's water resources and the aquatic life they support. A summary of the evolution is given in Table 13.2, which serves as an outline for the following discussion.[5]

Early U.S. Water Quality Laws

The evolution of U.S. water quality laws began with the Rivers and Harbor Act of 1899. Technically still in force, this legislation prohibits the discharge of refuse into all U.S. navigable waters. Though not aimed at pollution sources or specific contaminants, this act attempts to preserve the navigability of waterways by preventing blockages caused by waste discharges. Federal legislation on water pollution per se originated nearly half a century later with the Water Pollution Control Act of 1948. Up until this time, water pollution control laws had been enacted by state and local governments. Much like the first national law on air quality control, the role of the federal government in the 1948 Act was limited—apparently for the same reason. There was a reluctance to bring federal intervention into what had been perceived as the responsibility of state governments. The 1948 act did, however, introduce a federal loan program to assist municipalities in the construction of publicly owned treatment works (POTWs)—a program that was to have long-term ramifications.[6] In fact, the 1956 amendments to this act converted the loan plan to an outright grant program whereby the U.S. government would subsidize up to 55 percent of POTW construction costs. Aside from this revision, however, national water quality legislation remained weak.

---

[5]Much of the following is drawn from Adler, Landman, and Cameron (1993), pp. 5–10; Freeman (1990), pp. 97–108; and Freeman (1978), pp. 45–53.

[6]We will analyze the POTW grant program in the next chapter.

TABLE 13.2   Evolution of U.S. Water Quality Laws

Legislative Act	*Major Provisions*
Rivers and Harbor Act of 1899	Prohibits the discharge of refuse into all U.S. navigable waters without a permit.
Water Pollution Control Act of 1948	Called for the federal government to conduct research, implement surveys to study contamination, and provide loans to municipalities for construction of POTWs.
Water Pollution Control Act Amendments of 1956	Authorized state governments to set criteria to define water quality; strengthened federal government's role; established a grant program to subsidize construction of POTWs; instituted the enforcement conference.
Water Quality Act of 1965	Required states to establish ambient water quality standards, devise implementation plans, issue permits to satisfy standards, and set up a monitoring and enforcement program.
The Marine Protection, Research, and Sanctuaries Act	Regulates ocean dumping of materials that may harm health, the marine ecology, or the economic potential of the oceans; also acts as the domestic instrument that implements the international agreement called the London Dumping Convention.
Federal Water Pollution Control Act of 1972	Shifted the primary responsibility for water quality controls from the states to the federal government; established the first set of national goals for water quality; authorized EPA to establish technology-based effluent standards.
Clean Water Act of 1977	Postponed compliance deadlines for meeting the effluent standards; established new treatment standards for wastes sent to POTWs; strengthened controls on toxic pollutants.
Water Quality Act of 1987	Established federal subsidies to states for loans to finance POTW construction; required states to set up programs for nonpoint polluting sources.

Sources: Robert W. Adler, Jessica C. Landman, and Diane M. Cameron, *The Clean Water Act: 20 Years Later* (Washington, D.C.: Island Press, 1993), pp. 5–10; A. Myrick Freeman III, "Water Pollution Policy," in Paul R. Portney, ed., *Public Policies for Environmental Protection* (Washington, D.C.: Resources for the Future, 1990), pp. 97–108; A. Myrick Freeman III, "Air and Water Pollution Policy," in Paul R. Portney, ed., *Current Issues in U.S. Environmental Policy* (Baltimore, Md.: The Johns Hopkins University Press for Resources for the Future, 1978), pp. 45–53.

Attempting to address the deficiencies, Congress passed the Water Quality Act of 1965. For the first time, the law itemized specifically what state authorities were expected to accomplish with some provision for federal oversight. Chief among these responsibilities were setting ambient water quality standards, devising implementation plans on the effluent reductions needed to meet those standards, and issuing permits to limit polluters' discharges. While seemingly well defined, the new provisions met with failure. Why? State governments were ill prepared and poorly motivated for the important tasks assigned to them. A major obstacle was that states were unable to translate water quality standards into facility-specific discharge limits. Such a procedure calls for advanced and costly modeling techniques that state governments simply were unable to orchestrate. They also had difficulty identifying which dischargers were responsible for a water body not meeting the standards, so they had little leverage in enforcing the law. There was also an incentive problem, since states recognized that stringent discharge limits would discourage industry from locating in their jurisdictions.[7] Finally, there was a lack of consistency in how standards were set and enforced across the nation due to state-specific differences in resources and technological expertise. In sum, it was apparent that further reform was needed.

Evolving toward Today's Policy Position

The decade of the 1970s was a period of environmental policy reform. Responding to the continuing decline in national water quality and recognizing the failure of delegating virtually all control to state authorities, Congress passed two major pieces of federal water control legislation in 1972. One was the Marine Protection, Research, and Sanctuaries Act (MPRSA) whose primary objective was to regulate ocean dumping. For a discussion of this and other legislation protecting ocean waters, read Application 13.2. The other major law enacted in 1972 was the Federal Water Pollution Control Act (FWPCA)—considered to be a milestone in the evolution of U.S. water quality legislation. In fact, much of what guides U.S. policy today originated with this act.

It was through the FWPCA that primary responsibility for water quality shifted from the states to the federal government. National goals were defined for the first time, including one calling for the elimination of all polluting discharges by 1985. New technology-based effluent limitations were to be

---

Application 13.2

U.S. Policy to Protect Ocean Waters

Open ocean waters are generally in better environmental health than other types of surface waters. Part of the reason is that the sheer size of the earth's oceans allows them to disperse and dilute any pollutants they receive far more readily than other surface waters. Nonetheless, there are serious threats that jeopardize the quality of oceans and the marine life they support beyond the discharge of effluents from polluting sources. The image of wastes washed up on shorelines is still fresh in the minds of most Americans, and so too is the damage from oil spills like the *Exxon Valdez* incident in the spring of 1989. Deliberate ocean dumping and accidental oil spills are two problems that require special mandates. Hence, Congress passed legislative acts specifically to protect oceans and coastal waters—laws that complement the broad-based objectives of the Clean Water Act. Two of these are the Marine Protection, Research, and Sanctuaries Act (MPRSA), and the Oil Pollution Act of 1990 (OPA).

---

[7]Notice how this incentive problem arises—just as it does in states' development of implementation plans to control air pollution.

Application 13.2 (continued)

The Marine Protection, Research, and Sanctuaries Act (MPRSA)

In 1972, Congress passed the Marine Protection, Research, and Sanctuaries Act (MPRSA), also known as the Ocean Dumping Act. Its major purpose is to regulate ocean dumping of materials that may harm human health, the marine ecology, or the economic potential of the oceans. This Act is also the domestic instrument that implements the rulings of the London Dumping Convention, an international agreement on ocean dumping to which the United States is a party. Under the MPRSA, dumping of certain materials is explicitly prohibited, such as radiological, chemical, and biological warfare agents, high-level radioactive wastes, and medical waste. The dumping of other wastes such as dredged materials is controlled through permitting systems. The MPRSA also authorizes the Secretary of Commerce to designate certain areas of the marine environment as National Marine Sanctuaries and to authorize conservation and management of these areas. As indicated in the table below, these protected marine environments currently comprise well over 9,000 square nautical miles.

National Marine Sanctuaries

Marine Sanctuary	Designation Date	Location	Size (square nautical miles)	Description
Monitor	1975	Cape Hatteras, NC	1.0	A circular area over the wreck of the *U.S.S. Monitor*
Key Largo	1975	Upper Florida Keys	100.0	Coral reef
Channel Islands	1980	Santa Barbara, CA	1,252.0	Offshore, nearshore, and intertidal habitats
Gray's Reef	1981	Sapelo Island, GA	17.0	Submerged live-bottom reef
Gulf of the Farallones	1981	Along the central California coast	948.0	Diverse habitat for marine mammals and seabirds
Looe Key	1981	Lower Florida Keys	5.3	Florida reef tract
Fagatele Bay	1986	Tutuila Island America Samoa	0.2	Terraced coral reef ecosystem typical of South Pacific islands
Cordell Bank	1989	San Francisco, CA	397.0	Ocean waters surrounding a submerged mountain top
Florida Keys	1990	Off the Florida Keys	2,800.0	Coral reefs and other waters
Monterey Bay	1992	Along the central California coast	4,024.0	Marine mammals, seabirds, and the largest U.S. submarine canyon
Flower Garden Banks	1992	Off the Texas–Louisiana coast	41.7	Northernmost North American coral reef community
Stellwagen Bank	1992	Off the coast of Massachusetts	638.0	Whale summering ground, major fisheries
Hawaiian Islands Humpback Whale	1992	Off the Hawaiian Islands	500.0*	Whales and tropical coral reef resources

Note: *Final boundaries remain to be designated.

Source: U.S. Department of Commerce, NOAA, National Ocean Service, 1992, as cited in Council on Environmental Quality, *Environmental Quality, 23rd Annual Report* (Washington, D.C.: U.S. Government Printing Office, January 1993), p. 35.

Application 13.2 (concluded)

In 1988, the Ocean Dumping Ban Act was enacted by Congress to amend the MPRSA. Among its mandates is a ruling that called for an end to the dumping of sewage sludge and industrial waste by the close of 1991. The new act also regulates garbage barges and makes it unlawful for medical wastes to be disposed of in any coastal or navigable U.S. waters.

Oil Pollution Act of 1990 (OPA)

Oil spills from tanker accidents or offshore oil drilling platforms have made headlines all over the world. Perhaps the best known spill in U.S. waters is that of the *Exxon Valdez* on March 24, 1989. The environmental and economic damages of this accident were substantial. Experts place the assessment in the several billions of dollars. In the aftermath of this disaster, Congress recognized the need to pass additional legislation to control and respond to oil spills. In 1990, it enacted the Oil Pollution Act (OPA), which specifically amends provisions in the Clean Water Act to institute tougher controls on oil spills. One entire section of this act is dedicated to the Prince William Sound region where the *Valdez* incident occurred. The rest of the legislation is aimed at controlling and preventing the threat of oil pollution to all marine environments through directives on removal actions, liability assessment and compensation, and prevention.

Under the OPA, a National Contingency Plan is established to provide for efficient and effective action to remove oil and hazardous substance discharges. To execute this plan, the act instituted a National Planning and Response System activated in part by response teams formed by the U.S. Coast Guard. These oil spill strike teams comprise highly trained individuals who can carry out the objectives of the National Contingency Plan. Related rulings call for owners or operators of oil tankers, offshore facilities, and certain onshore facilities to develop their own response plans for a worst-case discharge of oil or some other hazardous substance or the threat of such an event.

Other important provisions in the OPA identify those parties responsible for removal costs, damages to natural resources and property, associated loss of profits or earning capacity, and costs of providing public services. The list of potentially liable individuals is all-encompassing, including owners or operators of vessels, pipelines, or onshore facilities as well as parties who would have been responsible for any abandoned ship, port, or facility just prior to its abandonment.

Congress also recognized the need to develop preventive initiatives to lessen the probability that accidents at sea will occur. Among these are provisions to strengthen the standards for obtaining licenses, certificates of registry, and merchant mariners' documents and to clarify the basis under which these may be suspended or revoked. Specific mention is made about testing for and responding to suspected drug and alcohol abuse by vessel operators or other personnel who serve in ''safety sensitive functions.'' There are other rulings aimed at improving the construction of oceangoing vessels. Here, the prevention strategy is to make the design standards for oil vessels more stringent. Included is a requirement for double hulls on certain oil-carrying vessels, though these provisions will not take effect for some time.

Sources: Marine Protection, Research, and Sanctuaries Act; Oil Pollution Act of 1990; U.S. Environmental Protection Agency, Office of Water, *Marine and Estuarine Protection: Programs and Activities* (Washington, D.C., February 1989); Council on Environmental Quality, *Environmental Quality, 23rd Annual Report* (Washington, D.C.: U.S. Government Printing Office, January 1993), pp. 34–35.

set within one year by the EPA as the primary instruments of U.S. water quality control.[8] The federal cost share of sewage treatment construction was increased to 75 percent, and a National Commission on Water Quality was formed to monitor policy effectiveness and to study any economic and technological implications. There was no question that the new law was meant to take a tough position against water polluting sources. But it soon became apparent that it was overly ambitious, falling far short of its objectives. When the newly established commission issued its first report in 1976, it stated that 20 percent of dischargers likely would not meet the first phase of compliance with the effluent limits, which had been targeted for 1977.[9] In fact, the EPA had not even defined all of the standards by that date, despite the one-year deadline. Citing hundreds of pending legal cases challenging the EPA-mandated limits and attempting to explain the observed lack of progress, the commission's report and recommendations prompted another round of revisions eventually enacted as the Clean Water Act (CWA) of 1977.

Making much needed midcourse corrections, the CWA of 1977 extended the compliance deadlines for meeting the effluent limitations. It also strengthened the law on toxic water pollutants. Still more extensions and revisions followed when the act later came up for reauthorization—these in the form of the Water Quality Act of 1987.[10] Passed over President Reagan's veto, the 1987 act authorized more federal monies to support POTW construction—$9.6 billion in federal grants through 1990 and another $8.4 billion through 1994 to subsidize construction loans to take over when the grant program expired. It also required states to establish programs aimed at nonpoint polluting sources and authorized federal funding of $400 million to support that effort.

The most recent reauthorization of the Clean Water Act began under the 102nd Congress with many hearings held by the Senate and House in 1991. The review process ignited intense discussion among Senate members, the EPA, and administration officials. In the interim, no analogous bill was introduced in the House of Representatives. An accumulation of disagreements so delayed the procedures that it soon became clear that the 102nd Congress would not complete the process. In June 1993, the reauthorization bill was reintroduced to the Senate of the 103rd Congress by Senators Baucus of Montana and Chafee of Rhode Island while an analogous bill was being written in the House of Representatives. President Clinton submitted his Clean Water Act Initiative to Congress for consideration in their deliberations, a summary of which is given in Application 13.3. The 103rd Congress concluded without reaffirming the 1972 law, leaving its successors to draft revisions to the nation's primary water quality legislation.[11]

---

[8]In the next chapter, we will investigate how these effluent limits are defined and conduct an economic analysis of their effectiveness.

[9]National Commission on Water Quality (March 1976).

[10]Though this Act officially changed the title of U.S. legislation, we will follow convention and refer to this legislation as the Clean Water Act.

[11]For more on the reauthorization process, see Knopman and Smith (1993) and Adler (1993).

Application 13.3

Reauthorizing the Clean Water Act: Clinton's Clean Water Act Initiative

As part of the process to reauthorize the Clean Water Act, Congress must evaluate existing policy, consider what needs to be changed, and take appropriate action to accomplish any needed reform. The Clinton administration submitted to Congress its proposal for policy revisions in the form of a Clean Water Act Initiative. The following are the most salient aspects of the Clinton plan.

- **Controlling Nonpoint Source Pollution: Polluted Runoff**

  The EPA would be responsible for specifying various measures to control runoff, and state officials would select which of these to apply to priority waters. Implementation would take place over a five-year period, after which a review would be conducted to determine the attainment of water quality standards. For those waters not meeting the standards, additional controls would be applied over a subsequent five-year period. Enforcement procedures would be established to assure proper action. Estimated benefits are expected to include improvements in 52 percent of impaired or threatened rivers and 63 percent of impaired or threatened lakes.

- **Controlling Stormwater in Urban Areas**

  Local governments would be given more flexibility in selecting control instruments to combat the problem of runoff from city streets and parking lots. By delegating more control to local jurisdictions, high priority areas could be targeted and controlled. Expected benefits are a reduction of 75 to 80 percent of sediments, toxics, and nutrients in developing urban areas and between 15 and 25 percent in urban areas already developed. Spending for this part of the Clinton Plan is estimated at $7.0 to $10.1 billion per year. Under current policy, costs to control urban runoff are estimated at between $23.6 and $24.5 billion annually.

- **Watershed Management**

  Watershed management is an integrated policy approach to controlling all water polluting sources by consolidating and coordinating resources to achieve objectives. The Clinton plan proposes the use of incentives to encourage states' adoption of a watershed management approach. State officials would be given flexibility to customize nonpoint source programs to suit specific needs and conditions in watersheds. Reporting requirements to the federal government and grant programs would be consolidated in an effort to reduce administrative burdens. Estimated cost increases to execute this approach are between $1.0 and $1.3 billion annually.

- **Federal Financial Assistance**

  Federal funding would be continued through 2004 to support the state revolving loan fund. A fee program would also help states recover costs incurred to implement various programs under the Clean Water Act. For example, states currently spend $394 million per year managing the national system of permits. Charging fees to permittees would help states recover some of these expenditures.

- **Toxics Control**

  Existing procedures for developing water quality standards and criteria are costly and time-intensive and need to be refocused. Releases of the most persistent toxic contaminants must be limited, and the EPA needs to be given greater authority to take immediate action as necessary. Multimedia strategies are proposed along with a plan to give more flexibility to industry in selecting the most cost-effective means to reduce toxic discharges.

Application 13.3 (concluded)

- **Strengthening Enforcement**

  Enforcement procedures must be streamlined and strengthened analogously to what has been done in other environmental laws. Citizens should also be given a more significant role in pursuing enforcement action.

- **Economic Incentives**

  Effluent trading between point sources or between point and nonpoint sources would be allowed under certain circumstances patterned

after trading plans introduced in the 1990 Clean Air Act Amendments. Preliminary EPA analyses estimate a potential savings of between $0.7 billion and $7.5 billion if existing command-and-control discharge limits were replaced by such trading provisions.

Source: *EPA Journal,* "President Clinton's Clean Water Initiative," *EPA Journal* 20, no. 1–2 (Summer 1994), p. 7; Mark Luttner, "President Clinton's Clean Water Act Initiative: Costs and Benefits," *EPA Journal* 20 no. 1–2, (Summer 1994) pp. 30–31.

Policy Objectives under the Clean Water Act

In the United States as in many industrialized nations, there are many laws aimed at protecting water quality, some directed solely at ocean waters, some at drinking water, others at wetlands, and some at specific water bodies.[12] Of these, none is more comprehensive than the Clean Water Act. While its provisions are not consistently stringent for all water resources and for all polluting sources, they *do* cover both ground and surface water, and they address both point and nonpoint sources of contamination. To understand the far-reaching intent of this major act, look at Table 13.3 which lists the national goals for water quality enacted by Congress. Of these, the three considered most important are those numbered (1) through (3), referred to as the **zero discharge goal,** the **fishable-swimmable goal,** and the **no toxics in toxic amounts goal,** respectively. These are implemented primarily through the technology-based effluent limits as well as the three approaches outlined in the fourth, fifth, and sixth goals stated in the act. These approaches address funding for POTW construction, areawide waste treatment management, and research and development, respectively. The seventh goal, which calls for the development of nonpoint source pollution programs, was added with the Water Quality Act of 1987.

zero discharge goal
A U.S. objective calling for the elimination of all polluting effluents into navigable waters by 1985.

The Zero Discharge Goal

The **zero discharge goal** calls for the elimination of all polluting effluents into navigable waters by 1985. The objective was an ambitious one. It was motivated by the ineffectiveness of states' control efforts prior to 1972 and by evidence that had been accumulating about the deterioration of U.S. water resources. For example, in 1969 the buildup of oil and industrial wastes in

---

[12]In Chapter 15, we will analyze U.S. policy to protect drinking water with a particular emphasis on the Safe Drinking Water Act.

TABLE 13.3 · Objectives and Policy Goals of the U.S. Clean Water Act

---

The objective of this Act is to restore and maintain the chemical, physical, and biological integrity of the Nation's waters. In order to achieve this objective it is hereby declared that, consistent with the provisions of this Act—

(1)   it is the national goal that the discharge of pollutants into the navigable waters be eliminated by 1985;

(2)   it is the national goal that wherever attainable, an interim goal of water quality which provides for the protection and propagation of fish, shellfish, and wildlife and provides for recreation in and on the water be achieved by July 1, 1983;

(3)   it is the national policy that the discharge of toxic pollutants in toxic amounts be prohibited;

(4)   it is the national policy that Federal financial assistance be provided to construct publicly owned waste treatment works;

(5)   it is the national policy that areawide waste treatment management planning processes be developed and implemented to assure adequate control of sources of pollutants in each State;

(6)   it is the national policy that a major research and demonstration effort be made to develop technology necessary to eliminate the discharge of pollutants into the navigable waters, waters of the contiguous zone, and the oceans; and

(7)   it is the national policy that programs for the control of nonpoint sources of pollution be developed and implemented in an expeditious manner so as to enable the goals of this Act to be met through the control of both point and nonpoint sources of pollution.

Source: Clean Water Act (Federal Water Pollution Control Act) as amended, Sec.101.(a).

Ohio's Cuyahoga River caused it to literally catch fire. Two years later, a report of Ralph Nader's investigation of U.S. water quality entitled *Water Wasteland* cited incident after incident of damage to U.S. waters caused by pollution.[13] Believing there was a need for a strong government response with a fixed deadline, the zero discharge goal was written into law.

The Fishable-Swimmable Goal

fishable-swimmable goal
An interim U.S. objective requiring that surface waters be capable of supporting recreational activities and the propagation of fish and wildlife by 1983.

The "fishable-swimmable" goal was written as an interim objective to be met until the zero discharge goal could be achieved. According to this objective, surface waters were to be capable of supporting recreational activities and the propagation of fish and wildlife by 1983. Recall that the Water Quality Act of 1965 charged states with the task of establishing ambient standards for water bodies in their jurisdictions, which would effectively define water quality for the nation. What the fishable-swimmable goal attempts to do is establish a

---

[13]Zwick and Benstock (1971), as cited in Adler et al. (1993), pp. 5–6.

baseline level of water quality across all states and to set a fixed deadline of July 1, 1983, by which this baseline would be achieved.

No Toxics in Toxic Amounts

no toxics in toxic amounts goal
A U.S. goal prohibiting the release of toxic substances in toxic amounts into all water resources.

The goal on toxic contaminants is to adopt a national policy prohibiting the release of these substances in toxic amounts into all water resources. Singling out toxic pollutants was in direct response to the observation of increasing numbers of water bodies contaminated by dangerous chemicals. Throughout the 1960s and 1970s chemical use had been on the rise. The discovery of new synthetic chemicals during that period, about which little was known, added uncertainty to the potential threat. Congress reacted by explicitly prohibiting dischargers from adding dangerous amounts of toxic effluents to the nation's waters.

These three critical goals were intended to be the guiding principles for achieving and maintaining water quality throughout the United States. In truth, none of these objectives were met by the stated deadlines nor have they since been achieved, though they are still the ultimate targets of policy initiatives. Part of the problem is that they are overly ambitious, like many of the provisions in the 1972 legislation in which they were introduced. It is also the case that implementation of U.S. policy has been inordinately slow and sometimes misguided—an observation we will return to later in this chapter and in the next chapter as well.

Identifying Pollutants under the Clean Water Act

Water can be polluted at virtually any point in the hydrological cycle and by many different contaminants. The contamination can arise either deliberately through illegal waste disposal or accidently such as when oil tankers spill their cargo into the oceans—a problem discussed in Application 13.4. Many pollutants are responsible for degrading the earth's water supplies, ranging from

---

Application 13.4

The Ecological and Economic Impacts of Recent Oil Tanker Spills

All too often, the media report on another oil tanker that has run aground, spilling its hazardous cargo into surrounding ocean waters. As recently as January 1994, a barge off the coast of Puerto Rico made national headlines—this one releasing 750,000 gallons of heavy oil into the ocean and damaging some of the region's renowned beaches. The largest spill in history involved 97 million gallons when two tankers collided in 1979 off the coast of Trinidad and Tobago. In the United States, the most damaging spill occurred in March 1989 when the *Exxon Valdez* ran aground in Alaskan waters and 11 million gallons of oil poured into Prince William Sound.

In January 1993, the second of two major oil spills within five weeks of one another made world headlines. Both occurred off the coast of the European continent. The first involved a Greek oil tanker named the *Aegean Sea* that ran aground in stormy seas off the coast of Spain in December 1992. The tanker split in two and dumped 23 million gallons of oil into the northwestern port of La Coruna. Early damage reports place a dollar value of $50 million on the destruction, a magnitude expected to rise as economic losses to the area's commercial shellfish beds are assessed. The second incident involved the Liberian-registered tanker *Braer,* carrying 26 million gallons of light crude oil. The 18-year old vessel lost power just south of the Shetland Islands in the North Sea and ran aground along the rocky coastline. Preliminary damage reports estimate the cost of this accident in the hundreds of millions of dollars.

In the aftermath of these accidents, society must contend with the environmental damage and the economic losses. Birds, fish, sea otters, and other marine life are killed or found coated with oil, struggling to survive. Coastlines are contaminated as the crude oil makes its way to shore. Some of the losses have market implications, such as regional economic losses in tourism and the destruction of commercially valued fish and shellfish. Even more difficult to assess are damages based on the existence value of the ecology—the ocean itself, the marine life it supports, and natural coastlines.

No one can accurately determine the numbers of birds, fish, and sea mammals destroyed as a result of these accidents. Even if this were possible, there is the daunting problem of assigning a dollar value to ecological quality and biological life. Nonetheless, analysts attempt to assess and monetize these damages along with other market effects. In the *Exxon Valdez* case, documented damages include the carcasses of thousands of sea otters and tens of thousands of marine birds. In the first week following the accident, animal experts collected 250 dead sea otters from the despoiled waters. Another 135 live animals were found covered with crude oil and already poisoned from ingesting the contaminant. Despite scientists' efforts to clean the animals, only 55 survived. In many cases, hypothermia was the cause of death, as the coating of oil interferes with the insulation normally provided by the animals' fur. Other otters died from damage to vital organs from oil ingestion. All told, between 3,500 and 5,500 sea otters were destroyed. An estimated 30,000 sea birds also were killed— among them the nation's prized bald eagle. Including these losses, dollar damages attributable to the *Valdez* incident have been estimated in the billions of dollars. Exxon must pay $4 billion in cleanup and criminal costs, but indications are that the company's share may end up even higher.

Given such damage statistics, a common argument is that more should be done to reduce the probability of oil spills. In the past, proposals to require tankers to have double hulls have been dismissed, generally because of the high costs involved. Such preventive initiatives typically have taken a back seat to ameliorative proposals that support better management of the spill *after* it has occurred. In the United States, delays in responding to the *Valdez* incident incited national outrage that prompted Congress to pass the 1990 Oil Pollution Act. This law has been credited with helping to minimize the impact of the 1994 spill in Puerto Rico.

Sources: Tom Kenworthy, ''Puerto Rico Oil Spill Tests Law Passed After Valdez,'' *Boston Globe,* January 10, 1994; William Miller, ''Oil Spill Threatens North Sea Wildlife,'' *Boston Globe,* January 6, 1993; Associated Press, ''Updating Previous Big Spills.'' *Boston Globe,* January 6, 1993; William E. Schmidt, ''Aground, Tanker Spills Oil on Shetland,'' *New York Times,* January 6, 1993; Peter H. Raven, Linda R. Berg, and George B. Johnson. *Environment* (New York: Saunders College Publishing; Harcourt Brace Jovanovich College Publishers, 1993, pp. 15, 197).

TABLE 13.4 Major Categories of Water Pollutants

Category	Description	Examples
Plant nutrients	Substances that promote the growth of aquatic plant life; high levels of nutrients in a water body indicate enrichment or eutrophication, which is the fertilization of a water body.	Nitrate and phosphate compounds
Sediment and other suspended solids	Small particles of solid pollutants suspended in water bodies, which resist removal by conventional means.	Organic and inorganic particles, including soil and silt
Pathogens	Microorganisms that can cause disease in humans, animals, and plants.	Bacteria, viruses, parasites
Inorganic chemicals	Chemical substances of mineral origin that are not of basically carbon structure.	Acids, road salt
Heavy metals	Metallic elements with high atomic weights that tend to accumulate in the food chain.	Mercury, chromium, cadmium, arsenic, lead
Organic compounds	Synthetics and animal or plant-produced substances containing primarily carbon, hydrogen, nitrogen, or oxygen.	Pesticides, plastics, oil, gasoline, detergents
Thermal modification	Elevated temperature of water bodies caused by the discharge of heated water from industrial processes and electricity generation.	Heated water
Radioactive substances	Substances that emit ionizing radiation during decay.	Radioisotopes

Sources: U.S. Environmental Protection Agency, Office of Communications, Education, and Public Affairs, *Terms of Environment, Glossary, Abbreviation and Acronyms* (Washington, D.C., September 1992); Raven, Peter H., Linda R. Berg, and George B. Johnson, *Environment* (New York: Saunders College Publishing; Harcourt Brace Jovanovich College Publishers, 1993).

---

toxic pollutant
A contaminant which upon exposure will cause death, disease, abnormalities, or physiological malfunctions.

conventional pollutant
An identified pollutant that is well understood by scientists.

nonconventional pollutant
A default category for those pollutants not identified as toxic or conventional.

excess plant nutrients to synthetic toxics. A descriptive list of the major categories of water pollutants is given in Table 13.4.

Introduced in the Clean Water Act of 1977, three categories of pollutants are relevant to national law: **toxic pollutants, conventional pollutants,** and **nonconventional pollutants.** These classifications came about to allow for tougher controls on toxic contaminants. As we will investigate in the next chapter, these play a role in how the technology-based effluent limits are implemented.

- A **toxic pollutant** refers to a contaminant which upon exposure will cause death, disease, behavioral abnormalities, genetic mutations, or physiological malfunctions in biological organisms or their offspring.
- A **conventional pollutant** is an identified pollutant that is well understood by scientists and may be in the form of organic waste, sediment, acid, bacteria, viruses, nutrients, oil and grease, or heat.
- A **nonconventional pollutant** is the default category for those pollutants not identified as toxic or conventional.

Classifying a pollutant as toxic is based on its degradability (i.e., its ability to break down into a less complex form), persistence (i.e., how long it remains in the environment), the presence of affected organisms and their importance, and the nature and degree of the effect of the pollutant on such organisms. Among the 65 toxic compounds and families of compounds listed in the Clean Water Act are such substances as benzene, chloroform, lead, mercury, and arsenic. This list translates into 126 individual toxic substances referred to as **priority pollutants.** Conventional pollutants are to include suspended solids, those classified as biological oxygen demanding (BOD),[14] fecal coliform, and pH.[15]

Defining Water Quality: Standard-Setting under the Clean Water Act

As originally required under the Water Quality Act of 1965, surface water quality is defined by **receiving water quality standards.** These state-established standards have two distinct components:

receiving water quality standards
State-established standards defined by use designation and water quality criteria.

1. The **use designation** for the water body.
2. **Water quality criteria** to sustain the designated uses.

The **use designation** identifies the intended purposes of a water body such as for irrigation or shellfishing. The **water quality criteria** give the biological and chemical water attributes necessary to sustain or achieve these designated uses, including a *maximum concentration of pollutants* allowed.

use designation
The component of receiving water quality standards that identifies the intended purposes of a water body.

water quality criteria
The component of receiving water quality standards that gives the biological and chemical water attributes necessary to sustain or achieve designated uses.

Use Designation[16]

States are authorized to decide the designated beneficial uses for all intrastate water bodies, subject to EPA approval. Among the uses they should consider are public water supplies, propagation of fish and wildlife, recreational activities, and agricultural purposes, as shown in Table 13.5. At minimum, designated uses must be sufficient to support swimming and some fishing in order to be consistent with the national **fishable-swimmable goal.** Furthermore, adoption of waste transport or waste assimilation as a designated use is specifically prohibited. This latter ruling refers directly to the assertion that pollution dilution is not a viable substitute for waste treatment.[17]

---

[14]This refers to the amount of oxygen needed by microorganisms to decompose organic compounds.

[15]See CWA, Sec.307.(a)(1) on toxic pollutants and Sec.304.(a)(4) on conventional pollutants; and U.S. EPA, Office of Water Regulations and Standards (September 1988), p. 9.

[16]The following is drawn from 40 CFR 131.10 Designation of Uses and U.S. EPA, Office of Water (March 1994).

[17]U.S. Congress, Congressional Research Service (1972), as cited in Adler (1993), p. 159; and Van Putten and Jackson (1986).

TABLE 13.5   **Individual Beneficial Uses for Water Bodies
as Recommended by the EPA**

Use	*Description*
Aquatic life support	The waterbody provides suitable habitat for survival and reproduction of desirable fish, shellfish, and other aquatic organisms.
Shellfish harvesting	The waterbody supports a population of shellfish free from toxicants and pathogens that could pose a human health risk to consumers.
Fish consumption	The waterbody supports a population of fish free from contamination that could pose a human health risk to consumers.
Drinking water supply	The waterbody can supply safe drinking water with conventional treatment.
Primary contact recreation—swimming	People can swim in the waterbody without risk of adverse human health effects (such as catching waterborne diseases from raw sewage contamination).
Secondary contact— recreation	People can perform activities on the water (such as canoeing) without risk of adverse human health effects from occasional contact with the water.
Agriculture	The water quality is suitable for irrigating fields or watering livestock.

Source: U.S. Environmental Protection Agency, Office of Water, *National Water Quality Inventory: 1992 Report to Congress* (Washington, D.C., March 1994), p. ES-3.

use-support status
A classification of a water body based on a state's assessment of its present condition relative to what is needed to maintain its designated uses.

Use-Support Status.   Periodically, state authorities must determine the **use-support status** of a water body by assessing its present condition and comparing it with what is needed to maintain its designated uses. One of five classifications is assigned to characterize use-support status of surface waters. As described in Table 13.6, these classifications are: (1) **fully supporting;** (2) **threatened;** (3) **partially supporting;** (4) **not supporting;** and (5) **not attainable.** States' findings on use-support status are submitted to the EPA, analyzed, and reported to Congress as part of a biennial National Water Quality Inventory required by the Clean Water Act.

Determining Use-Support Status: Water Quality Assessment.   Procedures to determine the use-support status of a water body are neither universal nor highly developed in all cases. As the knowledge base and data collection methods improve, more consistent evaluations should be forthcoming. At present, two types of surface water quality assessment data are collected: **evaluative data** and **monitoring data.** Of the two, **evaluative data** are the less scientific—typically collected without the use of quality controls or site-specific sampling. Examples include reports of fish kills associated with pollution, such as the data shown in Table 13.7, and information obtained from surveying fisheries officials. **Monitoring data** are obtained under more carefully

TABLE 13.6   Classifications of Use Support for U.S. Surface Water Quality

Use Support Level	Water Quality Condition	Definition
Fully supporting	Good	Water quality meets designated use criteria.
Threatened	Good	Water quality supports designated uses now but may not in the future unless action is taken.
Partially supporting	Fair (impaired)	Water quality fails to meet designated use criteria at times.
Not supporting	Poor (impaired)	Water quality frequently fails to meet designated use criteria.
Not attainable	Poor	The state has performed a use-attainability study and documented that use support is not achievable due to natural conditions or human activity that cannot be reversed without imposing widespread economic and social impacts.

Source: U.S. Environmental Protection Agency, Office of Water, *National Water Quality Inventory: 1992 Report to Congress* (Washington, D.C., March 1994), Table ES-1, p. ES-3.

TABLE 13.7   Evaluative Data on U.S. Fish Kills for 1990–1992 (43 states reporting)

Number of Fish Kills by Cause

Toxic pollutants	248 (15.3%)
Conventional pollutants	308 (19.0%)
Habitat modification	28 (1.7%)
Unspecified/unknown pollutants	369 (22.8%)
Natural causes	586 (36.2%)
Total number of fish kills	1,620*

Number of Fish Killed by Cause

Toxic pollutants	2,411,458 (27.0%)
Conventional pollutants	1,074,325 (12.0%)
Habitat modification	153,194 (1.7%)
Unspecified/unknown pollutants	1,259,614 (14.1%)
Natural causes	4,047,998 (45.2%)
Total number of fish killed	8,946,589

*Total does not equal sum of reported categories due to incomplete State data in some categories.

Source: U.S. Environmental Protection Agency, Office of Water, *National Water Quality Inventory: 1992 Report to Congress* (Washington, D.C., March 1994), Table E-7, pp. E-10–E-11.

controlled conditions. They may be gathered over the long run from sampling stations positioned near major dischargers or be collected at a point in time using intensive surveys to assess a specific area or study a particular condition. Because of the importance of sound water quality assessment, efforts are ongoing to improve procedures and data collection methods. One recent advance is the Environmental Monitoring and Assessment Program (EMAP) initiated by the EPA. The objective of the program is to systematically determine the quality of natural resources, including surface waters, using an integrated approach.[18] Application 13.5 discusses how this program is being implemented to improve the assessment of U.S. wetlands.

Application 13.5

Water Quality Assessment:
The EPA's EMAP-Wetlands Program

Scientists and environmentalists are keenly aware of the benefits of maintaining and preserving U.S. wetlands. Estimates claim that nearly 80 percent of our coastal fisheries and about one-third of endangered species depend upon these unusual water-dependent systems. The unique biological environment that characterizes wetlands supports the habitats of many species of waterfowl, reptiles, and mammals. Beyond these biological attributes, wetlands also act as a filtering system that naturally reduces the contamination of surface water and groundwater. Yet since the 1950s, the United States has witnessed an alarming loss of wetlands acreage blamed on population movements, economic development, and coastal area construction. Most estimates place the loss at nearly 50 percent.

Because so many of these regions have already been destroyed, public officials are trying to protect those that remain. To accomplish this, scientists must develop a well-defined procedure to assess the baseline conditions of wetlands, identify existing threats, and monitor changes over time. Responding to this need, the EPA has launched a new initiative called the Environmental Monitoring and Assessment Program for Wetlands (EMAP-Wetlands).* Through this program, the EPA plans to provide a quantitative assessment of *current* conditions and *long-term* trends on both a regional and national scale. The agency's objectives for EMAP-Wetlands are as follows.

- To quantify the status of wetlands through measures of ecological condition and potential threats.
- To monitor changes over time in condition, hydrology, contamination, and other factors affecting or stressing wetlands.
- To identify possible causes of degradation or improvement.
- To assess the effectiveness of policy initiatives and other control actions.
- To provide annual statistical data and regular interpretive assessments of the status and trends of wetlands.

To achieve these goals, the program must develop two critical parameters of environmental assessment: (1) good sampling strategies; and (2) a set of valid indicators. Eventually, the EMAP program plans to field-sample 3,200 wetlands and present reporting data on eight types of wetlands. At the outset, the following eight indicators will be measured:

1. Wetlands extent and type diversity.
2. Landscape indicators such as ratios of open water to vegetation.
3. Hydrological indicators such as water level and flood duration.
4. Sediment characteristics such as sedimentation rates and organic matter content.

---

[18]U.S. EPA, Office of Water (April 1992a), p. 8 and Chapter 11.

Application 13.5 (concluded)

5. Composition and abundance of vegetation diversity.

6. Composition and abundance of the vertebrate and macro-invertebrate community.

7. Chemical contaminants in sediments.

8. Nutrient content in sediments or vegetative tissues.

Through a series of pilot studies, the EMAP program calls for field testing on these indicators to assure their capacity to assess wetlands conditions.

Ultimately, the agency anticipates that the data collected will be invaluable to the EPA and Congress in making decisions on policy and wetlands management. In addition, these data can help state and federal decision-makers establish designated use categories and biocriteria as well as identify those wetlands in need of special regulatory controls. If successful, EMAP-Wetlands should contribute to the goal of preserving and protecting this valuable and threatened natural resource.

*Analogous applications of EMAP are also under development for surface waters, forests, near-coastal waters, agricultural lands, arid lands, and the Great Lakes.

Sources: Council on Environmental Quality, *Environmental Quality, 23rd Annual Report* (Washington, D.C.: U.S. Government Printing Office, January 1993), pp. 230–31, 235–36; U.S. Environmental Protection Agency, Office of Water, *National Water Quality Inventory: 1990 Report to Congress* (Washington, D.C., April 1992a), pp. 74–75.

Water Quality Criteria[19]

numeric criteria
Stated as concentrations of chemicals or pollutants allowed in water expressed in micrograms per liter (μg/L).

To assure that designated uses are achieved and maintained, states must either establish **water quality criteria** subject to EPA approval or adopt criteria set by the EPA itself. The EPA is responsible for developing and publishing criteria that reflect the most current scientific knowledge on all identifiable effects of pollution on health, aquatic life, and welfare. It must also publish information on the factors needed to restore and sustain the integrity of surface and ground waters. These criteria are pollutant-specific and may be expressed as **numeric criteria, narrative criteria,** or **biocriteria.**

narrative criteria
Expressed in concise, qualitative statements.

- **Numeric criteria** are stated as concentrations of chemicals or pollutants allowed in water expressed in micrograms per liter (μg/L).

- **Narrative criteria** are expressed in concise, qualitative statements, typically in a ''free from'' format, such as ''free from toxic pollutants in toxic amounts.''

biocriteria
Expressed in broad statements about the condition of an aquatic system, typically based upon the findings of biomonitoring procedures.

- **Biocriteria** are expressed as broad statements about the overall condition of an aquatic system, typically based upon the findings of biomonitoring procedures.

Narrative criteria and biocriteria are to be used only if numeric criteria cannot be established or as supplements to numeric criteria. In any case, all criteria must have a sound scientific basis, and if there are multiple uses designated

---

[19]The following is drawn from 40 CFR 131.11 Criteria; CWA, Sec.303; and U.S. EPA, Office of Water Regulations and Standards (September 1988), pp. 8–11.

for a water body, the criteria must be set to support the most sensitive use. The rules are more stringent for toxics. As a result of a 1976 Consent Decree between the EPA and the Natural Resources Defense Council and later mandated in the Clean Water Act of 1977, numeric criteria for the 126 priority toxics were to be established by the end of 1979.[20]

Analysis of Receiving Water Quality Standards

The **receiving water quality standards** are a critical element of U.S. water quality policy because they are linked directly to the nation's objectives, particularly the fishable-swimmable goal. However, the process of establishing these standards has been problematic as has their reliance on the effluent limitations for implementation.

Administrative Problems in Establishing Water Quality Criteria

A major source of contention is the poor performance of both the EPA and state officials in carrying out the tasks needed to define water quality criteria, particularly those for toxics. The EPA has been criticized for not having developed all the criteria documents needed to support states' use designations.[21] Because of this and other related problems, states have missed important deadlines. A recent report by the U.S. General Accounting Office (GAO) validates these assertions. According to this report, as of July 1991 the agency had issued only 108 human health criteria documents and 26 aquatic life criteria documents for the 126 priority pollutants. Hence, some toxic contaminants still lack numeric criteria despite the 1979 statutory deadline. For nonpriority pollutants, 9 human health and 10 aquatic life criteria documents have been published—most issued in the early to mid-1980s. Although revision of criteria is required under the Clean Water Act, only about one-third of the human health criteria and none of the aquatic life criteria have been updated. According to the EPA, the delay is due mainly to insufficient resources to develop the data and to conduct the analyses. Consequently, the agency has had to rely on results obtained from or published by the scientific community, which lengthens the process considerably.[22]

These long delays have taken their toll on states' participation in the standard-setting process. As of March 1991, only 24 states were in complete compliance with the ruling calling for state adoption of numeric criteria for toxics. According to EPA regional and state officials, part of the hesitancy is that some states question the scientific validity of the data or the analyses that

---

[20]Adler et al. (1993), p. 121.

[21]In Chapter 10, we discussed how criteria documents present a synthesis of available scientific evidence on the properties and effects of any known or suspected pollutant.

[22]U.S. GAO (July 1991), p. 29.

form the basis of the criteria documents. There is also concern about the out-dated information being used by the agency. Some states have indicated that effluent limits based on defined criteria are far too stringent, with some more restrictive than states' drinking water standards for the same pollutants. In other instances, the limits are set below detectable levels, complicating states' compliance efforts.[23]

There is also dispute about how federal policy identifies the most dangerous water pollutants. Government officials at both the EPA and at the state level argue that the 126 identified priority pollutants do not constitute a comprehensive list of the most dangerous toxic contaminants. For example, in 1989 a Connecticut official testified before a Senate Committee that many of the pollutants known to cause toxic effects on aquatic life in Connecticut waters were not priority pollutants. The EPA acknowledges that criteria are needed for many nonpriority pollutants that potentially cause serious health effects. Hence, it may be that the law is overregulating priority pollutants at the direct expense of underregulating more common and perhaps more dangerous contaminants.[24]

Absence of Benefit-Cost Analysis in Setting the Standards

When the states were called upon to establish receiving water quality standards, the law allowed them to specify different standards for each interstate water body within their jurisdictions. It was implied that they could use an evaluation of benefits and costs in setting these standards, but they were *not* required by law to do so.[25] Of course, the use designation had to be consistent with national goals, indicating at minimum a water quality level to support fishing and swimming—a goal that was solely benefit-based with no consideration given for economic costs.

Even in states' reports to the EPA on use-support status, benefit-cost assessment is not being done, even though the law calls for such an analysis. According to the Clean Water Act, states are called upon to submit a biennial water quality report in which, among other things, they must identify waters that have met the fishable-swimmable use designation. This report is supposed to include estimates of the associated costs and benefits of that achievement. The reference in the law is as follows:

> Each State shall prepare and submit . . . a report which shall include . . . an estimate of (i) the environmental impact, (ii) the economic and social costs necessary to achieve the objective of this Act in such State, (iii) the economic and social benefits of such achievement, and (iv) an estimate of the date of such achievement.

---

[23]U.S. GAO (July 1991), pp. 30–31.

[24]U.S. GAO (July 1991), pp. 17, 29. For a detailed discussion of the inadequacies in the water quality standard-setting process, see Adler et al. (1993), Chapter 4.

[25]Freeman (1990), p. 102.

Despite this requirement, most states report only physical, chemical, and biological changes in water quality and estimated changes in physical loadings from point and nonpoint sources. Only a few use models that translate these data into economic activities such as commercial fishing, and even fewer attempt to monetize the results. According to the most recent report to Congress,

> None of the States and Territories reporting on their water quality programs attempted to describe the full extent of economic benefits and costs associated with progress made in improving and protecting water quality conditions.[26]

Most information on the benefits and costs of water quality improvements is limited to the results of research studies focusing on a single location or a specific water body. A case in point is an academic study of the benefits of water quality improvements to marine sportfishing along the East coast. For a closer look at this study, which is being supported by the EPA, see Application 13.6. Efforts such as these may advance researchers' understanding about how best to measure water quality benefits on a comprehensive scale. In the interim, state officials are a long way from assessing the benefit categories recommended by the EPA, which are shown in Table 13.8. Even if data collection and assessment methods improve, there is currently no explicit mandate to assure that the benefit-cost decision rule is used to define water quality standards. Hence, there is no assurance that water pollution abatement will be set at an efficient level.

Application 13.6

How Much Is Cleaner Water Worth to Marine Sportfishing?

One of the more difficult problems in environmental policy analysis is estimating the incremental benefits to society of regulatory changes. The motivation of sound benefit estimation is more than academic. When policy-makers evaluate a legislative revision, they need to understand whether society gains as much as it has to give up. Tougher laws add regulatory costs of implementation, monitoring, and enforcement—costs that are passed on to society as higher product prices and increased taxes. In addition, there are implicit costs that society must bear. These costs are justified if society gains at the margin by the same amount, but measuring these associated benefits is easier said than

done. Nonetheless, its importance to policy development motivates private and public researchers to look for better and more accurate methods to estimate environmental benefits.

Most research studies focus on a particular water body or region as the context of their analysis. Such is the case for a University of Maryland study supported by the EPA, which is analyzing the coastal region that extends from New York to south Florida (excluding the Florida Keys). The selection is motivated by the economic activity being studied—marine sportfishing. Some 80 percent of all East coast marine sportfishing takes place in the area targeted by the study. Furthermore, the region

---

[26]U.S. EPA, Office of Water (March 1994), p. 18.

Application 13.6 (concluded)

is one where there are active pollution control initiatives in place as well as management plans for recreational fisheries.

The objective of this university research is to develop a database and a procedure that can be used to estimate the economic value of two related factors: (1) access to marine sportfishing; and (2) changes in the "catch rate" of various species, where catch rate is the average number of fish caught per fishing trip at a given site. The link between these two factors and economic benefits is a logical one. Water quality policy reform can improve the catch rate, which will in turn affect fishermen's decisions about where to fish, what species they fish for, whether they fish from the shore or from a boat (called the "fishing mode"), and even how often they go fishing. By measuring these changes in fishermen's behavior, researchers can make the link to a monetized benefit measure of improved fishing conditions that can be achieved through tougher pollution controls.

To determine catch rates, the analysis uses survey data collected by the National Marine Fisheries Service. Three broad categories of catch rates are defined by type of fish: big game fish (e.g., marlin and tuna), small game fish (e.g., bluefish and mackerel), and bottom fish (e.g., snapper and

grouper). Thus far, three different benefit estimates have been calculated:

1. A 20 percent increase in the catch rate of small game fish for both fishing modes at all sites would increase the average benefit of each fishing trip by $0.33.

2. A 20 percent increase in the catch rate of bottom fish by boat would increase the average benefit per trip by $1.27.

3. A 20 percent increase in the catch rate of large game fish would yield an increase in benefits of $1.56 per trip.

By publishing a detailed report of their findings, the university hopes their work will lay the ground work for other regional analyses. In addition, the model developed by the research will be capable of assessing interregional impacts, such as how changes in fishing conditions in Florida can affect fishing activity in the Chesapeake Bay region. Through efforts such as these, researchers can learn more about how best to measure environmental benefits, which in turn can help policy-makers make better and more informed decisions.

Source: U.S. Environmental Protection Agency, Office of Water, *National Water Quality Inventory: 1990 Report to Congress* (Washington, D.C., April 1992a), p. 164.

Lack of Consistency with the Technology-Based Effluent Limitations

Another problem with the standard-setting procedure relates to the use of federally mandated effluent limitations to achieve the states' receiving water quality standards. The source of contention is that the link between the water quality standards and the effluent limitations is blurred at best. Why? Because each is motivated differently—one by water usage and the other by technology. Since the effluent limits are technology-based, they are motivated by what is practical or feasible rather than by benefit-cost analysis or environmental criteria. The intent was to avoid the problem states had encountered of estimating the relationship between a predetermined water quality level and the discharge reduction needed to achieve it. However, it is precisely this relationship that is needed to map the effluent limits to the water quality standards.

TABLE 13.8   Classification of Economic Benefits of Water Quality Recommended by the EPA

Intrinsic Benefits
No current use by the individual:

Community benefits	Biocentric satisfaction of knowing that an ecological community is sustained for its own sake.
Existence benefits	Vicarious enjoyment from the knowledge that others are using the resource. Stewardship interest in providing an opportunity for others to use the resource in the future.

Potential future use by the individual:

Option benefits	Interest in securing an option to participate in an activity or use the resource at some point in the future.

Current Benefits
Indirect use by the individual:

Aesthetic benefits	Conditions enhance the characteristics of current adjoining fixed amenities, such as lakeside property.
Recreational benefits	Conditions enhance the characteristics of current adjoining transitory activities, such as hiking and photography.
Structural ecosystem benefits	Conditions maintain the functional ecosystem processes, such as stable climate and purification of land, air, and water.

Direct use by the individual:

Recreational benefits	Conditions enhance the characteristics of current water-contact activities, such as boating, swimming, and fishing.
Commercial benefits	Conditions enhance the characteristics of current production processes and activities.

Other uses:

Extractive commercial uses	Production processes where water is a medium for other goods (e.g., commercial fishing, medical industries).
Commercial navigation	Examples include dams, canals, and ports.
Agricultural irrigation	Water used as an input to production of crops.
Industrial processes	Water itself is used as an input to production (e.g., processing, cooling, and steam generation).
Municipal water	Water used for drinking, washing, and fire protection.

Source: Adapted from Research Triangle Institute, *Benefit-Cost Assessment Handbook for Water Programs, Volume 1,* prepared for the EPA, Economic Analysis Division, April 1993, Figure 3-1, p. 3-2 as cited in U.S. Environmental Protection Agency, Office of Water, *National Water Quality Inventory: 1990 Report to Congress* (Washington, D.C., April 1992a), Figure 12-1, p. 167.

Since the technological limits are applied uniformly within defined groups of point sources, they do not account for varying conditions across water bodies or for the different uses of water bodies designated by states. So, even if all dischargers met the effluent limits, there is no guarantee that water quality as the states have defined it would be achieved. In fact, it is precisely because of this possibility that the law requires states to identify those waters for which the effluent limitations are insufficient. Officially, these waters are to be labeled as "water quality limited" and placed in a priority ranking. More stringent controls must then be established, called **total maximum daily loads,** which specify the largest amount of pollution that can be received without violating the standards.[27] These additional rulings are necessary because the policy instrument—the effluent limitation—is not properly linked to the objective—the water quality standard.

To make matters worse, states have not been complying with this aspect of the law. According to a recent study of one EPA region, state officials do not give the matter priority because there is no statutory deadline for setting maximum daily loads. Other contributing factors are EPA delays in establishing regulations to define maximum loads and poor management procedures in tracking the development and implementation of these modified limits. As of 1989, maximum daily loads had been completed for only 1 of the 602 water quality limited segments in the region under study. A less dramatic but no less discouraging performance was observed in the New York region, where this task had been executed for only 4 of the area's 168 water quality limited segments.[28]

Apparently, many different factors are responsible for the observed delays and inconsistencies in the standard-setting process. Yet, virtually all of these are characteristic of a command-and-control approach to environmental policy. The Clean Water Act lacks incentive mechanisms to encourage support and compliance from state governments and from the polluting sources themselves. Such an approach must instead rely on layers of regulations that become difficult to implement, monitor, and enforce. States have little incentive to adopt criteria that they neither believe in nor are forced to accept. The EPA lacks the resources to carry out the letter of the law as it is written. The result? A process on which so much of the Clean Water Act depends has proceeded at a snail's pace, and the nation's progress toward achieving water quality has been delayed.

A Benefit-Cost Analysis of U.S. Water Quality Control Policy

Water quality is a goal about which there is little debate—at least from a qualitative perspective. Everyone wants to preserve and maintain clean rivers and lakes and to protect the earth's oceans from indiscriminate dumping. The issue is not a zero-one option of whether or not such goals are worth pursuing, but rather to determine the *extent* to which water contamination should be

---

[27]See CWA, Sec.303.(d)(1)(A) and U.S. GAO (January 1989), pp. 2–3.

[28]The study was conducted by the U.S. GAO focusing on EPA's Region X (i.e., the region including the states of Oregon, Washington, Idaho, and Alaska). See U.S. GAO (January 1989), pp. 2–4.

TABLE 13.9   Water Quality Trends 1972–1982

Type of Water Body	Improving (%)	Unchanged (%)	Declining (%)	Not known (%)
Streams (miles)	11	67	2	20
Lakes and reservoirs (acres)	2	62	10	26
Estuaries (square miles)	22	74	3	1

Source: Reprinted with permission of The Conservation Foundation, *State of the Environment: An Assessment at Mid-Decade* (Washington, D.C.: The Conservation Foundation, 1984), reported in Freeman (1990), Table 4-6, p. 118.

controlled. This assertion boils down to the tough issue of defining what is meant by ''water quality'' from a policy perspective. As is always the case in environmental policy, the question is, ''How clean is clean?'' Once this fundamental question has been addressed, a secondary issue is to evaluate *how* this goal, however defined, is to be achieved. Both issues are complex, but they can be addressed with considerable objectivity using the analytical tool of benefit-cost analysis. Using this decision rule, water control policy can be evaluated using the efficiency criterion. The task is difficult to execute in practice because of the usual measurement problems that plague an assessment of environmental benefits and costs. Nonetheless, relying on the careful work of well-respected environmental economists, we can examine the evidence and draw some qualitative, albeit guarded, conclusions.

Benefit-Cost Analysis of the FWPCA of 1972

The enactment of the Federal Water Pollution Control Act (FWPCA) of 1972 marked a major shift in U.S. policy toward stronger controls administered by the federal government. National objectives were established, and the EPA was authorized to set and implement technology-based effluent limits to achieve these goals. Because of its importance in the development of U.S. policy, the FWPCA has been a common subject of analysis—not all of it with favorable results. Part of the criticism is that overall water quality did not improve significantly as a result of the 1972 reforms. In fact, according to an assessment conducted by The Conservation Foundation, the majority of the nation's streams, lakes, and estuaries showed no change in water quality over the 1972 to 1982 period, as Table 13.9 indicates.[29] Similar findings were reported by states for the same period.[30] In any case, a review of water quality

---

[29] The Conservation Foundation (1984), pp. 106–08.

[30] However, according to the Council on Environmental Quality, these data do indicate some measure of accomplishment given an 11 percent growth in population over the period as well as a marked increase in water use. State trend data are given in the Association of State and Interstate Water Pollution Control Administrators in cooperation with the U.S. EPA, *America's Clean Water: The States' Evaluation of Progress, 1972–1982* (Washington, D.C., 1984) as cited in Council on Environmental Quality (1989), pp. 34–35.

trend data is insufficient evidence to evaluate the effectiveness of federal policy. First, it is not valid to assume that an observed favorable trend is entirely the result of regulatory controls. Water quality is influenced by other factors, such as use intensity, population growth, and industrial development. Secondly, even if the trend data *were* indicative of improved water quality and could be attributed to policy initiatives, these improvements or benefits must be considered along with the costs society incurred to achieve them.

While a number of studies have estimated and monetized the benefits of improved water quality, these analyses typically focus on a specific water body or a particular region. Furthermore, some examine only a single aspect of water quality such as recreational use or the value to the commercial fishing industry.[31] Only one analysis has been done which attempts to synthesize the findings of existing research to arrive at a comprehensive benefit measure of improved water quality attributable to the FWPCA of 1972. This landmark study was conducted by A. Myrick Freeman III in 1979 for the Council on Environmental Quality and later revised in 1982.[32] An overview of Freeman's findings follows, with all values expressed in 1984 dollars.

Estimating the Benefits of the FWPCA of 1972.   To arrive at a dollar value of the total social benefits (*TSB*) associated with the FWPCA of 1972, Freeman surveyed the findings of about 20 existing empirical studies. As shown in Table 13.10, he classified the benefit measures into four categories: (1) recreational use, (2) nonuser benefits, (3) commercial uses, and (4) diversionary uses. Adjusting for differences in price levels, Freeman arrived at an estimate of annual *TSB* for 1985 of between $5.7 and $27.7 billion, with a point estimate of $14.0 billion. This magnitude can be interpreted as the monetized annual benefit of achieving the effluent limitations mandated by the 1972 legislation.

Estimating the Costs of the FWPCA of 1972.   To estimate the comparable costs associated with the FWPCA, Freeman examined two sets of estimates—one provided by the Council on Environmental Quality (CEQ) and one by the EPA. The CEQ data use EPA estimates of the engineering costs of complying with the 1972 Act absent the additional spending associated with implementing the 1977 Amendments. According to these data, the average annual costs over the 1979 to 1988 period are about $23.2 billion. The EPA data are based upon legislative requirements as of December 1982 and therefore include *some* of the costs incurred by the 1977 revisions. These estimates show that the average annual costs are $30.8 billion. Freeman drew from both

---

[31]For a recent survey of some of these studies, see Cropper and Oates (1992), particularly Section IV.

[32]Freeman (December 1979) and (1982).

TABLE 13.10   Monetized Annual Benefits of the FWPCA as of 1985
($1984 billions)

Category	Range	Point Estimate
Recreation		
Freshwater fishing	$0.7– 2.1	$ 1.5
Marine sports fishing	0.1– 4.5	1.5
Boating	1.5– 3.0	2.2
Swimming	0.3– 3.0	1.5
Waterfowl hunting	0.0– 0.5	0.2
Subtotal	$2.6–13.1	$ 6.9
Nonuser benefits		
Aesthetics, ecology, property value	$0.7– 5.9	$ 1.8
Commercial fisheries	$0.6– 1.8	$ 1.2
Diversionary Uses		
Drinking water/health	$0.0– 3.0	$ 1.5
Municipal treatment costs	0.9– 1.8	1.3
Households	0.2– 0.7	0.4
Industrial supplies	0.7– 1.4	0.9
Subtotal	$1.8– 6.9	$ 4.1
Total	$5.7–27.7	$14.0

Note: Estimates are originally presented in Freeman (1982) in 1978 dollars. They have been converted to 1984 dollars using the implicit price deflator.

Source: A. Myrick Freeman III, *Air and Water Pollution Control: A Benefit-Cost Assessment* (New York: John Wiley & Sons, 1982), Table 8-3, p. 161 and Table 9-1, p. 170. Reprinted by permission of John Wiley & Sons, Inc.

sources and arrived at an annual estimate of total social costs (*TSC*) in 1985 within a range of $25 to $30 billion. Table 13.11 gives more detail on these cost estimations.

Benefit-Cost Comparison.   Now consider a comparison of Freeman's estimates, assuming they reflect the true benefits and costs to society. The range of values for *TSB* is between $5.7 and $27.7 billion, while the comparable *TSC* estimate is between $25.0 and $30 billion. Notice that the two sets of values overlap by only a small amount. We also can examine the relationship between Freeman's *point* estimate of *TSB,* $14.0 billion, and the midpoint of his *TSC* estimate range, $27.5 billion. In this case, the *TSC* of water quality control as of 1985 exceeds the associated *TSB*—a finding that indicates an inefficient outcome. This result is illustrated in Figure 13.2(a). Notice that at the abatement level associated with U.S. regulations as of 1985, A_{1985}, *TSC* is higher than *TSB*. Also note that A_{1985} is above the efficient level, A_e, where net benefits are maximized.

TABLE 13.11   Annual Costs of the FWPCA ($1984 Billions)

Annual Cost Estimate by Freeman, 1985*
Total $25.0–30.0

Annual Cost Estimates by the Council on Environmental Quality (CEQ)†

	Operation, Maintenance	Capital Costs‡	Total
1979			
Public	$ 2.3	$ 5.9	$ 8.2
Private	5.1	4.1	9.2
Total	$ 7.4	$10.0	$17.4
1988			
Public	$ 4.5	$13.7	$18.2
Private	7.8	7.4	15.2
Total	$12.3	$21.1	$33.4
1979–1988 (average)			
Public	$ 3.4	$ 8.1	$11.5
Private	6.1	5.5	11.7
Total	$ 9.5	$13.6	$23.2

Annual Cost Estimates by the EPA§

1981			
Public			$17.7
Private			7.5
Total			$25.2
1981–1990 (average)			
Public			$21.9
Private			8.9
Total			$30.8

*Source: A. Myrick Freeman III, *Air and Water Pollution Control: A Benefit-Cost Assessment* (New York: John Wiley & Sons, 1982), as cited in Freeman (1990), pp. 125–26.

†Source: Council on Environmental Quality, *Environmental Quality—1980* (Washington, D.C.: U.S. Government Printing Office, 1980b), as cited in Freeman (1990), Table 4-9, p. 125.

‡Interest on accumulated investment and depreciation.

§Source: U.S. Environmental Protection Agency, *Final Report: The Cost of Clean Air and Water* (Washington, D.C.: U.S. EPA, 1984a), Table 3, pp. 15–16, as cited in Freeman (1990), Table 4-10, p. 126.

The comparable marginal analysis is shown in Figure 13.2(b), where A_e corresponds to the point where the marginal social cost (*MSC*) curve intersects the marginal social benefit (*MSB*) curve. Notice that at A_{1985}, *MSC* exceeds *MSB*, and that this abatement level is to the *right* of A_e.

If Freeman's estimates are reasonable, the findings suggest that as of 1985, the United States was overregulating water quality. The marginal benefit to society was not justified by the marginal cost incurred, and too many resources were allocated to water quality controls. This result is symptomatic of any number of distinct problems. It could be that some or all of the water quality standards were too stringent, forcing an abatement level that was too expensive for the benefits received. Alternatively, the standards could have been set

FIGURE 13.2

Benefit-cost analysis
of the U.S. FWPCA
of 1972 as of 1985

(a) Total social benefits and total social costs

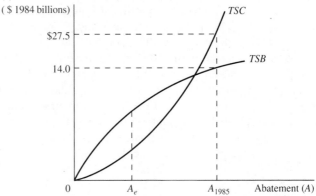

This model is based upon Freeman's estimates of the total social costs (*TSC*) and total social benefits (*TSB*) as of 1985 based on regulations given in the FWPCA of 1972. As the diagram shows, *TSC* > *TSB* in 1985, and abatement level A_{1985} is above the efficient level, A_e, where net benefits are maximized.

(b) Marginal social benefit and marginal social cost

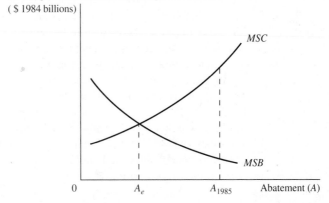

This model shows the comparable relationships to Figure 13.2(a) using marginal analysis. Notice that A_e in this depiction corresponds to the point where the marginal social cost (*MSC*) curve intersects the marginal social benefit (*MSB*) curve. In 1985 at abatement level A_{1985}, *MSC* > *MSB*. Notice that A_{1985} is to the right of A_e, suggesting that U.S. policy in effect at that time overregulated water quality.

Source: Values depicted based upon A. Myrick Freeman III, *Air and Water Pollution Control: A Benefit-Cost Assessment* (New York: John Wiley & Sons, 1982), Table 8–3, p. 161 and Table 9–1, p. 170. Reprinted by permission of John Wiley & Sons, Inc.

appropriately but the instruments used to implement them such as the permitting system or the effluent limits were not cost-effective.[33]

As in any empirical study, there are always caveats attached to the conclusions. In this case, the major drawbacks of Freeman's findings are associated with data limitations and the complications of synthesizing studies that are not directly comparable. In a recent publication, Freeman (1990) points out several reservations about the values used to support his conclusions. First, the EPA's cost estimates include expenditures associated with the added 1977 controls on toxics, though the associated gains are not captured in the benefit estimate. Second, he argues that these cost estimates suffer from the usual biases associated with the engineering approach.[34] Freeman suggests that the cost values are likely inflated, since they do not allow for the potential of more cost-effective decisions at the firm level or cost savings due to technological advances over time.

An independent commentary on Freeman's work argues further that the benefit estimate would likely be higher if existence and option values were included.[35] Although Freeman *does* attempt to include some valuation of ''nonuser benefits,'' the estimate for this category is highly uncertain because of the methods used in the underlying studies upon which it is based.[36] (Look back at Table 13.10. Notice that although the estimated range for this category is within a range of $0.7 billion and $5.9 billion, Freeman uses a conservative point estimate of $1.8 billion.) Recognizing the potential inaccuracies while defending his overall conclusion, Freeman argues that, even with a 20 percent *upward* adjustment to the benefit estimate and a 20 percent *reduction* in the cost values, the data still suggest an unfavorable outcome.[37]

Freeman's work, though not without limitations, is a valuable analysis in that it draws attention to the potential inefficiencies of the 1972 legislation. Taken in the context of the series of revisions to this legislation, we need to consider whether these post-1972 reforms accomplished much in terms of improving the efficiency of federal water quality policy. To examine this question, we next consider the benefits and costs of U.S. water pollution policy as of a more current period.

---

[33]If this were the case, then the cost estimates lie *above* the true *MSC* curve. We will analyze the permitting system and the effluent limits in more detail in the next chapter.

[34]Recall from Chapter 8 some of the reservations about using this approach, including uncertainty about price movements, availability of raw materials, and energy costs in future time periods.

[35]Howe (1991), p. 15.

[36]Freeman (December 1979), pp. 161–62.

[37]Freeman also discusses the difficulty of attempting to assess the overall benefit of water quality control given the heterogeneity of surface waters and the sensitivity of water quality indicators to sampling locations and time. He further points out that the benefit estimates used in his analysis measure only the gains from controls on point sources even though many bodies of water are seriously impaired by nonpoint sources (Freeman, December 1979, pp. ix–x).

Advances in Benefit-Cost Analysis of U.S. Water Quality Policy

An Updated Benefit Estimate of U.S. Water Quality Controls.   Assessing benefits continues to be the most difficult task in benefit-cost analysis of environmental policy. For water resources, the problem is exacerbated by the inadequate monitoring framework in the United States. Nonetheless, there have been some advances in research methods used to estimate environmental benefits. One in particular is the use of the Contingent Valuation Method (CVM), touted for its ability to capture existence value as well as user value of environmental resources.

A recent study conducted by researchers at Resources for the Future in Washington, D.C., uses the CVM approach to estimate the value of water quality improvements associated with U.S. regulations.[38] The researchers, Carson and Mitchell, surveyed individuals across the United States in 1983, asking them to assign a dollar value to the minimum levels of water quality specified in the Clean Water Act, that is, for boatable, fishable, and swimmable surface waters. As indicated in Table 13.12, usable responses were used to form a preliminary nationwide estimate of the total social benefits (*TSB*) of water quality at $29.2 billion per year. All values are expressed in 1990 dollars. The authors then combine this estimate with elements of Freeman's earlier findings that were not captured by their survey and arrive at an adjusted value of $39.1 billion. Notice that this estimate is considerably higher than what Freeman found, which is $20.1 billion in 1990 dollars when adjusted for inflation and number of households.[39] A final modification is made to adjust for changes in the number of households, the general price level, real income, and attitudes about water pollution up to 1990. Their final estimate of *TSB* is $46.7 billion per year as of 1990. This magnitude represents the value assigned to improvements in water quality from a baseline of nonboatable surface water quality to swimmable surface water quality.

Comparable Costs of U.S. Water Quality Controls.   Cost estimates are available from a number of government sources. Carson and Mitchell cite the most recently available cost data from the Department of Commerce, which indicate that 1988 annual costs of U.S. water quality control are approximately $37.3 billion expressed in 1990 dollars.[40] Another comprehensive data source cited is the EPA, whose estimates of annualized costs of water quality control

---

[38]See Carson and Mitchell (1993). For more detail on the authors' use of the Contingent Valuation Method, see Mitchell and Carson (1989). The reader also may wish to review the analysis of this method presented in Chapter 8.

[39]Carson and Mitchell explain that the difference is due to the greater measure of water quality improvement considered in their analysis. Recall that Freeman measures the benefit of achieving the effluent limitations, whereas Carson and Mitchell measure the benefit of achieving the swimmable goal. It is also possible that their estimate is higher because the CVM approach captures the existence value of clean water.

[40]Bratton and Rutledge (1990), pp. 32–38, as cited in Carson and Mitchell (1993).

TABLE 13.12   **Benefit Estimates of Water Quality Improvements: A Contingent Valuation Study** (expressed in 1990 dollars)

Survey Results of Contingent Valuation Study	
Water Quality	*Estimated Willingness to Pay (average per person per year)*
Boatable	$106
Fishable	80
Swimmable	89
Total	$275

Preliminary Estimate of Annual Economic Benefits Based on Survey Results

Economic benefit to achieve swimmable water quality from baseline of non-boatable quality

Range	$24–$45 billion
Point estimate	$29.2 billion

Adjusted Estimate of Annual Economic Benefits of Clean Water

Adjusted to add benefits of commercial usage and marine recreational activities from Freeman (1982)	$39.1 billion
Scaling for increases in real income and changes in attitude about water pollution from 1983 to 1990	$46.7 billion

Source: Drawn from Richard T. Carson and Robert Cameron Mitchell, ''The Value of Clean Water: The Public's Willingness to Pay for Boatable, Fishable, and Swimmable Water,'' *Water Resources Research* 29, no. 7 (July 1993), pp. 2445–54.

are shown in Table 13.13. Notice that the EPA data show a projected annual cost in 1990 of $50.6 billion. To be conservative, we use the information from both of these sources and assume that annualized total social costs (*TSC*) for 1990 are somewhere in the range of $37.3 to $50.6 billion, or about $44.0 billion as a midpoint estimate.[41]

An Updated Benefit-Cost Comparison for U.S. Water Control Policies.   To consider the efficiency implications of U.S. water quality control, we compare the *relative* magnitudes of the estimated *TSB* and *TSC*. In so doing, we observe that the *TSB* of $46.7 billion is slightly higher than the comparable *TSC* estimate of $44.0 billion. However, Carson and Mitchell suggest that costs are likely to rise above benefits in the future because of the

---

[41]While these cost estimates are quite comprehensive and include costs to *all* economic sectors, they do *not* capture the true social costs of water quality control because implicit costs are not included. Recall that implicit costs monetize the value of such policy effects as higher-priced products, restrictions on consumer and firm decisions, and job losses associated with production and technology changes. Since these data are not directly available, we rely on estimates of explicit costs, acknowledging that these values underestimate the true costs to society.

TABLE 13.13   EPA Cost Estimates of Water Quality and Drinking Water Control (billions of 1990 dollars)*

	Year				
Program	*1980*	*1987*	*1990*	*1995*	*2000*
Water quality†	$27.2	$41.0	$46.3	$57.5	$68.7
Drinking water	2.4	3.7	4.3	6.4	7.9
Total‡	$29.5	$44.7	$50.6	$63.8	$76.4

Notes:
*Estimates are originally given by the EPA in 1986 dollars; they have been adjusted to 1990 dollars using the CPI.
†Water quality costs are those pursuant to the Clean Water Act as amended in 1987 and the Marine Protection, Sanctuaries and Research Act of 1972.
‡Some totals do not agree with components shown due to rounding.
Source: U.S. Environmental Protection Agency, Office of Policy, Planning, and Evaluation, *Environmental Investments: The Cost of a Clean Environment* (Washington, D.C., December 1990), Table 2–1, pp. 2-2, 2-3.

FIGURE 13.3

Benefit-cost analysis of U.S. post-1972 water quality policy: total social benefits and total social costs.

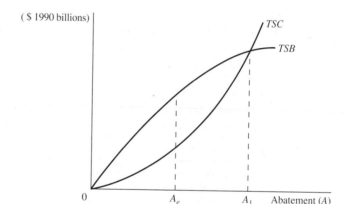

The efficient abatement level occurs where net benefits are maximized at point A_e, the point where *TSB* exceeds *TSC* by the greatest vertical distance. Based on available estimates for 1990, the abatement level for post-1972 U.S. regulations lies somewhere between 0 and A_1, where *TSB* is everywhere above *TSC*. Note, however, that there is no reason to assume that it coincides with point A_e.

spending needed to bring all surface waters up to the swimmable level. In any case, the comparison of *total* magnitudes as of 1990 does not indicate whether the associated abatement level is efficient. As Figure 13.3 illustrates, the efficient abatement level occurs where net benefits are maximized at point A_e, the point where *TSB* exceeds *TSC* by the greatest distance. Given the available estimates for 1990, we can conclude only that the associated abatement level lies somewhere between 0 and A_1 where *TSB* is above *TSC*. However, there is no reason to assume that this level coincides with A_e.

To determine whether or not this is the case, we need to compare marginal social cost (*MSC*) and marginal social benefit (*MSB*) as of 1990. Although

FIGURE 13.4

Benefit-cost analysis of U.S. water control policy for the 1985–1990 period: marginal social cost and marginal social benefit.

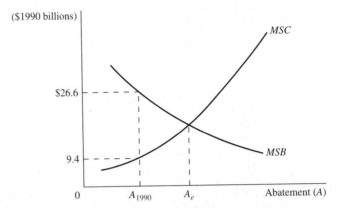

In this model, incremental costs for the 1985 to 1990 period are shown using the conventional marginal social cost (*MSC*) curve with an analogous interpretation on the benefit side. Notice that the 1990 abatement level, A_{1990}, occurs at a point *below* the efficient level, A_e, where *MSC* intersects *MSB*.

these magnitudes are not directly available, a rough approximation is possible by comparing *incremental* costs and *incremental* benefits over a relevant time period as long as the magnitudes are measured in constant dollars. In this context, the appropriate comparison is the incremental costs and benefits between 1985 and 1990, using Freeman's estimates for 1985 and Carson and Mitchell's for 1990. After converting all estimates to 1990 dollars, these incremental values are:

Incremental Control Costs for 1985–1990:

1990 control costs (EPA and Dept. of Commerce)	$44.0 billion
− 1985 control costs (Freeman)	34.6 billion
Incremental costs	$ 9.4 billion

Incremental Benefits for 1985–1990

1990 benefits (Carson and Mitchell)	$46.7 billion
− 1985 benefits (Freeman)	20.1 billion[42]
Incremental benefits	$26.6 billion

These calculations communicate an important result. Since the estimated incremental benefits are greater than the incremental costs, there is reason to believe that the post-1972 revisions to U.S. water legislation have not achieved an efficient abatement level. This result is illustrated in Figure 13.4, where

---

[42]As noted above, this magnitude is the value of Freeman's estimate after being adjusted by Carson and Mitchell for number of households and inflation.

incremental costs are shown using the conventional marginal social cost (*MSC*) curve with an analogous interpretation on the benefit side. Notice that the 1990 abatement level, A_{1990}, is *lower* than the efficient level, A_e, where *MSC* intersects *MSB*. This suggests that more stringent controls on polluting sources may be justified.

This assessment is an interesting one, but it is based on crude calculations. For one thing, as Carson and Mitchell assert, most U.S. waters are at a level above the nonboatable quality baseline assumed in the benefit estimate. Hence, costs to achieve swimmable quality are lower than they would be if all water bodies were actually at the baseline level. Furthermore, the calculations implicitly assume that the values between 1985 and 1990 are directly comparable, which is not the case on the benefit side. Because the 1990 benefit assessment is determined by the Contingent Valuation Method, it is a more comprehensive estimate than Freeman's because it includes some measure of existence value. Consequently, Freeman's estimate of $20.1 billion likely undervalues benefits for the 1985 period, which in turn means that incremental benefits likely are biased upward. It can be argued, however, that existence values in 1985 would not be large enough to change the *qualitative* result. In any case, until more accurate data are available, the conclusion that current U.S. regulations underallocate resources to water quality control is a tentative one at best.

Conclusions

The water on earth has some natural capacity to replenish itself through the various processes that make up the hydrological cycle. Likewise, water bodies have some ability to assimilate certain of the pollutants they receive. However, there is a limit to nature's restorative powers. Furthermore, the hydrological cycle that contributes to the restoration process is also the mechanism that can spread contamination—from the air to surface waters and to the groundwater below. Water pollution is pervasive, and virtually every form of human activity and many natural processes contribute to the problem.

Although water pollution *is* widespread, society has come to recognize the problem and has begun to take action. In the United States, water quality legislation has been expanded and strengthened over the last several decades. This evolution coupled with what are unquestionably ambitious national objectives would seem to suggest that policy officials have made a concerted effort to respond to the country's water pollution problems. Despite these assertions, most argue that whatever legislative progress *has* been realized, it has happened at far too slow a pace. There have been missed deadlines both in establishing effluent limitations and in setting the receiving water quality standards. Such delays have meant that ground and surface water deterioration has continued longer than it should have, human health has been placed at greater risk, and marine life and aquatic vegetation have been degraded or lost.

Even without the delays that admittedly have slowed the process, economic analyses suggest that the end result may not be an efficient solution. If this *is* the case, valuable resources are not being employed in their best possible use, and society is paying for the misallocation. Accepting that we cannot change the past, the real question is whether the nation can learn from its mistakes. There is still much to be done in revising existing policy and establishing new initiatives—a realization that is an integral part of Congress's recent deliberations to reauthorize the Clean Water Act.

An important motivation in moving national policy forward will be for Congress to consider how much progress has been made toward reaching national water quality objectives and at what measure of costs. Once done, it must determine how much of any realized improvement can realistically be attributed to existing policy. Finally, constructive revisions must be proposed, and feasible options formulated as needed. While it is easy to be critical of existing regulations, it is far more difficult to identify the problem and find effective and viable alternatives. In the next chapter, we will examine the control instruments currently used to achieve national objectives—in a very real sense a textbook exposition of what U.S. policy-makers are now undertaking as they continue to develop water quality policy for the nation.

Summary

- The earth's water supply comes from two major sources, surface water and groundwater. Surface waters are diverse and therefore are categorized as open ocean waters, ocean coastal waters, estuaries, inland waters, and the waters found in wetlands. Groundwater is an important water resource since it is available at every point on earth and is the only reliable source for many arid regions of the world.

- Surface water and groundwater are linked together by the hydrological cycle, a model that explains the movement of water from the earth's atmosphere to the surface and back into the atmosphere. The interdependence of the atmosphere and water supplies underscores the importance of protecting all natural resources from contamination.

- The two primary source categories of water pollution are point sources and nonpoint sources. A point source refers to any single identifiable source of pollution; a nonpoint source is one that cannot be identified accurately and degrades a water body in diffuse, indirect ways over a relatively broad area.

- Federal legislation on water pollution began with the Water Pollution Control Act of 1948, which introduced a federal loan program to assist municipalities in the construction of publicly owned treatment works. 1956 amendments to this act converted the loan plan to an outright grant program. Provisions in the Water

Quality Act of 1965 were the first to itemize states' responsibilities in pollution control with some provision for federal oversight.

- In 1972, Congress passed the Marine Protection, Research, and Sanctuaries Act (MPRSA) to regulate ocean dumping. It also enacted the Federal Water Pollution Control Act (FWPCA), which shifted primary responsibility from states to the federal government. This act defined the first set of national goals for water quality and established technology-based effluent limitations as the primary instrument of U.S. water quality control. Further amendments were accomplished through the Clean Water Act (CWA) of 1977 and the Water Quality Act of 1987.

- The three most important objectives of the Clean Water Act are (1) the zero discharge goal, (2) the fishable-swimmable goal, and (3) the no toxics in toxic amounts goal.

- Many pollutants are responsible for degrading the earth's water supplies. U.S. law distinguishes among three categories of pollutants: toxic pollutants, conventional pollutants, and nonconventional pollutants.

- Surface water quality is defined in the Clean Water Act by receiving water quality standards. These standards assign a use designation for each water body and identify water quality criteria necessary to sustain designated uses. Water quality criteria are pollutant-specific and may be expressed as numeric criteria, narrative criteria, or biocriteria.

- State authorities determine the use-support status of a water body by assessing its present condition and comparing it with what is needed to maintain its designated uses. One of five classifications are used to characterize the use-support status of surface waters: (1) fully supporting, (2) threatened, (3) partially supporting, (4) not supporting, and (5) not attainable.

- Two types of surface water quality assessment data are collected: evaluative data and monitoring data. Evaluative data typically are collected without the use of quality controls or site-specific sampling. Monitoring data are obtained under more carefully controlled conditions.

- One problem with the receiving water quality standards is that the EPA has not developed all the needed criteria documents to support states' use designations. Another criticism is that states are not required by law to use a benefit-cost evaluation to establish these standards. They also do not provide benefit and cost estimates associated with achieving national objectives. Finally, the link between receiving water quality standards and effluent limits is unclear since each is motivated differently—one by usage and the other by technology.

- According to a benefit-cost analysis of the Federal Water Pollution Control Act, the total social costs of regulatory control as of 1985 exceed the associated total social benefits. This may mean that too many resources were being allocated to water quality controls at that time.

- A more recent analysis, which used the Contingent Valuation Method to estimate benefits, found that as of 1990, the total social benefits of U.S. controls exceeded total social costs. Over the 1985 to 1990 period, estimates indicate that the incremental benefits exceeded incremental costs by $17.2 billion, suggesting that current legislation may underregulate polluting sources.

Key Concepts

surface water

groundwater

hydrological cycle

point sources

nonpoint sources

publicly owned treatment works
  (POTWs)

industrial facilities

combined sewer systems

technology-based effluent limitations

zero discharge goal

fishable-swimmable goal

no toxics in toxic amounts goal

toxic pollutants

conventional pollutants

nonconventional pollutants

priority pollutants

receiving water quality standards

use designation

use-support status

evaluative data

monitoring data

water quality criteria

numeric criteria

narrative criteria

biocriteria

Appendix
A Reference to Acronyms in Water Quality Control Policy

Environmental Economics Acronyms

CVM	Contingent Valuation Method
TSB	Total social benefits
TSC	Total social costs
MSB	Marginal social benefit
MSC	Marginal social cost

Environmental Science Acronyms

BOD	Biological oxygen demand
μg/L	Micrograms per liter

Environmental Policy Acronyms

CWA	Clean Water Act
CEQ	Council on Environmental Quality
EMAP	Environmental Monitoring and Assessment Program
FWPCA	Federal Water Pollution Control Act
MPRSA	Marine Protection, Research, and Sanctuaries Act
OPA	Oil Pollution Act of 1990
POTWs	Publicly owned treatment works

Review Questions

1. Use the concept of the hydrological cycle to explain how contamination of surface waters can also cause degradation of groundwater.

2. Refer to the Application on the Chesapeake Bay. Discuss both the natural and man-made conditions that are most responsible for the degradation of this water body.

3. Nutrients and pesticides are prevalent causes of water pollution. From an economic perspective, analyze why more has not been done to control agricultural runoff, the major source of these contaminants.

4. Identify two significant trends that characterize the evolution of U.S. water quality policy up through the 1987 Water Quality Act.

5. Using economic analysis, comment on the following statement: ''The Clean Water Act's zero discharge goal was doomed from the beginning.''

6. *a.* Discuss the major difficulties associated with estimating the benefits of water pollution abatement.

   b. Propose a policy approach which would promote states' use of benefit-cost analysis in setting and evaluating standards.

7. Reconsider the benefit-cost analyses of U.S. clean water policy offered by Freeman and by Carson and Mitchell. Are their different conclusions justified from a policy perspective? Why or why not? Are the respective estimation methods used by these researchers a factor in your assessment? Explain.

Additional Readings

Browner, Carol M. ''The Administration's Proposals: We Must Embrace a Watershed Approach.'' *EPA Journal* 20, no. 1–2 (Summer 1994), pp. 6–9.

Dahl, T. E. *Wetlands Losses in the United States: 1780's to 1980's.* Washington, D.C.: U.S. Department of the Interior and U.S. Fish and Wildlife Service, 1990.

Knopman, Debra S., and Richard A. Smith. ''20 Years of the Clean Water Act: Has U.S. Water Quality Improved?'' *Environment* 35, no. 1 (January/February 1993), pp. 17–20, 34–41.

Newman, Alan. ''A Blueprint for Water Quality.'' *Environmental Science and Technology* 27, no. 2 (1993), pp. 223–25.

Rogers, Peter. *America's Waters.* Cambridge, Mass.: MIT Press, 1993.

Satchell, Michael. ''Rape of the Oceans.'' *U.S. News & World Report,* June 22, 1992, pp. 64–68, 70–71, 75.

U.S. Environmental Protection Agency, Office of Water. *The Quality of Our Nation's Water: 1990.* Washington, D.C., June 1992.

U.S. General Accounting Office. *Water Pollution: Improved Coordination Needed to Clean Up the Great Lakes.* Washington, D.C., September 1990.

World Health Organization. ''Health Hazards of Water Pollution.'' In David H. Speidel, Lon C. Ruedisili, and Allen F. Agnew, eds. *Perspectives on Water: Uses and Abuses.* New York: Oxford University Press, 1988.

14 ACHIEVING WATER QUALITY

Controlling Point and Nonpoint Sources

As we discussed in the last chapter, U.S. water policy has a fairly long history and one that has been characterized by a series of significant revisions. Yet few would debate the need for further reform. While there has been measurable improvement in U.S. water quality, some water bodies continue to deteriorate, and most are still threatened by contamination—particularly the pollution from nonpoint sources. Furthermore, there is concern about certain of the policy instruments currently in use. A common criticism of U.S. water legislation is an overreliance on uniform technology-based limits and a lack of incentives to get the job done. An investigation of these and other issues form the agenda for this chapter.

Our objective is to analyze the major policy instruments used to control point and nonpoint sources of water pollution. Just as is the case for public officials and economic researchers, our policy analysis is hampered by insufficient data. Water monitoring, though improving, is not yet at a point where totally reliable and comprehensive information is available. In the interim, we make best efforts toward approximating the status of U.S. water resources, acknowledging whatever uncertainty clouds our conclusions. Accepting the limitations of our analysis, we can conduct a fairly thorough examination of what has been accomplished to date, where the weaknesses lie, and what types of revisions ought to be proposed.

Our analysis will cover the following aspects of U.S. water quality policy: (1) effluent limitations and permits to control point sources; (2) the grant program for publicly owned treatment works (POTWs); and (3) programs to control nonpoint sources. In each case, we present an overview of the control approach followed by an analytical evaluation. Where appropriate, the evaluation will be based upon the economic criteria of efficiency and cost-effectiveness. We conclude the chapter with a discussion of several proposed instruments that use market incentives to achieve water quality, some of them already in use on a limited scale. An appendix of acronyms is provided at the end of the chapter for reference.

Controlling Point Sources: Effluent Limitations

As evidence began to mount in the 1960s and early 1970s that U.S. waters were deteriorating, Congress realized that federal legislation needed a major overhaul. The result was a command-and-control policy approach dominated by the use of uniform pollution standards—a response not unlike the initial reaction to America's air quality problems.

An Overview of the Effluent Limits and National Permits

technology-based effluent limitations
Standards to control discharges from point sources based primarily on technological capability.

Instituted through the Federal Water Pollution Control Act (FWPCA) of 1972, **technology-based effluent limitations** are the primary control instruments through which U.S. water quality objectives are to be achieved. Following a command-and-control approach, these standards limit the amount of contaminants that may be discharged into surface waters by point sources. As technology advances, these EPA-established regulations are to be revised to identify currently available control measures and practices. Over time, the intent is that effluents can be completely eliminated to meet the zero discharge goal.

All point sources are subject to these end-of-pipe effluent limits, which vary by the type of polluting source, the age of the facility, and sometimes by the type of contaminant released. For example, publicly owned treatment works (POTWs) are required to meet a special set of secondary treatment standards based upon ''best practicable control technology.''[1] For *indirect* dischargers who release their effluents to these facilities, standards are established for the amount of pretreatment that must be done. Still other types of technology-based standards are defined for industrial dischargers who release their effluents *directly* into surface waters. A summary of the different types of effluent standards is given in Table 14.1, though the distinctions are sometimes more apparent than real. It is also important to note that, although there are different standards for different types of polluting sources, they are applicable *uniformly* to all individual polluters within each designated category.

National Pollutant Discharge Elimination System (NPDES)
A federally-mandated system of permits used to control effluent releases from direct industrial dischargers and publicly owned treatment works.

Once determined, pollution limits for direct industrial dischargers and for POTWs are communicated through a permitting system called the **National Pollutant Discharge Elimination System (NPDES)** administered by the EPA. In simplest terms, this system prohibits any *direct* discharges into

---

[1]Secondary treatment refers to the second step in the waste treatment process in which bacteria consume the organic elements of waste.

TABLE 14.1   **A Summary of Effluent Limits Specified in the Clean Water Act**

Standard	Polluting Source	Pollutant
Best practicable technology currently available (BPT) (phased out; replaced by BAT and BCT)	Direct industrial dischargers	EPA-specified water pollutants
Best available technology economically achievable (BAT)	Direct industrial dischargers (existing sources)	Toxic and nonconventional pollutants
Best conventional control technology (BCT)	Direct industrial dischargers (existing sources)	Conventional pollutants
Best available demonstrated control technology (BADCT)	Direct industrial dischargers (new sources)	Toxic, conventional, and nonconventional pollutants
Pretreatment standards	Indirect industrial dischargers (existing and new sources)	Pollutants not susceptible to POTW treatment or potentially damaging to POTW operations
Secondary treatment standards	POTWs	Oxygen-demanding substances and suspended solids

navigable waters without an NPDES permit.[2] These permits communicate precisely what the effluent limitations are as well as the requirements for monitoring and reporting. Though the EPA bears the overall responsibility of the program, states may be allowed to administer NPDES permits as long as certain federal requirements for an EPA-approved program are satisfied. As of 1992, 38 states and territories have assumed this responsibility.[3]

Defining effluent limits for direct industrial dischargers is a monumental task, since they must reflect technological differences across industry groups such as steel mills, pesticide manufacturers, and fertilizer manufacturers. In fact, recall from the previous chapter that problems associated with these standards caused serious delays that arguably slowed the nation's progress toward achieving its water quality objectives. For these and other reasons, these particular standards have been the subject of the most criticism by policy analysts, and hence we need to examine them more closely.

Technology-Based Standards for Direct Industrial Dischargers

While many factors are considered in setting the effluent limits for private commercial facilities, the most important is the technological capability of each industry, that is, what *can* be achieved by employing certain pollution control equipment and other technology. Because of this, these standards are

---

[2]Permits are *not* required for indirect dischargers whose effluents are released to permitted POTWs.

[3]Council on Environmental Quality (January 1993), p. 230.

best available demonstrated control technology (BADCT)
The technological basis for effluent limits applicable to new, direct industrial dischargers.

best available technology economically achievable (BAT)
The technological basis for effluent limits applicable to existing, direct industrial dischargers of nonconventional and toxic pollutants.

best conventional control technology (BCT)
The technological basis for effluent limits applicable to existing, direct industrial dischargers of conventional pollutants.

referred to as **technology-based effluent limitations.** However, polluting sources are allowed to choose the means by which the limit is achieved. This means that these effluent limitations are more accurately termed performance-based standards. These industry-specific standards are further delineated by the age of the polluting source much as is done for air quality standards, with differences outlined between new and existing sources.

According to the Clean Water Act, a new source is one whose construction was begun *after* proposed regulations for a standard applicable to that source have been announced. For *new* industrial point sources, the effluent limitations are more stringent than those for existing sources, based upon what the law calls **best available demonstrated control technology (BADCT).** In fact, wherever practical the BADCT limits are to explicitly prohibit effluent discharges.

For *existing* sources, two types of limits are applicable based on the type of pollutant released:

1. **Best available technology economically achievable (BAT)** standards for controlling nonconventional and toxic pollutants.

2. **Best conventional control technology (BCT)** standards, which are applicable to conventional pollutants.[4]

These limitations are to be considered minimum or baseline controls, allowing for more stringent standards to be used if needed to achieve the desired level of water quality for a particular water body. In setting the BAT standards, the ''best available technology'' for each industry is determined by a number of factors, including the processes used, the cost of achieving the effluent reduction, the engineering aspects of control techniques, energy requirements, and any impact on the environment beyond water quality. The determinants for the BCT standards add a consideration for the ''reasonableness of the relationship'' between the associated benefits and costs.

Analysis of Effluent Limitations on Point Sources

Notwithstanding the sense of immediacy that motivated the standards-based 1972 law, the command-and-control approach to U.S. water quality policy has been the subject of some debate. Much of the criticism has been lodged against the technology-based effluent limits, which have been blamed for the lack of progress achieved by U.S. policy. Among the recognized problems are long delays in establishing the standards, vague statutory definitions, meeting the zero discharge goal, and the lack of economic decision rules. These problems contribute to an inefficient solution to U.S. water pollution. Even

---

[4]The BAT and BCT standards replaced the **best practicable technology currently available (BPT)** standards originally mandated in the 1972 Federal Water Pollution Control Act. The BPT standards are still applicable in a few instances, but these too will be replaced eventually.

accepting the inefficiency, there is also strong evidence to suggest that the effluent limitations are not cost-effective. Let's take a closer look at these issues.

Administrative Delays

Under the 1972 law, industrial point sources were to achieve an initial phase of compliance with the BPT standards by 1977 followed by a second phase calling for attainment of the BAT standards by 1983. As it turned out, neither of these deadlines were met, with much of the blame pointed at the EPA. Although the agency was to have determined all the BPT standards within one year of the act's enactment, it failed by a wide margin. While the one-year time frame may have been overly ambitious, it is harder to defend why the EPA had not defined all the BPT standards by 1977—the date by which polluters were to have achieved compliance with them. In any case, the first phase deadline had to be postponed to 1983. The second phase was not only delayed but also redefined through a new set of standards for conventional pollutants— the BCT standards, with the BAT standards retained specifically for toxics and nonconventional pollutants.

Over the last 20 years, the EPA's track record has been slow in developing and revising effluent guidelines—the basis for the federal limitations. Reportedly, there are still many industrial categories not covered by guidelines, and some that have been established are seriously out of date. Such delays are particularly worrisome for toxic effluents, which pose relatively high environmental risks. The potential inequity of these risks is discussed in Application 14.1. Of the 51 sets of guidelines issued for point source categories, 35 are aimed specifically at toxics. However, 19 of these have not been revised in more than five years, and 9 of these 19 were established back in the 1970s.[5] What caused such delays? Part of the answer lies in how the standards were originally defined in the law.

Application 14.1

Toxic Fish Consumption: Are the Risks Equitable?

In 1992, the EPA issued a public warning that fish drawn from 46 U.S. riverways out of a test sample of 388 areas were not suitable for human consumption. The fish apparently had become contaminated by PCBs and a pesticide known as dieldrin, both of which are suspected carcinogens. In this case, the estimated *incremental* health risk is relatively minor. For example, scientists estimate that a

---

[5]U.S. General Accounting Office (GAO) (July 1991), p. 27.

Application 14.1 (continued)

monthly diet of two four-ounce fish fillets from the polluted waters over a 72-year lifespan would increase one's lifetime cancer risk by some amount greater than 1 in 10,000. However, since this adds to an already known cancer risk for all individuals, the advisory is considered appropriate. But this information leaves out an important point—whether the risk of exposure is the same for all members of society.

In February 1994, President Clinton issued an executive order mandating that all federal agencies consider ''environmental justice'' in their decision-making. What this means is that public officials must determine, not only the *degree* of risk associated with environmental pollution, but also the *relative* risk of exposure across various population groups. Although the potential for disproportionate risk to contaminated waters may seem unlikely, such an outcome is a very real possibility.

Setting aside cultural traditions, there are two distinct sets of motivations that affect an individual's decision to fish and consume the catch. One of these is purely recreational—fishing for sport. The other motivation is subsistence—a means to sustain a regular food supply. Individuals engaging in either or both types of fishing are at greater risk than the general population. It is true that those who fish purely for pleasure can minimize their risk by traveling to less polluted waters or by simply electing not to consume their catch. However, individuals who rely on fish and shellfish as part of their regular diet have limited options and therefore bear the highest relative risk of exposure to contaminated waters.

Researchers have tried to identify which population groups are most vulnerable to toxic contamination through fish consumption. Some studies suggest a relationship between race or ethnic origin and average per capita fish consumption. For example, survey data indicate that people of color consume more fish than the rest of the population. Other studies find that Asians and African Americans eat more seafood than Caucasians. It is also the case that certain Native Americans comprise

one of the largest subsistence fishing communities in the United States. Unfortunately, research on this latter group of Americans has been frustrated by a lack of data. The problem is that most studies use a sample of only *licensed* fishermen. Such data do not include *reservation-based* Native Americans because according to treaty rights, these individuals do not have to obtain a state fishing license.

To illustrate the risk implications of such consumption differences, we consider the findings from a recent survey study of Detroit residents. According to this investigation, the average daily fish consumption across the entire sample is 18.3 grams per person per day. This statistic by itself is disconcerting, since the standard used in the state of Michigan to regulate point source toxic releases is based on a much lower consumption rate of 6.5 grams per person per day. However, the equity implications are even more troubling. The highest consumption rate across all defined population groups is for off-reservation Native Americans, estimated at 24.3 grams per person per day. The comparable statistics for African Americans, other minorities, and whites, are 20.3, 19.8, and 17.9, respectively. These data suggest that the risk of exposure to contaminated waters is not shared equally across population groups. Even worse, the extent of the inequality may be far greater than the estimates imply, since reservation-based Native Americans are unavoidably excluded from the analysis.

If researchers could determine the cause of the relatively high consumption rate for Native Americans, it might be possible to make inferences about the on-reservation population. It is true that some tribes have a cultural tradition of fishing-based economies, but it is also believed that Native Americans living on reservations depend on subsistence fishing for economic reasons. If this hypothesis is correct, then both cultural and economic factors play a role in fish consumption rates. Thus, it may be the case that reservation-based Native Americans consume fish at a higher rate than the available data suggest and therefore face a high health risk from toxic exposure. In Michigan where this

---

Application 14.1 (concluded)

research was conducted, the health concern is particularly grave given the severe pollution problems in the Great Lakes region.

Although existing studies have not been able to uncover all the answers, research is ongoing to learn more about environmental equity. Furthermore, there is growing support for this issue from U.S. officials. Responding to President Clinton's executive order on environmental justice, EPA Administrator Browner said the following:

For too long, low income communities and minority communities have borne a disproportionate burden of modern industrial life . . . All Americans deserve to be protected from pollution—not just those who can afford to live in the cleanest, safest communities.

Sources: Patrick C. West, "Invitation to Poison? Detroit Minorities and Toxic Fish Consumption from the Detroit River," in Bunyan Bryant and Paul Mohai, eds., *The Proceedings of the Michigan Conference on Race and the Incidence of Environmental Hazards,* 1992, as cited in Adler et al. 1993, p. 57; Patrick C. West, "Health Concerns for Fish-Eating Tribes? Government Assumptions Are Much Too Low," *EPA Journal* 18, no. 1 (March/April 1992), pp. 15–16; U.S. Environmental Protection Agency, Office of Communications, Education, and Public Affairs, "Federal Actions Address Environmental Justice," *EPA Activities Update,* Washington, D.C., February 22, 1994a; Associated Press, "EPA: Fish Aren't Safe to Eat From 46 Waterways," *Brockton Enterprise,* November 20, 1992.

Imprecise and Inconsistent Definitions

water quality-related limitations
Modified effluent limits to be met if the desired water quality level is not being achieved, even if polluting sources are already satisfying the technology-based limits.

A fundamental problem with the effluent limitations is that they are not aligned with the nation's objectives. The basis of the standards is what is technologically feasible for each group of polluting sources—*not* what is necessary to achieve water quality. In fact, the potential inadequacy of these standards is implied by the statutes themselves. Modifications to the effluent limits are allowed in the form of **water quality-related limitations.** These are to be met by every polluting source if the desired level of water quality is not being achieved—even if a source is already satisfying the technology-based limits. While this may seem reasonable, it nonetheless speaks to the deficiency of the effluent limits. The very fact that modifications might be needed calls into question the characterization of these technology-based limitations as "best." The law acknowledges that these so-called "best" standards might not be sufficient to achieve water quality and further requires that some polluting sources abate beyond what has been determined as the "best conventional" or "best practicable" technology. Still more problems arise in attempting to establish and implement these limitations for designated categories of point sources. While the use of technology-based limits appears to be an objective and scientific approach to standard-setting, the law does not identify clearly what level of technology is appropriate. Phrases like "best practicable," "best available," and "best conventional" are not exact terms. Without more careful guidelines and objective decisions rules, officials are left with the difficult task of trying to *infer* what these terms mean and how to implement them in practice.[6]

---

[6]CWA, Sec. 302; Freeman (1990), pp. 106–07.

Meeting the Zero Discharge Goal

In retrospect, the zero discharge goal established in 1972 was overly ambitious. Furthermore, its call for the complete elimination of water polluting effluents is likely an inefficient objective. Nonetheless, it was the target set by Congress under federal law.[7] The Clean Water Act also requires that the EPA review existing standards and successively advance them toward a zero limit as new technology becomes available. Yet, the EPA's efforts in this regard has been something less than satisfactory. In the last 20 years, there have been only a few instances—among them onshore oil and gas wells—where this limit has been imposed. Although there is no comprehensive way to determine which of the existing effluent guidelines *should* have been moved to a zero discharge limit, there are indications that this may have been the case in certain instances. One example is the set of effluent standards for the organic chemicals, plastics, and synthetic fibers industry. Although the EPA knew that certain plants had the capacity to achieve the zero discharge goal, it did *not* impose a zero effluent limit on the industry. Reacting to this outcome, the Natural Resources Defense Council challenged the EPA's decision. Yet even after a federal appeals court required the agency to reassess its decision, the EPA did not change its ruling. Instead, it defended its position on the basis of differences across plants and its own lack of resources to further investigate the matter.[8]

The Absence of Economic Decision Rules

Economists and other policy analysts are quick to point out the absence of economic decision rules in guiding the specification of the BAT and BCT standards. To understand the implications of this deficiency, consider the following observations:

- The law does not mandate that the standards be set to maximize net benefits, which prevents the attainment of an efficient level of abatement.
- The standards are applied uniformly across dischargers within identified industrial groups, which disallows a cost-effective outcome.

Lack of an Efficiency Criterion.   The Clean Water Act does allow for many factors to be considered in setting the BAT and BCT standards beyond technological feasibility, including economic consequences. However, the provisions do little more than list the relevant factors, offering no guidance as to how they are to be used in decision-making. This is particularly problematic,

---

[7]For a more detailed discussion of the zero discharge goal, see Van Putten and Jackson (1986).

[8]Adler, Landman, and Cameron (1993), pp. 143–44.

since the determinants itemized in the law are many, and they cross over from engineering and scientific criteria to economic considerations.

In the definition of the BCT standards for conventional pollutants, there is a troubling lack of precision in the reference to benefits and costs. According to law, officials are to consider the "reasonableness of the relationship between the costs of attaining a reduction in effluents and the effluent reduction benefits derived." This is a far cry from setting abatement levels at the point where marginal benefits and costs are equal. Absent from the BAT standards is any reference to economic benefits. For these limits, which are applicable to toxic pollutants, only the cost of achieving the mandated effluent reduction is among the list of determinants.

Without congressional guidelines as to how all determinants, including economic ones, are to be measured and weighted relative to one another, the standards are left to discretion and subjective judgment. The result? Many disagreements and legal battles have ensued among industrial sources, government officials, and environmental groups, delaying the process on which much of the force of the law depends.[9] Beyond these general problems is the absence of any opportunity for the BAT standards to achieve an efficient level of abatement and only a very remote one for the BCT limits.

Cost-Ineffective Decision-Making.   As we have discussed in previous chapters, in instances where the law prevents the use of the efficiency criterion, a "second-best" economic solution is to select cost-effective policy instruments to achieve an objective. Cost-effectiveness requires that abatement levels be set to achieve equal marginal abatement cost (*MAC*) levels across all polluters. However, under the Clean Water Act, the *uniformity* of the effluent standards prevents such an outcome. Although the law allows for the limitations to be industry-specific, the associated effluent reductions must be achieved by all polluting sources within each industry group—regardless of firm-level differences in resource availability or technological expertise. If all dischargers must achieve the same standard, the only way the *MAC*s would be equivalent across polluters is if these polluting sources were identical. Since this clearly is not the case, the standards impose higher costs to society than is necessary.

Just how significant is the problem? Unfortunately, there is no research that provides a comprehensive answer to this question. However, some economic studies have attempted to quantify the cost implications of command-and-control instruments for specific water bodies. Table 14.2 summarizes the findings of some of these. Each analysis determines a ratio of the cost of implementing a command-and-control approach to that of the least-cost market-based method. In each case, the ratio is significantly greater than 1, meaning that the command-and-control approach is relatively more costly than the use of economic incentives.

---

[9]Freeman (1978), p. 55.

TABLE 14.2   **Cost-Effectiveness of Market-Based Controls:
Some Quantitative Studies**

Investigators and Year	*Command-and-Control Approach*	*Geographic Area*	*Ratio of Command-and-Control Cost to Least Cost*
Johnson (1967)	Equal proportional treatment	Delaware Estuary	3.13 at 2 mg/l DO 1.62 at 3 mg/l DO 1.43 at 4 mg/l DO
O'Neil (1980)	Equal proportional treatment	Lower Fox River, Wisconsin	2.29 at 2 mg/l DO 1.71 at 4 mg/l DO 1.45 at 6.2 mg/l DO
Eheart et al. (1983)	Equal proportional treatment	Willamette River, Oregon	1.12 at 4.8 mg/l DO 1.19 at 7.5 mg/l DO
Eheart et al. (1983)	Equal proportional treatment	Delaware Estuary in PA, DL, and NJ	3.00 at 3 mg/l DO 2.92 at 3.6 mg/l DO
Eheart et al. (1983)	Equal proportional treatment	Upper Hudson River in New York	1.54 at 5.1 mg/l DO 1.62 at 5.9 mg/l DO
Eheart et al. (1983)	Equal proportional treatment	Mohawk River in New York	1.22 at 6.8 mg/l DO

Note: mg/l = Milligrams per liter; DO = dissolved oxygen.
Source: U.S. Environmental Protection Agency, Office of Policy, Planning and Evaluation, *The United States Experience with Economic Incentives to Control Environmental Pollution* (Washington, D.C., July 1992), Table 2-1, pp. 2-3–2-5, citing Tietenberg (1985) and the original sources given in the table.

Underlying the problem of uniform standards is the lack of a reward system for efficient abaters to reduce their effluents beyond legal limits. In fact, it has been argued that the structure of the effluent limits acts as a market *disincentive* for technological innovation.[10] Based on the law, if a discharger were to develop a new technology to reduce effluents more efficiently, the limits would be tightened based on the innovative discovery. This response would impose higher abatement costs on *all* effluent dischargers, including the innovating entity. Furthermore, since the limits are used to establish performance-based rather than technology-based standards, the law would not require polluters to employ the new technology. Thus, there is no market opportunity and hence no monetary reward for new innovation. The result is that most dischargers tend to employ the same technology used to set the limits in the first place, even though they are not required to do so. The rationale is to avoid the potential of an official compliance inquiry that might arise if an alternative technology were used.

[10]Freeman (1978), p. 57.

Waste Treatment Management and the POTW Program

An important and sometimes controversial aspect of the Clean Water Act is the federal funding authorized by Congress to support the construction of publicly owned treatment works (POTWs). POTWs are potentially significant sources of water contamination. Among the pollutants released by these facilities are pesticides, heavy metals, viruses, and bacteria. Unless municipal waste water is properly treated, the associated pollution threatens ground and surface water drinking supplies, aquatic life, recreational opportunities, and the overall health and stability of ecosystems. Responding to the potential environmental risks, the Clean Water Act requires POTWs to satisfy technology-based secondary treatment standards and calls for significant federal appropriations to support this mandate. In fact, the fourth policy goal of the act specifically states:

> It is the national policy that Federal financial assistance be provided to construct publicly owned waste treatment works.

Investment in this program has been significant with a total federal outlay of $56 billion through fiscal year 1992.[11]

federal grant program
A program that provided major funding from the federal government for a share of the construction costs of POTWs.

The Pre-1987 Federal Grant Program

Prior to 1987, Title II of the Clean Water Act was devoted solely to waste treatment management. The voluminous and highly detailed set of provisions outlined the **federal grant program** for the construction of POTWs throughout the nation. Administered by the EPA, the program authorized federal funds of billions of dollars per year, starting in 1973 with $5 billion and ending in 1990 with $1.2 billion. The federal share of construction costs was set at a maximum of 75 percent until 1984, when it was reduced to 55 percent. Related to the grant program were provisions to facilitate the development of areawide waste treatment management plans for regions facing significant water quality problems due to urban-industrial concentration.[12] Approved plans were eligible for federal grant assistance.

State Revolving Fund (SRF) program
An initiative replacing the federal grant program that establishes state lending programs to support POTW construction and other projects.

Shift to the State Revolving Fund (SRF) Program in 1987

As part of the 1987 reauthorization, Title VI was written as the successor to Title II. Title VI authorizes capitalization grants to each state for establishing a revolving fund for water pollution projects. States are to provide 20 percent in matching funds to support the effort. This **State Revolving Fund (SRF)**

---

[11]U.S. EPA, Office of Water (March 1994), p. 231.

[12]These plans were to include an identification of treatment facilities to service the area over a 20-year period, a construction plan and time schedule, a regulatory program, and a means to identify and devise control methods for nonpoint sources.

program, which replaced the federal grants, was targeted to provide loans for POTW construction as well as for other environmental projects. As of 1990, every state and Puerto Rico had established an SRF program. Over $9 billion has been appropriated for this plan through 1994.[13]

Analysis of the POTW Funding Program

Most understand the motivation of the federal subsidy of POTW construction, given the potential health and ecological threat of inadequate waste treatment. Yet the issue is not whether the intent of the program is well founded but rather whether federal subsidies are an effective instrument to improve national water quality. To organize a study of this important component of U.S. water quality regulation, we consider three primary questions:

1. What is the relationship between the allocation of federal monies and any observed improvement in waste treatment across the United States?

2. To what extent is efficiency served in the federal aid plan and what incentives or disincentives are present?

3. What are the equity implications in terms of who actually pays for this funding?

Assessing the Accomplishments Attributable to Federal Subsidies

To argue that federal subsidies have been effective because municipal waste treatment has progressed measurably is falsely motivated. The problem is that such an argument implicitly assumes that the federal program is fully responsible for any observed improvement. In fact, there is evidence to suggest that this is not at all the case.

It *is* true that an increasing proportion of the population is served by facilities using at least secondary treatment. In 1960, of all people served by a wastewater facility this proportion was only 4 percent. By 1980 the proportion rose to 73 percent. More recent data show that as of 1988, 138 million Americans were being served by at least secondary treatment—an 84 percent increase over 1977.[14] Yet research indicates that the majority of federal grant monies only *displaced* local funds that would have been allocated to POTW construction had the national program not been in place.

A 1984 empirical study found the rate of fund displacement to be 67 percent, meaning that every additional dollar of federal money *permanently*

---

[13]U.S. EPA, Office of Water (March 1994), pp. 231–32.
[14]Council on Environmental Quality (1982), Table A-61, p. 295, as cited in Freeman (1990), p. 136; U.S. EPA (December 1990a), p. 2.

displaced 67 cents of municipal spending on POTW construction.[15] This finding means that roughly two-thirds of every dollar in federal grant money acted only as a *substitute* for local funding with only a third as *incremental* investment in POTW construction. The significance of this result is that the observed improvement in wastewater treatment across the nation cannot be attributed fully to the grant program. Since only a portion of the federal monies was incremental to what would have been spent at the local level, only a fraction of the improved water quality can be linked to the federal aid program. See Application 14.2 for more on this important conclusion.

Application 14.2

The POTW Grant Program: Displacement of Local Funding

In a 1984 empirical study, two researchers named Jondrow and Levy reported some interesting findings about the U.S. government's POTW grant program. Their investigation shows that every additional dollar of federal grants awarded *permanently* displaced 67 cents of municipal spending. The analysis further estimates that 28 cents of every dollar of unspent federal budget authority *temporarily* displaced (i.e., postponed) local expenditures on POTW construction. This latter form of displacement is associated mainly with the early phase of the federal program. At that point, local authorities had an incentive to delay expenditures while the federal program was getting under way or while awaiting federal approval of a proposed project.

According to Jondrow and Levy, these estimates translate to the following dollar values for 1973 at the start of the POTW grant program:

$1.05 billion in federal grants
− $714 million of municipal expenditures
    permanently displaced

$346 million
− $1.4 billion of municipal expenditure
    temporarily displaced

($1.06 billion) net addition to POTW
construction

Based on these calculations, the total displacement of municipal spending on sewer treatment in 1973 was approximately 200 percent. Thus, the federal program actually caused a *reduction* in overall funding for POTW construction of over $1 billion. According to the researchers, the high proportion of displacement in 1973 is explained mainly by the large amount of temporary displacement that is more likely to occur in the initial stages of the program. Hence, this displacement would be expected to decline as the program became more established. In fact, conducting an analogous exercise for 1980, Jondrow and Levy found that temporary displacement was much lower for the period. Nonetheless, total displacement was still a significant amount, estimated to be $2.5 billion or 64 percent of the total grant expenditures for that year.

Related statistics bear out the findings of Jondrow and Levy. According to a report conducted by the Congressional Budget Office, the $18 billion federal grant program authorized in 1972 marked a major shift of the financial burden for POTW construction from local governments to the federal level. Over the 1970 to 1977 period, the annual federal outlay under the grant program rose from $0.5 to $6.0 billion, with average local spending falling from $4.0 billion to $1.5 billion.

---

[15]Jondrow and Levy (1984), p. 176.

Application 14.2 (concluded) ·

Collectively, these data suggest that the POTW grant program did not contribute dollar for dollar to improvements in U.S. water quality. Given the enormous financial investment in the program, this conclusion cannot be taken lightly. In simplest terms, this outcome is a classic case of misallocated resources. One can only hypothesize about the loss in environmental quality that could have been achieved had these billions of dollars been more wisely spent.

Sources: James Jondrow and Robert A. Levy, "The Displacement of Local Spending for Pollution Control by Federal Construction Grants," *American Economic Review* 74, no. 2 (1984), pp. 174–78; U.S. Congressional Budget Office (CBO), *Efficient Investments in Wastewater Treatment Plants* (Washington, D.C.: U.S. Government Printing Office, 1985a), p. 4.

Inefficiencies in the Grant Program

That the grant program achieved something less than a dollar-for-dollar improvement is an important realization, but it is only part of the story. It turns out that the well-intended plan was plagued by a number of inefficiencies. One was that the original program as established in 1972 did not assure that federal funds were allocated where incremental benefits were expected to be highest, such as in areas suffering from the worst pollution problems. This misallocation was not addressed until Congress passed the 1977 amendments, which required states to establish priority lists of facilities most in need of financial assistance.

Another problem is that the federal aid package was directed toward proper *construction* of new POTWs, yet lacked any provision to encourage *maintenance* and *operation* of these facilities once they had been built. In the 1970s, the EPA's annual inspections of POTWs revealed that only about 30 to 50 percent were operating satisfactorily. Similar findings were reported by the U.S. General Accounting Office (GAO).[16]

Most if not all of the grant program's inefficiencies were due to one important void—a lack of incentives. Fundamental to the program's design was the share of costs to be absorbed by the federal government. Recall this was set at up to 75 percent until 1984. Such a large proportion shifted most of the spending away from local governments, leaving them little incentive to minimize costs in the building of treatment facilities. In fact, with the addition of special aid from federal and state governments, some municipalities had to raise as little as 5 percent of the overall construction costs. Consequently, some POTWs are larger and more elaborate than necessary, motivated by a desire to attract industry and promote growth. Such excess capacity is a waste of economic resources and has been blamed for the observed poor operating performance of certain funded facilities.[17]

---

[16]See Council on Environmental Quality (1976), p. 18, and U.S. EPA (November 1974), p. 16 reported in U.S. EPA (1975), p. IV-37.

[17]U.S. Congressional Budget Office (CBO) (1985a), pp. ix, 12.

Responding to such inefficiencies, the U.S. government made several changes to the program. Grant awards were cut to $2.4 billion per year through 1985—a significant reduction from the range in prior years of $4 billion to $6 billion. Starting in 1985, the federal cost share was reduced to 55 percent. Tighter restrictions on grant authorizations were instituted, such as limiting funds to servicing the needs of existing rather than projected population levels. This latter revision was an attempt to discourage the deliberate construction of excess capacity as a way to promote local economic growth.[18] Finally, the Water Quality Act of 1987 altered the basic premise of the program from outright construction aid to funding for state-administered revolving loans.

Notice that these changes shift more of the cost burden back to local governments. In so doing, municipalities must become more self-sufficient in developing revenue sources to fund wastewater treatment and therefore should be encouraged to make more cost-effective decisions. Furthermore, concern for higher sewer fees prompts local residents to take a more active role in assuring that local officials carefully consider costs. According to a statistical analysis done by the U.S. Congressional Budget Office (CBO), increases in the lifetime local cost share of up to about 50 to 60 percent *do* lead to efficiency improvements measured in terms of declines in lifetime unit costs.[19] Finally, by placing responsibility closer to the funded project, decisions can better reflect state and local needs.

Equity Implications

Beyond the efficiency issues, there are also equity considerations associated with the POTW program. Some municipalities had not yet been funded when the grant program was eliminated, placing a relatively higher cost burden on those communities. The inequity is greater for smaller, rural communities that are unable to take advantage of scale economies available to localities serving relatively large populations. The shift to the State Revolving Fund (SRF) program may have provided some measure of offset, however, since state-managed loans can be tailored through interest rates or grace periods to accommodate lower income or wealth levels of certain communities.[20]

On a broader scale, there is evidence that the grant program *did* provide for a more equitable tax burden across the national population. A 1980 study showed that federal cost-sharing reduces the burden imposed on the lowest income families from 0.6 to 0.4 percent of family income and increases the comparable burden of highest income families from 0.3 to 0.8 percent.[21] It is

---

[18]See U.S. CBO (1985a), p. 3. For more on the inherent incentive toward excess capacity, see Freeman (1978), pp. 63–64.
[19]For more detail on this study, consult U.S. CBO (1985a), Chapter II.
[20]U.S. CBO (1985a), pp. 54, 59–60.
[21]Gianessi and Peskin (1980).

not yet apparent as to how the allocation of the tax burden has been affected by the shift to the SRF program.

Controlling Nonpoint Sources[22]

In 1987, the federal government added a seventh policy goal calling for the development of programs to control nonpoint polluting sources.

> It is the national policy that programs for the control of nonpoint sources of pollution be developed and implemented in an expeditious manner so as to enable the goals of this Act to be met through the control of both point and nonpoint sources of pollution.

Nonpoint Source Management Program
A three-stage, state-implemented plan aimed at nonpoint source pollution.

This addition to the national list of objectives was in direct response to the growing awareness that these diffuse sources are major contributors to surface water and ground water pollution. Enacted officially as Section 319 of the Water Quality Act of 1987, the **Nonpoint Source Management Program** was launched as a three-stage plan to be implemented by states with federal approval and financial assistance. The first step of the program calls for states to prepare assessment reports in which they identify waters that cannot achieve or maintain water quality standards without some action taken toward nonpoint sources. They must also identify categories of nonpoint sources or specific point sources responsible for the problem.[23] In the second stage, states must develop management programs in which they designate **best management practices (BMP)** to reduce pollution from every identified category, subcategory, or individual nonpoint source, taking into account the impact on groundwater resources. As of 1992, 51 states and territories have full EPA approval of their management programs. The final step calls for implementation of these programs over a multiyear time period.

best management practices (BMP)
Procedures or strategies other than effluent limitations aimed at reducing pollution from nonpoint sources.

To support states' efforts, federal grants are available for up to 60 percent of the total costs incurred. Over the 1991 to 1993 period, federal appropriations totaled over $191 million. In 1991, the EPA issued final guidance on how these funds are to be awarded and managed. This guidance encourages states to focus on high-priority activities, such as dealing with high-risk nonpoint problems, promoting comprehensive watershed management, and protecting sensitive and ecologically significant waters such as wetlands, estuaries, and scenic rivers. In 1989, the EPA developed its *Nonpoint Source Agenda for the Future* to help define national goals for nonpoint source pollution and to find appropriate mechanisms to achieve them. Application 14.3 has more on this national agenda.

---

[22]The following is drawn from CWA, Sec.319. Nonpoint Source Management Programs and U.S. EPA, Office of Water (March 1994), pp. 247–48.

[23]A summary of these reports was published by the EPA in 1992 in *Managing Nonpoint Source Pollution.*

Application 14.3

The EPA's *Nonpoint Source Agenda for the Future*

Further improvements in U.S. water quality depend on policy efforts aimed at nonpoint polluting sources. To help define objectives for nonpoint source programs and ways to implement them, the EPA drafted a *Nonpoint Source Agenda for the Future* in 1989. This agenda outlines a comprehensive approach to controlling nonpoint sources and achieving the policy goals of the Clean Water Act. Working with state and local governments, the EPA hopes to eliminate what it perceives to be significant barriers that hinder successful implementation of nonpoint source control programs. To date, the following three barriers have been identified: (1) inadequate public awareness of the nonpoint pollution problem; (2) inadequate knowledge or transfer of knowledge of successful solutions to nonpoint pollution; and (3) inadequate incentives to correct nonpoint source pollution. The identification of these barriers gives the agenda direction and helps to establish priorities for state governments and local authorities. Implementation is to be carried out through five themes that characterize the agenda and hence the EPA's overall objectives. What follows is a brief description of each theme and some of the accomplishments to date.

Themes of the Nonpoint Source Agenda for the Future

Public awareness: To help states and local governments educate the public about the effects of nonpoint source pollution.

        Accomplishments to date: Efforts include the release of a brochure, poster, and various other educational materials to improve the general public's awareness of the problem.

Successful solutions: To assist state and local governments by establishing information networks to communicate feasible solutions to existing problems and strategies to avoid future problems.

        Accomplishments to date: The EPA has established a new publication called *Nonpoint Source News-Notes* to disseminate information on successful nonpoint source programs.

Economic forces: To provide financial incentives to prevent or reduce nonpoint source pollution and to eliminate any that encourage environmentally damaging activities.

        Accomplishments to date: The EPA has published a guidance document called *Share the Costs—Share the Benefits,* to explain to states how cost-share programs can be used to encourage best management practices (BMP).

Regulatory solutions: To assist states and localities in developing regulatory solutions through the use of a clearinghouse and information transfer workshops.

        Accomplishments to date: The primary instrument in use is the publication *Nonpoint Source News-Notes.* The EPA is also continuing to develop its storm water regulatory program authorized by the Clean Water Act and supports state and local efforts through grant funding.

Application 14.3 (concluded)

Themes of the Nonpoint Source Agenda for the Future (*concluded*)

Good science:	To develop scientific criteria and monitoring protocols that can be used to evaluate nonpoint source pollution and establish sound control programs at the state and local levels.
	Accomplishments to date: The EPA published *Biological Criteria—National Program Guidance for Surface Waters,* which documents the effective use of biological criteria and standards in state water quality programs.

Through this comprehensive agenda, the EPA hopes to provide the national leadership needed for states and local governments to identify, solve, and prevent the significant problem of nonpoint source water pollution.

Sources: U.S. Environmental Protection Agency, Office of Water, *National Water Quality Inventory: 1990 Report to Congress* (Washington, D.C., April 1992a), p. 149; U.S. Environmental Protection Agency, Office of Water, *Managing Nonpoint Source Pollution* (Washington, D.C., January 1992), pp. 7–10.

Analysis of Controls on Nonpoint Sources

There is no debate that the emphasis of water pollution control in the United States has been on point sources. Through 1987, policy officials focused their energies on developing standards, issuing permits, and monitoring these more visible and obvious sources of contamination. Over time, it became increasingly apparent that these efforts were incomplete. Nonpoint source pollution from land runoff and atmospheric deposition was continuing to threaten surface water and groundwater supplies, and existing policy was simply not designed to deal with it. EPA Administrator Carol Browner characterizes the extent of the problem today as follows:

> The single greatest remaining threat to America's rivers, lakes, and estuaries is polluted runoff, sometimes called nonpoint source pollution. Silt, pesticides, fertilizer, and other pollutants are carried off farms, suburban lawns, industrial plants, and city streets into water bodies whenever it rains.[24]

Efforts begun in 1987 to control nonpoint source pollution are progressing but still in their infancy. (The implementation phase began only in 1990.) Nonetheless, it is possible to investigate the general approach of this new national program. Since the 1987 provisions delegate much of the implementation to state governments, we need to consider the reasonableness of this

---

[24]Browner (Summer 1994), p. 6.

decision. What are the pros and cons? We also must evaluate what the federal government is doing vis-à-vis what is needed to support states' efforts.[25]

Delegating Control to the States: The Pros

One factor in support of delegating nonpoint source control to state governments is the variability of nonpoint source pollution. Not only are these sources difficult to identify and isolate, but the extent of the associated damage is highly unpredictable. A major source of the problem is land runoff from farms, city streets, mines, construction sites, and so on. Because runoff is influenced by precipitation, the resulting contamination is affected by many exogenous factors such as weather conditions, geological patterns, and soil conditions. Not only are these factors uncontrollable, but they also vary considerably from location to location. Logically, the use of broad-based, uniform controls is likely to be ineffective and difficult to implement. In a 1984 report on nonpoint source pollution, the EPA acknowledged this point:

> Flexible, site-specific, and source-specific decision-making is the key to effective control of nonpoint sources. Site-specific decisions must consider the nature of the watershed, the nature of the water body, the nature of the nonpoint source(s), the use impairment caused by the nonpoint source(s), and the range of management practices available to control nonpoint source pollution.[26]

Another factor influencing the coordination of effort between state and federal authorities is the relationship between nonpoint source pollution and land use practices. Land use practices include such activities as agriculture, mining, forestry, and urban development, all of which historically have been controlled by local governments. It therefore becomes a politically sensitive issue when the federal government sets policy that dictates how a state or local community is to use its own land resources. A good example is environmental policy affecting forestry—an industry that can harm the ecology but also often sustains local or regional economies. In some sense, the 1987 nonpoint source program attempts to address the interests of both sides by giving states the major responsibility of policy design and implementation, while assigning oversight to the EPA through its review of states' assessments and programs.

Delegating Control to the States: The Cons

Although there is some logic to controlling nonpoint pollution close to the source, state governments often lack the information they need to carry out their responsibilities. Data on the extent of water contamination are inade-

---

[25]Much of the following is drawn from U.S. GAO (October 1990), Chapter 2. Another comprehensive examination of policy on nonpoint source pollution is U.S. EPA, Office of Policy, Planning and Evaluation (June 29, 1992). A review of the EPA's 12 findings in this source is given in Adler et al. (1993), pp. 188–89.

[26]U.S. EPA (1984b), pp. xiii–xiv.

quate, due in large part to ineffective monitoring systems—a pervasive problem that affects all types of water contamination. Though the Clean Water Act requires states to assess surface waters and report the findings every two years, the law does not specify what proportion of these waters is to be included in the biennial review.[27] The extent of the data deficiencies in the context of nonpoint source pollution was discussed in a recent government report. One of the cited instances was the lack of assessment data on mining runoff. Reportedly, inactive ore and mineral mines in five states—California, Colorado, Idaho, Missouri, and Montana—are responsible for 80 percent of the nation's pollution arising from these types of nonpoint sources. Thousands of stream miles are affected from such contaminants as heavy metals and sedimentation. Yet state officials claim that only a portion of the problem has been assessed. In fact, a Colorado official reported that only 8,000 of that state's 50,000 abandoned mines have been studied for their environmental impacts.[28]

Adding to the dilemma is the fact that most state assessment data are collected from monitoring systems designed to detect point source pollution, which therefore do not give an accurate picture of the extent of damage from nonpoint sources. Insufficient monitoring data not only hinders environmental assessment but also impedes the evaluation of states' management programs and their designation of best management practices (BMP) to control nonpoint sources. Without proper monitoring systems, changes in contaminant levels cannot be properly measured. Hence, incentives to propose new plans or revisions to existing ones are limited at best.

Finally, there is always the potential problem of inconsistent pollution controls when state governments are in charge of policy implementation. Such inconsistencies are problematic, since water contamination in one state can flow downstream into another state's jurisdiction. Anticipating this possibility, Congress did provide for intervention by the EPA to arrange for interstate management conferences. If a state's water body is not meeting standards due to nonpoint sources in another jurisdiction, that state can petition the EPA to arrange a conference to solve the problem.

Analyzing the Federal Role in Nonpoint Source Controls

Although states have the primary responsibility for implementing nonpoint source controls, they require support from the federal government on a number of fronts. The problem is that policy resources dedicated to water quality have long been focused on point sources, and consequently some adjustments must be made at the federal level. To illustrate, we consider two areas in need of attention: (1) the allocation of resources between point and nonpoint source

---

[27]U.S. GAO (July 1991), pp. 21–22.
[28]U.S. GAO (October 1990), pp. 22–24.

TABLE 14.3   **Annualized Expenditures on Point versus Nonpoint Source Pollution Control ($1986 millions)**

Program	1972	1980	1987	1995	2000
Point source	$ 8,543	$ 22,116	$ 33,642	$ 47,300	$ 56,604
	(93.8%)	(97.2%)	(97.7%)	(98.1%)	(98.3%)
Nonpoint source	567	647	779	893	959
	(6.2%)	(2.8%)	(2.3%)	(1.9%)	(1.7%)
Water quality total*	$ 9,110	$ 22,763	$ 34,421	$ 48,194	$ 57,563
	(100%)	(100%)	(100%)	(100%)	(100%)

Note: Relative proportions are given in parentheses.

*Total excludes expenditures on drinking water controls.

Source: U.S. Environmental Protection Agency, Office of Policy, Planning, and Evaluation, *Environmental Investments: The Cost of a Clean Environment* (Washington, D.C., December 1990), Table 3-3, p. 3-3.

pollution policy; and (2) coordination of nonpoint source programs with other federal programs.

Resource Allocation.   Because of the historic emphasis on point source water pollution, federal funds are needed to fill information voids about nonpoint source pollution. For example, states need water quality criteria to develop standards suited to these diffuse sources of impairment. Unfortunately, the EPA's experience with establishing criteria for point source pollutants is not directly applicable, so the task is expected to be very time-intensive. Similarly, efforts must be made to improve the nation's monitoring technologies, or ''protocols'' as they are called. Here again, the work to date has focused on measuring contaminants released by point sources. It now must be extended to establishing better protocols aimed at the more complex problem of nonpoint source pollution. Attending to these needs will require substantial resources.

Table 14.3 shows the relative spending on point versus nonpoint source pollution control for selected years starting in 1972 and projected through the year 2000. The data clearly indicate the national emphasis on point source control. Notice also that the *proportion* of total spending dedicated to nonpoint source pollution shows a decline from 6.2 percent in 1972 to a projected 1.7 percent in the year 2000. Part of the reason is that the EPA is charged with much greater responsibility for controlling point sources. However, there are two other observations that are more difficult to explain. First, the EPA has not been aggressive in using the funds that *have* been authorized by Congress for nonpoint sources. Of the $400 million approved for Section 319 programs under the Water Quality Act of 1987, the EPA requested only $22 million through 1991 and an accumulated $200 million through 1993. Second, the proportion of funding across the two types of sources is *not* supported by relative risk analysis. A recent study showed that while health risks from point and nonpoint source pollution are comparable, nonpoint sources pose a much greater risk to ecosystems.[29] As we have discussed in previous chapters, policy controls do not always follow scientific findings on actual risk but instead are based on public perceptions of risk. Hence, more federal funding for nonpoint sources might be forthcoming if public awareness about the problem is improved—one of the themes of the EPA's *Nonpoint Source Agenda for the Future* discussed previously.

Coordination with Other National Programs.   Another important issue to be resolved at the federal level is the conflict between water quality objectives and other regulations. This becomes an issue for government programs supporting industries like agriculture and forestry, which are major contributors to nonpoint source pollution. Consider, for example, the agricultural commodity programs operated by the U.S. Department of Agriculture (USDA). These programs are designed to stabilize and support crop prices, which in turn protects the incomes of the nation's farmers. Over two-thirds of U.S. croplands are enrolled in these programs. To operationalize the price protection, an acreage base is established for a given program crop along with a crop yield based upon that acreage, both of which are determined from historical values. Farmers participating in this program cannot plant crops other than the so-called program crop, nor can they plant more than their base acreage in that crop. While such supply restrictions do help to maintain crop prices, they also promote practices that can lead to water contamination. A case in point is the incentive for farmers to specialize in certain program crops, since benefits are based on historical production levels. The problem is that repeated plantings of the same crop year after year depletes the soil and makes plantings more vulnerable to pests. Consequently, farmers tend to rely more on agrichemicals such as fertilizers and pesticides, both of which contribute to agricultural runoff—a problem responsible for the contamination of 50 to 70 percent of assessed U.S. surface waters.[30] Recognizing the conflict, the EPA and the USDA have begun to coordinate the Nonpoint Source Management Program with the USDA's projects. There have even been some arrangements for personnel sharing between the two—an initiative that has brought both agencies new insights that are proving valuable to their respective programs.[31]

---

[29]The issue of funding priorities between point and nonpoint sources is discussed in U.S. GAO (October 1990), pp. 49–53; and Adler et al. (1993), p. 256. Findings on relative risks between the two sources are given in U.S. EPA (August 1989).

[30]U.S. GAO (October 1990), pp. 15–17.

[31]For further information, consult U.S. GAO (October 1990), Chapter 4. A related discussion is given in Harrington, Krupnick, and Peskin (1985).

Proposals for Reform: Using the Market

On balance, federal officials have been slow to react to the inefficiency and cost-ineffectiveness of U.S. water quality policy. There are, however, indications that this trend might be changing. Following the lead of several European countries, the United States is beginning to consider the potential cost savings of using market-based approaches to water quality policy. In fact, some local governments are currently experimenting with these types of incentive-based policy tools. To analyze these economic instruments, we consider two market approaches to point source pollution control: effluent fees and tradeable effluent permits. We then extend the analysis to the more complex case of nonpoint source control by studying product charges and effluent reduction trading within a "bubble."

Market Approaches to Point Source Pollution

volume-based effluent fee
A per unit effluent charge based upon the quantity of pollution discharged.

pollutant-based effluent fee
An effluent charge based on the degree of harm associated with the contaminant being released, such as its toxicity.

Effluent Fees.   As discussed in Chapter 5, an **effluent fee** is a charge based on the discharge of pollution. In order for an effluent charge to provide an incentive for pollution reduction, it must be based either upon the volume or the type of effluent released. For example, a **volume-based** fee is imposed on a per unit basis so that polluters pay higher amounts for larger quantities of discharges. Similarly, to discourage the release of more damaging effluents like those containing toxics, the fee should be **pollutant-based,** meaning it is higher for discharges containing more harmful substances. A few countries like Germany, France, and the Netherlands have instituted effluent charges to control water contamination.[32] Application 14.4 discusses Germany's experience with this type of market-based instrument. Yet worldwide use of effluent fees is still limited. There are complications in setting the level of the fee, and because of the complexity, administrative costs can be prohibitive.[33]

Application 14.4

Germany's Effluent Charge System

Like most advanced countries, Germany experienced substantial economic growth and industrialization during the 1960s. By the early 1970s, this surge of development had taken its toll on

Germany's natural environment, particularly its water resources. In some regions, the contamination was so severe that it was impeding customary uses of some water bodies. There was also mounting

---

[32]For a summary of these particular effluent charge systems, see Hahn (1989).

[33]Several economists have examined the advantages and limitations of effluent fees or taxes. Examples include studies by Rose-Ackerman (1973, 1977) and Herzog (1976), each of whom gives the basic framework of an effluent charge approach with discussion of its real-world limitations. Russell (1979) discusses the major considerations in designing an effluent charge system.

international pressure from countries like Switzerland and the Netherlands who have a vested interest in shared water bodies like the Rhine River. As Germany began to evaluate its existing water protection policies, it could not deny the need for substantive reform.

Germany's first line of defense was to create the Cabinet Committee for Environmental Protection, which it established in 1971. By design, this body was assigned the responsibility of coordinating all environmental activities at the federal level of government. In one of its first official documents, the committee advocated the use of market-based instruments. Among its recommendations was the implementation of an effluent charge to help restore Germany's water quality. As proposed, this charge was to be levied on every discharger in an amount equal to the *incremental* damages caused by its effluents—precisely the kind of solution economists endorse.

Response to the committee's recommendation for an effluent charge was mixed. Support came from some international organizations that traditionally favor proposals based on the so-called "polluter-pays principle." Among these were the Organisation for Economic Cooperation and Development (OECD) and the 1972 World Environmental Conference sponsored by the United Nations. However, the Lander (i.e., all the states of the Federal Republic of Germany) opposed the shift to an economic approach to water quality control. Instead, they supported a more moderate transition with an *integration* of market-based instruments into the country's existing command-and-control structure. There was also strong opposition from most of Germany's industrial sector. However, as the concept of an integrated approach gained political support, this segment of Germany's economy focused its concerns on potential implementation problems such as how the fee would be determined and when it would be effected. Ultimately, a revised initiative was imposed, which integrated an effluent charge system into Germany's existing command-and-control regulatory framework.

In September 1976, the German government passed the Effluent Charge Law, which combined a discharge fee with a permit structure similar to the U.S. system. Implemented in 1981, the new law requires each German state to levy an effluent charge on all direct dischargers of such pollutants as settleable solids, chemical oxygen demand, mercury, cadmium, and toxicity to fish. One of the unique elements of this landmark legislation is a market-based incentive that encourages polluters to abate beyond the level needed for statutory compliance. This is accomplished by reducing a polluter's charge liability if it complies with federally mandated minimum standards. Studies indicate that this incentive feature has had its intended qualitative effect—at least in some German cities and towns. Reportedly, some municipalities and industrial dischargers claim that this aspect of the new law was the primary motivation for their increased investment in waste treatment.

From a financial perspective, the effluent charge adds substantially to government revenues. There is also anecdotal evidence that this instrument can provide significant cost savings. Germany's Council of Experts on Environmental Questions claims that an effluent charge can achieve a given level of water quality for about 33 percent less than if uniform standards were used. Finally, there are indications that the effluent charge may stimulate innovation in pollution abatement. According to the OECD, Germany's clean water technology market has grown considerably and is now the largest segment of its environmental protection market nationwide.

Sources: Gardner M. Brown, Jr. and Ralph W. Johnson, "Pollution Control by Effluent Charges: It Works in the Federal Republic of Germany, Why Not in the U.S?" *Natural Resources Journal* 24 (October 1984), pp. 929–66; and J. B. Opschoor and Has B. Vos, *Economic Instruments for Environmental Protection* (Paris: Organisation for Economic Cooperation and Development, 1989).

FIGURE 14.1

*Cost-effectiveness of
a per unit effluent fee*

Suppose the government sets a per unit effluent fee for releases of some toxic water pollutant. The decisions of two hypothetical firms are shown above, each facing different MAC curves but the same marginal effluent fee (MEF). Firm 1 faces MAC_1 and abates A_1 units of effluent, and Firm 2 faces MAC_2 and abates A_2 units. Although the individual abatement levels are different, the associated MAC incurred by each firm is the same.

To illustrate these issues, suppose the government sets a per unit effluent fee for releases of some toxic water pollutant. The outcome would be that each polluting source would abate up to the point where its marginal abatement cost (MAC) equaled the fee. Since all MACs would be equal, the effluent charge would yield a cost-effective solution. This is shown in Figure 14.1 for two hypothetical firms, each facing different MAC curves but the same marginal effluent fee (MEF). Firm 1 faces MAC_1 and abates A_1 units of effluent, and Firm 2 faces MAC_2 and abates A_2 units. Although the abatement amounts are different, the associated level of MAC for each firm is the same.

Recognize, however, that the combined abatement level achieved by all firms would not be efficient unless the marginal social cost of abatement (MSC) (i.e., the horizontal sum of all the individual MACs (MAC_{mkt}) plus the government's marginal cost of monitoring and enforcement (MCE)) were equal to the associated marginal social benefit of abatement (MSB). Identifying the MSB and the MSC in practice is very difficult, and the costs of collecting the necessary data to do so would likely be prohibitive. Even if this task were somehow accomplished, the solution would be efficient only in the aggregate and *not* for the specific water bodies affected. Unless the marginal benefits and costs at each pollution site were identical, the fee would not yield a waterbody-specific efficient outcome. For example, the fee would effectively overregulate polluters in regions where the associated marginal benefits of abatement were relatively low, such as in a sparsely populated location, and would underregulate polluters where the conditions were reversed, holding all else constant.

Such an outcome is shown in Figure 14.2, where it is assumed for simplicity that the MSC is the same for two regions, but there are different MSB curves—MSB_{low} in a low population area and MSB_{high} in a high population area. If the per unit effluent fee is set at MEF, each region will abate A_o units. Notice, however, that A_o is *above* the efficient level for the sparsely populated

FIGURE 14.2

Inefficiency of a national per unit effluent fee.

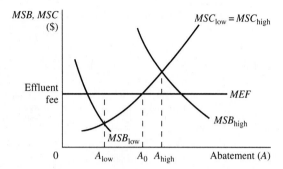

In the model above, the *MSC* is the same for two regions, but there are different *MSB* curves—*MSB*$_{low}$ in a low population area and *MSB*$_{high}$ in a high or densely populated area. If the per unit effluent fee is set at *MEF*, each region will abate A_o units. Notice that A_o is above the efficient level for the sparsely populated region, A_{low}, and below the efficient level for the densely populated region, A_{high}. If the objective were to achieve efficiency at the regional level, regulatory officials would have to establish a unique effluent fee for every location corresponding to the abatement level where the respective *MSB* and *MSC* were equal.

region, A_{low}, and *below* the efficient level for the densely populated region, A_{high}. Hence, if the objective were to achieve efficiency at the regional level, regulatory officials would have to impose a unique effluent fee for every location corresponding to the abatement level where the respective *MSB* and *MSC* are equal. The data required to implement such a complex plan coupled with the sophisticated monitoring needed would make this approach highly impractical—at least on a national scale. However, there are opportunities for states to institute such programs, and in fact some state officials have begun to do so. Officials in New York and California, for example, have instituted fees that are either volume-based or pollutant-based. A similar approach is being used by some POTWs.[34] These initiatives are extensions of the permit fees implemented through the National Pollutant Discharge Elimination System (NPDES). Normally, these charges are independent of the type or amount of effluent being discharged. Thus, the associated *MEF* is zero, offering no incentive for polluting sources to abate.[35]

[34]For POTWs, incentive effects appear to occur only for pollutant-based charges and not for those tied to volume. See Sims (1977) as cited in U.S. EPA, Office of Policy, Planning, and Evaluation (July 1992), p. 3-2. To date, there has been no comprehensive study of the incentive effects associated with analogous charges set through the NPDES.

[35]The EPA's Office of Policy, Planning, and Evaluation has launched a new project to devise a sliding-scale fee system based on the toxicity of discharges in the 12 states for which the agency currently writes NPDES permits. The revenues received under the new system would be held in a Water Pollution Trust Fund. Part of the monies would be used to cover administrative costs, with the remainder distributed to states for initiating pollution prevention practices. See U.S. GAO (July 1991), p. 39.

TABLE 14.4   Examples of Tradeable Effluent Permit Markets

State	Water Body	Pollutant	Type of Sources in Trades	Estimated Cost Savings ($ millions)
Wisconsin	Fox River	Biological oxygen demand	Point	$7.0
Colorado	Dillon Reservoir	Phosphorus	Point/nonpoint	1.0
Colorado	Cherry Creek Reservoir	Phosphorus	Point/nonpoint	na
North Carolina	Tar-Pamlico Basin	Nitrogen and phosphorus	Point/nonpoint	na

---

Note: na = Not available.

Sources: Hahn (1989); Elmore et al. (1984); and U.S. Environmental Protection Agency, Office of Policy, Planning and Evaluation, *The United States Experience with Economic Incentives to Control Environmental Pollution* (Washington, D.C., July 1992), pp. 5-15–5-16, which cites the work of O'Neil et al. (1983).

tradeable effluent permit market
The exchange of permits or ''rights to pollute'' among polluting sources.

Tradeable Effluent Permits.   An alternative economic instrument is the establishment of a **tradeable effluent permit market.** This could be implemented using the existing NPDES, by issuing each permit as a set of tradeable, per unit ''rights to pollute.'' As discussed in Chapter 5, there are potential gains from trading as long as *MAC*s differ across polluting sources. If a discharger does not need to release all the effluents allowed, it can hold the excess rights for future use or sell them to other dischargers. If it needs to release more than allowed by law, it must either abate more or buy the rights it needs from polluters holding an excess. Low-cost abaters will have excess rights which they would be willing to sell at any price greater than or equal to their *MAC*. High-cost abaters would be willing to buy these as long as the selling price is less than or equal to their own *MAC*. Market forces will establish a price for permits such that all firms abate to the point where the associated level of MAC is equal across firms—a cost-effective solution.

Table 14.4 lists some of the applications of tradeable effluent permit markets, including a frequently cited program designed to clean up the Fox River. In 1981, Wisconsin officials instituted this plan for one type of pollutant being released to the Fox River.[36] The initial allocation of permitted discharges was based on historical data and was valid for a five-year period. Officials expected that unequal *MAC*s among polluting sources would provide the impetus for active trading of effluent reduction credits. One researcher estimated that this market potentially could yield a cost savings of about $7 million. However,

---

[36]The pollutants targeted by the program are so-called BOD-based effluents. BOD stands for biological oxygen demand, which measures the amount of oxygen needed by microorganisms to decompose organic compounds. Hence, as the waste level in a water body rises, the BOD measure rises as well.

the savings have not materialized, since only one trade has taken place.[37] Why? Several conditions may justify the absence of trading in this case. For one thing, participants in the program still had to meet the federally established technology-based effluent limits. Since such standards constrain independent decision-making, they likely limit the incentive mechanism of the trading program. Furthermore, two of the major classes of dischargers involved, namely pulp and paper mills and municipal waste treatment plants, do not operate in competitive markets, which also dampens market forces. Finally, the key participants in the program did not fully support the plan, further limiting its potential for success.[38] These observations suggest that market conditions and existing regulatory constraints must be considered in the design of a successful trading program.

Market Approaches to Nonpoint Source Pollution

Using a market approach to reduce nonpoint source pollution is more complex because the problem itself is that much more difficult to identify. The dilemma becomes apparent if we reconsider a pricing instrument like an effluent fee in this context. Implementing this approach is problematic, since land runoff and atmospheric deposition arise from a number of sources. Since the contribution of each polluting source is indeterminate, an effluent fee cannot be implemented fairly—at least not in the usual sense. If policy-makers were to impose a uniform fee on all known contributors to a runoff problem, the result would be inequitable. The fees would be passed on to consumers of the goods produced at these sites through higher prices, and those individuals would bear most of the costs. However, the benefits of the reduced runoff would accrue primarily to individuals located near the waterway.[39] Because of these difficulties, an indirect approach can be used such as a **product charge** levied on the commodity whose usage adds to a known runoff problem.

product charge
A fee added to the price of a pollution-generating product based either on its quantity or some attribute responsible for pollution.

Product Charge.   An often cited example of using a **product charge** to control runoff is the use of a fertilizer tax. Since agricultural runoff is a major contributor of nonpoint source pollution, such a market instrument appears to have merit. Imposing a tax on fertilizer causes its effective price to rise, which in turn should reduce the quantity demanded of this pollution-generating commodity. In theory, the optimal tax is one that covers the marginal external costs associated with fertilizer use in the production of agricultural products.

---

[37]U.S. EPA, Office of Policy, Planning, and Evaluation (July 1992), p. 5-15, citing O'Neil et al. (1983) on the cost-savings estimation.

[38]Hahn (1989).

[39]Harrington et al. (1985). For a more in-depth analysis of the efficiency and equity considerations on nonpoint source controls in the agricultural sector, see Spurlock and Clifton (1982).

In practice, however, the operative issue is whether the demand response to the elevated effective price is sufficient to measurably reduce the runoff problem.

As of 1988, 46 states had imposed such a tax, but the rates apparently were too low to have much of an effect on fertilizer consumption. Tax rates range from $0.10 to $1.70 per ton—a very small proportion of the product's price, which is anywhere from $60 to $200 per ton. With taxes levied at no higher than a 2.5 percent rate, and usually much lower than that, the decline in consumption has been negligible.[40] Even if the rates were elevated, the effect on quantity demanded would likely not be sufficient to significantly mitigate the associated pollution problem. Since fertilizer is an important input in crop production, its demand is likely to be relatively price inelastic. In fact, studies of the use of such fees in Europe show that even with a tax rate of 50 percent, fertilizer usage is not significantly reduced.[41] Ultimately, the incremental benefit of these taxes tends to be not in the decline in fertilizer use but in the associated revenues that can be used to enhance environmental protection and fund research. Some $14 million are raised each year from these taxes in the United States.[42]

Effluent Reduction Trading within a "Bubble."   An alternative market-based approach to nonpoint source pollution is the use of an **effluent reduction trading policy** within a "bubble" (sometimes called a "bowl" to signify its use for a watershed). The premise is exactly the same as what underlies the use of a bubble to control air pollution. In simple terms, an overall abatement objective is established for a watershed, and then each polluting source is assigned an effluent limit. Once done, these sources are allowed to negotiate trades among themselves for "rights to pollute" issued as **effluent reduction credits** or **effluent allowances**.[43] **Effluent reduction credits** are issued if a polluter discharges *less* than what is permitted by law. **Allowances** are issued up front and give the polluter the right to release pollution in the future. Polluting sources have an incentive to trade as long as their *MAC*s are not equal at current abatement levels. Ultimately, the market will establish a price for each allowance or credit such that all polluters abate to the point where their respective *MAC* levels are equal. This approach has been used to allow trading between point and nonpoint source polluters as shown in Table 14.4. In theory, such trades should bring about efficiency gains, since abatement costs are typically much higher for point sources than they are for nonpoint sources.

effluent reduction trading policy
A market approach whereby an abatement objective is established for a watershed and sources are allowed to negotiate trades for "rights to pollute."

effluent reduction credits
Tradeable permits issued to a polluting source if it discharges a lower level of effluents than what is allowed by law.

effluent allowances
Tradeable permits issued up front to a polluting source that give it the right to release effluents in the future.

---

[40]U.S. EPA, Office of Policy, Planning, and Evaluation (July 1992), p. 3-5.
[41]U.S. EPA, Office of Water (January 1992), p. 196.
[42]U.S. EPA, Office of Policy, Planning, and Evaluation (July 1992), p. 3-5. For a discussion of some specific usage of such product charges, see U.S. EPA, Office of Water (January 1992), pp. 196–97.
[43]The reader may wish to review this distinction introduced in Chapter 5.

Perhaps the most frequently cited example of a point/nonpoint source trading program is one designed to clean up the Dillon Reservoir.[44]

The Dillon Reservoir is an important resource to Colorado, since it supplies Denver residents with more than half of their water supply. Over time, residential and industrial development in the area caused a serious pollution problem. The reservoir was receiving significant amounts of phosphorus, which was contributing to its decline. Officials tracked the damaging discharges and determined that over half was coming from nonpoint sources. The remainder was coming from 4 municipal treatment plants, 16 small treatment plants, and an industrial facility. Although these point sources were being controlled by discharge limits, they faced substantial marginal costs in trying to achieve them. More importantly, the large municipal treatment facilities faced much higher marginal abatement costs than the nonpoint sources in the watershed. The Dillon Reservoir problem was a textbook case of unequal marginal abatement costs across polluting sources where cost savings could be realized through a trading scheme.[45] With the EPA's support, officials in the area instituted a point/nonpoint source trading program. Initial allocations of phosphorus discharge limits were set, and trades were allowed between point and nonpoint sources on a 2-to-1 ratio.[46]

Despite the classic conditions at the Dillon Reservoir, active trading has been minimal. There are, however, some logical explanations for this outcome. For one thing, point sources in the Dillon area have become more efficient abaters over time. As they have, their abatement costs have declined, which in turn lessens their incentive to trade for pollution rights. Also, the region's economic development has begun to slow down, which necessarily lessens the amount of discharges and hence the need for market trades. Finally, the 2-to-1 trading ratio, while well intentioned, discourages trading, since point sources are allowed only 1 unit of effluent for every 2 credits they buy. Interestingly, it is reported that a few trades have been proposed between nonpoint sources at the Dillon Reservoir region, an outcome that was not anticipated by the

---

[44]Other programs include the Cherry Creek Reservoir in Colorado and a project under way in North Carolina to save the Tar-Pamlico basin. The latter is discussed in Hall and Howett (1994). See U.S. EPA, Office of Policy, Planning, and Evaluation (July 1992), pp. 5-15 and 5-16 from which much of the following discussion on the Dillon Reservoir is drawn.

[45]An EPA study suggests that there was a potential for over $1 million in cost savings. See Elmore et al. (1984) cited in Harrington et al. (1985). For a discussion of why these savings might not be realized, see Hahn (1989).

[46]A trading ratio of 2 means that point sources are allowed 1 unit of effluent for every 2 they purchase from nonpoint sources. A ratio greater than 1 favors point source reductions and discourages trades. Conversely, a ratio less than 1 favors reductions by nonpoint sources and encourages trades. For an analysis of these ratios and an overview of point/nonpoint source trading, see Letson (1992). A more rigorous study is given by Malik, Letson, and Crutchfield (1993).

program planners.[47] It is still too soon to predict the long-term success of such trading programs, since they are still relatively new. In any case, the experiences at the Dillon Reservoir may be valuable to other officials planning to establish similar markets.

Conclusions

An ongoing source of debate is the nation's dependence on a command-and-control approach to achieving water quality and the methods it uses to guide critical decisions. Since 1972, U.S. water control policy has been rooted in the use of technology-based effluent standards. There have been documented delays in setting these limits, which in turn have slowed states' efforts in achieving receiving water quality standards. Beyond the time problem, there is a lack of guidance in the law as to how the technological and economic determinants of these limits are to be considered relative to one another. An efficient abatement level is not likely, given the absence of any mandate to use benefit-cost analysis in defining these standards. Furthermore, because the effluent standards are applied uniformly within major groups of polluters, a cost-effective solution is also unlikely.

Another costly policy decision has been the federal funding of POTW construction. Studies show that these funds have served primarily to displace rather than supplement local spending, suggesting that observed improvements in waste treatment are not directly attributable to the billions of dollars spent at the federal level for this program. In addition, by removing much of the cost burden from municipalities, local officials had little incentive to make cost-conscious decisions in building waste treatment facilities. Policy-makers have recognized the problem and revised the law in an attempt to restore the incentive mechanisms removed by the long-term grant program.

Beyond this dependence on command-and-control instruments, there are gaps in the overall policy approach. Nonpoint polluting sources such as agricultural and urban runoff are major contributors to water contamination, and the United States has only begun to address this highly complex issue. The 1987 amendments initiated the Nonpoint Source Management Program, but this program cannot succeed unless resources are allocated to improving monitoring technologies and to advancing the knowledge base about nonpoint source pollution.

On balance, the federal government has virtually ignored market incentives in implementing water quality regulations. Economic instruments such as effluent fees and permit trading programs might be viable alternatives to the nation's current standards-based approach. In fact, the use of economic

---

[47]U.S. EPA, Office of Policy, Planning, and Evaluation (July 1992), pp. 5-15–5-16. The reader should consult Harrington et al. (1985), particularly pp. 29–30, for a clear explanation as to why trading might be more likely among nonpoint sources and other determinants of trading activity.

incentives is one of the themes of President Clinton's Clean Water Act Initiative—the administration's proposal for revision of the Clean Water Act. Our analysis of this major U.S. law illustrates how water quality policy development has been and continues to be an evolutionary process. Environmental controls must be continuously evaluated and revised to reflect new technologies, changes in natural conditions, and innovative proposals for better solutions.

Summary

- Point sources are subject to EPA-determined, end-of-pipe effluent limits that vary by the type of polluting source, the age of the facility, and sometimes by the type of contaminant released. Although there are different standards for different groups, they are applicable uniformly to all individual polluters within each designated group.

- Effluent limits for direct industrial dischargers and for publicly owned treatment works (POTWs) are communicated to dischargers through a permitting system called the National Pollutant Discharge Elimination System (NPDES).

- For new industrial point sources, the effluent limitations are more stringent than those for existing sources, based upon what the law calls best available demonstrated control technology (BADCT). Wherever practical, the BADCT are to explicitly prohibit effluent discharges.

- For existing industrial point sources, two types of limits are applicable based on the type of pollutant released—best available technology economically achievable (BAT) standards for controlling nonconventional and toxic pollutants, and best conventional control technology (BCT) standards for conventional pollutants.

- There have been delays in developing and revising the guidelines that serve as a basis for the effluent limitations. It is also the case that these limitations are not aligned with U.S. objectives, since they are based on what is technologically feasible rather than what is needed to achieve water quality. The EPA is also criticized for not imposing zero effluent limits where achievable in accordance with the nation's zero discharge goal.

- Economists and policy analysts object to the absence of economic decision rules in guiding the specification of the BAT and BCT standards. The Clean Water Act does not mandate that these standards be set to maximize net benefits, which prevents an efficient solution. Furthermore, they are applied uniformly across dischargers within identified groups, which disallows a cost-effective outcome.

- Prior to the 1987 revisions, Title II of the Clean Water Act outlined the federal grant program for the construction of POTWs. There were also provisions to facilitate the development of areawide waste treatment management plans for regions facing major water quality problems due to urban-industrial concentration. In 1987, Title VI was added as the successor to Title II, authorizing capitalization grants to states for setting up a revolving fund for various projects.

- One criticism of the POTW grant program is that the majority of federal monies only displaced local funding for new construction. Furthermore, federal aid was aimed only at construction of POTWs, with no provisions to assure proper operation and maintenance of these facilities. An economic issue is that the mandated federal cost share shifted most of the expenditures away from local governments, leaving them little incentive to minimize costs.

- Under the Nonpoint Source Management Program initiated in 1987, states must prepare assessment reports in which they identify waters unable to achieve quality standards without controls on nonpoint sources. They also must develop management programs in which they designate best management practices (BMP) to reduce pollution from every identified nonpoint source.

- One factor supporting states' responsibility for nonpoint sources is the location-specific nature of nonpoint source pollution. Another is the political sensitivity of federal controls on land use. On the opposite side are information deficiencies that hinder state governments' ability to carry out their responsibilities. There is also the potential problem of inconsistent control efforts, which become problematic when contamination flows downstream across jurisdictions.

- At the federal level, far less funding has been allocated to nonpoint source pollution than to point source contamination. There also have been conflicts between water quality objectives and the goals of other regulations and programs, such as those directed by the USDA.

- The United States is beginning to consider the potential cost savings of using market-based approaches to water quality policy. Some local governments are experimenting with these types of incentive-based policy tools.

- An effluent charge can be based either upon the volume or the type of effluent released. Germany, France, and the Netherlands have instituted these instruments, as have some state governments in the United States.

- Tradeable effluent permit markets could be implemented using the existing NPDES by issuing the permit as a set of tradeable, per unit "rights to pollute." Potential gains from trading exist as long as marginal abatement costs differ across polluting sources.

- Product charges can be levied on a commodity whose usage adds to a known runoff problem, such as fertilizers that contribute to agricultural runoff. An alternative approach is the use of an effluent reduction trading policy within a "bubble," which has been used to allow trading between point and nonpoint sources.

Key Concepts

technology-based effluent limitations
National Pollutant Discharge
   Elimination System (NPDES)
best available demonstrated control
   technology (BADCT)
best available technology economically
   achievable (BAT)

best conventional control technology
   (BCT)
water quality-related limitations
federal grant program
State Revolving Fund (SRF) program
Nonpoint Source Management Program
best management practices (BMP)

volume-based effluent fee
pollutant-based effluent fee
tradeable effluent permit market
product charge

effluent reduction trading within a
  ''bubble''
effluent reduction credits
effluent allowances

APPENDIX
A REFERENCE TO ACRONYMS IN WATER QUALITY
CONTROL POLICY

Environmental Economics Acronyms

MAC	Marginal abatement cost of a single polluter
MAC_{mkt}	Marginal abatement cost of all polluters
MCE	Marginal cost of enforcement
MEF	Marginal effluent fee
MSB	Marginal social benefit of abatement
MSB_{low}	Marginal social benefit of abatement in an area with a low population
MSB_{high}	Marginal social benefit of abatement in an area with a high population
MSC	Marginal social cost of abatement

Environmental Science Acronyms

BOD	Biological oxygen demand
DO	Dissolved oxygen
mg/l	Milligrams per liter

Environmental Policy Acronyms

BADCT	Best available demonstrated control technology
BAT	Best available technology economically achievable
BCT	Best conventional control technology
BMP	Best management practices
BPT	Best practicable technology currently available
FWPCA	Federal Water Pollution Control Act
NPDES	National Pollutant Discharge Elimination System
POTWs	Publicly owned treatment works
SRF	State Revolving Fund

Review Questions

1. *a.* Evaluate the use of ''technological attainability'' as the primary determinant of the effluent limitations.
   b. Economically analyze the use of *uniform* technology-based effluent limitations.

2. Discuss the incentive/disincentive implications of the federal assistanceprograms for POTW construction.

3. As an alternative to standards, one policy proposal is the use of permit trading between point sources of water pollution. Give the major reason why this is advantageous: (a) from an economic perspective; and (b) from an environmental perspective.

4. According to EPA Administrator Carol Browner,

> We've done the easy part of controlling pollution at the end of the pipeline. For the first time ever, we are tackling the hard part—the control of polluted runoff, which is the biggest remaining barrier we face in keeping the nation's waters clean.[48]

Working as part of the EPA's team, your assignment is to give a clear, objective presentation of a market-based approach to reduce nonpoint source pollution. Include in your discussion the theoretical issues and any practical concerns that must be addressed prior to implementing your proposal.

5. *a.* To help fight the problem of nonpoint source pollution associated with agricultural runoff, your state is contemplating charging an annual fee of $500 to every seller of pesticides. If this fee is to achieve an efficient solution, state specifically according to externality theory (a) what the $500 fee must represent; and (b) in which market.

   b. Illustrate graphically, labeling where and how the fee is imposed.

Additional Readings

Downing, Donna, and Stuart Sessions. "Innovative Water Quality-based Permitting: A Policy Perspective." *Journal of Water Pollution Control Federation* 57, no. 5 (May 1985), pp. 358–65.

Joeres, Erhard F., and Martin H. David, eds. *Buying a Better Environment: Cost-Effective Regulation Through Permit Trading.* Madison, Wis.: University of Wisconsin Press, 1983.

Knopman, Debra S., and Richard A. Smith. "20 Years of the Clean Water Act: Has U.S. Water Quality Improved?" *Environment* 35, no. 1 (January/February 1993), pp. 17–20, 34–41.

Krupnick, Alan J. "Reducing Bay Nutrients: An Economic Perspective." *Maryland Law Review* 47, no. 452 (1988), pp. 452–80.

Magat, Wesley A., and W. Kip Viscusi. "Effectiveness of the EPA's Regulatory Enforcement: The Case of Industrial Effluent Standards." *Journal of Law and Economics* 33 (October 1990), pp. 331–60.

---

[48]U.S. EPA, Office of Communications, Education, and Public Affairs (February 22, 1994b).

Oates, Wallace E., and Dianna L. Strassmann. ''Effluent Fees and Market Structure.'' *Journal of Public Economics* 24 (1984), pp. 29–46.

O'Neil, William B. ''The Regulation of Water Pollution Permit Trading under Conditions of Varying Streamflow and Temperature.'' In E. Joeres and M. David, eds. *Buying a Better Environment: Cost-Effective Regulation Through Permit Trading.* Madison, Wis.: University of Wisconsin Press, 1983, pp. 219–31.

U.S. General Accounting Office (GAO). *Water Pollution: Improved Monitoring and Enforcement Needed for Toxic Pollutants Entering Sewers.* Washington, D.C., April 1989.

PROTECTING
DRINKING WATER

The U.S. Safe Drinking Water Act

In 1993, 400,000 residents of Milwaukee, Wisconsin, became ill from a waterborne disease that was transmitted through the city's drinking water. Ultimately, more than 40 people lost their lives. Beyond the human suffering, an estimated sum of $37 million in wages and productivity was lost. How could a city's water supplies become so polluted? What went wrong? There are several theories—human error, aging facilities, illegal discharges, and monitoring failures among them. Another is that the disease outbreak was a result of poorly defined federal controls. The claim is that regulations divert attention and resources to lower-priority problems, which in this case caused officials to miss the warning signs of the contamination.[1] Whatever the reason, the Milwaukee incident sparked national concern about the potential for similar problems across America. It also triggered skepticism and criticism of U.S. drinking water policy. What regulations are in place to protect drinking water supplies? How effective is this part of U.S. water quality control policy?

Drinking water supplies depend on ground and surface water resources, both of which are protected by the Clean Water Act. However, this act requires a level of water quality to support aquatic life and recreational uses—a level that calls for far less stringent standards than those necessary to support safe drinking. Furthermore, although the Clean Water Act is comprehensive, its protection of groundwater resources is limited. Groundwater is the source of drinking water for half of the U.S. population and for 95 percent of rural Americans.[2] Hence, regulations beyond those in the Clean Water Act are necessary to minimize the risks of contaminated drinking water—precisely the motivation of the U.S. Safe Drinking Water Act.

---

[1]Smith (Summer 1994).
[2]U.S. EPA (August 1988), p. 52.

U.S. regulations on drinking water have an evolution with a century-long history—much of it dominated by the setting of bacteriological standards by public health officials. For many years, there was an absence of control over other types of contamination, including toxic chemicals and, ironically, harmful substances associated with water treatment procedures. In the United States, comprehensive legislation on drinking water was not passed until the 1970s—some 60 years after the first health standard had been established. Furthermore, it was not until the 1980s that provisions were added specifically to protect groundwater resources.

In this chapter, we focus on the nation's drinking water policy, which is governed by the Safe Drinking Water Act. Like the Clean Water Act, this legislation uses a standards-based, command-and-control policy approach—a characteristic we evaluate from an economic perspective. Our investigation is timely because this law—like the Clean Water Act—has recently come up for reauthorization before Congress. We begin with a brief review of the origin and evolution of drinking water standards and laws. From this point, we discuss the objectives of the Safe Drinking Water Act and the standards used to define drinking water quality for the nation. Once done, we analyze the federal standard-setting process, the performance of state and local governments in meeting these standards, and the cost implications for society. We then consider the economics of pricing water supplies. Once again, an appendix of acronyms is provided at the end of the chapter.

The Evolution of U.S. Safe Drinking Water Legislation

Throughout the early history of the United States, deaths caused by diseases such as cholera and typhoid fever were not uncommon. For many years, no one realized that these diseases were caused by bacteria living in water supplies used for drinking. It was not until 1854 that an epidemiologist named Dr. John Snow linked cholera to contaminated water. Another 30 years passed before specific bacteria were identified as the cause of waterborne disease. Armed with this evidence, the federal government enacted the Interstate Quarantine Act of 1893. As Table 15.1 shows, this was the first federal law in the evolution of U.S. drinking water controls. This act authorized the surgeon general to issue regulations to prevent the spread of disease from any foreign country to the United States or from one state to another. In 1912, the first water-related regulation was passed—a ruling that outlawed the use of a common drinking cup on interstate carriers.[3]

---

[3]McDermott (1973) as cited in Larson (1989).

TABLE 15.1   **Evolution of U.S. Drinking Water Legislation**

Legislation	*Major Provisions*
Interstate Quarantine Act of 1893	Authorized the surgeon general to issue regulations to prevent the spread of disease; led to the first U.S. water regulation passed in 1912 prohibiting the use of a common drinking cup on interstate carriers.
Public Health Service Act of 1912	Provided for the U.S. Public Health Service to set bacteriological standards for drinking water.
Revisions to Public Health Standards in 1925, 1942, 1946, 1962	Strengthened existing standards; required more stringent testing procedures; established maximum allowable concentrations for certain substances.
Safe Drinking Water Act of 1974	Authorized the EPA to establish drinking water standards; controlled underground injection activities and protected sole-source aquifers.
Safe Drinking Water Amendments of 1986	Accelerated procedures for the standard-setting process; provided greater protection of groundwater sources of drinking water; banned the use of lead in public drinking water systems.

Sources: Charles D. Larson, ''Historical Development of the National Primary Drinking Water Regulations,'' in Edward J. Calabrese, Charles E. Gilbert, and Harris Pastides, eds., *Safe Drinking Water Act: Amendments, Regulations and Standards* (Chelsea, Mich.: Lewis Publishers, Inc., 1989), pp. 3–15; H. McDermott, ''Federal Drinking Water Standards—Past, Present, and Future,'' *Water Well Journal* 27, no. 12 (1973), pp. 29–35; Andrew A. Dzurik, *Water Resources Planning* (Savage, Md.: Rowman & Littlefield Publishers, Inc., 1990); U.S. Congress, Office of Technology Assessment (OTA), *Protecting the Nation's Groundwater from Contamination*, vol. I (Washington, D.C.: U.S. Government Printing Office, October 1984), Chapter 3, pp. 64–75; Sidney M. Wolf, *Pollution Law Handbook: A Guide to Federal Environmental Laws* (New York: Quorom Books, 1988), Chapter 4, pp. 133–37.

Setting Standards to Protect Drinking Water

Recognizing that banning common drinking cups was of little value if the water itself was contaminated, federal authorities passed the Public Health Service Act of 1912—the first U.S. law to specifically call for drinking water health standards. As authorized, these standards were limited in scope— targeting only contaminants capable of spreading communicable waterborne diseases. Hence, in 1914 the Public Health Service set *bacteriological* standards for drinking water. Recognizing the potential health risks of other types of substances, the standards were expanded in 1925 to consider chemical characteristics like lead and copper. Over the next several decades, more revisions followed, each time adding more structure to the law and strengthening existing standards and controls.[4]

In the 1960s, there was a turn of events that was to change the direction of U.S. drinking water policy. In 1963, the Public Health Service formed an advisory committee to evaluate the existing drinking water standards and make appropriate recommendations. In 1967, the committee recommended that toxic contaminants be addressed—an advisory that *would* have led to limits on such chemicals as chlordane and DDT. However, it was argued that setting

---

[4]McDermott (1973) as cited in Larson (1989); Dzurik (1990), p. 61.

standards on toxics went beyond the jurisdiction of the Public Health Service, whose authority was limited to controlling communicable disease. Although the responsibility may have been misplaced, the concern was appropriate. Chemical usage was on the rise, pesticides were being detected in groundwater supplies, and the general public was becoming alarmed. A federal committee was formed in 1969 to evaluate the 1962 standards and make recommendations. It completed its work in 1971—one year after the EPA had been established. The newly established agency reviewed the committee's report, which ultimately became the cornerstone of new regulations. These were issued under the Safe Drinking Water Act of 1974 (SDWA), at which point the responsibility of protecting drinking water shifted from the Public Health Service to the EPA.[5]

The Safe Drinking Water Act of 1974 (SDWA)[6]

Capitalizing on the broader jurisdiction of the EPA, the Safe Drinking Water Act (SDWA) was aimed at protecting drinking water from *any* contaminant that could threaten human health or welfare—not just bacteria responsible for communicable disease. Primary standards were to be established for organic and inorganic chemicals, radionuclides, and microorganisms identified as having adverse effects on public health. Secondary standards, which were actually just guidelines, were to be defined to protect welfare by controlling such characteristics as taste and odor.

Not unlike other early environmental laws, the SDWA of 1974 was not without problems that ultimately caused major delays. It originally called for interim health standards to be set within 180 days. These were to be revised based on a coordinated effort between the EPA and the National Academy of Science (NAS), at which time they would become final regulations. These regulations were to establish pollution limits called maximum contaminant levels (MCLs) that the NAS believed would protect human health. The complex procedures coupled with the EPA's alleged lack of initiative delayed the process considerably. In fact, a litany of missed deadlines left many dangerous pollutants without standards for years. By the mid-1980s, relatively few contaminants had been regulated by the EPA, and most interim standards still had not been revised. These procedural problems and uneven compliance by public water utilities led to the 1986 Amendments—the law currently in force.

The Safe Drinking Water Amendments of 1986

The 1986 Amendments expanded federal controls on drinking water and corrected some of the failings of the original SDWA. To accelerate procedures for the standard-setting process, maximum contaminant levels (MCLs) were

---

[5]Larson (1989).

[6]Drawn from U.S. Congress, Office of Technology Assessment (OTA) (October 1984), Vol. I., Chapter 1, pp. 8–9, Chapter 3, pp. 64–75; Wolf (1988), Chapter 4, pp. 133–37.

required for a specific list of 83 contaminants according to a strict timetable over the 1987 to 1989 period. Responding to growing concerns about lead contamination, the amendments prohibited all future use of lead pipe and solder in public drinking-water systems, now known as the "lead ban." Other revisions attempted to provide better protection of underground drinking water supplies.

Although the SDWA of 1986 addressed some important concerns, most agree that further changes are needed. Numerous proposals for reform have been discussed as part of the most recent reauthorization of this act. Among these proposals was President Clinton's Safe Drinking Water Initiative, an outline of which is given in Application 15.1.

Application 15.1

Reauthorizing the Safe Drinking Water Act: Clinton's Safe Drinking Water Initiative

As part of the reauthorization of the Safe Drinking Water Act, Congress must evaluate the nation's current policy position, consider areas in need of revision, and contemplate recommendations for reform. The Clinton administration has proposed a number of changes in the form of a Safe Drinking Water Initiative. The following are key elements of the Clinton plan.

- **Regulating drinking water contaminants**

  Existing policy should be revised to authorize the EPA to consider any number of contaminants for regulation in lieu of the current requirement calling for standards on an additional 25 pollutants every three years.

- **Financing infrastructure**

  Analogous to the federal funding program authorized by the Clean Water Act, a State Revolving Fund should be established to help local communities and water utilities finance needed infrastructure. Under the proposal, $599 million would be authorized for 1994, $700 million for 1995, and $1 billion per year for 1996 through 1998.

- **User fees**

  States would be given the authority to establish a user program to assure sufficient

resources to implement the provisions of the Safe Drinking Water Act.

- **Special assistance for small water systems**

  States would establish programs to evaluate whether small water systems are viable and if they are capable of complying with new drinking water regulations. They would also be given the authority to prevent the establishment of nonviable systems and to consolidate noncompliant, nonviable systems as needed. Less costly treatment technologies would be established specifically for these smaller systems with special requirements for added precautions like source-water protection programs to assure public health protection.

- **Encouraging source-water protection**

  States would be required to develop source-water protection programs that would delineate drinking water protection areas and assess the threat of contamination in these areas. The purpose of this proposal is to prevent contamination from occurring and in so doing lower monitoring and treatment costs. As a further incentive, states could approve alternative monitoring and treatment processes for communities that have implemented an "enhanced" source-water

---

Application 15.1 (concluded)

protection program, where "enhanced" would be determined by the EPA.

• **Strengthened enforcement**

Enforcement of the Safe Drinking Water Act should be strengthened such that it is consistent with other environmental laws. Consolidation among multiple enforcement provisions should be done and any inconsistencies addressed. Clarification should be made that federal facilities must be in compliance with the law.

• **Training and certifying drinking water systems operators**

States would be required to establish training and certifying programs for all drinking water system operators. For those systems unable to meet the costs of training or hiring certified personnel, provision would be allowed for the hiring of part-time services or the sharing of services with other local systems.

Source: *EPA Journal,* "Safe Drinking Water Act Reform," *EPA Journal* 20, no. 1–2 (Summer 1994), p. 9.

Objectives of the Safe Drinking Water Act

Interestingly, the SDWA has no statutory objectives per se. However, according to the House of Representatives, the primary purpose of the act is as follows:

> To assure that water supply systems serving the public meet minimum national standards for protection of public health.

sole-source aquifers Those underground geological formations containing groundwater that are the only supply of drinking water for a given area.

To accomplish this goal, the SDWA of 1974 authorized three key directives: (1) to establish drinking water health standards applicable to public water systems; (2) to control underground injection activities that may threaten drinking water;[7] and (3) to protect **sole-source aquifers** (i.e., those that are the only source of drinking water for a given area).[8] The 1986 Amendments added another directive—this one aimed at protecting groundwater supplies used for drinking. The new provisions called for states to develop Wellhead Protection Programs that would safeguard areas around public water supply wells. As of 1992, 27 states and territories have EPA-approved programs.[9]

It is important to have some perspective about how these directives relate to those of other U.S. water quality laws. Compared to the Clean Water Act, which has a comprehensive span of control, notice that the Safe Drinking Water Act (SDWA) is more focused. Its aim is to define, monitor, and enforce

---

[7]This directive controls various underground wells, such as those used to inject wastes or fluids from oil production into the ground, to assure that these materials do not contaminate underground drinking water supplies.

[8]U.S. Congress, OTA (October 1984), Vol. I., Chapter 3, pp. 72–75, citing U.S. House of Representatives (1974) on p. 74.

[9]U.S. EPA, Office of Water (March 1994), pp. 298–99.

whatever standards are needed to assure that water drawn from the tap is safe for human consumption. First of all, note the phrase "drawn from the tap," suggesting that bottled water is *not* regulated through the SDWA. Assuring the potability of this water falls within the jurisdiction of the Food and Drug Administration—a matter discussed in Application 15.2. Second, it is important to realize that the goals of the SDWA are not independent of the Clean Water Act, which controls *all* water resources including those used for drinking. Since the rulings of the Clean Water Act are not stringent enough to assure the safety of drinking water, the SDWA imposes the tougher standards needed to assure potability. However, it does rely implicitly on the Clean Water Act to achieve a baseline level of water quality and to control the effluents of polluting sources.

Application 15.2

Who Regulates the Quality of Bottled Water?

By 1993, sales of bottled drinking water had grown into a thriving $2 billion market. To a large extent, these impressive revenues reflect consumers' uncertainty about the quality of public drinking water supplies. Some are concerned about aesthetic issues such as unpleasant odors and discoloration, and others about more serious threats like lead contamination. Whatever the specific cause, the response of many consumers is to substitute bottled water for tap water.

Implicit in households' decisions to purchase bottled water is the assumption that this substitute commodity is of higher quality than tap water. For this assumption to be valid, it must be the case that bottled water is subject to more stringent standards than is public drinking water or that suppliers of bottled water are closer to compliance with some set of universal standards than their public counterparts. Are either of these scenarios correct? To answer this important question, we need to examine and compare the regulations affecting private and public drinking water supplies.

To begin, the two types of water supplies are controlled by different regulatory entities. Public drinking water supplies are controlled by the Safe Drinking Water Act through standards administered by the EPA and state authorities. Bottled water quality falls within the jurisdiction of the Food and Drug Administration (FDA). The reason is that bottled water is considered a "food," and as such is part and parcel of the FDA's charge.

To assure consumer safety, the FDA requires that bottled water products be produced in compliance with FDA Good Manufacturing Practices. All such products must be clean and safe for human consumption, and they must be processed and distributed under sanitary conditions. Furthermore, according to a 1978 agreement, the FDA is to adopt the EPA's public drinking water standards for bottled water. As of 1991, this had been done for most, but not all, of the existing standards. The FDA also has its own standards, dealing with aesthetics and health concerns. As a further precaution, domestic bottled water producers who distribute their products interstate are subject to periodic, unannounced site inspections by the FDA and by state health officials. Within the industry, there is also some measure of self-regulation. One example is that all members of the International Bottled Water Association must be inspected each year by the National Sanitation Foundation, an independent laboratory.

What does all of this mean to the consumer? It is true that there are federal and state regulations in place to protect the quality of bottled water, and

Application 15.2 (concluded)

indeed there is consensus that bottled water is safe for human consumption. However, there is no reason to assume that it is *safer* to drink than ordinary tap water, since the same basic health standards are applicable to both.

Beyond this issue, there is also debate about whether bottled water is being unfairly or deceptively marketed. For example, it has been alleged that some bottled water is nothing more than ordinary tap water. Yet, its price can be as much as 1,000 times higher than the price of public water supplies. Further allegations have been made about misleading or even absent information about the true characteristics or sources of bottled water

products. To address these types of problems, the FDA has proposed new labeling requirements for bottled water that will provide consistency to such designations as "mineral," "distilled," or "sterile" and will require the identification of bottled water drawn from municipal supplies. Truth-in-labeling is not a new concept, but its application to the increasingly popular bottled water industry may be long overdue.

Sources: U.S. Environmental Protection Agency, Office of Drinking Water, *Bottled Water: Helpful Facts and Information* (Washington, D.C.), undated; Sue Kirchhoff "FDA Proposes Bottled Water Measure Up to Tap Standards," *Boston Globe,* January 1, 1993; U.S. Environmental Protection Agency, *Bottled Water Fact Sheet* (Washington, D.C.: March 1991).

Finally, the groundwater protection added in 1986 is indicative of the fragmentary U.S. approach to controlling groundwater contamination. There are many statutes implemented by different government agencies aimed at this important natural resource—arguably an ineffective approach with no unified oversight.[10] This outcome evolved from the false belief that groundwater was naturally protected from contamination because of its location within layers of soil and rock. In the 1970s, this assumption was called into question when pesticides were discovered in U.S. groundwater supplies. Since then, every state in the nation has discovered some amount of pollutants in its groundwater.[11] The most commonly observed groundwater contaminants as of 1990 are shown in Table 15.2. Public concern prompted a call for more aggressive legislative controls, and existing laws were amended in an attempt to address the problem. However, no single legislative act has ever been passed whose main objective is to protect groundwater resources.[12]

Pollutants Controlled under the Safe Drinking Water Act

The Safe Drinking Water Act controls *all* types of contaminants that may threaten human health and not just those linked to communicable disease. Its

---

[10]Among the laws with some provisions to protect groundwater are: the Comprehensive Environmental Response, Compensation, and Liability Act, the Federal Insecticide, Fungicide, and Rodenticide Act, the Resource Conservation and Recovery Act, and the Toxic Substances Control Act. For more detail on this important issue, the reader should consult U.S. Congress, OTA (October 1984), Vol. I., Chapter 3.

[11]U.S. EPA, Office of Pesticides and Toxic Substances (October 1991), pp. 1–2; U.S. Congress, OTA (October 1984), Vol. I., p. 3.

[12]U.S. Congress, OTA (October 1984), Vol. I., pp. 63, 73–75.

TABLE 15.2   States' Ranking of Groundwater Contaminants

(Based on 1990 Reports from 42 States and Territories)

Contaminant	Numbers of States Identifying as Prevalent
Nitrates	37
Metals	33
Pesticides	32
Petroleum	31
Volatile organic compounds	31
Brine	23
Synthetic organic compounds	21
Fluorides	21
Radioactive materials	18
Arsenic	17
Other agricultural chemicals	17
Other contaminants	14

Source: U.S. Environmental Protection Agency, Office of Water, *National Water Quality Inventory: 1990 Report to Congress* (Washington, D.C., April 1992a), pp. 115–16.

rulings refer to "contaminants" as any physical, biological, or radiological substances in water. The 1986 Amendments are much more specific, listing 83 contaminants for which drinking water standards are to be set. The listed substances fall into the following categories: volatile organic chemicals; synthetic organic chemicals and inorganic chemicals; microbials; lead and copper; radionuclides; disinfectants and disinfection by-products; pesticides and other inorganic and organic constituents. Every three years another 25 are to be added beginning in 1991. These are to be drawn from a so-called list of **priority contaminants** devised by an advisory group, published, and updated regularly.

priority contaminants
Pollutants for which drinking water standards are to be established based on specific criteria.

The following are among the criteria for selecting **priority contaminants:**

1. The contaminant must be known or expected to occur in a public water system.

2. The contaminant may have an expected adverse effect on human health.

Consideration of which substances are to be identified on the priority list shall include but not be limited to contaminants identified in the Comprehensive Environmental Response, Compensation, and Liability Act (also known as Superfund), and pesticides registered under the Federal Insecticide, Fungicide, and Rodenticide Act.[13] More on the problem of pesticides and other agricultural chemicals in drinking water is given in Application 15.3.

---

[13]We will discuss these two major legislative acts in the next module.

Application 15.3

Pesticides and Other Agrichemicals in U.S. Groundwater

Despite the natural protection afforded by the earth's layers of rock and soil, groundwater resources can be polluted by a variety of contaminants. Of particular concern in the United States are agricultural fertilizers and pesticides that reach this vital resource via runoff from America's expansive acreage of farmland.

Surveys conducted by federal, state, and local governments across the nation have revealed some troubling statistics about the quality of U.S. groundwater. In 1979, California conducted one such investigation, testing about 2,500 wells in that state. This landmark survey discovered small traces of the cancer-causing pesticide dibromochloropropane (DBCP) in the sample of tested wells—the first significant finding of pesticide contamination of U.S. groundwater supplies. In that same year, the chemical Aldicarb was discovered in New York's groundwater. Reacting to these reports, other states launched their own investigations, particularly those with large agricultural lands such as Florida, Minnesota, Iowa, and Wisconsin. Many discovered that their drinking water supplies also had been polluted, and some were forced to take immediate and drastic action. Florida, for example, closed over 1,000 wells found to be contaminated with ethylene dibromide (EDB). Responding to the accumulating evidence, the EPA suspended the use of DBCP in 1979 and EDB four years later.

As more contamination was discovered, monitoring efforts intensified as did research endeavors to determine the magnitude of the problem. Recognizing a need to assimilate the accumulating data, the EPA established the Pesticides in Ground-Water Data Base using information gathered from some 150 monitoring studies. In 1988, the agency published the results in the *Interim Ground-Water Data Base Report.* One of its findings was that 46 different pesticides had been found in the groundwater supplies of 26 states—all of which were believed attributable to conventional agricultural activities. Point sources such as spills and improper disposal of chemical containers were linked to 32 pesticides contaminating the groundwater in 12 states. Although the database was valuable in generally assessing the problem, it nonetheless was a collection of information gleaned from diverse sources. Hence, the EPA saw the need to establish a nationally sponsored baseline of groundwater contamination data from which to monitor progress over time. It was this recognition that motivated the National Pesticide Survey of Drinking Water Wells conducted between 1988 and 1990.

The national survey analyzed samples from 1,349 drinking water wells across all 50 states. The samples were tested for 127 pesticides, pesticide metabolites, and nitrates. Of the total sample of wells, 586 were among the 38,300 public community water systems in the United States, and the remainder were representative of the 10.5 million private domestic wells. In November 1990, the agency released the survey's Phase I report, which confirmed that agricultural chemicals had contaminated the nation's groundwater. The report asserted that approximately 10.4 percent of the community wells and 4.2 percent of the private wells in the sample had a detectable amount of at least one pesticide. Based on these sample data, the EPA drew inferences about the status of *all* wells throughout the nation. These inferences suggested that nearly 10,000 community drinking wells and about 446,000 private domestic wells in the United States were contaminated by at least one pesticide. The Survey Report went on to indicate, however, that contamination levels high enough to threaten human health are relatively rare. Specifically, less than 1 percent of private wells and no community drinking water wells are likely to be in this category.

Phase II of the EPA's survey report was completed in 1992 and is a statistical analysis of the findings in Phase I. This second phase was aimed at determining how various factors, such as well depth and chemical composition of pesticides,

Application 15.3 *(concluded)*

influence the presence and concentration of agri-cultural chemicals in groundwater. A number of statistical associations were identified, including a link between pesticide contamination and agricul-tural activity. The analysis also found that the transport of chemicals to well water is affected by numerous factors, including precipitation and the proximity of surface waters to drinking water wells.

Overall, the EPA contends that while pesticide contamination of groundwater exists, most of the nation's supplies are relatively "safe," at least in the short term. In those local areas where this is not the case, the EPA asserts that every effort must be made to address the problem and the associated health risks. The agency does acknowledge, how-ever, that detectable levels of pesticides in well water on a widespread scale may suggest a threat to groundwater quality in the long run. In this regard, the survey data establish the baseline needed to help monitor changes in contaminant levels over time. This trend data should be useful in formulating policy initiatives and designing na-tional strategies to protect U.S. groundwater supplies.

Sources: U.S. Environmental Protection Agency, Office of Pesticides and Toxic Substances, *Pesticides in Drinking-Water Wells* (Washington, D.C., September 1990); U.S. Environmental Protection Agency, Office of Pesticides and Toxic Substances, *Pesticides and Ground-Water Strategy* (Washington, D.C., October, 1991); U.S. Environmental Protection Agency, Office of Water, Office of Pesticides and Toxic Substances, *National Pesticides Survey: Update and Summary of Phase II Results* (Washington, D.C., Winter 1992).

Setting Standards to Define Safe Drinking Water

The most important directive of the SDWA is to set standards that define drinking water quality for the nation. Under the law, there are two types of standards: **primary standards** to protect human health and **secondary standards** to protect public welfare.[14] The distinction is an important one, both in how each is defined and how each is implemented.

Establishing National Primary Drinking Water Regulations

National Primary Drinking Water Regulations (NPDWR)
U.S. health standards for public drinking water supplies implemented uniformly throughout the country.

The emphasis of the SDWA is clearly on the primary or health standards for drinking water. These are applicable only to public water systems and are to be implemented *uniformly* throughout the country. More formally, these stan-dards are called **National Primary Drinking Water Regulations (NPDWR).** Each regulation consists of three parts:

1. A **maximum contaminant level goal (MCLG).**
2. A **maximum contaminant level (MCL).**
3. The specification of the **best available technology (BAT)** for public water supply treatment.[15]

---

[14]There is consistency between the meaning of the primary and secondary drinking water standards and that of the primary and secondary ambient air quality standards in the U.S.

[15]Each regulation must also outline requirements for monitoring, reporting, and public notification. U.S. EPA, Office of Water, (May 1992).

Setting the Goal: The MCLG.   One of the key elements of a primary drinking water regulation is the **maximum contaminant level goal (MCLG).** This defines the level of a pollutant at which no known or expected adverse health effects occur, allowing for an adequate margin of safety.[16] MCLGs are based on data obtained in the risk assessment process discussed in Chapter 7. Of particular relevance is the evidence on carcinogenicity of water contaminants. The MCLG for known or probable carcinogens is zero, meaning that no amount of such a contaminant is allowed in public drinking water. For any substance that is *not* a carcinogen, the MCLG is set according to the established reference dose (RfD) for that contaminant. Recall that an RfD is an estimate of the amount of a pollutant to which humans can be exposed over a lifetime without harm.[17] The key point to remember is that the MCLG is *not* an enforceable standard. Instead, it serves as a target or objective toward which the primary standard is to be aimed.

maximum contaminant level goal (MCLG)
That component of an NPDWR that defines the level of a pollutant at which no known or expected adverse health effects occur, allowing for a margin of safety.

Setting the Standard: The MCL.   Once the target or MCLG is established, the primary standard is set. The primary standard gives the **maximum contaminant level (MCL)** allowed in drinking water. It is to be set as close to the MCLGs as is feasible, where feasibility is defined through the BAT technology. More formally, an MCL is the highest permissible level of a contaminant in water delivered to any user of a public system. It is expressed as an **action level** measured in milligrams per liter (mg/L). Unlike the MCLGs, the MCLs are federally enforceable. Table 15.3 lists the MCLs for selected contaminants and their associated health effects.

maximum contaminant level (MCL)
That component of an NPDWR that states the highest permissible level of a contaminant in water delivered to any user of a public system.

action level
The manner in which MCLs are expressed, generally measured in milligrams per liter.

Defining Treatment Technologies.   The law requires that each national primary drinking water regulation identify the treatment technology that makes attainment of the required contaminant level feasible. This is characterized as the **best available technology (BAT)** observed under field conditions, taking account of cost considerations. Since this technology is not a requirement per se, the primary water quality regulations are more accurately characterized as performance-based standards.

best available technology (BAT)
The treatment technology that makes attainment of the MCL feasible, taking cost considerations into account.

Current Status of the National Primary Drinking Water Regulations (NPDWRs)

As of 1992, NPDWRs have been announced for 8 volatile organic chemicals, 38 synthetic organic chemicals and inorganic chemicals, fluoride, coliform and other microbiological contaminants, and lead and copper.[18] All standards

---

[16]The phrase ''margin of safety'' is also used in defining the primary health standards for air quality.

[17]As discussed in Chapter 7, an RfD is expressed in milligrams of a pollutant per body weight per day.

[18]U.S. EPA, Office of Water, ''Phase V Rule: Fact Sheet'' (May 1992).

TABLE 15.3   National Primary Drinking Water Standards for Selected Contaminants

Contaminant	MCL[a] (mg/L)	Health Effects
Organic chemicals		
Atrazine	0.003	Reproductive and cardiac effects
Benzene	0.005	Cancer risk
Carbon tetrachloride	0.005	Cancer risk
Chlordane	0.002	Cancer risk
Heptachlor	0.0004	Cancer risk
Styrene	0.1	Liver, nervous system effects
Vinyl chloride	0.002	Cancer risk
Inorganic chemicals		
Arsenic[b]	0.05	Dermal and nervous system toxicity effects
Asbestos	7 MFL[c]	Benign tumors
Cadmium	0.005	Kidney damage
Fluoride[b]	4	Skeletal damage
Lead	0.015	Central and peripheral nervous system damage; kidney damage;
Mercury	0.002	Kidney, nervous system damage
Radionuclides		
Beta particle and Photon activity	4 mrem/yr[d]	Cancer risk
Radium 226/228	5 pCi/L[e]	Bone cancer risk
Radon	300 pCi/L[e]	Cancer risk
Microbiological		
Turbidity	0.5–1.0 NTU[f]	Interferes with disinfection
Legionella	TT[g]	Legionnaire's disease (pneumonia); Pontiac fever
Viruses	TT[g]	Gastroenteritis

[a]MCLs are measured in milligrams per liter (mg/L) unless otherwise noted.

[b]MCL is currently under review.

[c]MFL = million fibers per liter, with fiber length > 10 microns.

[d]mrem/yr = millirem or 1/1000 rem per year.

[e]pCi/L = picocuries per liter.

[f]NTU = nephelometric turbidity unit.

[g]TT means treatment technique requirement in effect.

Source: U.S. Environmental Protection Agency, Office of Water, *Fact Sheet: National Primary Drinking Water Standards* (Washington, D.C., August 1991); U.S. Environmental Protection Agency, Office of Water, *Drinking Water Regulations and Health Advisories* (Washington, D.C., April 1992b).

are to be reviewed at least once every three years and must be amended whenever enhanced health protection is possible through changes in technology, treatment, or other means. For example, more stringent primary standards for lead in drinking water were announced by the EPA in 1991. As a consequence, public water supplies in many U.S. communities now exceed the lead action level. For more on the implications of this outcome, see Application 15.4.

Application 15.4

Strengthening Controls on Lead Contamination of Water Supplies

The adverse effects of lead exposure are well documented by scientific research. Health effects include learning disabilities, high blood pressure, mental retardation, stillbirths, and premature deaths. Children are the most susceptible population group. However, according to the Centers for Disease Control, lead exposure is the nation's number one *preventable* pediatric health problem. Tremendous gains already have been realized in reducing children's exposure to lead contaminated air—much of this attributable to the phaseout of lead in gasoline. Although this progress is significant, exposure to lead in other environmental media continues to be a serious problem. According to recent EPA estimates, 10 to 20 percent of a child's exposure to lead comes from drinking contaminated water, much of it from the deterioration of pipes, solder, and other plumbing materials. Ingestion of lead paint, contaminated soil, and dust particles accounts for the remaining proportion.

Responding to these statistics, the EPA tightened the lead standard for drinking water in 1991 to a maximum contaminant level (MCL) of 0.015 mg/L. Announcing the new standard, then EPA Administrator William K. Reilly stated,

> Today's action will reduce lead exposure for approximately 130 million people . . . We estimate approximately 600,000 children will have their blood lead content brought below our level of concern because of these standards.

Initial EPA estimates accompanying the announcement predicted that about 40,000 public water suppliers likely would fail to meet the new lead standard. Federal requirements call for 79,000 public water suppliers to monitor for lead at household taps in higher-risk residences, that is, those with new lead solder or lead service lines. According to the EPA's initial 1992 survey based on test data from 6,400 large water systems, approximately

13 percent did not meet the new lead standard. Of those cities with populations greater than 50,000, the following were found to have the highest lead content in their public drinking water supplies:

City	Lead Levels (parts per billion (ppb))
Charleston, South Carolina	165
Utica, New York	160
Newton, Massachusetts	123
Columbia, South Carolina	114
Medford, Massachusetts	113
Chicopee, Massachusetts	110
Yonkers, New York	110
Waltham, Massachusetts	76
Brookline, Massachusetts	72
Taylor, Michigan	69

The EPA estimates that only about 1 percent of water systems with elevated lead levels will have to treat source waters. The reason is that most of the lead content in drinking water comes from the public water delivery system and not the water supply itself. The contamination arises from corrosion of lead pipe service lines and plumbing solder. The "lead ban," which was legislated as part of the Safe Drinking Water Amendments of 1986, prohibits the future use of lead pipes, solder, or flux. Nonetheless, some older homes built before 1930 have lead waterpipes, and some newer homes built before the lead ban was enacted have copper pipes joined with lead-based solder. Consequently, in areas with a highly corrosive water supply, lead can leach out of these pipes or solder joints, contaminating the water that reaches residents. To combat this problem, treatment technologies have been developed to reduce water corrosivity. Congress also added more controls by passing the Lead Contamination Control Act of 1988, which calls for the repair or removal of water coolers that are not lead-free and bans the future sale and manufacture of these potential sources of contamination.

Beyond these comprehensive measures, the EPA is also using a public education program to communicate simple procedures households can follow to reduce their risk of lead exposure. The EPA advisory recommends that all tap water be allowed to run for about a minute before using it for cooking or drinking as a means to flush out any lead sediment from pipes. For homes in areas where the new action level is exceeded, further precautions are recommended, such as running tap water for several minutes before using and avoiding the use of hot tap water for drinking or cooking. These precautionary measures coupled with the strengthened federal regulations should lessen considerably the risk of lead exposure that threatens human health.

Sources: U.S. Environmental Protection Agency, Office of Communications and Public Affairs, "EPA Tightens Standards for Lead in Drinking Water," *Environmental News* (Washington, D.C., May 7, 1991); Timothy Noah, "EPA Finds Unsafe Lead Levels in Water," *The Wall Street Journal*, May 12, 1993; U.S. Environmental Protection Agency, Office of Water, *Lead Contamination Control Act* (Washington, D.C., July 1988).

Establishing National Secondary Drinking Water Regulations

secondary maximum contaminant levels (SMCLs)
National standards for drinking water that serve as guidelines to protect public welfare.

Protection of public welfare is the statutory objective of secondary drinking water standards. More to the point, these standards deal with contaminants that so impair aesthetics and other non-health-threatening characteristics like odor and taste that a substantial number of individuals may be forced to discontinue use of the public water system. Referred to as **secondary maximum contaminant levels (SMCLs),** these standards serve as guidelines to protect public welfare and are *not* enforceable by the federal government. Furthermore, unlike the primary standards, the secondary standards are not uniform, since they may vary with geographic or other conditions. Table 15.4 gives the SMCLs as of 1992 and the associated effects of each listed contaminant.

Enforcement of U.S. Drinking Water Standards

Primary Drinking Water Standards.   Enforcement of the primary drinking water standards is shared between the EPA and state governments. The major responsibility is assigned to states provided that certain criteria are met. Included among these is a state's adoption of drinking water regulations that are at least as stringent as the national regulations. States must also establish monitoring procedures and maintain proper records. The EPA may assume enforcement responsibility in emergency situations or if, for example, it discovers that a state has failed to take proper action.

Tampering with public water systems is subject to both criminal and civil penalties. According to the SDWA, tampering refers to the introduction of a contaminant into a public water system or interference with the operations of a public water system with the intention of causing harm. Any person

TABLE 15.4   U.S. Secondary Maximum Contaminant Levels (SMCLs)

Substance	*SMCL (mg/L)**	*Contaminant Effects*
Aluminum	0.05 to 0.2	Discoloration
Chloride	250	Taste; pipe corrosion
Color	15 color units	Aesthetic
Copper	1.0	Taste; staining of porcelain
Corrosivity	Noncorrosive	Aesthetic and health related (corrosive water can leach pipe materials, like lead, into water)
Fluoride†	2.0	Dental fluorosis (brownish discoloration of the teeth)
Foaming agents	0.5	Aesthetic
Iron	0.3	Taste; staining of laundry
Manganese	0.05	Taste; staining of laundry
Odor	3 threshold odor numbers	Aesthetic
pH	6.5–8.5	Water is too corrosive
Silver	0.10	Argyria (discoloration of the skin)
Sulfate	250	Taste; laxative effects
Total dissolved solids	500	Taste; possible relation between low hardness and cardiovascular disease; indicator of corrosivity (related to lead levels in water); can damage plumbing and limit effectiveness of soaps and detergents
Zinc	5	Taste

*SMCLs are expressed in mg/L unless otherwise noted.

†Indicates under review.

Source: U.S. Environmental Protection Agency, Office of Water, *Drinking Water Regulations and Health Advisories* (Washington, D.C., April 1992b); U.S. Environmental Protection Agency, Office of Water, ''Is Your Drinking Water Safe?'' (Washington, D.C., December 1991).

convicted of tampering with a public water system will be imprisoned for not more than five years or be made to pay a federal criminal fine.

Secondary Drinking Water Standards.   For secondary standards, the EPA has no enforcement responsibility. It simply communicates SMCLs to states as guidelines. If the EPA observes any noncompliance with the secondary regulations, the law requires it to do nothing more than notify the state.

Analysis of U.S. Safe Drinking Water Policy

Several aspects of the Safe Drinking Water Act (SDWA) have been criticized by environmental economists and policy analysts, particularly in light of reported incidents of contaminated drinking water supplies. One important concern centers around the standard-setting process at the federal level and the potentially inefficient outcome it generates. Are contaminant levels being properly determined? And if not, what are the ramifications? Another key issue is the subpar performance at the state and local levels in meeting the standards and maintaining adequate treatment facilities. Is the less-than-satisfactory track record the result of ill-defined standards, poor enforcement procedures, inadequate resources, or some combination of factors? To begin, let's consider the standard-setting process that forms the fundamental basis of the Safe Drinking Water Act.

The Federal Role: Setting the Standards

The statutory goals of the Safe Drinking Water Act (SDWA), that is, the maximum contaminant level goals (MCLGs), are defined as the level of a pollutant at which no adverse human health effects occur with a "margin of safety." Allowing for an adequate margin of safety seems to suggest a contaminant level where *no* individual would be harmed. Given the variability of human sensitivities, this seems to imply that at least some MCLGs must be set at zero. Notice that there is no mention of feasibility or cost considerations in setting these goals. They are purely benefit-based. Since the maximum contaminant levels (MCLs) are aimed at these goals, they too are benefit-based. Although the MCLs are to consider "feasibility" defined through technological availability, there is no legal requirement that the associated marginal costs of achieving the standard be balanced with the expected marginal gains. As is the case with any such regulation, the absence of an explicit balancing of costs and benefits at the margin means that efficiency is not being used to regulate drinking water supplies. And given the language of the MCLG, there is the potential for overregulation of some contaminants and inflated costs.

Consider the graph in Figure 15.1 that models the total social (health) benefits (*TSB*) and total social costs (*TSC*) of abating some hypothetical drinking water contaminant beyond the efficient level. If the MCL is set to maximize social health benefits, the resulting abatement level is A_1, corresponding to the point where the *TSB* curve reaches its highest level. In this case, A_1 is *above* the efficient level of abatement, A_e. Hence, the benefit-based standard would overregulate this contaminant, imposing unnecessarily high costs on society.

The Cost Implications.   A recent analysis of U.S. water quality policy cites the dramatic rise in treatment costs that have come about since the SDWA was enacted. Forecasts indicate that the typical American household will face a 50 percent increase in these costs by the year 2000.[19] Much of the increase in

---

[19]See Howe (1991), p. 15, citing *U.S. Water News* (January 1991), p. 10.

FIGURE 15.1

The inefficiency of benefit-based primary drinking water standards

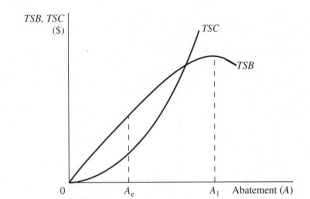

The model illustrates the relationship between the total social (health) benefits (*TSB*) and total social costs (*TSC*) of abating some hypothetical drinking water contaminant beyond the efficient level. If the maximum contaminant level (MCL) is set to maximize social health benefits, the resulting abatement level is A_1, corresponding to the point where the *TSB* curve reaches its highest level. In this case, A_1 is *above* the efficient level of abatement, A_e. Hence, the benefit-based standard would overregulate this contaminant, imposing unnecessarily high costs on society.

Regulatory Impact Analysis (RIA)
A document required under President Reagan's Executive Order 12291 that called for specific information about the potential benefits and costs associated with a "major" federal regulation.

regulatory costs is due to the more stringent requirements called for in the 1986 Amendments. According to estimates based on analyses done in late 1986 and early 1987, the annual costs of implementing these amendments are about $2.5 billion. The full breakdown of this magnitude by ruling and by type of cost is given in Table 15.5. A more recent report projects annualized control costs through the year 2000. These estimates are shown in Table 15.6 and assume full implementation of the SDWA. Notice how real costs are expected to rise over time—an outcome that may impede the EPA's ability to implement the law. The financial burden that these regulations place on state and local authorities is an important concern, particularly since many public water systems are already unable to comply with the law due to resource limitations.

What these findings imply is that both social costs and benefits are important considerations in the regulatory process. The premise is rooted in economic theory and recommended in President Clinton's Executive Order 12866 and previously in Executive Order 12291 issued by President Reagan. Under both presidential directives, the benefits and costs associated with a major regulatory action must be assessed or made public. Establishing or revising primary drinking water standards is an example of a government action subject to this requirement. In 1991 when the lead standard was revised, Reagan's Executive Order was in force, so the estimated benefits and costs were presented within a **Regulatory Impact Analysis (RIA).** We next consider the key results of this government-mandated benefit-cost analysis.

TABLE 15.5   **Estimated Annual Costs to Water Systems under the SDWA Amendments of 1986** ($1986 millions)*

Rule	Number of Systems Affected	Annualized Capital/ O&M Costs†	Average Annual Monitoring Cost	Total Annual Compliance Cost
Volatile organic chemicals	1,824	$ 32.7	$23.1	$55.8
Filtration	10,228	511.6	17.1	528.6
Total coliforms	200,183	0	75.2	75.2
Synthetic organic chemicals	2,284	45.4	32.2	77.5
Inorganic chemicals	1,896	123.2	12.4	135.6
Lead/copper corrosion control	43,927	302.2	32.9	335.2
Radionuclides	22,867	790.3	2.6	792.9
Disinfection	103,354	474.8	12.8	487.7
Total	‡	$2,280.2	$208.3	$2,488.5

*Most estimates presented result from regulatory and economic analyses conducted by the EPA in late 1986 and early 1987. Dollars are rounded to the nearest 100,000.

†Figures in this column include the estimated annualized costs over 20 years at a 10 percent discount rate and one year of annual operation and maintenance (O&M) expenses.

‡The number of water systems affected cannot be added together because some systems will be affected by multiple rules.

Source: U.S. General Accounting Office, *Drinking Water: Compliance Problems Undermine EPA Program as New Challenges Emerge* (Washington, D.C., June 1990), Table 4.1, p. 53.

TABLE 15.6   **Trend Data and Projections on Control Costs for Safe Drinking Water**

Year	Annualized Control Costs ($1986 millions)*
1986	$2,979
1987	3,111
1988	3,250
1989	3,415
1990	3,587
1991	3,926
1992	4,319
1993	4,586
1994	4,917
1995	5,350
1996	5,684
1997	5,949
1998	6,264
1999	6,491
2000	6,571

*These cost data assume full implementation at a 7 percent discount rate.

Source: Drawn from U.S. Environmental Protection Agency, Office of Policy, Planning, and Evaluation, *Environmental Investments: The Cost of a Clean Environment, A Summary* (Washington, D.C., December 1990), Table 2-1, pp. 2-2, 2-3.

The Regulatory Impact Analysis (RIA) for the New Lead Standard in Drinking Water[20]

In June 1991, the EPA announced a maximum contaminant level goal (MCLG) for lead of zero and a more stringent maximum contaminant level (MCL) of 0.015 mg/L. This new primary standard lowered the allowable lead level in drinking water from its former limit of 50 parts per billion (ppb) to 15 ppb measured at any point in a public water distribution system. Regulations for water treatment also were instituted to assure that the new action level would be met. These requirements include: (1) source water treatment; (2) optimal corrosion control treatment; (3) public education; and (4) lead service line replacement. Taken together, these regulations were expected to have a substantial financial impact on the regulated community—in excess of $100 million per year. Hence, by law the new rulings were subject to Executive Order 12291 and had to be accompanied by a Regulatory Impact Analysis (RIA) with a full description of the associated benefits and costs. Table 15.7 provides the detail.

Incremental Benefits of the New Lead Standard.   According to the RIA, the expected incremental benefits of the tougher lead standard for drinking water include reductions in damages to health and to materials. For health benefits, the qualitative assessment was described as a reduction in the exposure of 130 million people to lead in drinking water and a reduction in the blood lead level of an additional 570,000 children to below 10 micrograms per deciliter. To monetize these benefits, they were translated into avoided medical costs and estimated as within a range of $2.87 and $4.54 billion annually. Incremental material benefits were described as accruing to both public water facilities and to private households. These include such gains as longer pipe life, reduced leakages, extended life of water-using appliances, and fewer repairs. The estimated value of these benefits was $500 million per year. Combining these values, the aggregate incremental benefits associated with tightening the lead standard in drinking water were estimated at between $3.4 and 5.0 billion per year.

Incremental Costs of the New Lead Standard.   On the cost side, the RIA itemized annual expenditures for treatment, monitoring, education, and implementation, as shown in Table 15.7. The highest costs were assessed for treatment procedures at between $390 and $680 million per year. In the aggregate, the incremental costs of implementing the new lead action level were estimated at between $500 and $790 million per year.

---

[20]The following is drawn from U.S. EPA, Office of Ground Water and Drinking Water (May 1991), and U.S. *Federal Register* Vol. 56, No. 110, (June 7, 1991); Rules and Regulations.

TABLE 15.7   Estimated Benefits and Costs of the New Lead Standard: Results from the RIA

Incremental Benefits

Health Benefits

Descriptive assessment:

Reduction in the exposure of about 130 million people to lead in drinking water.

Reduction in the blood lead level of an additional 570,000 children to below 10 micrograms per deciliter.

Monetized annualized value (based on avoided medical costs):

From corrosion control and source water treatment:	$2.8 to $4.3 billion per year
From replacement of lead service lines:	$70 to $240 million per year

Material Benefits

Descriptive assessment:

Reduced damages to public water system pipelines, which extends pipe life and minimizes leakage.

Reduced damages to customers, such as less leakage, extended life of water-using appliances, less staining of clothing and water fixtures, and fewer repairs.

Monetized annualized value:

Accruing to households and water systems:	$500 million per year
Annualized Benefits	$3.4 to $5.0 billion per year.

Incremental Costs

Treatment, Implementation, Education Costs

Descriptive assessment:

Source water treatment; corrosion control treatment; lead-line replacement; public education; monitoring costs; state implementation impacts.

Monetized annualized value:

Treatment costs:	$390 to $680 million
Monitoring costs:	$ 40 million
Education costs:	$ 30 million
State implementation costs:	$ 40 million
Annualized Costs	$500 to $790 million per year.

Net Benefits

Annualized Net Benefits	$2.9 to $4.2 billion per year.

Note: Annualized costs for source water treatment, corrosion control, and lead-line replacement were derived from total capital costs, which were estimated to be between $2.9 and $7.7 billion.

Sources: U.S. Environmental Protection Agency, Office of Ground Water and Drinking Water, *Fact Sheet: National Primary Drinking Water Regulations for Lead and Copper* (Washington, D.C., May 1991); U.S. *Federal Register* Vol. 56, No. 110 (June 7, 1991); Rules and Regulations.

Net Benefits of the New Lead Standard.   Based on the benefit and cost estimates, the EPA determined that the annualized net benefits of tightening the standard for lead in drinking water were between $2.9 and $4.2 billion. Although these findings did not dictate the new action level, they did communicate in economic terms the net gain to society associated with the regulatory decision.

The State and Local Role: Compliance and Enforcement

Since the Safe Drinking Water Act relies heavily on a command-and-control approach, its success depends critically on sound monitoring and enforcement procedures that assure compliance with the primary standards. Public water systems are required to periodically sample water supplies, test them in an approved laboratory, and report the data to state authorities. In turn, these data are to be analyzed to determine if the system is meeting its monitoring responsibilities and if it is complying with the national standards. States are responsible for enforcement if any violations are noted, giving priority to those systems designated as "significant noncompliers (SNC)".[21] The EPA must step in if the state does not properly enforce the law.

Although these procedures may seem to be in order, a recent investigation conducted by the U.S. General Accounting Office (GAO) found that the extent of compliance by public water systems had been overstated by the EPA.[22] Part of the problem lies in the EPA's classification of SNCs versus "other noncompliers." The classification system was put into place to focus scarce resources on the worst offenders. However, according to the GAO, the SNC criteria are such that many serious violators are not being confronted. Deficiencies were identified at every level of government—the local water system, the state, and the EPA. Problems were discovered in the sampling and testing procedures conducted by community water systems. The GAO also found that states were not consistently reporting violations to the EPA. Since the EPA's data management system relies on state tracking systems for compliance information, its reporting of these data is sometimes inaccurate and overstated.

Another failing in the process is the inadequate enforcement action taken by both state authorities and the EPA, despite the added stringency provided by the 1986 Amendments. In its review of enforcement procedures in six states, the GAO found that states took timely and appropriate action in only 24 of the 95 SNC violations committed by 75 public water systems. Most notable was the observation that many SNCs remained in noncompliance for several years. In fact, 46 of the SNC cases reviewed, or nearly half, had met the SNC criteria for more than four years.

Why is the compliance record so poor? Some of the reasons are procedural, having to do with how states and the EPA respond to violations of federal law. However, even if these administrative issues were corrected, there would still be unresolved compliance issues due to both technological and economic considerations. A recent analysis done by the Natural Resources Defense Council reports that severely outmoded treatment facilities and failing

---

[21]The classification as an SNC is based on either the frequency of violations or the severity of the violations, such as the extent to which a system exceeds the MCL. See U.S. General Accounting Office (GAO) (June 1990), p. 14.

[22]U.S. GAO (June 1990).

water distribution systems characterize the majority of public water systems across the nation.[23] These technological problems are exacerbated by the absence of watershed protection approaches, which forces an overreliance on treatment techniques. With regard to economic considerations, the GAO argues that the SDWA imposes what it calls ''staggering costs'' upon public water systems faced with contamination problems. This is particularly true for small systems that are unable to finance the costs of corrective action and to compete for external funding. Of the 75 systems examined by the GAO, two-thirds served 500 or fewer people, and 87 percent served 3,300 or less.[24] This economic dilemma is worse in those cases where water prices are set below cost.

Responding to the funding problem, the EPA's Office of Drinking Water has launched a ''Mobilization Strategy'' to help state and local governments find alternative financing. Among its objectives are to offer assistance in obtaining resources, to identify low-cost technological solutions, and to inform the public about the associated health risks to elicit support for higher water rates. Although this effort is well intended, the need for such a strategy is likely related to inefficient decision-making. A balancing of benefits and costs may have avoided some of the costing difficulties public officials are facing. Another likely explanation is the lack of economically sound pricing practices for drinking water supplies—an issue we examine more closely.

Economic Principles in Pricing Water Supplies

At all levels of government, the costs of implementing the SDWA present a challenge. Not only are these costs inflated because of inefficient decision-making, but in many communities they are not properly reflected in the pricing of water supplies. Basic economic theory illustrates that resources are misallocated if the price of a good or service is not equal to the associated marginal social cost of production. In this context, society's marginal cost of *current* water usage includes the explicit costs incurred by water supply facilities plus the opportunity costs of forgone *future* consumption. All too often, water is priced at a fixed rate that is independent of use and therefore independent of rising marginal costs. The result is overconsumption. If present consumption is higher than its allocatively efficient level, future supplies will be adversely affected.

An International Comparison

An international comparison of water consumption patterns reveals two very interesting findings. First, U.S. per capita consumption is higher than most

---

[23]Cohen and Olson (March 1994).
[24]U.S. GAO (June 1990), p. 46.

FIGURE 15.2

International water prices: A comparison across selected industrialized countries (1989)

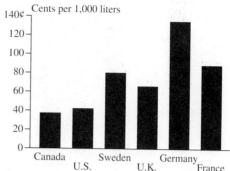

Cents per 1,000 liters

Note: Excludes cost of sewage treatment.

Source: Environment Canada, 1989 as cited in World Resources Institute, *The 1992 Information Please Environmental Almanac.* Copyright © 1991 by World Resources Institute. Boston, Mass.: Houghton Mifflin Company, 1992, p. 104. Reprinted by permission of Houghton Mifflin Co. All rights reserved.

nations around the world. For example, in 1990 the average American consumed approximately 2,161 cubic meters of water. Contrast this with the same statistic for Canada, which is reported at about 1,500 cubic meters, or for all of Europe, estimated at 750 cubic meters.[25] A second important observation is that water prices vary considerably across countries, as shown in Figure 15.2. Notice how European countries face much higher prices for water than the United States and Canada. And it is the European nations that have much lower consumption rates than their North American counterparts. Of course, this outcome is precisely what the Law of Demand predicts—that higher prices are associated with lower quantities consumed. What these data convey is that water use *is* price sensitive—an important observation given that some locations in the United States employ pricing policies that actually encourage inefficient water use. By examining these pricing practices in more detail, we can identify the inherent weaknesses and consider some economically sound alternatives.

flat fee pricing scheme
Pricing water supplies such that the fee is independent of water use.

flat rate pricing structure
Pricing water supplies to charge more for higher water usage at a constant rate.

Pricing Practices of U.S. Water Utilities

Table 15.8 provides data on the actual pricing practices of U.S. water supply utilities. Notice that many use a **flat fee pricing scheme,** that is, pricing that is independent of water use. Such an approach would be efficient only if the associated marginal cost were zero. Other utilities employ a **flat rate pricing structure,** which *does* charge more for higher usage but at a constant rate. This structure would be efficient only if marginal costs were constant and equal to the flat rate being charged. Neither of these pricing structures reflect the rising marginal social costs of water provision, and thus they act as a disincentive for consumers to economize on water usage.

[25]World Resources Institute (1992b), p. 102.

TABLE 15.8   Water Pricing Structures for Public and Private Water Utilities, 1982

| | Percent of Utilities | | | | | |
| | Small | | Medium | | Large | |
Pricing	*Public*	*Private*	*Public*	*Private*	*Public*	*Private*
Flat fee	13%	26%	4%	0%	5%	0%
Flat rate	6	0	15	0	15	0
Flat fee plus flat rate	29	26	28	15	10	0
Declining block	38	22	40	64	35	43
Increasing block	4	2	4	3	0	14
Other	8	20	8	18	35	43

Notes:

Flat fee:	A fixed fee paid monthly or annually which is independent of actual water use.
Flat rate:	A price that is a fixed amount per unit of water used.
Declining block:	A pricing scheme designed such that the per unit price declines as water use increases. Units are typically referred to as blocks, where each block represents a specific quantity of water.
Increasing block:	A pricing scheme designed such that the per unit price increases as water use increases.
Other:	All pricing schemes not mentioned above. Included in this category are pricing schemes that differentiate across consumer groups.

Source: U.S. Environmental Protection Agency, Office of Drinking Water, *Survey of Operating and Financial Characteristics of Community Water Systems* (prepared by Temple, Barker, and Sloan, Inc.), October 1982, as cited in U.S. Congress, Congressional Budget Office (CBO), *Financing Municipal Water Supply Systems* (Washington, D.C.: U.S. Government Printing Office, May 1987), pp. 6–7.

The other pricing methods represented in the table are the **declining block** and **increasing block** pricing structures. Each of these approaches allows for changes in per unit prices for different "blocks" of consumption levels, but obviously each works in the opposite direction of the other. Both pricing structures are illustrated graphically in Figure 15.3. Since they are motivated differently, we need to examine them more closely and consider how each affects water usage.

declining block pricing structure
A pricing scheme that allows the per unit price of different "blocks" or quantities of water to decline as usage increases.

Declining Block Pricing Structure.   Referring back to the data in Table 15.8, the **declining block** structure appears to be the predominant form of water pricing regardless of the utility size or the type of ownership. The reason for its prevalence appears to have its basis in the typical utility's cost structure. Throughout the United States, most water utilities tend to have high fixed costs and relatively low variable costs.[26] In an attempt to recover these high fixed costs, utilities encourage higher consumption levels with declining block pricing, as shown in Figure 15.3(a). In so doing, they can exploit available scale economies and incur lower average costs. From the utility's perspective,

---

[26]U.S. EPA, Office of Policy, Planning, and Evaluation (March 1991), pp. 4–7.

FIGURE 15.3

*Alternative pricing
structures of water*

(a) Declining block structure

The declining block pricing structure is the predominant form of water pricing. In the United States, most water utilities incur relatively low variable costs but high fixed costs. In an attempt to recover these fixed costs, utilities use declining block pricing to encourage higher consumption levels. In so doing, they are able to exploit available scale economies and incur lower average costs. From society's vantage point, this pricing scheme is inefficient because utilities are incorrectly using an **average cost pricing** framework as opposed to a marginal cost pricing framework.

(b) Increasing block structure

An increasing block pricing structure calls for a higher unit price as water consumption increases. This provides an economic incentive for more conservative water usage. Benefit-cost analysis is implicitly reflected in this approach. As each additional block of water is used, higher marginal costs are considered along with the marginal benefits of consumption.

the declining block price structure has merit. But from society's point of view, the pricing scheme is inefficient. Although this inefficiency arises for several reasons, the major culprit is that suppliers are incorrectly using average cost pricing as opposed to a marginal cost pricing framework.

**increasing block
pricing structure**
A pricing scheme
whereby the per unit
price of different
''blocks'' of water
increases as water use
increases.

Increasing Block Pricing Structure.   Looking again at Table 15.8, notice that the least common pricing practice is the use of an **increasing block pricing structure.** As illustrated in Figure 15.3(b), the customer pays a higher per unit price as water consumption increases—a practice that provides an economic incentive for more conservative water usage. Notice how benefit-cost analysis is implicitly reflected in this approach. As each additional block of water is used, higher marginal costs are considered along with the marginal benefits of consumption. Of course, unless the increasing price blocks accurately reflect society's marginal cost, the result will not be efficient. Also, there are implementation costs to be considered in instituting this pricing structure, since metering is necessary to track usage. This factor explains why some smaller utilities favor a flat rate system despite its inherent inefficiencies.

Based on this fundamental analysis, it is argued that the EPA and other government authorities should attempt to structure water pricing to reflect the associated marginal cost to society. A further consideration is to find ways to make such a pricing scheme financially feasible for all types of water utilities, including smaller facilities. Although this would be a challenging undertaking, it could make a measurable difference in both current and future water quality.

Conclusions

For more than 20 years, the Safe Drinking Water Act has been the legislation responsible for protecting human health from contaminated tap water. Like most environmental laws, this one has been the subject of debate and criticism—even more so as it recently came up for reauthorization before the U.S. Congress. Confidence in national drinking water policy has weakened in recent years. Right or wrong, most Americans had been fairly complacent about the quality of tap water. However, reports such as the EPA's 1992 survey on lead levels and the 1993 Milwaukee incident have made both private citizens and public officials question the effectiveness of U.S. drinking water policy.

By comparison to some environmental laws, the structure of the SDWA is markedly simple—a direct application of the command-and-control approach. It establishes contaminant limits designed to assure that public water supplies are safe for human consumption and relies on state and local authorities to make certain that these standards are met. From an economic perspective, such an approach is flawed. The standards are benefit-based, with no requirement for a balancing of marginal benefits and costs. Furthermore, there are no incentives to encourage compliance or to stimulate technological advance to meet the standards in a cost-effective manner. Instead, achieving safe drinking water relies on constant monitoring and enforcement—procedures that are difficult and costly to implement.

Beyond these problems are issues that arise from the relationship of the SDWA to other U.S. water quality laws, particularly the Clean Water Act. The Clean Water Act is designed to assure a baseline level of water quality—to meet the fishable-swimmable goal—for all surface water and groundwater supplies. For its part, the SDWA must achieve a comparatively higher level of quality solely for the water that arrives at the tap. It has no rulings to control effluent discharges and only limited provisions to protect underground sources of drinking water. If the Clean Water Act fails to achieve its goals, the objectives of the SDWA are that much harder to attain. The legislative interdependence is even more complex for groundwater resources, which are controlled under many different laws and programs.

Although it is easy to criticize a less-than-perfect outcome, it is far more difficult to find effective policy solutions. Because water resources are so diverse and at the same time interconnected, policy formulation is not straightforward, nor is the ongoing appraisal and revision process. Both the Clean Water Act and the Safe Drinking Water Act are rooted strongly in the command-and-control approach with standards providing the legislative muscle. Economists and other policy analysts argue the need for an integration of market-based incentives into this policy structure. Another recommendation is to launch initiatives to *prevent* water contamination and lessen the dependence on end-of-pipe treatment. These would be nontrivial revisions, but so too are the problems confronting the nation at this phase of its water quality policy development.

Summary

- The Interstate Quarantine Act of 1893 was the first federal law in the evolution of U.S. drinking water standards. The Public Health Service Act of 1912 called for the establishment of standards to prevent the spread of communicable waterborne diseases. These standards were set in 1914 and revised a number of times over the next several decades.

- The Safe Drinking Water Act of 1974 (SDWA) was aimed at protecting drinking water from any contaminant that could threaten human health or welfare. It established primary standards to protect human health and secondary standards to protect welfare. The 1986 Amendments expanded federal controls on drinking water and corrected some of the failings of the original SDWA. This legislation has recently come up for reauthorization before Congress.

- The primary purpose of the Safe Drinking Water Act is to assure that public water systems meet minimum standards to protect human health. The 1986 Amendments identified 83 contaminants for which drinking water standards were to be set and required that another 25 be added every three years starting in 1991.

- Under U.S. law, there are National Primary Drinking Water Regulations (NPDWRs) aimed at protecting human health. Each regulation consists of a maximum contaminant level goal (MCLG), a maximum contaminant level (MCL), and a specification of the best available technology (BAT) for public water supply treatment.

- The MCLG defines the level of a pollutant at which no known or expected adverse health effects occur, allowing for an adequate margin of safety. The MCL is the highest permissible level of a contaminant in water delivered to any user of a public system. It is set as close to the maximum contaminant level goal (MCLG) as is feasible. The BAT represents the feasible treatment technology capable of meeting the standard, taking account of cost considerations.

- Secondary Drinking Water Regulations establish secondary maximum contaminant levels (SMCLs) for pollutants that impair aesthetics and other characteristics like odor and taste. These are nonenforceable, federal guidelines aimed at protecting public welfare.

- Enforcement of the primary drinking water standards is shared between the EPA and state governments. The major responsibility is assigned to state governments, provided that certain criteria are met.
- The Safe Drinking Water Act (SDWA) does not call for a balancing of benefits and costs in setting the maximum contaminant levels (MCLs). Hence, efficiency is not being used to regulate drinking water quality. Since the primary standards are benefit-based, some drinking water contaminants may be overregulated.
- According to a recent government study, the extent of compliance by public water systems has been overstated by the EPA, and enforcement action has been inadequate. In addition to procedural problems, there is evidence that outmoded treatment facilities and failing water distribution systems characterize the majority of public water systems.
- Many U.S. communities use improper pricing practices of water supplies, such as a flat fee, flat rate, or declining block structure, none of which account for rising marginal costs. The result is overconsumption of water resources, since such practices do not provide an incentive for conservation.

Key Concepts

priority contaminants
primary drinking water standards
secondary drinking water standards
National Primary Drinking Water
 Regulations (NPDWR)
maximum contaminant level goal
 (MCLG)
maximum contaminant level (MCL)

action level
best available technology (BAT)
secondary maximum contaminant level
 (SMCL)
flat fee pricing scheme
flat rate pricing structure
declining block pricing structure
increasing block pricing structure

APPENDIX
A REFERENCE TO ACRONYMS IN DRINKING WATER QUALITY CONTROL

Environmental Economics Acronyms

TSB	Total social benefits
TSC	Total social costs

Environmental Science Acronyms

mg/L	Milligrams per liter
ppb	Parts per billion
RfD	Reference dose

Environment Policy Acronyms

BAT	Best available technology
NAS	National Academy of Science
MCL	Maximum contaminant level
MCLG	Maximum contaminant level goal
RIA	Regulatory Impact Analysis
SDWA	Safe Drinking Water Act
SMCL	Secondary maximum contaminant level
SNC	Significant noncompliers

Review Questions

1. In what ways did the Safe Drinking Water Act Amendments of 1986 best address the shortcomings in the law? In what ways did it fail?

2. *a.* Explain the practical difference between the MCLG and the MCL.

   b. Draw the relationship of marginal social benefit and marginal social cost for the MCLG for lead, assuming it is set at an efficient level. Intuitively explain your model.

3. Support or refute Congress's decision to make the secondary drinking water standards *not* enforceable by the federal government.

4. According to the EPA, uncontrolled disposal of pesticide residues and containers contributes significantly to groundwater contamination and hence threatens drinking water supplies. Design and evaluate a deposit/refund system for pesticide containers.

5. Determine the water pricing structure that is used in your hometown. Using the criterion of allocative efficiency, defend the current practice or propose an alternative pricing structure.

Additional Readings

Dziegielewski, Benedykt, and Duane D. Baumann. ''Tapping Alternatives: The Benefits of Managing Urban Water Demands.'' *Environment* 34, no. 9 (November 1992), pp. 6–11, 35–41.

Dzurik, Andrew A. *Water Resources Planning.* Savage, Md.: Rowman & Littlefield Publishers, 1990.

Gordon, Wendy. ''Federal Protection of Ground Water.'' In David H. Speidel, Lon C. Ruedisili, and Allen F. Agnew, eds. *Perspectives on Water: Uses and Abuses.* New York: Oxford University Press, 1988, pp. 326–29.

Howitt, Richard E., Dean E. Mann, and H. J. Vaux Jr. ''The Economics of Water Allocation.'' In Ernest A. Engelbert with Ann Foley Scheuring, eds. *Competition for California Water.* Berkeley, Calif.: University of California Press, 1982, pp. 136–62.

MacLeish, William H. ''Water, Water, Everywhere, How Many Drops to Drink?'' *World Monitor,* December 1990, pp. 54–58.

Mazari, Marisa. ''Potential for Groundwater Contamination in Mexico City.'' *Environmental Science and Technology* 27, no. 5 (1993), pp. 794–802.

Newman, Alan. ''A Blueprint for Water Quality.'' *Environmental Science and Technology* 27, no. 2 (1993), pp. 223–25.

Tomsho, Robert. ''Cities Reclaim Waste Water for Drinking.'' *The Wall Street Journal,* August 8, 1994, pp. B1, B6.

Waxman, Henry. ''Amending the Safe Drinking Water Act: View from Congress.'' *EPA Journal* 20, no. 1–2 (Summer 1994), pp. 32–33.

World Health Organization. ''Health Hazards of Water Pollution.'' In David H. Speidel, Lon C. Ruedisili, and Allen F. Agnew, eds. *Perspectives on Water: Uses and Abuses.* New York: Oxford University Press, 1988.

The Case of Solid Wastes and Toxic Substances

In 1978, the state of New York urged 1,000 families to leave their homes and ordered an emergency evacuation of 240 others—all residents of a Niagara Falls community known as Love Canal. Built on a site that 30 years earlier had been a chemical dumping ground, the ill-fated Love Canal was eventually declared a disaster area by President Carter. In 1982, the residents of Times Beach, Missouri, learned that their groundwater and soil contained dangerously high levels of dioxins—the result of contaminated road oil that had been used in the town 11 years earlier. Times Beach was completely evacuated. In 1987, what came to be known as the "garbage barge" hauled some 3,100 tons of New York's trash for months in the Gulf of Mexico and the Caribbean, searching for a place to deposit its decaying and foul-smelling cargo. These events and countless others awakened society to the potential risks of solid waste pollution and exposure to toxic chemicals.

The full extent of these problems is not completely known, and efficient solutions appear to be just as elusive. Not only are *current* waste generation and disposal practices at issue, but also the damages caused by waste mismanagement of the *past*. In a broad sense, there are two interrelated issues to be addressed—excess waste generation and the use of toxic substances that eventually become part of the waste stream. Chemicals leaking from buried waste and mismanaged disposal sites have caused serious damage to human health and the ecology—some of it irreparable. Less severe, but nonetheless cause for concern, is the growth rate of municipal trash generation—millions of tons of bottles, cans, food scraps, and the like. In many communities, residents and public officials are still searching for cost-effective ways to collect and dispose of the accumulating heap. What makes these problems all the more troubling is that the environmental damage cuts across all media—land, water, and air.

Policy development aimed at solid waste pollution got a late start in the United States, and most argue that current legislation is still inadequate and ill defined. In the 1960s and 1970s, U.S. environmental policy was firmly focused on controlling air and water pollution, but little in the way of substantive federal legislation was passed during this period to manage and reduce the solid waste stream. Why the lack of initiative? For one thing, population centers had remained fairly compact for a long time and seemingly were able to manage the amount of wastes being generated. Managing solid wastes was viewed as a local responsibility and not one that required national action. Furthermore, the problems associated with the treatment and disposal of chemical wastes, particularly synthetics, did not accelerate until the 1970s.[1] Regardless of the logic of these explanations, there is one root cause that underlies all of them. Society failed to recognize the significance of solid waste as an environmental and health risk. The result? Policy-makers are having to play catch-up with a problem that, at least until recently, has been advancing both in magnitude and severity.

In this module, we assess this important environmental and social dilemma and analyze the solutions brought forth by government. In Chapter 16, we focus on hazardous waste pollution—the risks it poses to society and the federal legislation designed to minimize those risks. Chapter 17 examines the challenges of managing nonhazardous wastes and the policy efforts of both the federal and lower levels of government. Our focus shifts in Chapter 18, where we analyze federal laws aimed at controlling pesticides and other toxic substances *before* they are introduced into commerce and eventually enter the waste stream. Not unlike our analyses of air and water degradation, the tools of economic analysis are used throughout to assess the effectiveness of government in responding to environmental risks.

---

[1]U.S. EPA, Office of Solid Waste and Emergency Response (October 1985).

MANAGING HAZARDOUS SOLID WASTE AND WASTE SITES

An official order to evacuate homes and businesses following the discovery of a hazardous waste leak is a chilling reminder of the potential risks of solid waste pollution. All too often, there are accounts of strange odors emanating from basements, tainted water supplies, or health symptoms for which doctors have no diagnosis—reports that are eventually linked to a waste accident or cover-up from years past. Once-thriving communities in the United States like Love Canal, New York, and Times Beach, Missouri, actually became ghost towns because of the toxic effects of hazardous waste. Why did the problem reach such a level before something was done?

By the time federal policies were formulated in the United States, the nation was already suffering from the ill effects of mismanaged hazardous wastes that had been accumulating for decades. At the same time, the growth rate of the waste stream was rising due to urban development, industrialization, population growth, and increasing chemical usage. There was also a glaring lack of information about the magnitude of the problem. In fact, some argue that we still do not have a complete picture of the extent and severity of solid waste pollution in this country. What we *do* know is that the damage extends to all environmental media, which means that the effects are widespread, difficult to control, and costly to society. Accepting this characterization, it should not be surprising to learn that there are *several* major legislative acts aimed at the dilemma. While some deal with the damage from *past* mismanagement, others attempt to control the *present* solid waste stream.

Investigating this multidimensional control approach is the objective of this chapter. Our aim is to explain the policy position of the United States in dealing with hazardous waste. The operative issue is whether or not existing policy is effective and if not, whether there are viable alternatives that can and should be implemented. We begin with an overview of the hazardous waste problem and a brief discussion of how the federal response evolved. We then focus on the two major U.S. laws aimed at hazardous waste—the Resource Conservation and Recovery Act (RCRA) and Superfund. Here, the goal is to explain the overall intent and structure of these laws so that they can be analyzed from an economic perspective. An appendix of acronyms is provided for reference at the end of the chapter.

Characterizing the Hazardous Waste Problem[1]

hazardous solid wastes
Any unwanted materials or refuse capable of posing a substantial threat to health or the ecology.

waste stream
The series of events starting with waste generation and including the transportation, storage, treatment, and disposal of solid wastes.

Hazardous solid wastes are any unwanted materials or refuse capable of posing a substantial threat to health or the environment. A diverse range of substances fall into this broad category, so it is useful to consider the hazardous constituents of wastes as part of meaningful subgroups like pesticides and synthetic chemicals as listed in Table 16.1. Notice from the table that these substances serve important functions in productive activity. Often, the properties that make them useful in production are precisely those that make them dangerous to society once they enter the **waste stream**. The **waste stream** refers to the series of events starting with waste **generation** and proceeding though the **transportation, storage, treatment,** and **disposal** of these materials. Environmental and health risks arise both because of excess generation and improper management of these materials once they enter the waste stream.

The Magnitude and Source of the Problem

In the United States, estimates of annual hazardous waste generation range anywhere from 250 to 500 million tons. This translates to about 1 ton per person annually.[2] Nations everywhere must deal with the risks of accumulating hazardous wastes. In Canada, for example, the reported annual level of hazardous wastes is 3.63 million tons, or about 0.14 tons per person, and in Italy, the level is estimated at 4.01 million tons, or 0.07 tons per person.[3] Third-world countries are also confronting the problem as they evolve into more industrialized economies. These developing nations also have to contend with wastes deliberately dumped inside their borders by firms from advanced countries seeking to avoid the costs of and regulatory constraints on disposal.[4]

---

[1]Following the literature and government data reporting, we have omitted from this discussion any reference to medical wastes and radioactive wastes.

[2]McCarthy and Reisch (1987) and U.S. Congress, Office of Technology Assessment (OTA) (March 1983) as cited in Wirth and Heinz (1991), p. 43. These values are based upon that portion of hazardous wastes controlled by U.S. regulations. Absent this qualifier, the grand total is estimated to be 1.3 billion tons per year, of which about 75 percent is controlled by the Clean Water Act.

[3]Direct international comparisons cannot be made with precision given differences in definitions and estimating methods across nations. The statistics cited are drawn from selected data in World Resources Institute (1993), ''Country Comparisons,'' pp. 333–640.

[4]Kharbanda and Stallworthy (1990), p. 105.

TABLE 16.1   Types of Hazardous Substances

Acids and Bases

Description: Acids are characterized as having a low pH between 0 and 6, and bases as having a high pH between 8 and 14. Highly acidic or basic substances are corrosive, meaning they can deteriorate other materials. In the waste stream, discarded acids and bases can corrode the containers in which they are stored and leach into land and nearby waterways.

Uses: Acids and bases are frequently used in processes such as plating procedures and metal stripping.

Heavy Metals

Description: Heavy metals include lead, arsenic, cadmium, barium, copper, and mercury. They are highly toxic and do not readily break down in the human body. Thus, their presence in the waste stream poses a potentially serious health threat.

Uses: These metals possess properties that are useful in plating and production processes and in numerous commodities. Some have special properties, such as copper, which is an excellent conductor of electricity and is highly resistant to corrosion.

Reactives

Description: Reactives are substances that behave violently when combined with air or water. Included are explosives and flammables, substances that react strongly when combined with oxygen, giving off large amounts of heat in the process. Common examples are petroleum or natural gas by-products. The instability of reactive substances makes them potentially harmful in the waste stream. Leaking of reactives like petroleum from storage tanks can contaminate soil and water resources.

Uses: Reactives are useful in certain industrial processes. For example, laboratories use these chemicals to accelerate a reaction, and plastics manufacturing uses them to speed up polymerization to harden plastic.

Synthetic Organic Chemicals

Description: Synthetic organic chemicals are man-made substances that are hydrocarbon based, some created from relatively new processes like chemical splicing and molecular engineering. Two important subcategories of synthetic organic chemicals are solvents and pesticides.

Uses: Many synthetics are highly resistant in use, making them valuable to industrial applications. Polychlorinated biphenyls (PCBs) formerly were used as insulators in transformers because of their resistance to heat and electrical charges.*

Solvents

Description: Solvents are liquids that can dissolve or disperse one or more substances. Examples include ethylene, benzene, pyridine, and acetone.

Uses: Solvents are used for a variety of industrial processes, such as degreasing, stripping, cleaning, and thinning procedures.

Pesticides

Description: Pesticides are used to prevent, destroy, or repel, any unwanted form of plant or animal life. These include insecticides, rodenticides, herbicides, and fungicides. Some are highly resistant, which allows them to persist in the environment for a long time without the need for frequent reapplication. Some are nearly insoluble in water, making their use as insecticides on crops resistant to rainfall. Many are acutely toxic.

Uses: These substances are used mainly in agriculture but also in such industries as textiles, paper, and wood production treatment.

*The highly toxic nature of PCBs led eventually to a 1976 ban on their manufacture, processing, distribution, and use in the United States, except in completely enclosed electrical equipment.

Sources: Drawn from Russell W. Phifer and William R. McTigue Jr., *Handbook of Hazardous Waste Management* (Chelsea, Mi.: Lewis Publishers, Inc., 1988), Chapter 3; Samuel S. Epstein, M.D., Lester O. Brown, and Carl Pope, *Hazardous Waste in America* (San Francisco: Sierra Club Books, 1982), pp. 14–26; U.S. Environmental Protection Agency, *Meeting the Environmental Challenge: EPA's Review of Progress and New Directions in Environmental Protection* (Washington, D.C., December 1990a), p. 120.

TABLE 16.2   Environmental Degradation at U.S. Hazardous Waste Sites as of 1991

Reported Impacts	*Percent of Sites Affected**
Groundwater	85.2%
Drinking water	73.1
Soil	72.1
Surface water	50.4
Air	26.0
Vegetation	10.5
Animal life	7.8
Human health	6.6

*Sites included in the report are those designated by the United States as on its National Priorities List, that is, those that pose the greatest threat to human health and the ecology.

Source: Council on Environmental Quality, *Environmental Quality, 22nd Annual Report* (Washington, D.C.: U.S. Government Printing Office, March 1992), Table 90, p. 338, citing U.S. Environmental Protection Agency, *Superfund NPL Characterization Project: National Results* (Washington, D.C., 1991).

There is no doubt that the problem of hazardous waste is worldwide, and there is no question that there are serious risks in ignoring it.

All environmental media—the atmosphere, ground and surface waters, and soil—are vulnerable to hazardous waste contamination. Ocean pollution, soil contamination, disease, fish kills, and livestock loss are among the potential damages. The health and ecological effects can be severe and long term, particularly from exposure to persistent pollutants like PCBs and DDT that bioaccumulate in the environment. As shown in Table 16.2, water and soil contamination are the most prevalent type of damage linked to hazardous waste sites. Contamination of drinking water can occur when rainwater absorbs pollutants as it runs through disposal sites. The resulting **leachate,** as it is called, can pollute ground and surface waters—damage that is very costly and sometimes impossible to rectify. Surrounding soil can be polluted in the same way. Food crops grown in such contaminated soil absorb pollutants that are later ingested by humans and animals. Particularly vulnerable are households living near hazardous waste sites. One of the most often cited cases of an entire community affected by the contamination is Love Canal, New York. A brief account of the story is given in Application 16.1.

Just who is responsible for generating all these toxic waste materials? It turns out that every sector of the economy—households, industry, government, and institutions—contributes to the hazardous waste stream.[5] While none of these sources should be ignored, there is no question that most hazardous wastes are generated by industry. In the United States, some 99

leachate
Water that runs through waste disposal sites and absorbs pollutants.

---

[5]For example, U.S. households dispose of an estimated 385 million gallons of used motor oil each year—literally 35 times more than the *Valdez* spilled into Alaskan waters in 1989.

Application 16.1

The Hazardous Waste Site Called Love Canal

In the late 1880s, an entrepreneur by the name of William T. Love began excavation of a canal that would connect the upper and lower ends of the Niagara River in upper New York State. Envisioned as the future site of a major industrial complex, the Love Canal project was designed to make use of the enormous supply of hydroelectric power that would be provided naturally by the 280 foot drop between the two ends of the river. Before the innovative plan was completed, alternating current (AC) was developed, and the once futuristic Love Canal project lost its appeal. Love's visionary complex was never finished, but one segment of the partially constructed canal remained. It simply filled with water, and for a time was used for swimming.

In the 1940s, Hooker Chemical and Plastics Corporation (then Hooker Electrochemical Corporation), through agreement with the canal's owner, Niagara Power and Development Corporation, began using the site to dump its chemical wastes. Ultimately buying the canal to use as a dump site, Hooker discarded over 21,000 tons of chemicals into the Love Canal over the period 1942 to 1952. Among the toxic wastes were benzene derivatives, dioxins, and trichlorophenol (TCPs) contaminated with a highly potent carcinogenic substance called TCDD. According to one source, TCDD is so lethal that less than three ounces could kill all the residents of New York City (Epstein et al., 1982, p. 93).

Some years later, the postwar construction boom that characterized America in the 1950s prompted the city of Niagara Falls to condemn the properties surrounding the canal to make room for a new school and a residential area. In 1953, Hooker signed the canal over to the city for $1 in exchange for a release from any liability for damage associated with the dump site. Despite the obvious danger, the canal was filled in, and construction proceeded. The school opened in 1955, and hundreds of homes were built. Beyond that, the newly constructed community was anything but normal.

Buyers of the new homes were unaware of the chemical dump site. Soon after moving in, they began to complain about fumes coming from the former dump site and chemical burns their children got from playing in nearby fields. Lawns and gardens refused to grow, and pools of black liquid began to surface in backyards and open fields. In the mid-1970s, the same black sludge started to seep into basements after heavy rains. Finally, in 1977 after numerous complaints, the city called in a consultant to investigate. The findings confirmed the residents' worse fears—toxic chemicals had leached from the canal and contaminated the ground and surface water.

One resident named Lois Gibbs took action, suspecting that her son's history of health problems might have been caused by the chemical leaks. She began a petition drive to get the school closed. As she did, the residents began to make the painful discovery that their community had suffered an unusual number of birth defects, miscarriages, and other health problems—some of them chronic. In August 1978, the state health commissioner announced that the school would be closed, and some—but not all—families would be evacuated and their homes bought by the state. It was then that the once local environmental disaster became national news. Meanwhile, some families were still living in the community. Unsatisfied that the state's action was sufficient, Gibbs continued to fight.

What followed was a complex and bitter struggle for Gibbs and the other Love Canal residents. Despite mounting evidence, the state's response to the problem continued to be less than adequate. Gibbs and the other residents formed the Love Canal Homeowners Association, Inc. and began to take matters into their own hands. Every level of government eventually became involved along with many public agencies, health officials, independent researchers, and the local and national media. In 1979, the Department of Justice filed a

Application 16.1 (concluded)

series of lawsuits against Hooker Chemical, the city of Niagara Falls, the city's board of education, and the Niagara County Health Department. In 1980, the EPA announced preliminary findings from a pilot study of the residents that showed chromosomal damage in 11 of the 36 persons tested. While the validity of that study has since been questioned and is still the focus of contention, it did seem to be an important catalyst in helping to get the remaining residents out of the area. In May 1980, President Carter declared Love Canal a disaster area, and that summer, $15 million in grants and loans was offered to the state of New York to purchase new homes for the relocated families. In October, President Carter signed a bill to permanently evacuate all families from the ill-fated community, but *not* because of any proven environmental hazard, rather for the mental anguish they had suffered.

This unfortunate event has no ending in the usual sense, since there are still many unanswered questions that will likely remain that way, but a few follow-up facts are in order. Billions of dollars in lawsuits were filed against Hooker Chemical— some by state and local government and numerous others by private individuals. Lois Gibbs went on to become an environmental activist, establishing

the group Citizen's Clearinghouse for Hazardous Waste in 1981. The EPA issued a much criticized report in 1982, indicating that the area was again safe for habitation, adding that the level of contamination in most of the area was not significantly different than what existed in other industrial areas of that region. Two years later, a clay cap was placed over a 40-acre area in Love Canal, and the EPA announced its plans to dredge the area and incinerate the toxic wastes.

It is difficult to sort through the sequence of events that is today referred to simply as Love Canal. On balance, most agree that government officials made some serious mistakes, and as a consequence, some of the facts of the Love Canal disaster have been lost. Bureaucratic entanglements, botched cleanup attempts, political infighting, and questionable scientific studies are unfortunately all part of the Love Canal saga. However, the event *did* awaken the world to the potential dangers of toxic wastes, and because of that Lois Gibbs and her neighbors won an important battle.

Sources: Samuel S. Epstein, M.D.; Lester O. Brown; and Carl Pope, *Hazardous Waste in America* (San Francisco: Sierra Club Books, 1982), Chapter 5; Lois Marie Gibbs, *Love Canal: My Story* (Albany: State University of New York Press, 1982); Melanie L. Griffin, ''The Legacy of Love Canal,'' *Sierra*, January/February 1988, pp. 26–28.

percent of industrial hazardous wastes comes from so-called large-quantity generators, those producing over 2,200 pounds per month. Another 1 million tons per year are added by small-quantity generators, producing between 220 and 2,200 pounds per month. This latter group includes such diverse entities as biological laboratories, automobile repair shops, dry cleaners, greenhouses, art museums, and exterminators. As shown in Table 16.3, the chemical and petroleum industries are responsible for generating most of the hazardous waste in the United States, with 79 percent attributable to the former. The distribution is also skewed geographically, with the eastern, midwestern, and southern United States producing more than the western and Rocky Mountain regions.[6]

---

[6]U.S. EPA (August 1988), p. 80.

TABLE 16.3   Hazardous Waste Generation in the
United States by Major Industry*

Industry	Percentage of Hazardous Waste Generation
Chemical	79.0%
Petroleum refinery	7.0
Transportation equipment	1.0
Fabricated metals	1.0
Primary metals	1.0
Electrical equipment	0.4
National security	0.4
Other	9.0

*Excludes radioactive wastes.

Source: U.S. Environmental Protection Agency, *Environmental Progress and Challenges: EPA's Update* (Washington, D.C., August 1988), p. 80, Figure L-2, from U.S. Environmental Protection Agency, Office of Solid Waste, *National Screening Survey of Hazardous Waste Treatment, Storage, Disposal, and Recycling Facilities* (Washington, D.C.)

From an economic perspective, any adverse effects associated with the use and disposal of hazardous substances are negative externalities. Hence, government policy is needed to regulate markets where the problem arises and attempt to internalize the external costs. In the United States, the early development of solid waste policy was anything but aggressive. Most argue that this segment of environmental legislative history should be characterized as having been *reactive*—even passive at times. This lack of spirited attention to solid waste problems by federal officials was matched by the same absence in the private sector. The environmentalism of the 1960s was preoccupied with fouled rivers and streams, urban smog, and threatened wildlife, paying little attention to accumulating mounds of trash and risks of chemical wastes.[7]

The Evolution of U.S. Solid Waste Policy

It is often suggested that the U.S. government did virtually nothing in the way of controlling solid wastes until *after* the Love Canal saga made national news in the late 1970s. This suggestion on face value is erroneous. The primary piece of federal legislation on solid wastes, the Resource Conservation and Recovery Act, had been passed by Congress two years *prior* to that infamous event. Furthermore, the draft version of the Superfund legislation dealing with abandoned and uncontrolled hazardous waste sites had been completed in October 1978—only two months after the nation first learned about Love Canal

---

[7]One important exception was the 1962 work of Rachel Carson, *Silent Spring*, which warned of the risks of pesticide chemicals.

TABLE 16.4   Overview of U.S. Legislation on Hazardous Solid Wastes

Legislative Act	*Major Provisions*
Solid Waste Disposal Act (SWDA) of 1965	Provided financial assistance to state and local governments in planning solid waste disposal programs; initiated a national research plan aimed at finding better waste disposal methods.
Resource Recovery Act of 1970	Encouraged recycling and technological controls to reduce waste at the generation point; continued to promote land disposal of wastes in local communities and emphasize nonhazardous solid waste.
Resource Conservation and Recovery Act (RCRA) of 1976	Represented the first U.S. official position on hazardous waste control; established a "cradle-to-grave" management system for controlling hazardous waste; delegated the administration of nonhazardous waste primarily to state governments.
The Hazardous and Solid Waste Amendments of 1984	Reauthorized RCRA and broadened federal control by adding owners and operators of underground storage tanks and all small quantity waste generators to those regulated under RCRA; shifted emphasis from land disposal to waste reduction and toward improved treatment technologies for hazardous wastes; elevated the standards for hazardous waste facilities with new requirements for safety measures.
Comprehensive Environmental Response, Compensation, and Liability Act (CERCLA) of 1980 (known as Superfund)	Called for the preparation of a national inventory of hazardous waste site information from which to identify sites posing the greatest threat to health and the ecology; placed these sites on the National Priorities List (NPL); designated a fund of $1.6 billion to clean up NPL sites and pay for associated damages.
Superfund Amendments and Reauthorization Act (SARA) of 1986	Reauthorized CERCLA; increased the fund to $8.5 billion to be financed primarily from feedstock taxes; called for the initiation of federal action on 375 sites within a five-year period; promoted permanent cleanup technologies.

Sources: Sidney M. Wolf, *Pollution Law Handbook: A Guide to Federal Environmental Laws* (New York: Quorum Books, 1988), Chapters 6, 7; U.S. Environmental Protection Agency, Office of Solid Waste and Emergency Response, *The New RCRA Fact Book* (Washington, D.C., October 1985); Resource Conservation and Recovery Act of 1976; Hazardous and Solid Waste Amendments of 1984; Comprehensive Environmental Response, Compensation, and Liability Act of 1980; Superfund Amendments and Reauthorization Act of 1986.

and well before the related publicity that continued into 1980.[8] The point is that the United States *did* have a national policy agenda on solid waste in the 1970s, but the legislation had passed with little scrutiny and was not fully responsive to the magnitude of the problem. Hence, while Love Canal was not the catalyst for *introducing* federal solid waste legislation, this event and others like it motivated public officials and private citizens to give the matter more attention. Several federal laws and amendments speak to this evolution as shown in Table 16.4. An overview of the chronology that ties together these laws and their primary objectives follows.

---

[8]Landy et al. (1990), p. 140.

Federal Recognition of the Solid Waste Problem

U.S. policy on waste control originated with the Solid Waste Disposal Act (SWDA) passed in 1965. Its primary objectives were to provide financial assistance to state and local governments in planning waste management programs and to initiate a national research plan aimed at finding better disposal methods. In 1970, this seminal waste legislation was amended by the Resource Recovery Act. More significant in intent, this act marked a slight shift in emphasis from disposal to conservation by encouraging recycling and technological development to reduce waste generation. At this stage of the evolution, however, the emphasis continued to be on *nonhazardous* waste and the use of land disposal in local communities.[9] Over time, the increasing use of chemicals, the addition of synthetic chemicals to production processes, and the more frequent occurrence of waste site contamination problems led to a shift in the legislative trend. Congress saw the need to strengthen controls on waste management practices with specific rulings aimed at hazardous waste materials.

Developing Policy to Control the Risks of Hazardous Wastes

In 1976, the Resource Conservation and Recovery Act (RCRA) was passed by Congress as amendments to the original Solid Waste Disposal Act. The hallmark of RCRA was that it signified the first federal policy position explicitly aimed at hazardous wastes. A distinct set of regulations within the act

cradle-to-grave management system
A command-and-control policy approach to regulating hazardous solid wastes throughout every stage of the waste stream.

established a **"cradle-to-grave" management system** for controlling these materials. The metaphor refers to a policy strategy for controlling, managing, and tracking these wastes throughout every stage of the waste cycle, as shown in Figure 16.1. A separate set of provisions delegated the administration of nonhazardous waste primarily to state governments.[10]

Congress reauthorized and strengthened RCRA through The Hazardous and Solid Waste Amendments of 1984.[11] The new provisions reinforced the evolving policy shift away from land disposal and toward waste reduction efforts and better treatment technologies. Standards for hazardous waste facilities were strengthened with new requirements for safety measures such as groundwater monitoring equipment and leachate collection systems. Control was broadened by adding two groups of facilities to those regulated under RCRA—owners and operators of certain underground storage tanks and all small-quantity waste generators. At the time, this latter group added about 175,000 entities to those already bound by federal law. Stringent rulings were

---

[9]U.S. EPA, Office of Solid Waste and Emergency Response (October 1985).

[10]The provisions applicable to hazardous waste are given in Subtitle C of RCRA. In the next chapter, we will investigate and analyze the rulings in Subtitle D of RCRA aimed at nonhazardous, municipal solid wastes.

[11]Despite the change in title, conventional practice is to use the acronym RCRA to refer to this legislation.

FIGURE 16.1

The "cradle-to-grave" management system under RCRA: controlling, managing, and tracking the hazardous waste stream

Source: U.S. Environmental Protection Agency, Office of Solid Waste, *Solving the Hazardous Waste Problem: EPA's RCRA Program* (Washington, D.C., November 1986), p. 11.

imposed on underground storage tanks that house potentially dangerous substances. In addition to requiring safety equipment such as leak detection systems, RCRA also assigned financial responsibility to tank owners and operators for any environmental damages should a leak occur. Application 16.2 has more on the potential risks of underground storage tanks.

Beyond RCRA's controls on *current* solid waste management, guidelines and financial support were needed to address the damages caused by *past* contamination and to clean up abandoned and uncontrolled hazardous waste sites. On the heels of the Love Canal dilemma, the Comprehensive Environmental Response, Compensation, and Liability Act (CERCLA), or Superfund

Application 16.2

Hazardous Wastes from Leaking Underground Storage Tanks

Current estimates indicate there are over 5 million underground storage tanks containing petroleum products or other hazardous substances in the United States. About 2 million of these are regulated under RCRA. The practice of burying storage tanks was done as a safety measure to prevent fires—an objective that was effectively accomplished. Ironically, these tanks have now become the source of a serious environmental hazard. Some 400,000 of the underground storage tanks in the United States are believed to be leaking—a number expected to rise in the future. These tanks are so large, even a small pinhole can lead to a serious waste problem. About 49 percent of the regulated storage tanks in the United States are filled with petroleum and owned by gasoline stations, with another 47 percent owned by industries that store petroleum for their own use, such as airports, farms, golf courses, and firms with large trucking fleets. The remaining 4 percent are filled with other chemicals stored for industrial use.

A major source of concern is that the inventory of buried tanks is aging, making leakages that much more likely and increasingly so as time goes on. It turns out that many of these tanks were placed in the ground in the 1950s and 1960s during the oil boom of that era. Studies have indicated that about one-third of fuel storage tanks in the United States are over 20 years old or of unknown age. Unfortunately, many of these older vessels were constructed of bare steel, making them totally vulnerable to corrosion. Adding to the dilemma are all the abandoned storage tanks left by defunct gas stations that failed during the OPEC crisis of the 1970s. In these cases, it is feared that the tanks may not have been closed properly. Since so much time has passed, determining ownership and responsibility for any discovered leaks is difficult at best.

According to the EPA, the primary cause of leaks is corrosion of steel tanks, a naturally occurring process that results when the surface of the tank comes in contact with the soil and begins to

return to its original state, iron oxide, or what most refer to as rust. Other important causes of leaks are spills and overfills. Spills occur when the hose that delivers the contents is pulled from the entry pipe before it has completely drained, and overfills result from trying to add more product than the tank can hold. Piping failures and loose fittings for attachments such as pumps and vent lines can also be the cause of leakages into the surrounding environment.

Leaks from underground storage tanks or their piping can contaminate groundwater and soil, poison crops, cause fires or explosions, and harm human health. Human exposure can occur through direct contact with contaminated soil or water or via inhalation of toxic emissions. Aside from breathing dangerous vapors released into a nearby building, inhalation also can occur during showering with contaminated water when volatile components are released. This form of exposure is often commensurate with drinking the water. For example, the calculated risk to humans from exposure to benzene, a carcinogenic substance found in gasoline, is the same for drinking 2 liters of water per day as it is for showering 15 minutes per day at 113 degrees Fahrenheit.

Prompt action is needed to remove or repair any damaged underground tanks, to clean up any contamination that has already occurred, and to compensate those who have suffered as a consequence. Just as important is the need to research new technologies in tank design, leakage detection systems, and alternative storage facilities to prevent the problem from recurring.

Source: U.S. Environmental Protection Agency, *Environmental Progress and Challenges: EPA's Update* (Washington, D.C., August 1988); pp. 102–05; U.S. Environmental Protection Agency, *Meeting the Environmental Challenge: EPA's Review of Progress and New Directions in Environmental Protection* (Washington, D.C., December 1990a), p. 16; U.S. Environmental Protection Agency, Office of Solid Waste and Emergency Response, *Leaking Underground Storage Tanks and Health: Understanding Health Risks from Petroleum Contamination* (Washington, D.C., January 1992).

as it is more commonly known, was passed in 1980. Under this law, the federal government was authorized to clean up contaminated sites and to recover damages from parties identified as responsible. Past and present owners of hazardous waste site facilities were required to notify the EPA of conditions at these sites by 1981. This baseline information along with data collected on an ongoing basis would comprise a national inventory of hazardous waste sites called the **Comprehensive Environmental Response, Compensation, and Liability Information System (CERCLIS).** This system is used to identify those sites posing the greatest threat to human health and the ecology—a classification formally referred to as the National Priorities List (NPL). The first "Superfund" of $1.6 billion was established to finance the clean up of priority sites and to pay for associated damages.

Comprehensive Environmental Response, Compensation, and Liability Information System (CERCLIS)
A national inventory of hazardous waste site data.

As it turned out, CERCLA was a national failure on two counts. First, the $1.6 billion Superfund was used to remediate only eight of the thousands of contaminated sites across the nation.[12] Secondly, according to the U.S. General Accounting Office (GAO), the CERCLIS inventory did not assess the full magnitude of the problem as was its intended purpose.[13] These failures were the primary motivation for the revision and reauthorization of CERCLA through the Superfund Amendments and Reauthorization Act (SARA) passed in 1986. SARA brought the Superfund up to $8.5 billion. This was to be financed primarily from **feedstock taxes,** including $2.75 billion from a petroleum tax and $1.4 billion from a tax on raw chemicals.[14] An important reform was the promotion of *permanent* cleanup technologies to replace short-term solutions of burying toxic wastes or transferring them from one site to another. Another was a requirement to initiate federal action on 375 sites within a five-year period. Yet, despite these changes, Superfund continues to be the source of political debate and social controversy.

feedstock taxes
Taxes levied on raw materials used as inputs in production.

In February 1994, the Clinton administration announced its proposal for major changes in the Superfund program. In an attempt to cut the program's high costs and to accelerate procedures, Clinton's plan calls for limitations on the liability of responsible parties, more flexible cleanup standards, and an $8.1 billion trust fund to cover disputed liability claims.[15] The proposal, like many others dealing with environmental issues, never made it through the 103rd Congress. Hence, the future of Superfund along with other major environmental laws remains uncertain until a new Congress determines their fate.

---

[12]Wolf (1988), p. 227.

[13]U.S. General Accounting Office (GAO) (December 1987), pp. 2–3.

[14]Another $2.5 billion was to come from corporate income taxes, $1.25 billion from federal appropriations, and the remainder from interest and recovered costs (Wolf 1988), p. 227.

[15]U.S. EPA, Office of Communications, Education, and Public Affairs (February 22, 1994c); Regan, Weber, Roush, and Kelly (April 25, 1994).

Controlling Hazardous Wastes: RCRA

source reduction
Preventive strategies to reduce the quantity and toxicity of hazardous wastes at the point of generation.

waste management
Control strategies to reduce the quantity and toxicity of hazardous wastes at every stage of the waste stream.

To minimize the risks of hazardous waste pollution, efforts must be made to reduce both the quantity and toxicity of the waste stream. Most agree that two general approaches are needed to achieve these broad-based objectives. The first is **source reduction,** a preventive strategy aimed at the generation stage. The second is to undertake sound **waste management** practices to control those wastes that cannot be eliminated. While RCRA's objectives make a general reference to preventive strategies, there is little question that management of the waste stream is the primary emphasis. A command-and-control framework characterizes the implementation plan, just as is true for federal clean air and water initiatives.

Primary responsibility for controlling hazardous wastes is assigned to the federal government—mainly through the EPA. However, Congress provided little guidance as to *how* the agency should design and implement its newly drafted policy position effected by the 1976 RCRA. This absence of legislative muscle is often blamed for what became long delays in launching the federal program and in deflecting opposition from those most affected by the new regulations. Just as critical to the policy challenge was the great uncertainty about the extent of hazardous waste pollution. Absent the obvious sources that had become national news, no one—not even major federal agencies—had a complete picture of the problem. The EPA's response was to devise a command-and-control approach intended to give structure to what must have seemed little more than ordered chaos.

The "Cradle-to-Grave" Management Approach[16]

The RCRA program emerged as the **"cradle-to-grave" management system**—a multipronged, command-and-control approach to regulating hazardous waste. Its four major components are:

1. The **identification** of hazardous wastes.
2. A **national manifest system** for tracking and monitoring the movement of wastes.
3. A **permit system** for **treatment, storage, and disposal facilities (TSDFs).**
4. The development of **standards** for these facilities.[17]

Identification of Hazardous Wastes.[18]   A fundamental element of the management system is a procedure for identifying those wastes considered to

---

[16]Much of the following is drawn from U.S. EPA, Office of Solid Waste (November 1986).
[17]U.S. Congress, OTA (1983), Chapter 7.
[18]See 40 CFR Part 261, Identification and Listing of Hazardous Waste.

characteristic wastes
Hazardous wastes identified as those exhibiting certain characteristics that imply a substantial risk.

listed wastes
Hazardous wastes that have been pre-identified by government as having met specific criteria.

manifest
A document used to identify hazardous waste materials and all parties responsible for its movement from generation to disposal.

permitting system
A control approach that authorizes the activities of TSDFs according to predefined standards.

general regulatory standards
Standards applicable to all types of TSDFs that control generic functions.

technical regulatory standards
Standards that outline specific procedures and equipment requirements for each type of TSDF.

be hazardous and therefore subject to federal regulations. The rules are highly detailed, since an error of omission would allow a dangerous material to escape federal control. Essentially, a waste is considered hazardous under the law if it falls into one of several categories. As is conventional practice, one of these categories is called **characteristic wastes**—those exhibiting attributes that imply a substantial risk. In the United States, these attributes are ignitability, corrosivity, reactivity, and toxicity. Another category is a set of **listed wastes**—those preidentified by the EPA as having met certain criteria such as the presence of toxic or carcinogenic constituents. Based upon these categories, waste generators are responsible for determining which of their wastes are hazardous and assuring that these are managed to comply with federal law.

The National Manifest System for Tracking Wastes.   If a generator chooses to transfer any hazardous wastes off-site for treatment, storage, or disposal, that movement is tracked by the **national manifest system.** Once the wastes are ready for transport, the generator must prepare a document called a **manifest** that identifies the hazardous material and all the parties responsible for its movement. The document remains with the shipment from the point of generation through to its final disposal. The objective is clear— to assure that dangerous waste materials are accounted for through every phase of the waste cycle, reducing the opportunity for illegal dumping.

The Permit System.   While the tracking system monitors the *location* of hazardous waste, a **permitting system** is used to control its management at **treatment, storage, and disposal facilities (TSDFs).** Every TSDF must obtain a permit in order to operate. The permitting process is stringently controlled, since its purpose is to ensure that TSDFs meet federal **standards,** many of which are aimed at protecting groundwater from waste contamination.

Standards.   Two sets of standards control the waste management practices of TSDFs. **General regulatory standards** apply to *all* types of TSDFs and control generic functions like inspections, emergency plans, and participation in the manifest program. There are also **technical regulatory standards** that outline procedures and equipment requirements for specific types of waste facilities. For example, storage facilities must follow careful procedures to avoid leakages into the surrounding environment and subsequent exposure to humans, animals, and plant life. Disposal sites must use technologies such as cover systems, liners, and leakage-detection systems.

Although these four components of the "cradle-to-grave" system provided much-needed controls over the hazardous waste stream, the program was inadequate in one important respect—it did not indicate nor even suggest a hierarchy of preferred methods for managing these wastes. This omission meant that virtually nothing was being done to slow the overuse of land at the disposal stage.[19] From a broader perspective, it also meant that national policy was not supporting preventive strategies to reduce the *size* of the hazardous waste stream. Responding to this inadequacy, Congress passed the Hazardous and Solid Waste Amendments of 1984. Unlike its predecessor, these amendments outline in detail how hazardous wastes are to be controlled and explicitly set forth restrictions on land disposal. In so doing, the law prioritizes hazardous waste treatment technologies, which is intended to provide an incentive for source reduction and hence prevention of hazardous waste pollution.

Moving toward Pollution Prevention

Several references in the 1984 Amendments speak to the policy shift away from land disposal and toward more preventive solutions. The law's general provisions were revised to include the following mandate:

> Reliance on land disposal should be minimized or eliminated, and land disposal, particularly landfill and surface impoundment, should be the least favored method for managing hazardous wastes.

Other rulings outline specific prohibitions on the land disposal of untreated hazardous wastes except under certain conditions. These stringent controls are intended to encourage facilities to find alternatives that prevent pollution. To reinforce the emphasis on prevention, the 1984 law added the following to RCRA's statement of objectives:

> The Congress hereby declares it to be the national policy of the United States, that, wherever feasible, the generation of hazardous waste is to be reduced or eliminated as expeditiously as possible.

Although the cradle-to-grave system remained in force, certain of its elements were revised in support of the nation's broader policy goals. For example, a new ruling requires waste generators to state on the manifest that they have taken steps to minimize the quantity and toxicity of wastes. A related revision calls for TSDF permit applicants to certify that they have instituted a program aimed at these same objectives.[20]

Monitoring and Enforcement

RCRA includes an extensive monitoring and enforcement plan executed through mandatory site inspections of hazardous waste facilities. One priority at these inspections is to assure compliance with groundwater monitoring rules and labeling requirements. Minor violations may be punished by the revocation or suspension of the facility's permit or by a civil penalty of up to $25,000

---

[19]For more detail, see Fortuna and Lennett (1987), Chapter 9.
[20]RCRA, Sec.3002(b) and Sec.3005(h).

per day for each violation. For serious violations, criminal penalties may be imposed. If the violator knowingly endangers another person by committing these violations, the fine shall be as much as $250,000 per person or $1 million for an organization. In 1991, 364 federal enforcement actions were undertaken for RCRA violations, and another 291 were executed in 1992.[21]

Analysis of U.S. Hazardous Waste Policy

The nation's cradle-to-grave management system is a classic example of a command-and-control approach to environmental policy. As such, it relies primarily on rules and standards instead of incentives, decreasing the likelihood of an efficient or cost-effective outcome. To investigate this hypothesis, we consider several aspects of the RCRA program: (1) the identification of hazardous waste; (2) the standard-setting process; (3) the manifest system; and (4) the 1984 land restrictions.

Risk-Based, Uniform Rules of Identification

Central to RCRA's control approach are the rulings that govern the identification of a hazardous waste. Two aspects of this process merit consideration. One is the absence of risk-benefit analysis in defining the identifying categories, and the other is the uniformity in how these categories are implemented.

To begin, the law requires that hazardous waste be identified according to characteristics and criteria that are risk-based. Although the rulings attempt to accurately identify the risks of exposure to hazardous waste, they include no provision for balancing these risks with the benefits provided by these materials before they enter the waste stream. That being the case, all wastes satisfying these criteria are regulated with the same stringency regardless of how they originated. Consequently, a waste material associated with a product or process that is vital in use is treated under the law in exactly the same way as one generated from an output of relatively low value to society.[22]

Another problem is that the identifying criteria are applied *uniformly*. There are no qualifiers to allow for differences in the *degree* of toxicity across various waste constituents. Effectively, the procedure sets up a zero-one decision-making process that translates to a set of *uniform* standards. If a waste falls into one of the predefined categories, it is hazardous; if not, it is nonhazardous by default. The law does not allow for any flexibility in determining

---

[21]See Council on Environmental Quality (January 1993), pp. 85–86.

[22]It is interesting to note that certain wastes are exempt from this identification process, such as those associated with the production or development of crude oil and natural gas. The importance of these products suggests that a risk-benefit assessment may have been used to justify these exemptions. It is also true that the initial RCRA was passed during a period of great uncertainty about U.S. oil supplies.

how much of a given substance poses a hazard to society. Yet there can be wide variation in the risk of exposure to the same quantity of different hazardous substances.[23] From an economic perspective, ignoring this variation is allocatively inefficient. Since there are known differences in risk across hazardous waste constituents, it is also true that the respective marginal benefits of abating these constituents are different. If marginal abatement costs are the same, society's welfare could be improved by allocating more resources to abating relatively high-risk substances and fewer to those posing a lower risk. Yet there is no provision in the law for such flexibility.

Benefit-Based, Uniform Standards

RCRA controls hazardous waste management primarily through standards imposed on the key participants in the waste cycle, that is, the generators, the transporters, and the treatment, storage, and disposal facilities (TSDFs). According to the law, these standards are to be established "as may be necessary to protect human health and the environment."[24] Such a mandate clearly defines the standard-setting process as benefit-based with no consideration for economic costs. The lack of cost considerations is particularly problematic for standards with long-run implications. Examples include the technical standards for TSDFs relating to groundwater monitoring, closure, and postclosure procedures. Standards on postclosure procedures guide a facility's activities for 30 years after a facility is closed. The purpose is to prevent active hazardous waste facilities from becoming problem sites after they cease operation—undoubtedly a response to the nation's mounting concerns with thousands of abandoned and uncontrolled sites. Although the intent appears to be well motivated, the long-term nature of these standards assures that compliance costs will be significant. Yet costs are not allowed to influence the standard-setting process.[25] As long as this is the case, the standards so fundamental to federal policy will likely not be set to achieve allocative efficiency.

Another criticism of the standards-based approach is that with few exceptions, it offers states no flexibility in how they administer RCRA's hazardous waste program. While state officials are allowed to submit their own plans, these are approved only if they are equivalent to the national program or consistent with those applicable in other states.[26] There is virtually no provision for site-specific differences—either in the facilities themselves or in the types of wastes they handle. As we have discussed in other contexts, the lack of consideration for such differences means that the criterion of cost-effectiveness likely will not be met.

---

[23]For more detail, see U.S. Congress, OTA (1983), Chapter 6.
[24]RCRA, Sec.3004.(a).
[25]See 45 F.R.33, 159-60 as cited in U.S. Congress, OTA (1983), pp. 283–85.
[26]RCRA Sec.3006.(b).

Failures of the Manifest System

One of the more prominent elements of RCRA's cradle-to-grave approach is the manifest system. Under the law, the transport of any hazardous waste material is tracked from the point of generation all the way through to its final disposal—with virtually no exceptions. Congress's intent in establishing this elaborate tracking procedure was to deter illegal disposal and reduce the adverse effects associated with such practices.[27] The system is a definitive command-and-control instrument. There are no incentives, no pricing mechanisms, and no options. It was a no-nonsense response to a tough problem, and in that sense the approach was understandable, albeit inefficient. Why? Because its objective is solely benefit-based—to halt the progression of damage caused by mismanaged hazardous waste materials. Characteristic of the RCRA program, economic considerations play no role in its design or implementation.

Beyond the efficiency implications, a more fundamental issue is the overall effectiveness of the manifest plan. It turns out that despite its elaborate design, the tracking system has not been a major factor in controlling hazardous wastes because of its limited scope. For all its complexity, the tracking system applies only to wastes that are transported off-site by the generator. According to estimates, these represent only 4 to 5 percent of the nation's hazardous waste stream. Most large firms manage their wastes on their own premises. It is smaller businesses, particularly those in crowded urban areas, that rely on other facilities to treat and dispose of their wastes.[28] It *is* true that this proportion should increase over time due to the 1984 revision to make small-quantity generators subject to RCRA. Nonetheless, it is expected to remain a small fraction of the total hazardous waste stream.[29]

Finally, the high compliance costs associated with the tracking program sets up the potential for a perverse outcome. To understand this claim, consider the following. Hazardous waste generators that typically rely on off-site facilities have three options available to them: (1) they can legally dispose of their wastes by complying with the manifest system; (2) they can attempt to evade the law and illegally discard their wastes; or (3) they can reduce the amount of wastes they generate. Assuming that generators wish to maximize profits, they must consider the *relative* costs of these options in their decision-making. When the United States instituted the manifest system, it elevated the costs of legal disposal, making both source reduction *and* illegal disposal relatively cheaper and hence more attractive options from a profitability perspective. The key question is—which of the two options will firms pursue?

---

[27]U.S. GAO (February 22, 1985), p. 3.

[28]Wirth and Heinz (1991), p. 47; U.S. EPA, Office of Solid Waste (November 1986), p. 9.

[29]Assuming these smaller entities would use off-site facilities instead of absorbing the cost of obtaining an on-site permit, the U.S. Congressional Budget Office (CBO) estimated that the amount of waste managed off-site should rise from about 4 percent in 1983 to 10 percent by 1990 (U.S. CBO, 1985b, p. 50).

While there is some anecdotal evidence that ''midnight dumping'' has diminished since RCRA was passed, there is no definitive answer to this critical question.[30] Until such evidence is available, there is no reason to dismiss the possibility that this well-intended program might promote the very practice it sought to deter—illegal hazardous waste disposal.

From nearly every perspective, RCRA's track record during its early years was less than impressive. There were major delays in implementation, more than a few policy reversals, several potential loopholes, and many questions about its effectiveness. These observations were largely responsible for Congress's enactment of the hard-hitting 1984 Amendments. Attempting to solve a litany of problems, these Amendments continue to rely upon command-and-control policy instruments. There is still a glaring absence of economic incentives in the law, though the land restrictions may have been an exception.

Market Implications of the 1984 Land Restrictions

As the nation's hazardous waste program was evolving in the late 1970s, it became apparent that existing policy was doing nothing to halt the overuse of land disposal. One reason why landfilling had become so prevalent was that its price was typically much lower than that of other disposal options. This differential is due in part to more significant scale economies for landfilling relative to alternative practices, particularly waste incineration. For example, large-sized landfills face unit costs of $23 to $49 per metric ton, while large incineration facilities incur much higher unit costs of $80 per ton.[31] The problem is that these values are *private* costs and do not account for the external costs of environmental damages. If these latter costs were internalized, prices would be higher and any misallocation corrected. An appropriate economic solution would be to use a pricing instrument designed to capture the true social costs of all hazardous waste services. In 1984, policy-makers chose instead to use a command-and-control approach—an explicit restriction on landfilling. This policy decision *does* have economic consequences, though the net effect is not clear-cut.

Restricting the land disposal of hazardous waste elevates the costs of providing these services, which should be reflected in higher prices to waste generators. Just as in our analysis of the manifest system, we need to ask how generators are likely to respond. As profit-maximizers, they would consider the relative costs of all available options. Again, they could reduce the amount of waste they generate or they could maintain their waste level and seek an alternative waste management practice. The difference here is that alternative waste management does not necessarily mean illegal disposal. Waste generators could use less landfilling by employing a treatment method like incineration to reduce the volume of wastes to be disposed of. Although the options

---

[30]Wirth and Heinz (1991), p. 47.

[31]U.S. EPA (March 1, 1984), as cited in Hahn (1988), pp. 201–30.

FIGURE 16.2

The impact of land restrictions under RCRA's 1984 Amendments

(a) Market for land disposal services

(b) Market for incineration services

As a result of the higher costs associated with the 1984 land restrictions, the *MPC* and *MSC* for land disposal shift up, causing the private market solution to decrease from L_0 to L_1. Because production is lower, the associated external costs are smaller as well, declining from area *abc* to area *def*. If the waste generator uses less landfilling because it pursues source reduction, the net result of the 1984 rulings is an improvement for society measured by this external cost reduction. However, if the generator does not reduce its level of wastes, then the decrease in land disposal must have been achieved by using some alternative waste management practice, such as incineration. Increased use of incineration is shown as a shift to the right of *MSB* in that market, which increases equilibrium output from I_0 to I_1. As a result, external costs in this market have increased from area *ghi* to area *gjk*. Unless the decline in external costs in the landfilling market outweighs the increase in the incineration market, the 1984 land restrictions would achieve no net reduction in the external costs borne by society.

are complex, we can gain some insight by modeling the two *legal* options facing the waste generator: (1) substituting treatment for disposal; and (2) using preventive strategies to achieve source reduction. By way of illustration, we use incineration as the representative treatment method.

Pre-1984 Market Equilibrium. The two relevant markets are shown in Figure 16.2—land disposal in panel (a) and incineration in panel (b). Marginal private benefit (*MPB*) curves represent the decisions of waste generators, which are identical to marginal social benefit (*MSB*) functions, assuming no consumption externalities. On the supply side, marginal private cost (*MPC*) curves denote the decision-making of the respective waste service facilities. The *MPCs* are distinct from the marginal social cost (*MSC*) curves to indicate that negative externalities are associated with production in each market, with each marginal external cost (*MEC*) implied by the vertical distance between each pair of *MPC* and *MSC* curves. Prior to the 1984 land restrictions, private equilibrium in each market is determined by the intersection of *MPC* and *MPB*. In the landfill market, the pre-1984 equilibrium output level is L_0. The total measure of external costs associated with that output level is the area between

MPC and *MSC* up to that point, or triangular area *abc.* In the incinerator market, the initial equilibrium output level is I_0 and area *ghi* represents the analogous measure of external costs in that market.

Post-1984 Market Equilibrium.   Now consider the effect of the 1984 land restrictions. These rulings lead to higher operating costs in the land disposal market. In Figure 16.2(a), *MPC* shifts up to *MPC′*, and *MSC* rises by the same amount to *MSC′*. The result is a decline in landfill use from L_0 to L_1. Because production is lower, the associated external costs are smaller as well, declining to area *def.* Notice that the land restrictions do not eliminate the market inefficiency, since there is nothing in these rulings that causes external costs to be internalized by the market participants. It *is* the case, however, that the total external costs associated with land disposal have declined. Hence, if waste generators use less landfilling because they pursue source reduction, the 1984 rulings should reduce the health and ecological damages caused by hazardous wastes, holding all else constant. However, if generators do *not* reduce their level of wastes, then the decrease in land disposal must have been achieved by using some alternative waste management practice. Assuming the alternative is the use of incineration, we need to consider how the effects in that market affect the net result.

Increased use of incineration is shown in Figure 16.2(b) as a shift right of *MSB* to *MSB′*, which increases private equilibrium output from I_0 to I_1. This outcome was predicted by the U.S. Congressional Budget Office (CBO), which forecasted that the 1984 restrictions would increase the quantity of waste incinerated from 2.7 million metric tons (MMT) in 1983 to more than 11 MMT by 1990.[32] Notice however that at the higher equilibrium level, external costs have increased to area *gjk.* What can we conclude from this observation? Unless the decline in external costs in the landfilling market outweighs the increase in the incineration market, the 1984 land restrictions would achieve no net reduction in the external costs borne by society.

Obviously, a key issue is to determine the extent to which source reduction is undertaken in response to the 1984 RCRA land rulings. The outcome is difficult to predict. In part, the problem is that there are many factors that influence a firm's decision to reduce waste—an issue discussed in Application 16.3.[33] Despite the inherent difficulties, the CBO conducted an analysis of how the 1984 RCRA Amendments might be expected to affect waste

---

[32]U.S. CBO (1985b), Table 14, p. 49.

[33]There are also other changes in the 1984 Amendments that confound the outcome. One of these is the increase in demand for all off-site waste services, which is expected to occur as a result of expanding RCRA's span of control to include small quantity waste generators. This increase in demand would add still more pressure on rising prices of disposal services.

Application 16.3

INFORM's Study of Industrial Source Reduction Activities

gWhat motivates a firm to reduce its waste generation? Once the decision is made, how do firms determine the best course of action? Answers to questions like these are usually known only to industry insiders and corporate decision-makers. Fortunately, independent research on these issues recently has been conducted by INFORM, a nonprofit organization located in New York. The results of this 10-year effort provide new evidence on what factors determine industry's efforts to engage in **source reduction** activities.

To better understand the motives of source reduction and the eventual outcome, INFORM used a case study approach to examine pollution prevention strategies and the results achieved by a sample of 29 highly diverse organic chemical plants. An initial survey was conducted during 1985. A follow-up study was later undertaken to document changes instituted between 1985 and 1990 by the 27 plants that had remained in operation. To assure a representative depiction of the industry, the sample of plants was drawn from three states: California, New Jersey, and Ohio. Similarly, INFORM made certain to include different types of facilities distinguished by such characteristics as size, degree of centralization, type of production process (i.e., pure batch or exclusively continuous), and output produced (e.g., pesticides, adhesives, drugs, and paints).

Over the five-year period, source reduction activities grew from 44 distinct actions in 1985 to 146 in 1990. Based on the more recent study year, activities in the following table were documented by INFORM:

Source Reduction Activities

Type of Source Reduction Activity	Number of Activities	Number of Companies Reporting Activities
Process changes	64	16
Operational changes	44	16
Equipment changes	20	12
Chemical substitutions	15	8
Product changes	3	2

Overwhelmingly, chemical plant managers elected to change a production process or institute an operational change such as using different maintenance procedures or cleaning methods. Product changes were the least common activity.

INFORM's analysis revealed important information about what motivates these environmentally responsible decisions. The most commonly reported reason for initiating a source reduction action was given as the costs and overall problems of waste disposal—cited as the reason for 53 activities. The increasing burden of regulation was the second most common response, associated with 50 source reduction actions, and appears to be an increasingly important factor in these decisions based on the five-year trend. Other determinants cited by the survey participants were liability issues, process costs, worker safety, and community relations.

INFORM's comprehensive case study approach also reported on the eventual outcome of the plants' source reduction actions. The 1985 survey found that all activities yielded a waste reduction of approximately 7 million pounds per year. A dramatic

Application 16.3 (concluded)

improvement was documented for 1990—a combined reduction in wastes for all activities of 180 million pounds per year. While these statistics are impressive, more insight can be gained by examining other data from INFORM's 1990 report that quantify the effectiveness of source reduction.

Factor	Amount
Average reduction	68 percent
Average increase in product yields	6.8 percent
Average quantity reduced/activity/ year	2,405,621 lbs.
Total quantity reduced during the study period	180,421,596 lbs.
Average dollars saved/activity/year	$484,616
Total dollars saved during the study period	$28,592,367
Average dollars spent/activity	$946,612
Total dollars spent during the study period	$48,277,197
Average payback period	12.2 months*
Average length of time to implement	8.8 months

*This average payback period is based upon only those activities where both dollars spent and dollars saved were reported. Also, the three highest figures for the payback period (i.e., 889, 70, and 48 years) were excluded because they were much higher than other values reported.

These data capture the economics of waste reduction and the market incentive for firms to participate in pollution prevention activities. For example, the average cost of a source reduction action is estimated to be $946,612, while each is estimated to save a facility an average of about $485,000 per year. The payback period, or the amount of time needed to recoup the original investment, is estimated to be about one year on average.

Apparently, waste reduction is beginning to take hold in the industrial sector. The INFORM study offers insight about the internal decision-making and monetary outcome associated with this important preventive activity. These findings help to validate the environmental and economic gains associated with source reduction. Moreover, they should be of direct use by other firms in planning the design and implementation of similar strategies.

Source: U.S. Environmental Protection Agency, Office of Pollution Prevention, *Pollution Prevention 1991: Progress on Reducing Industrial Pollutants* (Washington D.C., October 1991), pp. 63–66.

generation levels. Table 16.5 presents the CBO's industry-specific estimates of pre- and post-1984 waste generation both with and without source reduction. If industries undertake no waste reduction, aggregate hazardous waste generation is estimated to increase from 265,595 thousands of metric tons in 1983 to as much as 280,364 in 1990—roughly a 5.6 percent increase. At the other extreme is the best possible outcome, which assumes sufficient incentives to encourage waste reduction. In this case, aggregate waste generation is estimated to *decline* by about 14 percent between 1983 and 1990, even allowing for waste growth associated with higher production levels.[34]

---

[34]U.S. CBO (1985b), Table 13, p. 48.

TABLE 16.5   **Changes in Waste Generation by Industry Associated with the 1984 RCRA Amendments** (thousands of metric tons)

Industry	Quantity in 1983	Quantity in 1990 No Waste Reduction*	Quantity in 1990 with Waste Reduction†
Chemicals and allied products	127,245	136,678	115,167
Primary metals	47,704	49,597	41,611
Petroleum and coal products	31,358	29,213	25,526
Fabricated metal products	25,364	25,493	11,820
Rubber and plastic products	14,600	17,954	17,252
Miscellaneous manufacturing	5,614	5,856	5,001
Nonelectrical machinery	4,859	5,717	4,831
Transportation equipment	2,977	3,243	2,781
Motor freight transportation	2,160	2,160	1,836
Electrical and electronic machinery	1,929	2,313	1,557
Wood preserving	1,739	2,095	1,743
Drum reconditioners	45	45	16
Total	265,595	280,364	229,141
Percent change from 1983	—	+ 5.6	− 13.7

*Assumes no waste reduction efforts by industry in response to the 1984 RCRA Amendments. Projection of waste levels in 1990 based on growth in industrial output levels forecasted by the CBO generation model. Decreases in waste quantities therefore result from declining levels of industrial and waste-producing activities.
†Assumes waste reduction efforts by industry.
Source: U.S. Congress, Congressional Budget Office, *Hazardous Waste Management: Recent Changes and Policy Alternatives* (Washington, D.C.: U.S. Government Printing Office, 1985b), Table 13, p. 48.

Table 16.6 presents the estimated costs associated with these waste generation magnitudes. With no waste reduction activity, aggregate costs rise from $5,779 million in 1983 to $11,201 million in 1990, measured in 1983 dollars—nearly a doubling of real expenditures to comply with the new regulations. If these estimates are reasonable, it is likely that firms will initiate waste reduction activities. If so, under the most favorable assumptions, the CBO estimates that the increase in 1990 compliance costs will be limited to about $2.7 billion.[35] These findings suggest that at least one aspect of U.S. hazardous waste policy—the land restrictions—may provide an economic incentive to help achieve the national goal of reducing hazardous waste generation. Absent this single element of the law, U.S. policy relies on a command-and-control approach that fails to achieve either efficiency or cost-effectiveness. This is a disconcerting observation, particularly since other nations and even some state governments have used market instruments successfully to help control hazardous waste pollution.

---

[35]The dollar expenditures would increase even with the decline in generation because of more stringent requirements for treatment and disposal methods in the 1984 Amendments. U.S. CBO (1985b), Table 15, pp. 50–51.

TABLE 16.6   Estimated Change of Annual Costs for Hazardous Waste Management for 1983 and 1990 ($1983 millions)

Industry	1983 Cost*	1990 Cost, No Waste Reduction	1990 Cost with Waste Reduction	Percentage Change with Waste Reduction
Chemicals and allied products	$1,544	$ 3,122	$2,283	48%
Primary metals	1,243	2,302	1,661	34
Fabricated metal products	899	1,191	735	−18
Rubber and plastic products	798	2,026	1,771	122
Miscellaneous manufacturing	267	356	308	15
Nonelectrical machinery	254	324	279	10
Motor freight transportation	229	247	247	8
Transportation equipment	191	360	286	50
Electrical and electronic machinery	156	237	163	4
Petroleum and coal products	136	940	634	366
Wood preserving	56	91	61	9
Drum reconditioners	6	6	2	−67
Total	$5,779	$11,201	$8,429	
Incremental change from 1983	—	+$5,422	+$2,650	
Percent change from 1983	—	+93.8%	+45.9%	

*Assumes full compliance with RCRA before the 1984 Amendments.

Source: U.S. Congressional Budget Office, *Hazardous Waste Management: Recent Changes and Policy Alternatives* (Washington, D.C.: U.S. Government Printing Office, 1985b), Table 15, p. 51.

Market Instruments in Hazardous Waste Control Policy

A fundamental shortcoming of command-and-control instruments is that they do not cause the external costs of environmental pollution to be brought into the private market transaction. As long as these costs are ignored, resources are overallocated to pollution-generating activities. Market instruments attempt to use the price mechanism to make polluters confront the full costs of their actions and respond accordingly. Since there are significant risks associated with hazardous waste pollution, the external costs can be enormous. Hence, if price were somehow made to reflect these costs, polluters—or in this context hazardous waste generators—would have a powerful incentive to engage in source reduction activities.

A conventional market approach to waste control policy is the use of a **pollution charge,** which can be implemented as a **waste-end charge.** A waste-end charge is so named because it is effected at the time of disposal based on the quantity of waste generated. Until the late 1980s, the Netherlands levied such a charge on companies that stored, treated, or disposed of chemical waste.

pollution charge
A fee charged to the polluter that varies with the amount of contaminants released.

waste-end charge
A fee implemented at the time of disposal based on the quantity of waste generated.

Austria imposes a charge on the disposal and export of both hazardous and nonhazardous wastes. In each case, the waste-end charge elevates the effective price of waste management services. If the charge is high enough, it should *discourage* waste generation and *encourage* source reduction. One of the more successful international uses of such a market instrument is one that was designed and implemented by the German State of Baden-Württemberg. Officials there have employed a variable rate charge on hazardous waste and are monitoring its effect on waste generation. What they have observed is that this pricing mechanism does appear to be high enough to encourage waste reduction.[36] In the United States, similar economic approaches have been employed by state governments in designing and implementing their hazardous waste programs—an issue discussed in Application 16.4. Despite the international evidence and the experience of state governments, federal hazardous waste policy has employed no analogous market instruments to date.

Application 16.4

Using the Market to Control Hazardous Wastes

Although the feedstock tax imposed under CERCLA may appear to have been motivated by the incentives of a product charge, its true intent was to provide a reliable source of funds for the nation's remediation program. Beyond this revenue-raising initiative, the use of a tax to reduce hazardous waste generation remains exclusive to state governments. While some states had introduced waste levies before the Superfund tax was effected, most imposed their own version of a pollution charge after the feedstock tax became law. Typically, this instrument was implemented as a **waste-end charge.**

As of 1984, there were 20 states actively taxing hazardous wastes at or beyond the point of generation. Technically, such a waste-end charge is imposed to encourage waste reduction. However, this motivation is not universally apparent. In fact, revenue-raising appears to be the overriding influence in more than a few instances. Many states use the revenues to finance monitoring costs or cleanup expenditures at sites where damages have occurred. Some add the waste tax revenues to their general funds, forcing environmental needs to compete for these funds along with all other state programs.

The table below lists some of the key features of state tax programs, each aimed at some phase of the hazardous waste stream. As these data indicate, the characteristics of these market instruments vary considerably from state to state.

---

[36]OECD (1989a), OECD (1991), and *Landesabfallabgabengesetz,* Article 4, as cited in U.S. EPA, Office of Policy, Planning, and Evaluation (July 1992), p. 9-1.

State Waste-End Tax Systems in 1984

State	Treated Wastes Taxed	Higher Rate for Off-Site Management	Who Pays	Highest Possible Tax Rate ($/ton)
Alabama	Yes	Yes	Generator and facility operator	$10.00
California	Yes	No	Generator and facility operator	45.66
Colorado	Yes	No	Facility operator	2.00
Connecticut	Yes	Yes	Generator	10.00
Illinois	Yes	Yes	Facility operator	6.60
Indiana	No	No	Facility operator	1.50
Iowa	Yes	Yes	Facility operator	50.00
Kansas	Yes	Yes	Generator and facility operator	5.00
Kentucky	Yes	Yes	Generator	11.00
Louisiana	Yes	Yes	Facility operator	10.00
Maine	Yes	Yes	Facility operator	33.00
Minnesota	Yes	No	Generator	70.40
Mississippi	No	Yes	Facility operator	9.00
Missouri	Yes	No	Generator and facility operator	26.00
New Hampshire	Yes	Yes	Generator	36.60
New York	Yes	Yes	Generator	12.00
Ohio	No	Yes	Facility operator	8.99
South Carolina	No	No	Facility operator	7.00
Tennessee	No	Yes	Generator	7.00
Wisconsin	No	No	Facility operator	0.14

Source: U.S. Congress, Congressional Budget Office, Office of Technology Assessment (OTA), Statement of Joel S. Hirschhorn for the Hearing Record, Senate Committee on Environment and Public Works, 98:2 (September 10, 1984).

Several observations about these data are noteworthy. First, notice that the statutory incidence, that is, the party on whom the tax is levied, is not universal. Some states impose the tax directly on the generator at the first stage of the waste stream. Others levy the charge at the postgeneration phase by taxing the facility operator, such as a storage or treatment facility. Some, like Alabama and Kansas, broaden the impact of the instrument by taxing both phases of the cycle. Revenue motivations aside, taxing the generator offers a stronger incentive for waste reduction than does imposing the charge on a facility engaged in treatment, storage, or disposal.

The rate of the tax also differs widely across the 20 jurisdictions, with maximum rates ranging from as low as $0.14 per ton in Wisconsin to as high as $70.40 per ton in Minnesota. Also of interest is a comparison of the rates charged to generators relative to those charged to facility operators. In 1984, the average rate charged to hazardous waste generators was $24.50 per ton—almost double the average rate imposed on facility operators of $12.80. The difference might be an incremental amount above what is needed to fund a state's waste management program, intended as an incentive for generators to reduce wastes. Finally, notice that some states allow for a differential that penalizes off-site waste management, likely to acknowledge the added risks of waste transport and to cover the costs of monitoring off-site disposal activities.

More refined data would show even more state-specific differences, such as varying rate schedules based on waste characteristics like volume, degree of hazard, or type of management technology. If these differences properly reflect local economic and environmental conditions, the use of a hazardous waste tax at the state level may be far superior than any uniform charge imposed at the national level.

Sources: U.S. Congress, Congressional Budget Office, *Hazardous Waste Management: Recent Changes and Policy Alternatives* (Washington, D.C.: U.S. Government Printing Office, 1985b), p. 82; U.S. Congress, Congressional Budget Office, Office of Technology Assessment (OTA), Statement of Joel S. Hirschhorn for the Hearing Record, Senate Committee on Environment and Public Works, 98:2 (September 10, 1984); Craig E. Reese, "State Taxation of Hazardous Materials," *Oil and Gas Tax Quarterly* 33 (1985), pp. 502–26.

Managing Uncontrolled Hazardous Waste Sites: CERCLA

By most accounts, the Comprehensive Environmental Response, Compensation, and Liability Act of 1980 (CERCLA), more commonly known as Superfund, is considered a landmark legislative act because its intent is solely remedial rather than preventive. Despite its precedent-setting intent and a $1.6 billion fund, the 1980 law failed to execute on its commitments. The 1986 Amendments attempted to address these failures, but many problems still remain. To understand why, we need to investigate the basic elements of this important national policy.

Response and Cleanup

Superfund gives the federal government broad authority to respond whenever there is a release or the threat of a release of a hazardous substance, which it identifies as:[37]

> (i) one that has been so designated under any of the following: the Water Pollution Control Act; the Solid Waste Disposal Act; the Federal Water Pollution Control Act; the Clean Air Act; and the Toxic Substances Control Act; and
> (ii) one that may present substantial danger to health, welfare, or the environment when released.[38]

National Contingency Plan (NCP)
A comprehensive set of regulations that outlines official response actions to a release or the threat of a release of a hazardous substance.

Notification of any release exceeding amounts specified in the law (one pound unless stated otherwise) is to be made to the National Response Center (NRC). Failure to do so is punishable by fine or imprisonment. To implement these response actions, a comprehensive set of regulations was established called the **National Contingency Plan (NCP)**. The NCP outlines the procedures to put Superfund into action, a summary of which is given in Table 16.7. By executive order, response activities are delegated to the EPA and are to be carried out through removal actions or remedial actions.

removal actions
Official responses to a hazardous substance release aimed at restoring immediate control to the site.

Removal Actions.   Removal actions are responses aimed at restoring immediate control to a release site. An example is an emergency cleanup of a chemical spill at a waste site or at the scene of an accident involving a transporter of hazardous chemicals. Depending on conditions, the removal action may include barricading a contaminated site, providing temporary drinking water supplies or shelter to nearby residents, or securing hazardous waste containers. These activities are undertaken only as short-term measures.[39]

---

[37]CERCLA, Sec. 101(14) and Sec.102(a).

[38]Since these descriptions are purposefully comprehensive, CERCLA *does* itemize certain exclusions, among them petroleum, natural gas, natural gas liquids, liquefied natural gas, or synthetic gas usable for fuel.

[39]U.S. EPA (August 1987); U.S. EPA, Office of Solid Waste and Emergency Response (May 1992).

TABLE 16.7   The National Contingency Plan: Phases of Response Actions

Phases	*Response Action*
Phase I: Site Discovery and Notification	Report the release to the National Response Center (NRC) and the affected state.
Phase II: Preliminary Assessment	Determine the nature, extent, and source of the release and the magnitude of the hazard using available data; make recommendation for further action.
Phase III: Immediate Removal Action	Implement appropriate immediate removal action such as measuring and sampling; removing hazardous substances from site; restraining spread of release; preventing access to site; controlling the source of release; recommending evaluation of threatened population; or any other emergency measures.
Phase IV: Site Evaluation and Determination of Appropriate Response Level	Conduct site evaluation; collect data; determine amount, type, and location of hazardous substances and potential for migration; determine appropriate response level; recommend site for immediate removal, planned removal, National Priorities List (NPL) remedial action candidate, or no further action.
Phase V: Planned Removal	Determine if site qualifies for planned removal; take appropriate response action to reduce or eliminate risk; action is completed when serious risk is abated *or* 6 months/$1 million limit is reached.
Phase VI: Remedial Action	Evaluate NPL sites and determine appropriate remedy as follows: conduct preliminary assessment; take initial remedial action if needed; perform remedial investigation; assess alternatives; determine appropriate extent of remedy from alternatives; proceed with chosen action if state assurances and contribution requirements are met and if fund-financing is approved.
Phase VII: Cost Recovery and Documentation	Complete documentation of government response action.

Source: Drawn from U.S. Congress, Office of Technology Assessment (OTA), *Technologies and Management Strategies for Hazardous Waste Control* (Washington, D.C.: U.S. Government Printing Office, 1983), Chapter 7, Table 57, pp. 306–07.

remedial actions
Official responses to a hazardous substance release aimed at achieving a more permanent solution to the site.

National Priorities List (NPL)
A classification of hazardous waste sites posing the greatest threat to health and the ecology.

Remedial Actions.   Remedial actions are long-term responses aimed at finding a more permanent solution to a release site. Several steps are involved, making the process very time-intensive. Following the official identification of a problem, called site discovery, a complete assessment is made of all available information, and an inspection is ordered to sample soil, ground and surface water, and to document the site layout. The findings ultimately are evaluated using a risk ranking system that assigns a numerical score to a site based on its inherent risks. If the site receives a 28.50 score or higher out of a 100-point maximum, it is placed on the **National Priorities List (NPL).**[40] As of 1992, 1,275 sites were listed on the NPL, and it is expected that about 100 more will be added each year. Only if a site is listed on the NPL can remedial actions be undertaken by the federal government. The rest are relegated to state and local officials for an appropriate response.

_____

[40]U.S. EPA, Office of Emergency and Remedial Response (June 1992), p. 9.

Once a site is placed on the NPL, a feasibility study is done, which involves a complete examination of the site and an appraisal of available cleanup options. This can take from 18 to 30 months and can cost up to $1 million. The action plan selected and support for the decision are documented and used in efforts to recover funding from parties responsible for the release. Design work follows to adapt the action plan to the specific attributes of the site. This stage takes another 12 to 18 months and adds another $1 million on average to the tally. Finally, the actual site cleanup or remedial action begins. On average, the total cost is $25 million per site and can take years to accomplish. Because the costs of remedial action are so high and the damage so extensive, there are more sites needing cleanup than there are funds available. The EPA uses a prioritization strategy whereby the agency's headquarters and its regional offices arrive at a consensus as to which sites are most in need of attention.[41]

Compensation, Liability, and Enforcement

potentially responsible parties (PRPs)
Any current or former owner or operator of a hazardous waste facility and all those involved in the disposal, treatment, or transport of hazardous substances to the contaminated site.

Superfund gives the EPA authority to force those parties responsible for a hazardous substance release to correct the problem and pay for the damage. This is accomplished either through an administrative order or by bringing a civil action against the responsible party. According to current law, so-called **potentially responsible parties (PRPs)** include any existing or former owner or operator of a hazardous waste facility as well as those involved, however remotely, in the disposal, treatment, or transport of hazardous substances to the contaminated site. The extent of the financial accountability is similarly extensive—to include all costs of removal or remedial action and any damages to natural resources or human health.[42] From an economic perspective, the intent is to force guilty parties to internalize the externality of whatever market transaction contributed to the release.

cost recovery actions
Steps taken by the EPA to recover its cleanup costs from those parties responsible.

If the EPA undertakes abatement action directly, it is financed through the Superfund. The agency can recover its cleanup costs from those parties responsible through **cost recovery actions.** The law also allows the federal government to sue for punitive damages. Any funds so recovered are returned to the budget for future response actions.

Emergency Planning

Title III of the Superfund Amendments and Reauthorization Act of 1986 is a free-standing piece of legislation known as the Emergency Planning and Community Right-to-Know Act. The purpose of this act is to inform citizens about the existence and potential release of hazardous substances and to provide a

---

[41]U.S. EPA, Office of Solid Waste and Emergency Response (May 1992), p. 6; U.S. EPA, Office of Emergency and Remedial Response (June 1992), pp. 10–12.
[42]CERCLA, Sec.107.(a).

planning system for emergencies. To develop the planning system, each state government must devise and implement a comprehensive plan to deal with a hazardous substance release.

A related objective of Title III is to keep the public informed about the production of hazardous substances and their discharge into the environment. To accomplish this goal, Title III has a number of reporting requirements. One of these calls for annual toxic chemical release reports from facilities that manufacture, process, or use specific chemicals in an amount that exceeds a mandated threshold. Data from these reports are used to compile what is called the **Toxics Release Inventory (TRI),** a national database about releases of hazardous substances. All data are published annually by the EPA and are available to the general public. Currently, information is collected on more than 300 chemicals and 20 chemical categories.

Toxics Release Inventory (TRI)
A national database that gives information about hazardous substances released into the environment.

An Analysis of Superfund

In concept, the Comprehensive Environmental Response, Compensation, and Liability Act (CERCLA) is the most unusual of all U.S. environmental laws. Unlike RCRA and other environmental legislation like the Clean Air Act, Superfund is not a regulatory program. Rather, its aim is to clean up the damage at uncontrolled or abandoned hazardous waste sites, using liability standards to identify the potentially responsible parties and make them pay for their actions.[43] While the overall intent is beyond reproach, the implementation of Superfund's tough mandates has produced mixed results.

Assessing Superfund's Performance

By most accounts, Superfund's Remedial Program has moved at a snail's pace. Table 16.8 gives data on identified CERCLIS and NPL sites for the 1980 to 1992 period and the number of sites removed each year. As of 1992, only 43 sites had been removed out of the 1,275 NPL sites. Further, it is argued that even the small number of removed sites is an inflated measure of Superfund's progress, since the EPA has not in all cases properly addressed the potential of recurring problems.[44] This argument relates to the selection of an appropriate risk management strategy for dealing with these sites. If benefit-cost analysis guided the decision-making, the high costs of cleanup would be used to determine how far remedial actions should go in cleaning up a site. Opponents of such an approach argue that the associated risks of a hazardous release should be reduced to zero or close to it, implying that a pure risk

---

[43]For an interesting discussion of how CERCLA is part of an important trend in U.S. environmental policy, see Humphrey and Paddock (1990).
[44]See U.S. Congress, OTA (1985).

TABLE 16.8   CERCLIS and NPL Sites, 1980–1992

Year	Sites Listed (number, cumulative)		NPL Sites Removed (number per year)
	CERCLIS	*NPL*	
1980	8,000	na	na
1981	10,500	na	3
1982	13,934	na	na
1983	16,307	545	0
1984	18,836	541	0
1985	22,455	857	0
1986	25,161	887	8
1987	27,507	950	0
1988	29,613	1,174	7
1989	31,522	1,224	9
1990	34,000	1,200	1
1991	35,798	1,185	9
1992	35,984	1,275	6

na = Not available.

Sources: Council on Environmental Quality, *Environmental Quality, 23rd Annual Report* (Washington, D.C.: U.S. Government Printing Office, January 1993), Table 93, p. 415; U.S. Environmental Protection Agency, Office of Emergency and Remedial Response, *Superfund Progress—Aficionado's Version* (Washington, D.C., June 1992), p. 4 (for 1992 values).

standard ought to be employed. Both arguments are firmly entrenched in the issue of "how clean is clean?" Until this is resolved, significant amounts of resources may be wasted—a major cost to society.

What's Wrong with Superfund?

Superfund's lack of success cannot be blamed on any single factor. There are many reasons that explain its generally disappointing track record, all of which tend to fall into two major categories. The first is the lack of information about the extent of the problem, both at the outset of the program and throughout its implementation. The second source of failure is linked to the structure of the program and the absence of incentives to advance the remediation process.

Information Problems.[45]   The EPA faces many problems in dealing with the aftermath of decades of careless dumping. A major obstacle is that the agency had to start at ground zero with very little data on the extent of the nation's hazardous waste site problem. As information first began to accumu-

---

[45]Much of the following is drawn from U.S. GAO (December 1987), Table 2.1, p. 14, Chapter 3; and U.S. EPA (March 1987) cited on p. 22 of this GAO report.

late the EPA learned that the dilemma was far worse than it had anticipated. In spite of these higher-than-expected reports, there is a strong contention that all the significant problems still have not been identified. At issue is to determine how much of this information gap is within the EPA's control.

A major criticism of the Superfund program is that there has been insufficient federal control, direction, and financial support for state programs aimed at identifying potential Superfund sites. While all states are required under RCRA to submit an inventory of any sites ever used for hazardous waste disposal, the methods used to comply with this requirement are not consistent. Furthermore, there is a lack of initiative in how states identify sites in need of remedial action, relying mainly on private citizens' complaints. The EPA has been criticized for not providing sufficient guidance or funding to rectify this problem, choosing to allocate its budget solely to cleanup activities. In the 1984 RCRA Amendments, Congress authorized $25 million over a four-year period for assistance to states in developing their waste site inventories, but the EPA *never* requested any of this funding. Superfund officials defend their position by asserting that evaluating states' programs is not realistic given that the agency is no longer appropriating grant monies for this purpose. Moreover, they argue that EPA's top priority is to assess and remediate identified sites—*not* to look for new ones.

Inadequate state reporting is only part of the problem. According to the U.S. General Accounting Office (GAO), there are other data gaps caused by the EPA's regional offices not properly aggregating state-reported data. In a 1987 study of site identification in five states, the GAO found that over 800 sites were missing from the CERCLIS inventory, and some of these are believed severe enough to qualify for the NPL. Of the 232 sites that the GAO could identify, 83 percent were reported by states but not listed by the appropriate EPA regional office. The GAO estimates that the true number of CERCLIS sites is in the range of 130,340 to 425,380—markedly different from the 27,507 that were officially listed in the study year.

Beyond these data problems, there is also a lack of knowledge about the most effective technologies to accomplish the complex cleanup task. The many phases of remedial action are extremely time-intensive and costly. Presumably, experience will help to shorten the time horizon. In the interim, the EPA is continuing its cleanup efforts and at the same time pursuing cost recovery settlements from responsible parties to help defray Superfund's enormous expense. Recent data on the progress of enforcement efforts are given in Table 16.9. On this front some headway has been made, though it is too soon to fairly assess this aspect of the program.

Lack of Incentives.   Like the provisions of RCRA, the Superfund legislation is distinguished by the conspicuous absence of market mechanisms. Even the feedstock taxes used to fund the $8.5 billion Superfund are aimed mainly at

---

TABLE 16.9   Superfund Enforcement

Activity	Total 1992		Program-to-Date*	
	Actions (number)	Value ($millions)	Actions (number)	Value ($millions)
Total RP response settlements†	78	$285.8	1,616	$5,954.0
RD/RA settlements	27	241.3	360	3,862.3
Total unilateral orders issued‡	54	172.8	722	1,567.3
UAOs issued for RD/RA	19	0.7	153	1,289.2
Total AOCs signed	32	1.4	983	1,329.4
AOCs for RD (only)	2	—	14	—
Cost recovery referrals to the Department of Justice	18	22.8	459	798.4
Total cost recovery settlements	63	22.6	1,113	592.3
Total cost recovery collections	—	55.9	—	359.1

Note: RP = responsible party; UAO = Unilateral administrative order; AOC = Administrative order on consent; RD = Remedial design; RA = Remedial action.

*Values are through fiscal year 1991.

†Does not include State Lead Settlements, and Federal Facilities Inter-Agency Agreements. Includes RD/RA settlements below.

‡Includes UAOs issued for RD/RA.

Source: U.S. Environmental Protection Agency, Office of Emergency and Remedial Response, *Superfund Progress—Aficionado's Version* (Washington, D.C., June 1992), p. 13.

---

raising revenues rather than encouraging decisions to improve the environment. Since these taxes are levied on oil and certain raw chemicals, it may seem as if they are product charges aimed at deterring the use of these hazardous substances. However, Congress's decision to target these materials was motivated by the need for a substantial and fairly reliable tax base from which to collect much-needed revenues.[46] Despite the statutory label of ''environmental taxes,'' these levies offer little incentive to diminish hazardous waste pollution.

Other incentive issues arise in how liability is established under Superfund. In the law itself as well as in how the courts have inferred Congress's intent, the determination of who is responsible for damages and to what extent is all-encompassing and unyielding. Motivated by the knowledge that the $8.5 billion fund would not be nearly enough to pay for the massive cleanup, Congress and the courts use whatever legislative and judicial muscle necessary to impose the ''polluter-pays principle.'' While the intent was to achieve swift action against the guilty parties and advance the remediation process, the plan backfires because it sets up an unexpected and perverse incentive.

---

[46]SARA added another revenue source in 1986, calling for a new tax based on a mandated percentage of corporate income. U.S. EPA, Office of Policy, Planning, and Evaluation (July 1992), p. 3-5; CERCLA, Title II; and SARA, Part VII, Sec.59A.

strict liability
A legal standard that
identifies individuals
as responsible for
damages even if
negligence is not
proven.

**joint and several
liability**
A legal standard that
identifies a single
party as responsible
for all damages even
if that party's
contribution to the
damages is minimal.

The problem is rooted in how the law identifies a potentially responsible party (PRP) and in how the liability is defined. In establishing legal responsibility, the courts use the concepts of strict liability and joint and several liability.[47] **Strict liability** means that individuals can be held liable even if negligence is not proven. **Joint and several liability** means that a single party found liable for damages can be held responsible for *all* associated costs even if that party's actual contribution to the damages is minimal.[48] The use of such tough legal standards was intended to save the government the complex and time-intensive process of proving negligence and then determining what proportion of costs each PRP must pay.[49] There was also the expectation that the use of joint and several liability would encourage an identified PRP to name all other responsible parties at a given site.

Unfortunately, these expectations proved to be off the mark. Recognizing the potential to be held accountable for *all* costs at a named waste site, few PRPs were willing to come forward with information. Furthermore, because joint and several liability assigns the entire costs of cleanup on a single party, there was a strong financial incentive for a liable party to use delay tactics or to incur the relatively lower costs of litigation to fight the charges.[50] As a consequence, the well-intended legal standards have led to long delays and a diversion of resources from cleanup to litigation proceedings. In fact, a 1985 study puts the estimate of legal expenses at about 55 percent of the total dollars expended on remediation.[51]

As a matter of record, EPA Administrator Carol Browner stated the following about the need for Superfund reform:

> Although the clock ran out on Superfund reauthorization this year, a broad-based coalition for reform was established. That coalition, ranging from corporation to small businesses to environmentalists, developed a vital blueprinting for change . . . One in four Americans live within four miles of a Superfund toxic waste site and many businesses, particularly small businesses, are still unfairly burdened—ultimately change is essential.[52]

---

[47]Interestingly, these legal concepts are *not* written into Superfund's provisions. They were initially in the bill submitted before Congress, but were removed as part of an agreement between the House of Representatives and the Senate before signing it into law. However, the courts took the initiative, and reinstated these notions based on what they perceived to be Congress's intent (Mazmanian and Morell 1992, p. 36).

[48]It is also true that the use of these liability standards under Superfund extends well beyond what is imposed under traditional common law. For example, causality does not have to be shown to establish liability under Superfund, as is the case under common low. Hence, there is no need to show proof that a defendant's wastes are those that caused the damage. All that is necessary is evidence that the defendant is a PRP. See Anderson (1989), pp. 427–32 for more detail.

[49]For an interesting article that discusses the issue of cost allocation in detail, see Butler, Schneider, Hall, and Burton (1993).

[50]Mazmanian and Morell (1992), pp. 36–37.

[51]Light (1985), p. 10205.

[52]U.S. EPA, Office of Communications, Education and Public Affairs (October 17, 1994).

Conclusions

Most would agree that U.S. hazardous waste policy has broadened and strengthened considerably over the past two decades. As the evolution continues, we observe public officials beginning to integrate preventive initiatives into the overall policy solution. By addressing the generation of hazardous waste *before* it becomes a problem, the nation can avoid some of the associated health and ecological risks, not to mention the high costs of correcting the degradation. Yet in spite of these favorable assessments and the acknowledgement that some measure of progress has been made, there are still questions about the efficiency and cost-effectiveness of current U.S. policy.

With 20/20 hindsight, it is apparent that the federal government should have acted sooner to respond to the risks of hazardous waste pollution. But such an assessment assumes full information—a luxury the United States clearly did not have. Confronted with tough problems, a marked lack of data, and a very angry constituency, Congress sought policy instruments that they thought would be direct, uncompromising, and capable of achieving a swift resolution. Given this motivation, it is not surprising that the major laws on hazardous solid waste are couched within a command-and-control framework. Understanding this motivation, however, does not change the fact that such a policy approach came at some measure of sacrifice—a loss of efficiency and cost-effectiveness. Exacerbating the problem, many of Congress's intentions were not carried out as planned. Not only did most of the initiatives lack incentive mechanisms, but many were set in motion without a full understanding of the extent of the problem. As such, they were destined for failure. Such was the fate of the Superfund legislation, a unique body of law that continues to be a source of contention among government officials, industry, and private citizens.

Midcourse corrections might save the nation considerable expense in executing its policy missions and could restore the level of environmental risk to an acceptable level more quickly. The strategy has to be directed both at repairing the damage from the past and seeking ways to reduce and more efficiently manage the present waste stream. Congress must decide a new course of action to reauthorize the Superfund law. Among its considerations is the recommendation for a major overhaul of this legislation endorsed by the Clinton administration. If nothing else, policy-makers seem to have recognized the need for reform and the importance of using risk management strategies in all environmental initiatives—even in the absence of extensive information. Such an awareness may be significant to what appears to be a critical phase in the evolution of U.S. hazardous waste policy.

Summary

- Hazardous solid wastes are any unwanted materials or refuse capable of posing a substantial threat to health or the environment. The risks associated with hazardous waste pollution arise because of excess waste generation and mismanagement of the waste stream.

- Estimates of annual generation of hazardous waste in the United States range from 250 to 500 million tons. Every sector of the economy contributes to the hazardous waste stream, but industry is responsible for the largest proportion. Chemical producers generate about 79 percent of all the hazardous wastes in the United States.

- All environmental media are vulnerable to contamination if hazardous wastes are improperly managed. Human health risks arise from such problems as contamination of drinking water and soil in which crops are grown.

- U.S. policy on solid wastes originated with the Solid Waste Disposal Act (SWDA) enacted in 1965. This act was amended in 1970 by the Resource Recovery Act and later by the Resource Conservation and Recovery Act (RCRA) in 1976. RCRA represented the nation's first official policy position on hazardous waste control. Congress reauthorized and strengthened RCRA through The Hazardous and Solid Waste Amendments of 1984.

- The Comprehensive Environmental Response, Compensation, and Liability Act (CERCLA), or Superfund, was passed in 1980. This act was aimed at identifying and cleaning up the nation's worst, inactive hazardous waste sites and to recover damages from responsible parties. CERCLA was revised in 1986 through the Superfund Amendments and Reauthorization Act (SARA), which brought the Superfund budget up to $8.5 billion.

- Under RCRA, a command-and-control hazardous waste program was devised, commonly referred to as the "cradle-to-grave" management approach. Its four components are: (1) the identification and listing of hazardous waste; (2) a national manifest system; (3) a permit system for treatment, storage, and disposal facilities (TSDFs); and (4) the setting of standards for these facilities.

- One problem with RCRA is that the characteristics and criteria used to identify hazardous waste are risk-based with no provision to consider the benefits of these materials before they enter the waste stream. Another problem is that the identifying categories are applied uniformly with no qualifiers to allow for differences in the *degree* of toxicity across various waste constituents.

- The standards applicable to TSDFs are benefit-based with no consideration for economic costs. Hence, it is not likely that allocative efficiency will be achieved. Furthermore, with few exceptions, the standards are applied uniformly. There is virtually no provision for site-specific differences, likely disallowing a cost-effective solution.

- The manifest system is a command-and-control instrument that is benefit-based in motivation. Economic considerations played no role in its design or implementation. It has not been a major factor in reducing risk because of its limited scope.

- The land restrictions imposed with the 1984 Amendments caused land disposal facilities to face higher costs and elevate their prices. In response, generators could either initiate waste reduction or alter their waste management practices. Although these rulings may reduce the external costs borne by society, inefficiency is not eliminated.

- One market-based approach to hazardous waste management is a waste-end charge levied at the time of disposal. Several nations employ such an instrument, as do many state governments in the United States.

- Under CERCLA, the federal government can undertake a response action whenever there is an actual or potential release of a hazardous substance that may present imminent danger to public health or welfare. The National Contingency Plan (NCP) outlines procedures to implement these activities either as removal actions or remedial actions. The EPA can force the parties responsible for a release to undertake abatement action.

- Title III of SARA is a free-standing piece of legislation known as the Emergency Planning and Community Right-to-Know Act. Its purpose is to inform citizens about potential releases of hazardous substances and to provide a planning system for emergencies. One of its reporting requirements calls for data that are used to form the Toxics Release Inventory.

- Superfund's provisions have produced mixed results. One reason is the lack of information about the extent of the problem. The second source of failure is the lack of incentives to enhance the remediation process. The use of strict liability and joint and several liability have led to delays and the diversion of resources from cleanup to litigation proceedings.

Key Concepts

hazardous solid wastes
waste stream
leachate
"cradle-to-grave" management system
Comprehensive Environmental
    Response, Compensation, and Liability
    Information System (CERCLIS)
feedstock tax
source reduction
waste management
characteristic wastes
listed wastes
national manifest system
permitting system

treatment, storage, and disposal facilities
    (TSDFs)
general regulatory standards
technical regulatory standards
pollution charge
waste-end charge
National Contingency Plan (NCP)
removal actions
remedial actions
National Priorities List (NPL)
potentially responsible parties (PRPs)
cost recovery actions
Toxics Release Inventory (TRI)
strict liability
joint and several liability

APPENDIX

A REFERENCE TO ACRONYMS IN HAZARDOUS WASTE POLICY CONTROL

Environmental Economics Acronyms

MPB	Marginal private benefit
MSB	Marginal social benefit
MEC	Marginal external cost
MPC	Marginal private cost
MSC	Marginal social cost

Environmental Science Acronyms

MMT	Millions of metric tons

Environmental Policy Acronyms

CERCLA	Comprehensive Environmental Response, Compensation, and Liability Act
CERCLIS	Comprehensive Environmental Response, Compensation, and Liability Information System
NCP	National Contingency Plan
NPL	National Priorities List
NRC	National Response Center
PRP	Potentially responsible party
RCRA	Resource Conservation and Recovery Act
SARA	Superfund Amendments and Reauthorization Act
SWDA	Solid Waste Disposal Act
TSDFs	Treatment, storage, and disposal facilities

Review Questions

1. Consider the various provisions in RCRA that discourage land-based waste disposal. Identify and explain one aspect of the law that is command-and-control in approach and one that is incentive-based.

2. Propose an alternative method of identifying hazardous waste that is more efficient than the one mandated under RCRA without compromising the objective of risk reduction. Support your proposal with a well-defined risk management strategy.

3. Use benefit-cost analysis to qualitatively evaluate the Superfund remedial action program.

4. Recommend an incentive-based reform that would improve states' identification of hazardous waste sites.

5. *a.* An ongoing debate about the Superfund program is the determination of the optimal abatement level, characterized as the "how clean is clean" problem. Choose one of the risk management strategies and propose how it might be used to resolve this issue.

   b. In your view, why has there been no movement to initiate such a proposal?

Additional Readings

Dower, Roger C. "Hazardous Wastes." In Paul R. Portney, ed. *Public Policies for Environmental Protection.* Washington, D.C.: Resources for the Future, 1990, pp. 151–94.

Fortuna, Richard C., and David J. Lennett. *Hazardous Waste Regulation: The New Era.* New York: McGraw-Hill, 1987.

Friedland, Steven I. "The New Hazardous Waste Management System: Regulation of Wastes or Wasted Regulation?" *Harvard Environmental Law Review* 5, no. 71 (1981), pp. 89–129.

Gerrard, Michael B. *Whose Backyard, Whose Risk.* Cambridge, Mass.: The MIT Press, 1994.

Hoffman, Andrew J. "An Uneasy Rebirth at Love Canal." *Environment* 37, no. 2 (March 1995), pp. 4–9, 25–31.

Hong, Peter, and Michele Green. "The Toxic Mess Called Superfund." *Business Week,* May 11, 1992, pp. 32–34.

Kunreuther, Howard, and Ruth Patrick. "Managing the Risks of Hazardous Waste." *Environment* 33, no. 3 (April 1991), pp. 13–15, 31–36.

Landy, Marc K., Marc J. Roberts, and Stephen R. Thomas. *The Environmental Protection Agency: Asking the Wrong Questions.* New York: Oxford University Press, 1990.

Levenson, Howard. "Wasting Away: Policies to Reduce Trash Toxicity and Quantity." *Environment* 32, no. 2 (March 1990), pp. 10–15, 31–36.

National Academy of Sciences. *Reducing Hazardous Waste Generation: An Evaluation and a Call for Action.* Washington, D.C.: National Academy Press, 1985.

Ritter, Don. "Challenging Current Environmental Standards." *Environment* 37, no. 2 (March 1995), pp. 11–12.

U.S. Congress, Office of Technology Assessment (OTA). *Serious Reduction of Hazardous Waste.* Washington, D.C.: U.S. Government Printing Office, September 1986.

U.S. Environmental Protection Agency, Office of Solid Waste and Emergency Response. *RCRA Environmental Indicators: FY 1991 Progress Report and Implementation Plan for the Future.* Washington, D.C., January 1992.

MANAGING MUNICIPAL SOLID WASTE

municipal solid waste (MSW)
Nonhazardous wastes disposed of by local communities.

Every local community has to deal with collecting and disposing of what most of us offhandedly call trash—that collection of cans, bottles, food scraps, newspapers, lawn clippings, and old furniture that characterizes everyday living. **Municipal solid waste (MSW),** as it is more formally termed, is a widespread, environmental problem. How could such a mundane matter as everyday trash become an issue? Mainly because society has seen it as exactly that—a routine part of living that merits no particular attention. As long as the unsightly pile of old newspapers and garbage leaves the street corner, most citizens give the matter little thought—that is, until some public official proposes a new landfill site on the next block. The typical reaction is a negative one—dubbed the ''not in my backyard,'' or ''NIMBY,'' syndrome. This response coupled with the growth trend in municipal waste generation and an aging disposal system have left many communities with a difficult problem.

As part of the nonhazardous waste stream, municipal solid wastes pose no *direct* threat to human, animal or plant life. Nonetheless, there are risks to society and the ecology if too much is generated or if it is improperly managed. Like many other countries around the world, the United States has depended on landfills to dispose of its MSW. Unsanitary conditions at these sites can contaminate water and soil with disease-spreading bacteria. A more serious risk is the release of toxic substances into the environment. Toxic contamination can arise from natural decomposition processes or the presence of household or industrial hazardous substances mixed in with municipal refuse. There is also the risk of atmospheric pollution caused by gases released from waste decomposition or from the incomplete combustion of incinerated wastes.

Given the potential damages, public policies are needed to control waste management practices, to find ways to recover and reuse waste materials, and to develop new technologies. In the United States, much of the responsibility for these policies is delegated to state and local governments with some measure of federal oversight. Such an approach allows for more flexibility in devising waste management programs than is the case for hazardous waste controls. In some communities, innovative policies have been developed to deal with MSW, including the use of market instruments to achieve environmental goals.

In this chapter, we consider the risks of MSW pollution and analyze the policy response to these risks in the United States. To understand the motivation of government programs and regulations, we begin by characterizing the generation and composition of this waste stream. Here, we use international comparisons to provide context to our discussion of U.S. data. Once done, we outline the delegation of responsibilities between federal and state governments given by the Resource Conservation and Recovery Act (RCRA). We then present a market model of MSW management services and explore potential sources of inefficiency. This discussion prepares the way for an economic analysis of various market instruments used by state and local governments to manage the MSW stream.

Characterizing Municipal Solid Waste

Observing a Trend

Many U.S. communities have been observing an increase in the size of the MSW stream, a phenomenon that is only partly linked to population growth. As shown in Table 17.1, *per capita* generation rates are also rising, suggesting that the characterization of Americans as a "disposable society" may be well placed. In-built product obsolescence, persuasive advertising that encourages excessive consumption, and reliance on prepared and therefore heavily packaged food products are all contributing factors. Despite this apparent growth

TABLE 17.1   **Trend Data on U.S. Annual MSW Generation from 1960 to 1990 by Weight**

	1960	*1970*	*1980*	*1990*
Total MSW generated by weight (millions of tons)	87.8	121.9	151.4	195.7
Total population (thousands)	180,671.0	203,984.0	227,255.0	249,924.0
Per capita MSW (pounds per day)	2.7	3.3	3.7	4.3

Source: U.S. Environmental Protection Agency, Office of Solid Waste and Emergency Response, *Characterization of Municipal Solid Waste in the United States: 1992 Update* (Washington, D.C., July 1992a), Table 1, p. 2-2 and Table 35, p. 5-2.

trend in MSW generation, the development of better waste management practices has lagged behind.

For years, the United States and most European countries have depended primarily on landfills to dispose of MSW, a practice that at least for a time seemed a reasonable solution. In the 1980s, reports of a "capacity crisis" warned that many municipal landfills were running out of space and others were being closed for improper waste management practices. More recently, counterarguments have emerged stating that the so-called capacity crisis in the United States was exaggerated, occurring in only certain locations. These reports point out that the rash of dump closings has involved mainly small sites, and that increased recycling, greater use of waste incineration, and a sluggish economy have contributed to what is now a surplus of landfill space in some areas. Indeed, some communities have been able to negotiate lower contract prices with trash management firms, suggesting that the reported glut in disposal capacity may be real—at least in some regions. Yet, some major waste companies continue to argue that landfill space is declining.

In either case, there is no debate that the MSW disposal system in the United States is aging. According to a recent report from the Congressional Office of Technology Assessment, 70 percent of MSW landfills in the United States began operation before 1980. Many lack proper controls such as waterproof cover systems, suitable liners to prevent leaching, or leachate collection systems. The absence of well-engineered controls creates a potential for serious environmental problems, such as methane gas explosions, the accumulation of bacteria, and contamination to ground and surface waters. These concerns are exacerbated when even small proportions of hazardous waste are mixed in with the nonhazardous materials.[1]

The Composition of MSW in the United States

product groups
Categories of products that make up the MSW stream identified as durable goods, nondurable goods, packaging and containers, food, and yard trimmings.

To get a sense of what comprises MSW in the United States, we can examine its composition both by the types of products being discarded and the kinds of materials entering the waste stream. The designated **product groups** are durable goods (e.g., appliances, furniture, and tires), nondurable goods (e.g., magazines, clothing, motor oil, batteries, and household cleansers), packaging and containers, food, and yard trimmings. Figure 17.1(a) gives the relative proportions by weight of these product groups based on the 195.7 million tons of MSW generated in 1990. Notice that packaging and containers account for nearly a third of this total, or 64.4 million tons. The **materials groups** identified in MSW are paper and paperboard, yard waste, food waste, glass, metals, plastics, textiles, rubber, and wood. Proportions by weight for these categories are shown in Figure 17.1(b).[2] According to these data, paper and paperboard

---

[1]U.S. Congress, Office of Technology Assessment (OTA), (1989), p. 284.
[2]U.S. EPA, Office of Solid Waste and Emergency Response (July 1992a).

FIGURE 17.1

Proportion by weight of products and materials generated in U.S. municipal solid waste in 1990

(a) Products

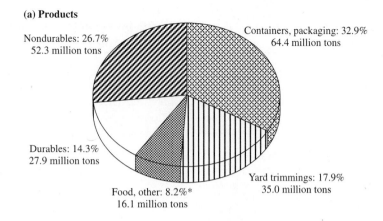

Nondurables: 26.7%
52.3 million tons

Containers, packaging: 32.9%
64.4 million tons

Durables: 14.3%
27.9 million tons

Yard trimmings: 17.9%
35.0 million tons

Food, other: 8.2%*
16.1 million tons

(b) Materials

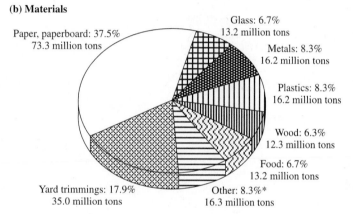

Paper, paperboard: 37.5%
73.3 million tons

Glass: 6.7%
13.2 million tons

Metals: 8.3%
16.2 million tons

Plastics: 8.3%
16.2 million tons

Wood: 6.3%
12.3 million tons

Food: 6.7%
13.2 million tons

Yard trimmings: 17.9%
35.0 million tons

Other: 8.3%*
16.3 million tons

*"Other" refers to rubber, leather, textiles, and other miscellaneous waste materials, where each of these subcategories makes up less than 4 percent of the total MSW in 1990.

Source: U.S. Environmental Protection Agency, Office of Solid Waste and Emergency Response, *Characterization of Municipal Solid Waste in the United States: 1992 Update* (Washington, D.C.: U.S. EPA, July 1992a), Figure ES-1, p. ES-4; Figure ES-3, p. ES-5.

materials groups
Categories of materials found in the MSW stream identified as paper and paperboard, yard waste, food, glass, metals, plastics, textiles, rubber, and wood.

represent the largest proportion by weight of discarded materials in 1990, accounting for 37.5 percent of the total.

Composition data by materials convey information about how manufacturing decisions ultimately affect waste accumulation. Table 17.2 gives trend data on the materials content of the nation's MSW for the 1960 to 1990 period. Notice that the generation of paper and paperboard has grown fairly steadily over time, rising from 29.9 million tons, or 34.1 percent of the total, in 1960 to 73.3 million tons, or 37.5 percent, in 1990. Paper wastes are procyclical, meaning that the amount varies directly with the economic business cycle. This explains why the total weight of paper wastes in 1975, a recession year,

TABLE 17.2   Trend Data on MSW Generated in the United States: 1960–1990 by Materials

	Millions of Tons*						
	1960	*1965*	*1970*	*1975*	*1980*	*1985*	*1990*
Materials in products							
Paper and paperboard	29.9	38.0	44.2	43.0	54.7	61.5	73.3
Glass	6.7	8.7	12.7	13.5	15.0	13.2	13.2
Metals	10.5	11.1	14.1	14.3	14.5	14.2	16.2
Plastics	0.4	1.4	3.1	4.5	7.8	11.6	16.2
Rubber and leather	2.0	2.6	3.2	3.9	4.3	3.8	4.6
Textiles	1.7	1.9	2.0	2.2	2.6	2.8	5.6
Wood	3.0	3.5	4.0	4.4	6.7	8.2	12.3
Other†	0.1	0.3	0.8	1.7	2.9	3.4	3.2
Subtotal—materials in products	54.3	67.5	84.1	87.5	108.5	118.7	144.6
Other wastes							
Food wastes	12.2	12.7	12.8	13.4	13.2	13.2	13.2
Yard trimmings	20.0	21.6	23.2	25.2	27.5	30.0	35.0
Miscellaneous inorganic wastes‡	1.3	1.6	1.8	2.0	2.2	2.5	2.9
Subtotal—Other wastes	33.5	35.9	37.8	40.6	42.9	45.7	51.1
Total MSW generated by weight	87.8	103.4	121.9	128.1	151.4	164.4	195.7

	Percent of Total*						
	1960	*1965*	*1970*	*1975*	*1980*	*1985*	*1990*
Materials in products							
Paper and paperboard	34.1	36.8	36.3	33.6	36.1	37.4	37.5
Glass	7.6	8.4	10.4	10.5	9.9	8.0	6.7
Metals	12.0	10.7	11.6	11.2	9.6	8.6	8.3
Plastics	0.5	1.4	2.5	3.5	5.2	7.1	8.3
Rubber and leather	2.3	2.5	2.6	3.0	2.8	2.3	2.4
Textiles	1.9	1.8	1.6	1.7	1.7	1.7	2.9
Wood	3.4	3.4	3.3	3.4	4.4	5.0	6.3
Other†	0.1	0.3	0.7	1.3	1.9	2.1	1.6
Subtotal—materials in products	61.8	65.3	69.0	68.3	71.7	72.2	73.9
Other wastes							
Food wastes	13.9	12.3	10.5	10.5	8.7	8.0	6.7
Yard trimmings	22.8	20.9	19.0	19.7	18.2	18.2	17.9
Miscellaneous inorganic wastes‡	1.5	1.5	1.5	1.6	1.5	1.5	1.5
Subtotal—Other wastes	38.2	34.7	31.0	31.7	28.3	27.8	26.1

*The sum of any given column may not add to total due to rounding.

†The category "Other" in products is primarily associated with disposable diapers. Also included are electrolytes and other materials in lead-acid batteries not classified as plastics or metals.

‡Miscellaneous inorganic wastes includes such materials as soil, stones, and bits of concrete.

Source: U.S. Environmental Protection Agency, Office of Solid Waste and Emergency Response, *Characterization of Municipal Solid Waste in the United States: 1992 Update* (Washington, D.C., July 1992a), Table 1, p. 2-2.

is less than it was in 1970. The fastest growing segment of MSW in the United States is plastics, which has risen steadily from 0.4 million tons in 1960 to 16.2 million tons in 1990. This growth rate is just as impressive when viewed on a proportionate basis, at less than 1 percent of 1960's total MSW by weight to over 8 percent of the total in 1990. These data explain why there has been a surge of interest in recycling plastics, an issue discussed in Application 17.1.

Application 17.1

The Facts on Recycling Plastics

Over the last 40 years, plastics have shown up in everything from food packaging to automobiles. As inputs in production, plastics have intrinsic characteristics that are highly desirable—lightweight, durable, moldable, and inexpensive. Over the last three decades, plastic use in the United States has risen by over 10 percent per year. Accepting the premise that the waste stream is partly determined by product design, the intensified use of plastics in manufacturing and packaging is a phenomenon that should affect the composition of solid wastes. Indeed, this is precisely what has been observed. The growth rate of plastic wastes has been substantial. In the United States, generation grew by 49 percent (measured by weight) over the 1980 to 1985 period and by 40 percent from 1985 to 1990. These wastes include durable goods, such as appliances and furniture, nondurable goods like disposable diapers and trash bags, and containers and packaging. Relative to the total MSW stream, plastic wastes represent 8.3 percent of the total by weight, but by volume, they account for a much higher proportion—21.1 percent. Containers and packaging are by far the largest proportion of plastic wastes, representing 7.1 million tons in the United States in 1990, or nearly 44 percent of the plastics waste stream.

Beyond the sheer quantity of plastic wastes, these materials also can endanger the environment. According to the EPA, most of the wastes collected during harbor surveys and beach cleanups are plastics, ranging from condoms to plastic fishing gear.

In addition to the aesthetic degradation of such littering, disposal of plastics in surface waters threatens virtually all forms of marine life. Entanglement in as well as ingestion of plastic debris have caused serious injury and even claimed the lives of many fish, birds, and marine mammals. Plastics also contain such additives as colorants, stabilizers, and plasticizers, some of which include toxics like cadmium and lead. Reportedly, 28 percent of the cadmium and 2 percent of the lead found in MSW arise from plastics.

Exacerbating the problem, the recovery rate for plastic wastes in the United States has been poor. In 1985, only 0.1 million tons or less than 1 percent of all plastic wastes generated, was recovered. In 1990, the figure rose to 0.4 million tons, or roughly 2.2 percent of the total. However, the EPA estimates that about 31.5 percent of plastic soft drink bottles and their so-called base cups were recovered in 1990. Why is the overall recovery rate for plastics so poor? And why are the rates for certain plastic items so much better than others? The answers to these questions are directly related to the evolving markets for recycled plastic products. The bottom line is that recycled plastics have to compete with virgin materials. For any recycled product to be competitive, all three steps in the recycling process—collection, separation of materials, and manufacture of new products—must be executed efficiently.

One of the key issues in producing recycled plastic is the resin content. Plastics are made from a variety of different types of resins. For example, soft drink bottles are made of the resin called polyethylene terephthalate (PET), while food containers and foam cups are made from polystyrene (PS). Currently, there appear to be sizable and lucrative markets for products made from single resins but not for commodities produced from mixed plastics, which command a lower market value. The problem is, even though many products are made of only a single resin, all of these end up together in the waste stream. To achieve a homogeneous collection of a particular resin, different kinds of plastics have to be identified and separated after collection—a costly step in the recycling process. An important problem is that plastic wastes often are not easily identified, even by experts. Sometimes different kinds of resins are bonded together or nonplastic substances are adhered to the plastic content. Gone unnoticed, such mixtures contaminate the recycled material, making it completely unusable. Finally, recycled plastics must be pure, that is, free from contaminants such as paper fragments, food residues, and metals. Hence, processors must clean used plastic products thoroughly, separate out the desired resins, dry out the material, remelt it, and form it into pellets to be sold to manufacturers—all costly procedures.

In order for plastic waste recovery rates to improve, cost-effective methods must be developed to more easily identify different types of plastics and to more readily separate them into batches of single resins. Until these technologies are developed, recycling will continue to focus on easily recognizable plastic wastes that accumulate in large amounts. This explains why soft drink bottles and milk containers currently account for the greatest majority of recycled plastic. It also explains why many packaging manufacturers have begun to label their containers with a recycling symbol and a code number that identifies the resins that were used. The code system is summarized in the table below.

Markets for recycled plastics are still in their infancy. Currently, recycled soft drink bottles are used to produce fiberfill for coats and sleeping bags, carpeting, and bottles for household cleaners. Milk jugs are being recycled into children's toys, flower pots, and base cups for soft drink bottles. Recycled polystyrene containers are being made into cafeteria trays, toys, and insulation. These uses are likely just the tip of the iceberg. If so, the lure of profits from new market opportunities may stimulate the needed technology to give recycled plastics a much stronger presence in the marketplace. If this occurs, we should observe higher recovery rates for plastic discards and an overall reduction in the MSW stream.

Sources: Resource Integration Systems, Ltd., and Waste Matters Consulting, Portland, Oregon, *Decisionmaker's Guide to Recycling Plastics.* Prepared for The Oregon Department of Environmental Quality Solid Waste Reduction and Recycling Section and U.S. EPA, Region X, Solid Waste Program. December 1990, pp. 7–9; U.S. Environmental Protection Agency, Office of Solid Waste and Emergency Response, *EPA's Report to Congress on Methods to Manage and Control Plastic Wastes* (Washington, D.C., February 1990); U.S. Environmental Protection Agency, Office of Solid Waste and Emergency Response, *Characterization of Municipal Solid Waste in the United States: 1992 Update* (Washington, D.C., July 1992a), Tables 1 and 2, pp. 2-2, 2-3, and Table 7, p. 2-12.

Plastic Container Coding System

Code	Resin	Examples of Product Use
1	Polyethylene terephthalate (PET) or (PETe)	Soft drink bottles; food and medicine containers; blister-pack.
2	High-density polyethylene (HDPE)	Containers for milk, yogurt, detergents; boil-in-bag pouches.
3	Polyvinyl chloride (PVC)	Construction pipe; meat wrap; cooking oil bottles.
4	Low-density polyethylene (LDPE)	Garbage bags; coated paper; milk bottle caps.
5	Polypropylene (PP)	Yogurt containers; office furniture.
6	Polystyrene (PS)	Foam dishes and cups; cassette tape cases.
7	Expanded polystyrene (EPS)	Egg cartons; meat and poultry trays.

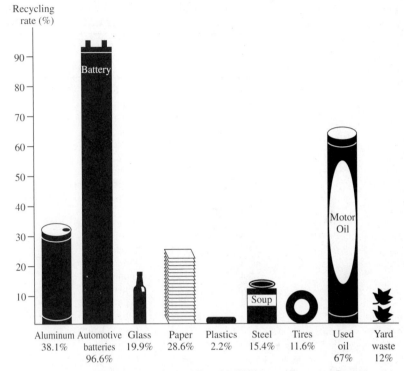

Source: U.S. Environmental Protection Agency, Office of Solid Waste and Emergency Response, *Environmental Fact Sheet*, ''Recycling Municipal Solid Waste: Facts and Figures.'' Washington, D.C., #EPA/530-SW-91-024, July 1992b.

Recycling rates for plastics and the other components of MSW as of 1990 are shown in Figure 17.2.

International Comparisons

Proper management of the MSW stream is a universal objective. Table 17.3 shows per capita MSW generation (measured in pounds per day) for the top 50 waste-generating nations in the world. Notice that the major industrialized nations and the oil-producing countries are at the upper end of MSW generation rates. What is also apparent from the data is that Americans are among the highest MSW generators in the world.[3] Notice how the U.S. data compares with other industrialized nations such as Germany and Japan. For example,

[3]These data have been compiled by World Resources Institute based on available country statistics. Because they are intended to provide a broad international comparison of waste generation rates, they are drawn from a number of sources and are based on methods and assumptions that are not necessarily the same as those used to prepare national data. Hence, these statistics, which are undated, are not directly comparable to domestically compiled data such as those reported by the EPA for the United States.

TABLE 17.3   International Data on Municipal Solid Waste Generation: The Top 50 Nations Ranked by per Capita Generation Rates

Country	Waste (lbs. per capita per day)	Rank	Country	Waste (lbs. per capita per day)	Rank
Australia	4.2	1	Spain	1.9	26
New Zealand	4.0	2	Germany	1.8	27
France	4.0	3	Iceland	1.8	28
Canada	3.7	4	Hungary	1.6	29
United States	3.3	5	Greece	1.5	30
Norway	2.9	6	Italy	1.5	31
Netherlands	2.6	7	Portugal	1.5	32
Denmark	2.6	8	Soviet Union (former)	1.3	33
Finland	2.4	9	Czechoslovakia	1.3	34
Bahrain	2.4	10	Albania	1.3	35
United Arab Emirates	2.4	11	Bulgaria	1.3	36
Saudi Arabia	2.4	12	Austria	1.3	37
Kuwait	2.4	13	Poland	1.3	38
Oman	2.4	14	Romania	1.3	39
Israel	2.4	15	Indonesia	1.3	40
Qatar	2.4	16	Colombia	1.2	41
Iraq	2.4	17	Guatemala	1.1	42
Luxembourg	2.2	18	Liberia	1.1	43
Switzerland	2.2	19	Cote d'Ivoire	1.1	44
United Kingdom	2.2	20	Malta	1.1	45
Belgium	2.0	21	Gabon	1.1	46
Sweden	2.0	22	Kenya	1.1	47
Japan	2.0	23	Trinidad and Tobago	1.1	48
Ireland	2.0	24	Cape Verde	1.1	49
Singapore	1.9	25	Mozambique	1.1	50

Japan's per capita rate of 2.0 pales in comparison to the U.S. statistic. Some of the international differences are attributable to the amount of packaging used by producers. For example, in 1988, it was estimated that the average American generated some 463 pounds of packaging waste. Citizens of both the European Community and Japan are said to have produced at least 25 percent *less* than that amount.[4] These variations also may reflect cultural preferences, environmental awareness, economic conditions, or government regulations. Of course, statistical comparisons across nations are not totally reliable. Estimation methods and even the definitions used for MSW are often different. Nonetheless, even assuming some measure of inaccuracy, the United States is clearly at the high end of worldwide MSW generation rates.

---

[4]McCarthy (Winter/Spring 1993).

There is also considerable variability in recycling rates across nations. In the United States, the national MSW recycling rate for 1990 was just over 17 percent. Japan and many European countries have practiced recycling for much longer than the United States, and their national averages reflect their experience. Japan in particular is touted as the nation with the highest national recycling rate for municipal wastes, quoted by most as being above 50 percent. Other nations with land constraints similar to Japan's such as The Netherlands also recycle about half of their local solid wastes.[5] Again, direct international data comparisons must be adjusted for political, cultural, economic, and demographic distinctions that affect the recyclability of manufactured products and the effectiveness of recycling programs.

The Policy Response: An Overview

As mentioned in the previous chapter, there is a set of provisions within the Resource Conservation and Recovery Act (RCRA) that apply to nonhazardous waste, including MSW.[6] For the most part, the responsibility of nonhazardous waste management is assigned to states with supervision and support provided by the federal government. This delegation of authority implies that policymakers view MSW controls as a responsibility best undertaken close to the source. Not every community faces the same problems, and even among those that do, the degree of environmental risk can vary considerably across localities. Factors such as town population, age of a landfill, and the proximity of ground and surface water sources to landfills are among the conditions affecting the outcome.

States' Responsibilities

According to RCRA, states are to develop their own waste management plans, but these must meet certain federal requirements. For example, state plans must include provisions to close or upgrade existing open dumps and to prohibit the establishment of new ones. They also must require that nonhazardous wastes be either used for resource recovery or be properly disposed of such as in a sanitary landfill. Some flexibility is allowed to account for state- or regional-specific factors that may affect the MSW stream, such as the industry profile in the area, the local availability of markets for recovered material, and population density.

RCRA also requires states to establish whatever regulatory powers they need to comply with the law. Typically, states pass their own legislation to meet federal requirements and to fulfill their responsibilities as outlined in

---

[5]Kharbanda and Stallworthy (1990), pp. 148–51.
[6]These provisions are given in Subtitle D of RCRA.

their state plans. Some have used incentive-based approaches such as providing grant monies for their cities and towns to set up waste management programs. Others have passed laws calling for local governments to set up recycling plans. One example is New Jersey's 1987 recycling law, discussed in Application 17.2. Some have passed more stringent laws *mandating* that local governments and disposal facilities recycle—among them, Connecticut, Oregon, Rhode Island, Washington, and Wisconsin.[7]

Application 17.2

State Recycling Goals: New Jersey's Solid Waste Initiative

Following the lead of states like Oregon and Rhode Island, New Jersey enacted a mandatory recycling law in 1987. The legislation calls for a statewide recycling rate of 15 percent for the first year and a 25 percent rate for each year thereafter. To implement the law, all of New Jersey's 21 counties must develop and submit a recycling plan as part of their solid waste plans. The law specifies that at least three materials must be recycled. While it does not mandate what these three must be, it is generally assumed that they will be newspapers, aluminum cans, and glass containers—materials that constitute much of the typical household waste stream.

The statewide recycling efforts are to be financed by a $1.50 per ton facilities surcharge, which officials estimate will generate approximately $12 million in revenues each year. These funds will be allocated to the program participants as follows:

New Jersey Recycling Payouts	
40%	Tonnage grants to counties and municipalities
35	Low-interest loans to businesses; for research and market development
10	Public education and awareness programs
8	Program grants for counties
7	Administration

While this revenue-sharing provides some incentive for counties and municipalities to participate in the program, New Jersey authorities took further steps to assure the program's success. For example, several incentive mechanisms were established, including a 50 percent tax credit for industries purchasing new recycling equipment. There is also a requirement that 45 percent of the state's paper purchases be spent on recycled paper to promote markets for recyclables. In addition, authorities have established an infrastructure throughout the state with recycling coordinators positioned within each county and municipality to develop and implement local recycling plans and to communicate important information to program participants.

Despite the complexities of orchestrating a recycling program in a state with a 7.5 million population and 567 municipalities, New Jersey has enjoyed remarkable success thus far. During 1989, just two years after the recycling law went into effect, about 20 percent of its residential and commercial solid waste and almost 39 percent of its entire solid waste stream were being recycled—wastes that would have found their way to New Jersey's limited landfills were it not for the 1987 law. As of 1990, about 88 percent of New Jersey's municipalities were participating in the program,

[7]U.S. EPA, Office of Solid Waste and Emergency Response (November 1989), pp. 16–17.

Application 17.2 (concluded)

and the state showed measurable progress toward achieving its target of a 25 percent recycling rate.

As the data in the table below indicate, New Jersey's recycling initiative compares favorably with what other states are doing across the country.

Apparently, New Jersey has set a realistic recycling goal and has achieved a high rate of participation among its population—undoubtedly the result of its integrated network of government officials and its built-in incentive plans. States planning to institute their own recycling programs might learn much from New Jersey's experience.

Sources: U.S. Environmental Protection Agency, Office of Solid Waste, *Recycling Works! State and Local Solutions to Solid Waste Management Problems* (Washington, D.C., January 1989), pp. 20–22; National Solid Wastes Management Association (NSWMA), *Recycling in the States: Mid-Year Update 1990* (Washington, D.C.: NSWMA, 1990).

State Recycling Goals and Outcomes

State	Date of Law	Goal	Recycling Rate	Percent of Population Served*
Oregon	1983	—	22–25%[a]	74%
Rhode Island	1986	Maximum possible[b]	15% residential	70% residential
			20% commercial	100% commercial
Massachusetts	1987	56% by 2000[c]	8–12%	Not known
New Jersey	1987	25% by 1992	20%, 39%[d]	500 of 567 municipalities
Vermont	1987	40% by 2000	15–17%	15%
Florida	1988	30% by 1994	10%[e]	Over 10%
Michigan	1988	50% by 2005	13–15%	Not known
Pennsylvania	1988	25% by 1997	4%	30%
Maine	1989	50% by 1994	16%[f]	Not known
Virginia	1989	25% by 1995	8–10%	27%
Washington	1989	50% by 1995	29%[g]	Majority of population

Notes:

Information shown is based on a survey of state recycling coordinators conducted during July and August of 1990. The states represented had the most complete data.

*By curbside collection or a materials recovery facility.

[a]Includes used oil.

[b]Municipalities must achieve at least 15% recycling. Yard waste composting cannot be counted toward meeting the goal.

[c]The goal calls for a 46% recycling rate and a 10% reduction in 1990 per capita waste generation rates by 2000.

[d]The 39% recycling rate includes scrap metal, batteries, construction and demolition material, and other non-MSW waste, as well as leaves collected for composting. The 20% rate does not include leaves.

[e]Yard waste, appliances, construction and demolition debris, and tires may count for 50% of recycled waste to meet goals.

[f]Includes nonhazardous industrial waste.

[g]Includes scrap metal, cars, tires, and lead acid batteries. Does not include yard waste for composting.

Source: National Solid Wastes Management Association (NSWMA), *Recycling in the States: Mid-Year Update 1990* (Washington, D.C.: NSWMA 1990). Reprinted with permission of National Solid Wastes Management Association.

In further support of such efforts, in October 1991 President Bush signed Executive Order 12780, entitled the Federal Recycling and Procurement Policy. This directive required all federal agencies to step up their recycling efforts and to foster the development of markets for recycled products. A recycling coordinator and a council on Federal Recycling and Procurement Policy were created to oversee the program.[8] While the response was a positive one, this initiative falls far short of what some other nations are doing. For example, in the same year that President Bush signed this Executive Order, Germany passed a new ordinance that is much more aggressive in its approach toward recycling, as Application 17.3 explains.

Application 17.3

Germany's Green Dot Program

Communities everywhere are actively seeking better policy solutions to managing municipal solid wastes. One approach that is gaining in popularity is the development and implementation of *national* recycling programs. Such initiatives are aimed at reducing the amount of trash that otherwise ends up in landfills or incinerators.

A commonly cited example of a national recycling plan is Germany's packaging ordinance. According to a recent press report, this 1991 law is the most ambitious recycling program in the world. The progressive mandate set recycling targets of 72 percent of glass, tinplate, and aluminum and 64 percent of cardboard, paper, plastic, and composites to be met by July 1, 1995. To achieve these ambitious objectives, Germany's ordinance stipulates that industry is to be responsible for the collection and recycling of all its packaging. If businesses' efforts fail to meet the statutory targets, the German government will institute costly deposits on essentially all packaging.

Responding to these tough requirements, firms have collaborated to form a private, nonprofit company, called Duales System Deutschland (DSD) (meaning a dual system), to provide collection and recycling services to consumers. Through its network, DSD assures that used packaging will be collected and sent to a proper recycling facility. To facilitate the collection phase, DSD distributes yellow bins and bags for all packaging waste other than glass containers, which continue to be collected via drop-off plans already in place. The avowed objective of this newly created enterprise is to make its services available to at least 90 percent of Germany's residents.

Of course, such an undertaking does not come cheap. DSD's start-up costs have been estimated to be in the neighborhood of $10 billion, while its operating expenses are expected to be $1 billion per year. To finance these fixed and variable costs, DSD sells to participating companies the right to use a ''green dot'' on their packages, a symbol that guarantees that the packaging is eligible for the services provided by DSD. The price of a green dot varies with the amount of packaging on each product and its recyclability. At the start of the program, the average price was about one cent per package.

Thus far, reported statistics indicate some progress has been made. For example, by April 1992, both domestic- and foreign-based firms had purchased 5,000 licenses for DSD's ''green dots'' to

---

[8]Council on Environmental Quality (March 1992), pp. 112–14.

Application 17.3 (concluded)

assure the use of its services for some 40 billion packaging units. Consumers have responded just as vigorously—even more so than was forecasted by analysts. Original predictions were that the Green Dot program would result in the collection of about 100,000 tons of plastics per year, but these estimates were far off the mark. In 1993, German households accumulated nearly four times these projections.

An added benefit of Germany's program has been the positive response of foreign corporations that participate in German markets. Instead of changing the packaging of only those commodities shipped to Germany, some firms have elected to make the requisite design changes across the board. For example, Hewlett-Packard has redesigned its office machine packaging on a worldwide basis— a true example of a positive externality. Such universal adjustments likely pay dividends in the long run, since firms avoid the costs of producing multiple packaging versions for the same commodity to meet country-specific regulations. Moreover, manufacturers that meet the most demanding national laws are prepared to satisfy other countries' new policies as they are brought closer to Germany's high standards.

While response to Germany's new ordinance has been favorable, the Green Dot program that supports it is not without problems. DSD lost more than $300 million during its first full year of operation. To counter this loss, prices of the "green dot" will have to be increased. While raising the fee may cover the shortfall, someargue that these higher rates,which are passed on to consumers, could make the program fail on economic grounds. A further problem involves the potential for fraud in the program. Apparently, some companies are putting the "green dot" symbol on their products without paying for it. In fact, one Duales spokesperson claims that approximately one-third of the green dots that appear on products are fraudulent. Misuse of the system is responsible for at least some of the imbalance between DSD's collection costs and its revenues. Finally, the German government has not yet adjusted its capacity to handle the sharp rise in accumulated recyclables triggered by the new ordinance, and there is concern about its ability to accommodate so rapid a change.

Despite the need for adjustments to the program, the German government and its corporate sector are credited with initiating an innovative recycling plan. It appears that the program is serving as a prototype for other national recycling laws. France and Austria already have launched their own versions of the German program, while the United States and Japan are in the process of examining the logistics of such a national plan. In fact, there is some discussion in the United States about proposing a national recycling law based on Germany's progressive new plan.

Sources: Cynthia Pollock Shea, "Getting Serious in Germany," *EPA Journal* 18 no. 3, July/August 1992, pp. 50–52; Frances Cairncross, "How Europe's Companies Reposition to Recycle," *Harvard Business Review,* March–April, 1992, pp. 34–45; Associated Press, "German Recycling Is Too Successful," *Brockton Enterprise,* July 27, 1993.

Federal Responsibilities

Based on RCRA's provisions for nonhazardous wastes, the federal government must provide financial and technical assistance to states in designing and implementing their waste management plans. It also must encourage states to conserve resources and assist them in finding ways to maximize the use of recoverable resources. The EPA is responsible for establishing minimum criteria for sanitary landfills and other land disposal sites. Approximately 227,000 such facilities are regulated under RCRA. The criteria are designed to prevent the transmission of disease, to ensure the safety of residents and facility employees, and to protect endangered species, crops, ground and surface water, air, and floodplains.[9] Facilities not meeting the criteria are considered to be open dumps and must be closed or upgraded in accordance with specific rules.

In September 1991, new regulations were issued to establish tougher standards for land disposal sites starting in 1993. These new rules are to be effective throughout the useful life of a facility plus 30 years after its closure. In addition to the risk reduction provided by these tougher rules, the revisions are expected to encourage source reduction and recycling on a national scale.[10] New regulations also were issued for waste-to-energy incineration facilities. These establish controls on various air emissions and assure proper combustion conditions. These rulings are of special importance, since there are about 150 municipal waste-to-energy facilities currently in operation in the United States.[11] Prior to this time, the EPA had established *guidelines,* but no regulatory controls per se, for MSW incineration facilities.

The Current Policy Direction

integrated waste management system
An EPA initiative to guide state MSW plans that promotes the combined use of source reduction, recycling, combustion, and land disposal ranked in order of preference.

Because states are responsible for their own nonhazardous waste plans, they have the flexibility to develop cost-effective programs. Although some states have submitted bona fide plans, the general response rate has been poor. Many states have not complied at all, and among those that have, some have submitted plans that are now badly out of date.[12] Reportedly, both the absence of enforcement and a depletion of federal funds to assure compliance are responsible. Responding to this shortcoming, the EPA has begun to guide state authorities in developing programs based on an **integrated waste management system.** This system promotes using a combination of techniques and programs aimed at source reduction, recycling, combustion, and land disposal—in that order. To determine how states are responding to the new initiative, we need to develop a general market model of MSW services. This provides the analytical tool with which to assess the cost-effectiveness and efficiency of various state programs.

Modeling the Market for MSW Management Services

In the market for MSW services, the relevant commodity is actually a combination of several distinct activities—the collection, transportation, and disposal of municipal solid waste. Based on this output definition, we

---

[9]U.S. EPA, Office of Solid Waste (November 1986).
[10]U.S. EPA, Office of Solid Waste and Emergency Response (November 1989), pp. 18–19 and pp. 108–09; Council on Environmental Quality (March 1992), pp. 112–13.
[11]Council on Environmental Quality (January 1993), p. 134.
[12]Denison and Ruston (1990), pp. 258–59.

FIGURE 17.3

The market for municipal solid waste services

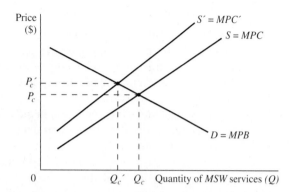

This model illustrates the market for MSW management services. The hypothetical demand or *MPB* curve and the supply or *MPC* curve determine the competitive equilibrium price of MSW services, P_c, and the equilibrium quantity, Q_c. The impact of Congress's decision to tighten federal controls on landfill disposal causes the *MPC* to shift upward to *MPC′* elevating equilibrium price to P_c' and causing a decline in quantity to Q_c'. The decrease in quantity of MSW services may mean that generators are using a source reduction strategy. It might also be the case that the generation rate is the same but generators are recycling more of their wastes. Finally, they might be maintaining the same generation rate *and* the same recycling rate but be engaging in illegal disposal to get rid of some of their wastes.

model the market for MSW services in Figure 17.3, using some hypothetical demand (*D*) or marginal private benefit (*MPB*) curve and some supply (*S*) or marginal private cost (*MPC*) curve. Together, these curves determine the competitive equilibrium price or fee for MSW services, P_c and the equilibrium quantity, Q_c.

The Supply of MSW Services

The supply side of the MSW services market represents the production decisions of private firms under contract with cities and towns or those of municipalities who provide these services directly to the community. In this market, the costs of production reflect the expenses of operating a fleet of disposal trucks, managing an approved landfill or incinerator, and labor. Under the usual assumptions about production and diminishing returns, the *MPC* exhibits a positive slope. Among the nonprice factors affecting supply in this market are land availability and government regulation.

Consider, for example, the impact of Congress's decision to tighten federal controls on landfill disposal. These tougher standards led to the closing of several hundred landfills that were unable to meet the law's new requirements. This outcome along with the NIMBY syndrome limited the availability of landfill space in some locations. As a result, landfill prices, or **tipping fees** as they are called, have risen. As Figure 17.3 shows, this outcome is modeled as an upward shift of *MPC,* which causes an increase in price to P_c' and a decline in equilibrium quantity to Q_c'.

tipping fees
Prices charged for disposing of wastes in a facility such as a landfill.

The Demand for MSW Services

The demand side of this market represents the purchasing decisions of MSW generators. In this context, the quantity response to changes in price takes on an important meaning about how wastes are managed. To understand this, reconsider the decline in quantity from Q_c to Q_c' due to the regulation-induced price increase described in Figure 17.3. How might generators change their behavior to achieve this reduction in quantity? One possibility is that they use a source reduction strategy and produce less trash. Another is that they generate the same amount of trash but demand less services because they recycle. Finally, they might maintain the same generation rate *and* the same recycling rate, but engage in illegal disposal to avoid the higher price of MSW services.[13] Which of these options is chosen depends upon their availability to the generator and the prices of these options relative to the price of MSW services. Recognizing the natural market response of demanders to higher-priced MSW services, a local community can encourage recycling by offering a cost-effective program to its residents.[14] In the absence of such a program, some generators may be motivated to illegally dispose of their wastes.

The demand, or *MPB,* of municipal waste services also responds to certain nonprice changes. For example, more affluent individuals tend to generate larger amounts of trash, since they purchase more products and replace them more frequently. Thus, demand for MSW services likely would shift to the right as the income of a community rises, holding all else constant. Another nonprice determinant of demand is tastes and preferences. As generators become more environmentally responsible, we would expect their demand for these services to decline as they adjust their purchases toward products with less packaging. In sum, waste generators in each community likely face a uniquely shaped demand curve that responds somewhat predictably to both price and nonprice changes.

If actual MSW markets behaved in accordance with this model *and* if there were no externalities, we could conclude that MSW markets achieve an efficient solution where $MPC = MPB$. However, it turns out that these conditions typically are violated in actual MSW markets. The resulting resource misallocation is an important issue that merits further investigation.

---

[13]Jenkins (1993), pp. 4–6.

[14]Recent data indicate that the design and implementation of recycling programs produce varying results on disposal reduction and on local budgets. According to a recent study conducted by Franklin Associates, curbside recycling generates high costs that do not appear to be justified by the associated benefits. Nationally, this type of recycling plan is estimated to lower disposal by only 2.5 percent compared to more conventional drop-off programs that achieve a 4.5 percent decrease. See Bailey (October 4, 1994).

FIGURE 17.4

Modeling a fixed fee system for MSW services

In most communities, a **fixed fee** per household or per commercial establishment is charged for MSW services. Since the fee is the same regardless of the quantity of waste generated at each location, this type of pricing scheme is known as a **flat fee pricing system.** The waste generator is charged nothing for any additional containers of trash beyond the first one, which means that the price does not reflect rising *MPC*. Instead, demanders are effectively paying a *marginal* price of zero, and hence have no incentive to reduce wastes. More formally, the market price under this scenario is being determined *as if* the *MPC* is zero, or coincident with the horizontal axis. Under such a scenario the market equilibrates where $MPC = MPB = 0$, at Q_o. Compared to the competitive equilibrium, too many resources are being allocated to MSW services.

Resource Misallocation in the Market for MSW Services

There are two distinct problems that arise in most MSW services markets, and both are associated with the supply side of the market:

1. The pricing of MSW services does not properly reflect the rising *MPC* associated with increases in production levels.

2. The production of MSW services gives rise to negative externalities.

Let's consider each of these problems in turn.

fixed fee or flat fee pricing system
Pricing MSW services independent of the quantity of waste generated.

Flat Fee Pricing of MSW Services.   In most communities, suppliers charge a **fixed fee** per household or commercial establishment for MSW services. Since the fee is the same regardless of the quantity of waste generated at each location, this type of pricing scheme is known as a **flat fee pricing system.** Notice that the waste generator is charged nothing for any additional containers of trash beyond the first one, which means that the price does not reflect rising *MPC*. Demanders effectively pay a *marginal* price of zero, and hence have no incentive to reduce wastes. More formally, the market price under this scenario is being determined *as if* the *MPC* is zero. This phenomenon is illustrated in Figure 17.4, where the *MPC* is shown coincident with the horizontal axis. Notice that under such a scenario, the market equilibrates where $MPC = MPB = 0$ at Q_o. Compared to the competitive equilibrium, too many resources are being allocated to MSW services. In communities where MSW services are publicly provided, the price mechanism is further dampened because the fee is not explicitly communicated but rather collected through property taxes. But whether these services are publicly or privately provided, the use of a fixed fee has serious efficiency implications.[15]

Negative Externalities.   Even if waste generators are charged a fee equal to the *MPC,* there may still be a resource misallocation if production of MSW services gives rise to negative externalities. Such an outcome is not uncommon in waste management markets. For example, Application 17.4 reports on the

Application 17.4

Garbage or Resource? The Case of Scrap Tires

One person's trash is another person's treasure—an appropriate commentary on the market for recyclables. Some solid waste can be returned to productive use, provided there is an active market for the recycled material. Encouraging waste generators to recycle is important, but it is only part of the story. Recycling sets up a reliable supply of inputs that presumably can be used in the production of some new commodity. However, in order for this market to be viable, there must be a healthy demand side of buyers willing and able to purchase these recycled materials at the going market price. If not, society can expect a trade-off of one problem for another—a waste heap for a glut of unwanted recycled materials.

An interesting case is the market for scrap tires. Current estimates place the total number of discarded tires at approximately 3 billion—a nontrivial disposal problem that is increasing at the rate of 242 million per year in the United States alone. The common practice of replacing all four tires when only one or two have worn out explains some of the growth rate. Another explanation is the dwindling demand for retreads—the result of both safety concerns and falling prices for new tires. Numbers aside, there is also a degradability issue. Technology advances in tire production have made these products almost indestructible. The result? The nation faces a growing disposal problem that seems to defy the usual solutions. Statistics bear out the magnitude of the dilemma. In the United States, fewer than 7 percent of scrap tires are recycled into alternative products like asphalt pavement, car mats, mud guards, and playground swings. Another 5 percent are exported, only 11 percent are incinerated for fuel value by pulp and paper mills, power plants, and cement factories, and the remaining 78 percent end up in stockpiles, landfills, and illegal disposal sites.

Environmentally, the costs of dealing with discarded tires can be significant. Stockpiles of used tires attract rodents and form traps for accumulating gases and water. Stagnant water becomes a breeding ground for mosquitoes that can carry diseases such as encephalitis and yellow fever. Accumulating gases can turn these trash heaps into fire hazards. Major fires at tire stockpiles are unfortunately not an uncommon occurrence. Most notable was a tire inferno in Canada that ultimately cost that nation nearly $30 million to extinguish. In landfills, old tires occupy a tremendous amount of volume, and they tend to float up to the surface and break through landfill covers.

---

[15]Wirth and Heinz (1991), pp. 48–49.

Application 17.4 (concluded)

In the face of such environmental risks *and* the enormous supply of used tires, there is a powerful incentive to find some productive use for this burdensome contribution to the solid waste stream. The reward is obvious. Not only would such a discovery rid society of an environmental problem, but it might also be an economic windfall. For this to occur, there has to be a market incentive. But so far, all the existing uses for whole discarded tires or processed scraps are so meager that they cannot keep up with the current disposal rate, much less put a dent in the huge stockpile.

Most experts agree that the use of scrapped tires as an energy source makes good sense from an energy efficiency standpoint. Their heat value exceeds that of coal, at about 12,000 to 16,000 Btus per pound. However, environmental and economic factors have been major stumbling blocks to expanding the use of scrap tires for energy recovery. Because of both air quality and aesthetic impairment, there is strong resistance to siting an energy facility that is dependent on scrap tires for fuel. Until recently, most tire-to-energy technologies have been relatively dirty, resulting in atmospheric emissions that are unacceptable by today's standards. But a new patented technology devised by a New Mexico firm—Titan Technologies—appears to hold promise.

Titan's newly developed process bakes six-inch squares of tire chips instead of burning whole tires or tire shreds. According to company officials, the process uses a closed system of catalytic drums and requires relatively low temperatures—about 450 degrees Fahrenheit. The result is a conversion process that yields by-products that are much less damaging to the environment. Furthermore, Titan operates at a large scale—much larger in fact than conventional waste-to-energy facilities. Exploiting scale economies allows Titan to achieve lower unit costs and market its energy at a competitive price. This "buy-back rate" is critical to the viability of this particular waste-to-energy market. Currently, unit costs of production are so high that buy-back rates are competitive only in certain regional markets like the Northeast and California, where competing energy supplies are expensive. Finding ways to lower unit costs means that tire-to-energy production may be able to service a national market. If this economic feasibility is established, demand for scrap tires should be stimulated, and the environmental hazard markedly reduced.

By definition, entrepreneurs look for profitable opportunities and find ways to cash in on them. In this case, the profit seekers had the vision to recognize the nation's heap of used tires as a potential resource in a lucrative new market. Society could have much to gain if others follow the lead of Titan Technologies.

Sources: Robert Metz, "N.M. Firm is Ready to Roll into the Tire Recycling Industry," *Boston Globe*, December 28, 1993, p. 34; U.S. Environmental Protection Agency, Office of Solid Waste and Emergency Response, *Summary of Markets for Scrap Tires* (Washington, D.C., October 1991); U.S. Environmental Protection Agency, Office of Policy, Planning, and Evaluation, *Economic Incentives: Options for Environmental Protection* (Washington, D.C., March 1991), pp. 2-13–2-15.

negative externalities associated with tire disposal and a new technology that may help reduce these effects. In the MSW services market, external costs may be due to groundwater contamination, air pollution from incineration, or impairment of aesthetics. As we have illustrated in other contexts, such a production externality is captured by a marginal external cost (*MEC*) curve, which must be added to the *MPC* to identify the marginal social cost (*MSC*) of producing the good. Assuming no externalities on the demand side, the marginal social benefit (*MSB*) of consumption is the same as the *MPB* function. The efficient solution is determined where the *MSC* equals the *MSB,* as

FIGURE 17.5

Allocative inefficiency in private markets for MSW services: the presence of a negative externality

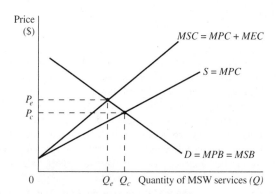

A resource misallocation may arise if production of MSW services gives rise to a negative externality. The external costs might be due to groundwater contamination, air pollution from incineration, or impairment of aesthetics. Such a production externality is captured by a marginal external cost (*MEC*) curve, which must be added to the *MPC* to identify the marginal social cost (*MSC*) of producing the good. Assuming no externalities on the demand side, the marginal social benefit (*MSB*) function is the same as the *MPB*. The efficient solution is determined where the *MSC* equals the *MSB*. Notice that the efficient output level occurs at Q_e, which is *lower* than the private market outcome, Q_c.

illustrated in Figure 17.5. (To avoid confounding the effect of the externality with that of charging a fixed fee, we show the *MPC* as a positively sloped curve.) Notice that the efficient output level is Q_e, which is *lower* than the private market outcome, Q_c.

To summarize, we observe that private MSW markets typically do not yield an efficient outcome. The use of fixed fees distorts the signaling mechanism of price, effectively removing the incentive to economize on trash generation. The private market's disregard for external costs leads to a further distortion. Singularly or in combination, these factors contribute to an overallocation of resources to waste services and an overproduction of municipal trash. Is there any solution to these problems? Actually, a number of pricing schemes can be used to correct the inefficiency. As we are about to discover, they are precisely what is suggested by economic theory.

A Market Approach to MSW Policy[16]

In recent years, some communities have begun to institute market-based policies aimed at reducing the problems associated with MSW. Of interest are three approaches that directly exploit the signaling mechanism of price. These are **back- or waste-end charges, front-end or retail disposal charges,** and **deposit/refund systems.**

---

[16]Much of the following is drawn from Wirth and Heinz (1991), pp. 48–65, Jenkins (1993), and U.S. EPA, Office of Solid Waste and Emergency Response (February 1991).

FIGURE 17.6

Modeling a waste-end charge to restore efficiency in the market for MSW services

This model illustrates how a **waste-end charge** can be implemented to achieve efficiency in the market for MSW services. Because such a charge varies with the quantity of waste, it avoids the market distortion caused by a flat fee pricing scheme. To achieve efficiency, the waste-end charge must be set to cover the *MSC* at the efficient equilibrium, where *MSB* is exactly equal to *MSC*. In the model shown above, the appropriate per unit fee would be set equal to P_e.

Back-End or Waste-End Charges

back-end or waste-end charge
A fee implemented at the time of disposal based on the quantity of waste generated.

As discussed in the previous chapter, a **waste-end charge** is so named because it is implemented at the time of disposal based on the quantity of waste generated. Because such a charge varies with the quantity of waste, it avoids the market distortion caused by a flat fee pricing scheme. To achieve efficiency, the waste-end charge must be set to cover the *MSC* at the efficient equilibrium. This solution is illustrated in Figure 17.6, with the appropriate per unit fee shown as P_e. Notice that this fee is a *price per unit of waste* to be paid by all generators, which is very different from charging a *price per household,* as is done under a flat fee system.

unit pricing scheme
Common designation for the use of a waste-end charge.

flat rate pricing
A unit pricing scheme that charges the same price for each additional unit of waste.

variable rate pricing
A unit pricing scheme that charges a different price for each additional unit of waste.

In practice, programs that use waste-end charges are called **unit pricing** schemes to indicate that prices for MSW services are charged on a per-unit-of-waste basis. The units may be measured either by weight or by volume generated, though the latter is more commonly used at the present time. The same price can be charged for each unit, called **flat rate pricing,** or the price can vary, called **variable rate pricing.** Perhaps the best known example of a community having implemented unit pricing is the city of Seattle. In fact, Seattle's program has come to be the prototype upon which other communities have modeled their own MSW unit pricing plans. The program is implemented by having each MSW generator register with the city for the number and volume of trash containers it expects to use in a week. Based on the registration, a fee is calculated using a schedule of volume-based prices.[17]

---

[17]Seattle uses a schedule of bimonthly fees based on trash can capacity. In 1988, these were reported as follows: $10.70 for a 19-gallon can; $13.75 for a 32-gallon can; $22.75 for a 60-gallon can; and $31.75 for a 90-gallon can. See Seattle Solid Waste Utility (1988), as cited in Wirth and Heinz (1991), pp. 50–51.

By moving from a fixed fee schedule to a unit pricing program, two important market incentives are restored. First, unit pricing communicates to generators that increased waste services are associated with a nonzero marginal cost of production, ideally the marginal social cost.[18] Effectively, this provides an incentive to economize on waste generation by using a source reduction strategy. Secondly, by elevating the price of collection and disposal, the *relative* price of alternative approaches declines. Given that recycling and disposal are substitute activities, the change in relative prices may encourage more recycling, which means less disposal. There are also favorable equity implications, since unit pricing does not force small MSW generators to subsidize larger ones, as is the case with a flat fee system.[19] Finally, while there is the theoretical possibility that unit pricing may encourage illegal disposal, there is little evidence that this activity is increasing dramatically in communities where such programs are in use.[20]

Beyond these theoretical arguments, there is a fair amount of anecdotal and empirical evidence that unit pricing is a viable policy instrument. For example, Seattle officials have observed that trash disposal in landfills has declined since unit pricing was introduced. In the early 1980s, the typical single-family residence was disposing about three and one-half 30-gallon receptacles each week. In 1988, 60 percent of the city's households had subscribed to one 32-gallon container per week, and this proportion rose to 87 percent a year later.[21] An analysis of the experience of Tacoma, Washington, which has instituted a program similar to Seattle's, shows that a 10 percent increase in fees resulted in a 2 percent decline in waste disposal.[22] More formal evidence is presented by Robin Jenkins (1993), who conducted a rather extensive statistical study on unit pricing. The results show that the effect of switching from a fixed fee to a volume-based fee of 50 cents per container is a decrease in waste per person per day of 0.2 pounds. This translates to an estimated decline of 3,650 tons per year for a community of 100,000 people or 18,250 tons annually for a community of 500,000 people. Proportionately higher effects are found for successively higher fees.

As the evidence accumulates, more and more communities are following Seattle's lead and moving to unit pricing programs. In fact, some local authorities have enhanced the prototype to improve its efficiency. For example,

---

[18]According to Jenkins (1993), p. 90, Seattle's fees do not cover the marginal external cost of MSW services.

[19]Furthermore, concerns about the regressiveness of unit pricing is being handled by Seattle and other communities by allowing special rates for low-income groups or senior citizens. See, for example, Wirth and Heinz (1991), p. 51 and U.S. EPA, Office of Solid Waste and Emergency Response (February 1991).

[20]See U.S. EPA (September 1990), cited in Wirth and Heinz (1991), p. 52, and Goldberg (February 1990), pp. 98–104, cited in U.S. EPA, Office of Policy, Planning, and Evaluation (March 1991), p. 2-9.

[21]Seattle Solid Waste Utility (1988), as cited in Wirth and Heinz (1991), p. 51.

[22]See Goddard (1990), as cited in Wirth and Heinz (1991), p. 51.

"bag-and-tag" approach
A unit pricing scheme implemented by selling stickers or tags to be applied to waste receptacles of various sizes.

one of the problems with Seattle's "per-can" pricing plan is that the preregistered number of receptacles on which the fee is based is not always an accurate forecast of actual trash generation. Consequently, generators can be charged a full rate even if some receptacles are half full or not used at all. Recognizing this potential inefficiency, some communities have instituted more flexible programs whereby generators purchase stickers for receptacles of various sizes. Then, they *choose* how many receptacles they need each period and simply apply the prepaid stickers to the receptacles used.[23] Application 17.5 discusses this so-called **"bag-and-tag" approach,** which has met with some success in Perkasie, Pennsylvania.

Application 17.5

"Bag-and-Tag" Systems: An Alternative to Seattle's Per-Can Pricing Scheme

Although the city of Seattle has been receiving national acclaim for its innovative unit pricing waste program, the market-based plan has not been without its problems. One in particular is that per-can pricing schemes are based upon residents' *forecasts* of their waste generation rate, which may or may not be accurate. As a result, some generators end up paying for disposal services on a full can of trash even if it is half empty or not used at all.

This potential inefficiency has prompted some communities to design modified versions of the Seattle prototype, called "bag-and-tag" systems. Under these plans, the advantages of unit pricing are maintained, but residents have the flexibility to assure that they pay only for the wastes they generate. One way these systems are implemented is by providing collection and disposal services only to trash placed in specially designated containers sold by the municipality. Program participants purchase in advance a supply of these trash bags, typically available in various sizes and priced accordingly. In each collection period, residents use only as many of the prepaid trash bags as they need. A variation of the system operates from the same premise except that stickers or tags are sold

by the municipality, and these are then affixed to residents' own trash containers. In either case, the inefficiency of the per-can pricing plan is resolved while maintaining the advantages of unit pricing.

In the late 1980s, High Bridge, New Jersey, instituted a tag pricing system, charging residents an annual fee for 52 stickers. In 1989, the annual charge was set at $200 per household, which covered the program's administrative costs plus the disposal cost of one container per week for each household. Restrictions on maximum weight and volume are imposed on a per-sticker basis. To provide greater flexibility to residents, additional stickers can be purchased from the town or traded between low-use and high-use residents.

At about the same time as High Bridge got its plan under way, the town of Perkasie, Pennsylvania, began selling town-issued trash bags to implement its unit pricing program. To distinguish between low and high waste generators, Perkasie uses a differential charge based on bag size. A 20-pound trash bag commands a price of $0.80, while the larger 40-pound container is sold for $1.50. All of Perkasie's trash bags have a "tree logo" to distinguish them from receptacles used by nonparticipants. Like the

---

[23]Wirth and Heinz (1991), p. 51.

Application 17.5 (concluded)

High Bridge plan, residents pay for services only on the quantity of waste generated in a given period and not on a predetermined and likely inaccurate forecast.

Assessing the success of these alternative unit pricing programs is difficult given their relatively brief existence. Nonetheless, preliminary estimates of waste reduction under each program are impressive. For example, in its first 10 months of operation, High Bridge officials reported a 24 percent decrease in waste tonnage. An even greater decline of 40 percent was observed after Perkasie's first full year of operation. However, such statistics can belie undesirable changes in behavior. Hence, provisions must be made to assure that the observed declines are reflecting reduced waste generation and not an increase in illegal disposal practices. For its part, Perkasie plans to enforce its prohibition of backyard burning, a practice which may have increased under its new pricing plan.

Overall, the use of unit pricing systems appears to be gaining momentum—partly because of increasing landfilling costs and partly because it makes good economic sense. Current estimates indicate that a growing number of communities across the country are implementing or considering some form of unit pricing to deal with municipal solid waste. Local officials can build on the successes enjoyed by communities like Seattle, High Bridge, and Perkasie, and learn from their mistakes. As they do, the powerful influence of price may help control solid waste pollution.

Sources: Timothy E. Wirth and John Heinz, *Project 88—Round II Incentives for Action: Designing Market-Based Environmental Strategies* (Washington, D.C., May 1991), pp. 49–53; U.S. Environmental Protection Agency, Office of Policy, Planning, and Evaluation, *Economic Incentives: Options for Environmental Protection* (Washington, D.C., March 1991), pp. 2.7–2.12; Timothy Tregarthen, "Garbage by the Bag: Perkasie Acts on Solid Waste," *The Margin,* September/October 1989, p. 17.

Front-End or Retail Disposal Charges

front-end or retail disposal charge
A fee levied on a product at the point of sale designed to encourage source reduction.

An alternative pricing scheme aimed at the MSW problem is the use of a **retail disposal charge.** In contrast to a waste-end charge imposed on *wastes* at the point of *disposal,* a retail disposal charge is levied on *products* at the point of *sale.* Since such a charge is instituted at the pregeneration stage, its objective is to encourage pollution prevention through source reduction.[24] This includes motivating manufacturers to seek out product designs and packaging that are more environmentally responsible.

From a practical perspective, local conditions tend to dictate when a retail disposal charge might be more appropriate than a waste-end charge. For example, a waste-end pricing scheme should be coordinated with a recycling program to deter illegal disposal. Hence, if a community has not instituted such a plan, a better option might be to use a front-end charge. A similar argument applies to communities where there is a predominance of multiunit

---

[24]While source reduction is also possible from using unit pricing, it is not assured. All that can be said with certainty is that unit pricing schemes encourage a decline of waste *disposal.* But this may be achieved through an increase in recycling with no change in the waste generation rate. Conversely, front-end or retail disposal charges directly encourage a decline in waste *generation* by reducing the quantity demanded of a product *before* it enters the waste stream.

FIGURE 17.7

*Modeling a retail
disposal charge to
correct a
consumption
externality: the
market for household
batteries*

The disposal of batteries poses an environmental risk to society because they are made with heavy metals like mercury or cadmium. Battery consumers do not consider the external effects, so the *MPB* effectively overstates the true marginal benefits of consumption. This means that the *MSB* is actually *below* the *MPB*. In the absence of government intervention, equilibrium output is Q_c, determined where *MPB* intersects *MPC*. The efficient output level is lower, determined by the intersection of *MSC* and *MSB* or Q_e. (For simplicity, we assume that no production externalities exist, so *MSC* = *MPC*.) To correct the inefficiency, government can impose a retail disposal charge on batteries at the point of sale equal to the difference between *MSB* and *MPB* at Q_e. We can model the imposition of the charge as a shift up of *MSC* by distance *xy*, resulting in an effective price to the consumer of P_R.

residences, making waste-end fees difficult to implement. Finally, a front-end charge can be used to complement a waste-end charge system to discourage the use of products that yield either large amounts of waste or wastes that pose a particular threat to health or the environment. Examples include such products as motor oil, batteries, and automobile tires.

To better understand the environmental and economic consequences of retail disposal charges, consider the market for household batteries. Batteries are made with heavy metals like mercury or cadmium, so their disposal poses an environmental risk to society. Battery consumers do not consider the external effects, so the *MPB* effectively overstates the true marginal benefits of consumption. This means that the *MSB* is actually *below* the *MPB,* as shown in Figure 17.7.[25] In the absence of government intervention, equilibrium output is determined where *MPB* equals *MPC*, or Q_c. However, the efficient output level is lower, determined by the intersection of *MSC* and *MSB* or Q_e. (For simplicity, we assume that no production externalities exist, so *MSC* = *MPC*.) To correct the inefficiency, government can impose a retail disposal charge on batteries at the point of sale equal to the difference between *MSB*

<hr>

[25]The externality is not modeled as an *MEC* added to the *MPC* because in this case it is *not* associated with the production side of the market. Rather, the externality arises from *consumption* or the demand side. Hence, the externality must be *deducted* from the *MPB* curve to show that the true benefits to society, the *MSB*, are reduced by the amount of the environmental damage. For a more rigorous and detailed analysis of this type of externality, the interested reader is referred to Tresch (1981).

and *MPB* at Q_e. In Figure 17.7, we model the imposition of the charge as a shift up of the *MSC* by distance *xy,* resulting in an effective price to the consumer of P_R.[26]

Retail disposal charges are being used both internationally and domestically. For example, Finland and Norway have imposed these charges on products packaged in nonreturnable containers. The specific aim of these fees is incentive-based—to encourage consumers to move away from such commodities and substitute those that have returnable and reusable containers. Sweden also uses retail disposal charges for a number of products, including batteries made of cadmium or mercury. While part of the objective is to diminish the damage caused by disposal of these products, the charge is also being used to generate revenue.[27] Domestically, retail disposal charges are imposed on a multitude of products by many state governments. Table 17.4 lists some common applications. Most of the target products and materials are those expected to generate high external costs. For example, Maine imposes a $5 charge on major appliances, and Louisiana charges $2 for each tire sold.

Deposit/Refund Systems

deposit/refund system
A two-part pricing scheme that imposes an up-front charge for potential damages caused by improper waste disposal that is reimbursed at the end of the product cycle if proper action is taken to avoid those damages.

An alternative market instrument that can mitigate MSW pollution is a **deposit/refund system,** which is actually a two-part pricing scheme. It imposes an up-front charge for potential damages caused by improper disposal, and it allows for a refund of that charge at the end of the product cycle if the consumer takes proper action to avoid those damages. Typically, the consumer must return the product or its container for recycling or safe disposal. The formal model of this system was presented in detail in Chapter 5, so it is not repeated here. More relevant to this discussion is the conceptual relationship between this instrument and the other two pricing schemes. Notice that the deposit is imposed at the time of purchase exactly like a retail disposal charge. The refund attempts to reduce disposal and encourage recycling much like a waste-end charge.

This innovative economic instrument has gained acceptance both domestically and internationally. In the United States, deposit/refund systems are aimed primarily at beverage containers and lead-acid batteries, as Table 17.5 indicates. Similar applications are common in other countries as well. For example, Denmark, Finland, Norway, Sweden, and The Netherlands all use deposit/refund systems for beverage containers. Some nations have gone a step further or at least are investigating the prospect. Norway has introduced a deposit/refund mechanism on car hulks. New car buyers pay a deposit at the

---

[26]It matters not whether the retail disposal charge is levied on the seller or the buyer of the product, since economic incidence (i.e., the party who ultimately bears the burden of the fee) is not determined by statutory incidence (i.e., the party who is initially charged the fee). For more detail, the reader can consult any good principles of microeconomics text.

[27]See Organisation of Economic Development (1989a), pp. 55–66. It is sometimes argued that the revenue objective tied to retail disposal charges is more important than the incentive goal, since the resulting difference in price is not sufficient to affect purchasing decisions. This is sometimes cited as a drawback of these types of pricing instruments.

TABLE 17.4   State Retail Disposal Taxes

State	Waste	Amount of Tax
California	Tires	$0.25
Florida	Multiple materials	$0.01 per package
Louisiana	Tires	$2.00
Maine	Tires	$1.00
	Major appliances	$5.00
Nebraska	Multiple materials	0.015 percent of sales
New Jersey	Multiple materials	0.0225 percent of sales
North Carolina	Tires	1 percent of price
Oklahoma	Tires	$1.00
Oregon	Tires	$0.50
Rhode Island	Beverages	Wholesale tax of $0.04 per case
	Multiple materials	Sales tax exemption on biodegradable returnable items
Tennessee	Beverages	6 percent of soda receipts and $0.50 per barrel of beer
Utah	Tires	$1.00–2.00
Virginia	Tires	$0.50
	Beverage	0.06 percent of sales
Washington	Tires	$1.00
	Multiple materials	0.015 percent of sales
Wisconsin	Tires	$2.00

Source: Drawn from Tellus Institute, Boston, Mass. (1991), as cited in Frank Ackerman, ''Taxing the Trash Away,'' *Environment,* June 1992, pp. 2-5 and 43. Reprinted with permission of Frank Ackerman.

TABLE 17.5   State Deposit/Refund Programs

State	Product	Amount of Deposit
California	Beverage	$0.02
Connecticut	Beverage	$0.05
	Batteries	$5.00
Delaware	Beverage	$0.05
Iowa	Beverage	$0.05
Massachusetts	Beverage	$0.05
Maine	Batteries	$1.00
	Beverage	$0.03–$0.05
Michigan	Beverage	$0.05
New York	Beverage	$0.05
Oregon	Beverage	$0.02–$0.20
Vermont	Beverage	$0.05
Washington	Batteries	$5.00

Source: Drawn from Tellus Institute, Boston, Mass. (1991) as cited in Frank Ackerman, ''Taxing the Trash Away,'' *Environment,* June 1992, pp. 2-5 and 43. Reprinted with permission of Frank Ackerman.

a deposit/refund mechanism on car hulks. New car buyers pay a deposit at the time of purchase and receive a larger refund if the automobile is returned to a designated recovery site when it is no longer wanted. The Netherlands and Denmark are considering the use of this approach for batteries.[28] Similarly, the United States is contemplating a broader use of deposit/refunds for such commodities as lubricating oil, industrial solvents, and pesticide or fertilizer containers.

Conclusions

Municipal solid wastes—the simple by-products of production and consumption—have become a local public issue in communities everywhere. Today, most agree that former claims of a landfill crisis were exaggerated. Even the famous ''garbage barge'' story of 1987 has been explained as the result of a botched business deal. Nonetheless, the world was listening and in the absence of 20/20 hindsight responded to what it heard. Private citizens began to change their behavior—avoiding products with excess packaging and participating in local recycling programs, and they turned to government for broader solutions.

In retrospect, many argue that people responded to false signals—a crisis that did not exist and unfounded predictions of doom and gloom. This assertion is probably true, at least to a point. However, it is wrong to conclude that there were no solid waste issues to resolve and no environmental risks to manage. Open dumps *had* become a health hazard, and most of society had been ignorant of the potential problems of excess waste generation and poor waste management practices. Having said this, a more relevant question is whether the response itself—both by private citizens and by government, however motivated, was and is appropriate.

In the United States, Congress passed laws to restrict the use of land for waste disposal and to replace the nation's open dumps with modern, sanitary landfills. It then delegated the responsibility for devising local waste management programs to the states, encouraging plans that promoted waste reduction and recycling. The land restrictions and the landfill rulings added costs to local waste management, and some states responded with market instruments that reflected these costs.

What was the result of these policy moves? At this stage, the most accurate assessment is that these efforts have yielded mixed results. Some waste generators are pursuing source reduction activities, while others are illegally disposing of their wastes. Some states and local governments have developed successful, cost-effective recycling centers, while others are struggling with expensive curbside programs that have placed a heavy tax burden on their residents. Add to this the series of debates about the viability of markets for

---

[28]Organisation of Economic Development (1989a), pp. 82–88.

recycled materials. Netting it out, these observations imply that municipal waste policies are still evolving, and public officials at all levels of government need to consider some needed reforms. Much can be learned from observing market responses to regulatory decisions and revisions. Rising prices for waste disposal and gluts of recycled materials are important signals to policy-makers about how and where to make strategic changes. If these signals are not ignored, future policy should approach more efficient and cost-effective solutions to the problem of municipal solid waste.

Summary

- In 1990, containers and packaging accounted for the highest proportion by weight of all discarded products in the U.S. municipal solid waste (MSW) stream. Across all materials, paper and paperboard represented the highest proportion by weight. The fastest growing segment of MSW in the United States is plastics.

- Internationally, the major industrialized nations and the oil-producing countries are among the highest MSW generators. Some of the international differences are attributable to the amount of packaging used by producers. The variations also may reflect cultural preferences, environmental awareness, economic conditions, or government regulations.

- One set of provisions in the Resource Conservation and Recovery Act (RCRA) is concerned with the management and control of nonhazardous wastes, including the municipal solid waste stream. For the most part, this section of the law assigns the responsibility of nonhazardous waste management to states with supervision and support provided by the federal government.

- Under RCRA, states are required to develop their own waste management plans, but these must meet certain requirements to receive federal approval. They also must establish whatever regulatory powers they need to comply with RCRA, such as enacting legislation to meet federal requirements. Some have passed laws requiring recycling by certain entities or calling for local governments to set up recycling centers.

- The federal government must provide financial and technical assistance to states in designing and implementing their waste management plans. It also must encourage states to conserve resources and help them find ways to maximize the use of recoverable resources. The EPA must establish minimum criteria for sanitary landfills and other land disposal sites.

- Although some states have developed waste management plans, the general response rate has been poor. The EPA has begun to actively encourage state authorities to use an integrated waste management system. This system promotes the use of a combination of programs aimed at source reduction, recycling, combustion, and land disposal, in that order.

- Resources are misallocated in private MSW services markets that charge a fixed fee per household or per commercial establishment. Since the fee is the same regardless of the quantity of waste generated at each location, this type of pricing scheme is known as a flat fee pricing system. The inefficiency occurs because the constant price does not properly reflect rising *MPC* and because production of MSW services gives rise to a negative externality.

- A waste-end charge is implemented at the time of disposal based on the quantity of waste generated. Because such a charge varies with the quantity of waste, it provides an incentive to economize on waste generation and avoids the inefficiency of a flat fee system. In practice, programs using waste-end charges are referred to as unit pricing schemes to indicate that prices for MSW services are charged on a per-unit-of-waste basis.

- Retail disposal charges are levied on the product at the point of sale. Since this charge is imposed at the pregeneration stage, its objective is to encourage pollution prevention through source reduction.

- A deposit-refund system imposes an up-front charge for potential damages caused by improper disposal and allows for a refund of that charge at the end of the product cycle if the consumer takes proper action to avoid those damages.

Key Concepts

municipal solid waste (MSW)	unit pricing
product groups	flat rate pricing
materials groups	variable rate pricing
integrated waste management system	''bag-and-tag'' approach
tipping fees	front-end or retail disposal charge
fixed fee or flat fee pricing system	deposit/refund system
back- or waste-end charge	

Review Questions

1. *a.* Summarize a specific municipal solid waste problem in your hometown or one that recently has been reported in the media. Use the specific stages of the waste stream in your discussion.

   b. What policies have been proposed or implemented to address the problem you describe? Analyze these policies from an economic perspective.

2. Using what you have learned about market-based incentives, suggest a policy initiative that would discourage land disposal in the United States.

3. Refer to the Application on New Jersey's recycling program. Identify which elements of the program are command-and-control in approach and which are market-based.

4. Using the information in Application 17.3, compare Germany's Green Dot program to U.S. national initiatives on recycling. In your view, which is likely to be more effective in the long run? Explain.

5. Diagram a general model of MSW management services. Show the simultaneous effect of the federal restrictions on landfills *and* rising consumer

awareness of the benefits of "green packaging." Assuming a private competitive market, predict the effect on the price and quantity of MSW services.

6. Consider the following model of a hypothetical market for MSW management services:

$$MPB = 25 - 2Q$$
$$MPC = 4 + Q$$
$$MEC = 0.5Q,$$

where Q is the number of trash containers per household per month.
   a. Quantitatively determine the effect of the resource misallocation due to:
   (i) the presence of the negative externality;
   (ii) the use of a flat fee pricing system in the presence of a negative externality.
   b. Support your answer to part (a) with a graphical model.
   c. Determine the dollar value of a waste-end charge that would restore efficiency to this market. Explain your answer intuitively.

7. *a.* Contrast the Seattle per-can pricing program with Perkasie's bag-and-tag approach both from an environmental and an economic perspective.
   b. Why might weight-based unit pricing for MSW management be more advantageous than volume-based programs?

Additional Readings

Bailey, Jeff. "Curbside Recycling Soothes the Soul, But Cost Is High." *The Wall Street Journal,* January 19, 1995.

Boerner, Christopher, and Kenneth Chilton. "False Economy: The Folly of Demand-Side Recycling." *Environment* 36, no 1 (January/February 1994), pp. 6–15, 32–33.

Daley, Beth. "Illegal Disposal of Trash Spreads." *Boston Globe,* March 6, 1994.

Erwin, Lewis, and L. Hall Healey Jr. *Packaging and Solid Waste: Management Strategies.* New York: AMACOM, 1990.

Martin, Mary. "Truly Fashionable Recycling: Plastic Bottles Get New Life as Polyester Fiber." *Boston Globe,* March 3, 1994.

Miranda, Marie Lynn; Jess W. Everett; Daniel Blume; and Barbeau A. Roy, Jr. "Market-Based Incentives and Residential Municipal Solid Waste." *Journal of Policy Analysis and Management* 13, no. 4; 1994, pp. 681–98.

Platt, Brenda A.; Neil Seldman; Bernd Granke; and Bernd Mayer. *Garbage in Europe: Technologies, Economics, and Trends.* Washington, D.C.: Institute for Local Self-Reliance, May 1988.

Repetto, Robert; Roger C. Dower; Robin Jenkins; and Jacqueline Geoghegan. *Green Fees: How a Tax Shift Can Work for the Environment and the Economy.* Washington, D.C.: World Resources Institute, 1992.

Thompson, Claudia. *Recycled Papers.* Cambridge, Mass.: The MIT Press, 1992.

CONTROLLING TOXIC CHEMICALS

Production, Use, and Disposal

Toxic substances are extensively regulated in the United States. Air toxics, for example, are controlled under the Clean Air Act. The discharge of hazardous pollutants into waterways is governed by the Clean Water Act, and the Resource Conservation and Recovery Act (RCRA) regulates the hazardous solid waste stream. Notice how all these federal laws deal with the *release* of toxics into the environment. In this chapter, we study legislation aimed at controlling chemical substances *before* they become residuals and enter the waste stream—when they are formulated and produced.

Approximately 5 percent of the U.S. economy is engaged in the production of chemicals and allied products. Over 65,000 chemical substances are produced in this country, with more than 1,000 new ones introduced each year.[1] While this increasing reliance on chemicals has added to the variety, durability, and usefulness of products available to society, there has also been a very real cost. Certain of these chemicals, such as polychlorinated biphenyls (PCBs) and the pesticide dichloro-diphenyl-trichloroethane (DDT), pose a threat to human health and ecosystems. In some cases the risks are not fully understood until long after the damage has been done.

Recognizing the potential risks of chemical usage and the impact of toxic residuals in the waste stream, Congress passed the Federal Insecticide, Fungicide, and Rodenticide Act (FIFRA) and the Toxic Substances Control Act (TSCA). These two laws, each from a different vantage point, control the production, distribution, and consumption of pesticides and other chemicals. By instituting controls before these substances are introduced into commerce, those that pose an unacceptable risk can be restricted in use or even banned. In so doing, the toxicity of the hazardous waste stream should be abated and the associated environmental risks reduced. Notice that this approach is preemptive because it eliminates the need to treat and dispose of some amount

---

[1] U.S. EPA (August 1988), p. 126.

of hazardous residuals. The underlying premise is that the waste stream is part of a larger cycle that originates with the design and development of products. Hence, regulating hazardous substances at the pregeneration phase of the waste stream is an effective way to prevent pollution.

In this chapter, our objectives are to understand the intent of FIFRA and TSCA, to analyze their implementation, and to evaluate their effectiveness using economic criteria and decision rules. To organize our investigation, we begin with an overview of the Federal Insecticide, Fungicide, and Rodenticide Act (FIFRA)—its evolution and its current regulatory structure. Following this presentation, we conduct an analysis of this act and its overall control approach. An analogous treatment is used to study the Toxic Substances Control Act (TSCA). At the conclusion of these two parallel discussions, we conduct a comprehensive analysis of U.S. policies on solid waste and toxic substances that have been the focus of this module. Risk-benefit analysis is the primary approach used in this summary evaluation. An appendix of acronyms is provided at the end of the chapter.

An Overview of U.S. Pesticide Controls: FIFRA

A Brief Retrospective[2]

Congress enacted the Federal Insecticide, Fungicide, and Rodenticide Act (FIFRA) in 1947 and charged the Department of Agriculture with its administration. Its statutory purpose was to control the production, storage, distribution, sale, use, and disposal of all pesticide products. However, its primary aim was to regulate pesticide labeling to protect against fraudulent products. In 1970, the newly established EPA assumed responsibility for FIFRA, and two years later Congress passed amendments to the act as the Federal Environmental Pesticide Control Act. These amendments changed virtually every aspect of the original law, shifting its focus to health and environmental protection. A key revision was the requirement for registration of new pesticides and the reevaluation and reregistration of those already on the market. Pesticide registration continues to be the chief regulatory instrument of federal controls on pesticides.

Over time, further revisions were made—many based on scientific advances or newly developed testing technologies. Part of the reform has been to require more sophisticated test data from registrants to determine if modifications or better safeguards are needed in labeling, packaging, or formulations. Not unlike other major policies, U.S. pesticide initiatives have sometimes proven to be overly ambitious. In fact, of the approximately 600

---

[2]The following section is drawn from U.S. EPA, Office of Pesticides and Toxic Substances (December 1988); U.S. EPA (August 1988), pp. 113–19; and Wolf (1988), p. 154.

pesticides needing reregistration under FIFRA, the EPA had issued registration standards for only about 185 of them by the late 1980s. These standards are important, as each includes a review of available data, a listing of information needed for reregistration, and a statement of the current regulatory position on the pesticide.

In 1988, Congress passed the FIFRA Amendments—the set of rulings currently in force. These revisions improved registration and reregistration procedures and authorized a fee system to help pay for the reregistration process. The amendments also strengthened the EPA's control over the storage, transportation, and disposal of pesticides, including labeling of both the pesticide and its container. Added to the EPA's responsibilities was to regulate the use, disposal, refill, and reuse of pesticide containers. The purpose was to prevent the damages these substances can cause after they enter the waste stream. Congress also rescinded one of the agency's responsibilities—that of accepting stocks of suspended and canceled pesticides and disposing of them at the government's expense. Instead, the EPA can require registrants and distributors to handle a recall. Application 18.1 reports on the disposal dilemma that arose following the U.S. cancellation of ethylene dibromide in 1984.

Controlling New Pesticides through Registration

pesticide registration
Formal listing of a pesticide with the EPA that must be approved based upon a risk-benefit analysis before it can be sold or distributed.

risk-benefit analysis
A decision rule that assesses the risks of an environmental hazard along with the benefits to society of not regulating that hazard.

A major objective of FIFRA is to require the **registration** of all pesticides *before* they can be distributed or sold.[3] Registration is subject to EPA approval based upon a **risk-benefit analysis.** The EPA is to assure that the benefits of using the substance outweigh the associated health and ecological risks. Hence, the law *implicitly* identifies those pesticides associated with unreasonable adverse effects by denying their registration. Based on the law, a pesticide may not be registered if: (1) its composition does not warrant its proposed claims; (2) its labeling does not comply with the law; (3) it will not perform its intended function without causing unreasonable adverse effects on the environment; *or* (4) it cannot be used in widespread practice without generating unreasonable adverse environmental effects. Since FIFRA's original enactment in 1947, over 50,000 pesticides have been registered for use in the United States—most before their risks were fully understood.[4] Advances in risk assessment are helping officials reduce the probability of making uninformed

---

[3]FIFRA defines a pesticide as (1) any substance or mixture intended to prevent, destroy, repel or mitigate any pest; and (2) any substance or mixture intended as a plant regulator (i.e., a substance that alters plant behavior such as growth rate), defoliant (i.e., a substance that removes plant leaves), or desiccant (i.e., a chemical that absorbs moisture). FIFRA Sec.2.(t) and Sec.2.(u).

[4]U.S. EPA (August 1988), p. 115. Today, there are about 25,000 formulated products registered for use in the United States. See U.S. EPA, Office of Pesticides and Toxic Substances (May 1991), p. 2.

Application 18.1

Pesticide Cancellation: The Case of Ethylene Dibromide

In 1948, a new pesticide was introduced to commercial markets—ethylene dibromide (EDB). Its effectiveness was borne out by its extensive use on fruits, vegetables, and stored grain. Over 35 years later, it was learned that EDB caused cancer in laboratory animals and was found to be linked to soil and groundwater contamination. In 1984, the EPA halted most uses of the product. All supplies of the toxic EDB immediately became unusable and unwanted material—effectively becoming part of the hazardous waste stream. Since the EDB cancellation predated the 1988 FIFRA Amendments, the EPA was bound by law to dispose of any of the unused pesticide if requested to do so. It also had to compensate users and manufacturers for any costs incurred from the emergency action.

As a consequence of the cancellation, the EPA was left with a huge stockpile of EDB wastes and no known method of safe disposal. Pending a decision as to how the disposal would be accomplished, the pesticide was held in storage. In 1986, an ominous discovery was made—drums filled with EDB in a Missouri warehouse were found to be leaking. News of the incident alerted the general public to the serious problems of pesticide waste disposal.

The EPA had planned to neutralize the EDB stock through a chemical process that had been tested only in laboratories, but the plan had been delayed by mechanical problems. When the agency attempted to remove the EDB from the leaking drums, which by that time had begun to corrode, toxic vapor emissions were discharged into the atmosphere. The EPA spent $1.5 million before it determined that the chemical treatment it had been considering for EDB was not viable for all formulations. It then looked into incineration that could somehow accommodate the corrosivity of the substance. That option was expected to cost between $6 million and $8 million. As of 1990, all stocks of EDB had finally been disposed of.

In terms of understanding the risks of managing pesticide wastes, there are likely no clearer examples than those that arise when pesticides are canceled on a mass scale. In addition to the EDB suspension, the United States has had to deal with two other emergency cancellations—one for 2,4,5-T/silvex and another for dinoseb. As of 1990, the EPA was still in the process of disposing of dinoseb, an herbicide and crop desiccant it banned in 1986. Expected disposal costs for this pesticide have been estimated at over $100 million. Beyond these emergency actions, the United States has canceled the registrations of 34 pesticides and halted the use of 60 toxic, inert ingredients in pesticide formulations as of 1990. Although the EPA no longer must accept supplies of suspended and canceled pesticides, registrants and distributors have to be prepared to handle a recall. The potential difficulties of finding safe disposal methods for canceled pesticides and the risks of interim storage underscore the importance of risk assessment within the registration process and the need to develop safer, less toxic substitutes.

Source: U.S. Environmental Protection Agency, *Environmental Progress and Challenges: EPA's Update* (Washington, D.C., August 1988), pp. 128–33, 118; U.S. Environmental Protection Agency, *Meeting the Environmental Challenge: EPA's Review of Progress and New Directions in Environmental Protection* (Washington, D.C., December 1990a), pp. 18–20.

registration decisions and prevent the use of any pesticide posing an unreasonable risk to society.

pesticide tolerances
Legal limits on the amount of pesticide remaining as a residue on raw agricultural products or in processed foods.

At the time of registration, the EPA also sets legal limits or **tolerances** on the amount of a pesticide that may remain as a *residue* on raw or processed food without causing an unacceptable health risk. In effect, the registration acts as a license for use, and the tolerances specify the conditions under which that use is approved. Tolerances are enforced by the Food and Drug Administration (FDA) according to the provisions of the Federal Food, Drug, and Cosmetic Act (FFDCA). While seemingly straightforward, a recent decision based on one of the provisions of the FFDCA, now known as the Delaney Clause, has effectively prohibited adding any substance with even a negligible carcinogenic risk to food.[5] The implications of this controversial issue are the subject of Application 18.2.

Controlling Existing Pesticides through Reregistration

pesticide reregistration
The formal reevaluation of a previously licensed pesticide already on the market.

One of the more important aspects of the 1988 FIFRA Amendments are the rulings dealing with the **reregistration** of previously licensed pesticides. As a result of the reevaluation process, many unsafe pesticides have been restricted in use or banned. Examples include agricultural uses of chlordane and virtually all uses of DDT and ethylene dibromide (EDB). As harmful chemicals like these are restricted or eliminated, industries and consumers must find alternative, and presumably less toxic, pesticides. Consequently, some amount of hazardous pollution should be *prevented* instead of having to be remediated after the fact.

In 1988, approximately 600 groups of pesticide active ingredients were targeted for reregistration. Thus far, registration standards have been issued on less than a third of these.[6] The process is a major undertaking, and the 1988 amendments were intended to accelerate what had been an inordinately slow procedure. To expedite the process, deadlines were imposed for the series of tasks needed to complete the reregistration procedure. These tasks are described in a five-phase approach, which is detailed in Table 18.1. The process begins with the EPA listing all pesticide active ingredients needing to be reevaluated. Once done, formal requests are made of registrants to supply updated information on each pesticide, which is then summarized and evaluated by the EPA. The first four phases were scheduled for completion by 1992, with the final phase to be executed by 1997.[7]

Based on original estimates, the nine-year reregistration process should cost about $250 million. To help defray these expenses, fees are charged to

---

[5]Kimm (January/February/March 1993).

[6]The 194 registration standards that have been issued represent approximately 350 active ingredients that account for 85 to 90 percent of the volume of pesticides used in the country. U.S. EPA, Office of Pesticides and Toxic Substances (May 1991), p. 4.

[7]U.S. EPA, Office of Pesticides and Toxic Substances (June 1991).

Application 18.2

Pesticide Residues and the Delaney Clause

One of the provisions of Section 409 of the Federal Food, Drug, and Cosmetic Act (FFDCA), called the Delaney Clause, is perhaps the most controversial piece of environmental legislation ever passed in the U.S. Named after its sponsor, former U.S. Representative James Joseph Delaney of New York, the 1958 law effectively bans the use of any food additive found to cause cancer—no matter how negligible the degree of risk might be. Under Section 409 of FFDCA dealing with processed foods, pesticide residues are considered food additives. Hence, the Delaney Clause directly affects the use of pesticides based upon the residue that remains after processing. As it turns out, the provision has even more far-reaching implications because the EPA has elected to coordinate its decisions on pesticide residues in raw food with those applicable to processed foods. In fact, in a recent federal appeals court decision in July 1992, it was ruled that the EPA cannot allow any pesticide residues in processed food that exceed what is allowed on raw food if the pesticide poses *any* measure of carcinogenic risk—no matter how small.

Part of the EPA's charge is to set a legal limit or *tolerance* on the amount of pesticide residue allowable on raw food and on processed food. These tolerances are specified at the time of pesticide registration. Some of the controversy associated with the Delaney Clause arises because of a statute in Section 409 called the "flow-through" provision. In essence, this provision says that processed foods will be considered safe if the residues remaining are not in excess of what has been established for raw foods under Section 408. Because of the relationship between these two sections in the FFDCA, the EPA coordinates its policies on setting tolerances for residues on raw food with those applicable to processed foods. Through this "coordination policy," as it is called, the EPA will not approve the use of a pesticide for use on raw foods under Section 408, if this use could result in a violation under Section 409 for processed foods.

While all of this is fairly complicated, there seems to be some logic to this approval system. However, the problem is that some pesticides concentrate during processing, and the resulting concentration may cause the remaining residue to exceed the approved tolerance level for raw foods. If so, the pesticide then becomes subject to separate approval under Section 409 and the Delaney Clause. Thus, if the pesticide is associated with even the smallest measure of carcinogenic risk, its use will be banned. It will be prohibited from use not only for processed food, but because of EPA's "coordination policy," for raw food as well—even though the carcinogenic risk may be unrelated to the concentration.

This coordination policy has come under fire, since tolerance levels under Section 408 are supposed to be set using risk-benefit analysis, unlike those under Section 409 which, because of the Delaney Clause, are to be risk-based. Nonetheless, the effect of the EPA's coordination policy coupled with the recent court interpretation of Delaney is that pesticides with negligible carcinogenic risks will be banned from use if they concentrate during processing. Paradoxically, other pesticides with higher carcinogenic risks may be allowed for use on raw foods because if they do not concentrate during processing, they do not require a Section 409 ruling. Hence, the court's ruling can hinder the use of safer pesticides and can therefore have far-reaching effects on the world's food supply—arguments presented by the EPA. Nonetheless, the court's decision still stands based upon the law as written. Effectively, the courts have placed the onus of any needed legislative changes on Congress. According to the courts, if Congress wants the EPA to use something other than a zero-risk standard when setting these residue tolerances, then Congress has to change the law.

In addition to these legislative and policy complications, there is also contention about the reliability of data on the amount of pesticide residues

Application 18.2 (continued)

Pesticide Residues in Domestic Foods, by Commodity Group, 1978–1991

	Commodity*				
Year	Grains and Grain Products	Milk, Dairy Products, and Eggs	Fish, Shellfish, and Meats	Fruits	Vegetables
1978	54%	43%	80%	48%	34%
1979	54	47	81	58	35
1980	52	36	71	53	40
1981	43	32	77	56	37
1982	42	34	72	49	36
1983	42	32	61	52	41
1984	54	31	75	38	33
1985	52	22	65	36	34
1986	60	21	68	57	39
1987	57	24	73	50	37
1988	49	19	72	51	35
1989	44	13	65	44	32
1990	46	9	68	49	38
1991	42	22	42	51	32

*Percent of samples with residues found.

Source: Food and Drug Administration, "Food and Drug Administration Pesticide Program Residues in Foods," *J. Assoc. Off. Anal. Chem.*, vols. 71–74, 1988, 1989, 1990, 1991; N. J. Yess, M. G. Houston, and E. L. Gunderson, "Food and Drug Administration Pesticide Monitoring of Foods: 1978–1982," *J. Assoc. Off. Anal. Chem* 74 (1991a), pp. 265–72; N. J. Yess, M. G. Houston, and E. L. Gunderson, "Food and Drug Administration Pesticide Monitoring of Foods: 1983–1986," *J. Assoc. Off. Anal. Chem.* 74 (1991b), pp. 273–80, cited in Council on Environmental Quality, *Environmental Quality, 23rd Annual Report* (Washington, D.C.: U.S. Government Printing Office, January 1993), Table 100, p. 424.

on food products *and* the scientific assessment of the associated risks. The table above presents data on the percentage of samples of major food groups found to contain pesticide residues. These data suggest the need for ongoing study of pesticide residues and their associated health effects. However, as the pesticide controversy has come to the forefront, questions have been raised about the reliability of these data and other information obtained from pesticide manufacturers. In fact, in 1991 the EPA stated that data obtained through the National Food Basket Survey appeared to be unreliable, an observation that warranted investigation. After careful inquiry, indictments were filed against a laboratory executive and other staff members for falsifying data submitted through the survey. Of course, once this happened, the results of studies that had used these data were discredited.

Exacerbating the data problems is uncertainty about the methods used to assess the risks of pesticide residues on foods. Some scientists have argued that the reliance on dose-response models, which are based on elevated exposures to laboratory animals, may generate conclusions that inflate the risk measure. For example, one of the authors of a recently released University of California study stated, "you may be killing cells and causing cancer from the high dose, not the chemical." On the opposite side of the debate are those who argue that the EPA's current policy for setting tolerance levels seriously underestimates pesticide risks. These critics point to such issues as the agency's lack of attention to so-called inert ingredients in pesticide products and the absence of consideration for multiple effects that arise when more than one pesticide is used on the same crop.

Application 18.2 (concluded)

This scientific controversy, the Delaney Clause, and a recent report by the National Academy of Sciences (NAS) on the vulnerability of children to pesticide risks have prompted officials to rethink the nation's policy position on pesticides. While the United States maintains that current food supplies are safe, officials want to reaffirm and strengthen national efforts to assure the protection of human health. Given the complex issues of pesticide usage and the significance of the implica-tions, this is one public policy process that will likely take years to resolve.

Sources: Victor J. Kimm, ''The Delaney Clause Dilemma,'' *EPA Journal,* January/February/March 1993; Council on Environmental Quality, *Environmental Quality, 23rd Annual Report* (Washington, D.C.: U.S. Government Printing Office, January 1993), p. 87, Table 100, p. 424; Marilyn Chase, ''Scientists Term Food-Pesticide Cancer Risk Overrated,'' *The Wall Street Journal,* October 9, 1992; Sonia L. Nazario, ''EPA Under Fire for Pesticide Standards,'' *The Wall Street Journal,* February 17, 1989.

TABLE 18.1   **The Five-Phase Reregistration Process under the 1988 FIFRA Amendments**

Phase	Timetable	Description
I. Listing of active ingredients	10 months from enactment	The EPA publishes lists of pesticide active ingredients that are subject to reregistration and inquires whether registrants intend to seek registration.
II. Declaration of intent and identification of studies	Completed in 1990	Registrants are to respond to EPA requests and to identify any missing or inadequate scientific studies needed to satisfy data requirements under the revised law. The first installment of the reregistration fee is due.
III. Summarization of studies	Completed in October 1990	Registrants must summarize existing studies to expedite EPA's review process, commit to generate or share the cost of generating new data if studies are not available, and pay the final installment of the reregistration fee.
IV. EPA review and data call-ins	Completed in July 1992	The EPA must complete its review of registrants' submissions under Phase II and III and issue whatever requirements are necessary to complete all data requirements.
V. Reregistration decisions	To be completed in 1997	The EPA conducts a comprehensive investigation of all data submitted and decides whether to reregister the pesticide.

Sources: Federal Environmental Pesticide Control Act, Sec.4; U.S. EPA, Office of Pesticides and Toxic Substances, *For Your Information: Pesticide Reregistration* (Washington, D.C., June 1991).

registrants which are expected to yield about $14 million in revenues annually. For every active ingredient that a registrant plans to use on a major food or animal feed crop, reregistration fees are $150,000. For active ingredients *not* used for major food or feed crops, the fee is between $50,000 and $100,000. There is also an annual maintenance fee for each pesticide product, which is estimated to be about $425 per product for the first 50 products and $100 each after that.[8]

Are these high costs worth the effort? The fact is, controlling pesticides poses a tough problem for policy-makers and for society as a whole. As a group of substances, pesticides can contribute positively to agriculture and other industries and in so doing to the well-being of society. Yet exposure to these substances can harm the ecology and cause serious health problems like cancer, birth defects, and neurological impairments. Both sets of factors need to be considered in a risk-benefit analysis. Hence, the $250 million expense to administer the reregistration process may be warranted if it facilitates government's ability to conduct such an analysis and properly manage whatever risks are justified by the associated social benefits.

Analysis of FIFRA

Risk-Benefit Analysis under FIFRA

No pesticide may be distributed or sold unless it has been registered with the EPA, and registration is denied for any substance associated with ''unreasonable adverse effects on the environment.'' Thus, the statutory definition of this phrase implicitly identifies the standard used to evaluate pesticides:

> The term ''unreasonable adverse effects on the environment'' means any unreasonable risk to man or the environment, taking into account the economic, social, and environmental costs and benefits of the use of any pesticide.[9]

Notice that unlike most U.S. environmental laws, FIFRA explicitly calls for a consideration of the costs and benefits of pesticide use in determining unreasonable risk. This clearly suggests the need for risk-benefit analysis. That is, the risks of using a pesticide measured in terms of health and ecological effects should be weighed against the associated benefits such as increased crop yields.

It turns out, however, that risks are the dominant factor in the EPA's registration decisions. For *new* pesticides, risks are evaluated from data on health and environmental effects submitted by manufacturers as part of the registration application. Hence, the onus of proving that risks are not ''unreasonable'' lies with the producer. If risks are found to be negligible, the EPA

---

[8]U.S. EPA, Office of Pesticides and Toxic Substances (December 1988), p. 5.
[9]FIFRA, Sec.2.(bb).

generally assumes that benefits exist based upon the manufacturer's willingness to absorb the high cost of registration. If risks are found to be *greater* than negligible, the manufacturer typically has to formulate a risk reduction strategy or show that the benefits exceed the risks.[10] When the EPA conducts a special review of an *existing* pesticide, a formal benefit analysis is done. In these instances, benefits are measured by determining biological effects, such as changes in agricultural yields, and then these effects are monetized to obtain an economic value.[11]

Problems in Risk Assessment

At least in principle, the nation's approach to pesticide control appears to have merit. So, why is U.S. pesticide policy the subject of such intense debate? Probably the best answer is that there is much uncertainty about the associated risks despite the widespread exposure. Many scientists question the EPA's methods of assessing pesticide risks. Some argue that the risks are underestimated, citing the agency's lack of attention to inert ingredients or the cumulative effects from using multiple pesticides in combination. Others assert that the opposite is true, claiming that findings from animal bioassays overstate the potential harm to humans. In its defense, the EPA contends that it has neither the staff nor the financial resources to undertake a complete reevaluation of all pesticides in use, even if there were consensus about appropriate risk assessment procedures. Beyond these issues, there is also concern about how tougher pesticide controls would affect agricultural productivity. Without viable pesticide substitutes, there could be serious implications for world food supplies.

A New Policy Direction

In 1993, a report by the National Academy of Sciences (NAS) triggered what appears to be a major shift in U.S. pesticide policy and perhaps a resolution to at least some of the questions. What the NAS found was that America's children are not being sufficiently protected from pesticides risks by U.S. policy. At the core of this assessment is that the smaller size of children and their diets make them more vulnerable to pesticide risks. Almost immediately, the Clinton administration announced its intention to develop a new pesticide plan—a joint effort by the EPA, the FDA, and the U.S. Department of Agriculture. One of the proposed provisions is to make a health-based standard the

---

[10]Generally, manufacturers try to reduce the risks or withdraw the registration application. U.S. General Accounting Office (GAO) (March 1991), pp. 3, 9.

[11]Such an assessment also may be conducted if the EPA wishes to cancel a registration on an emergency basis. One benefit assessment method used is called partial budgeting, which uses the value of lost crop yield plus the cost of alternative pest control methods. Another method uses agricultural modeling to estimate changes in crop prices. See U.S. GAO (March 1991), pp. 3–4.

**Integrated Pest
Management (IPM)**
A combination of
control methods
aimed at encouraging
more selective use of
pesticides and greater
reliance on natural
deterrents.

major factor in pesticide review with less consideration allowed for the economic implications for farmers. Officials claim that the objective of the new plan is to *reduce* pesticide use—not just regulate it. The goal is to promote what is known as **Integrated Pest Management (IPM)**—a collection of methods to foster more selective use of pesticides and greater reliance on natural deterrents. In support of this objective is an incentive-based proposal to encourage chemical manufacturers to develop alternative products.[12]

Notice that this proposal has a much different focus than current U.S. policy. If it succeeds, the United States will embrace a more preventive approach to the pesticide problem. Rather than adding more restrictions on how these substances can be used, the new program would encourage pesticide reduction—a more direct means of mitigating environmental risk.

An Overview of U.S. Legislation on Toxic Substances: TSCA

The Policy Response to Chemical Risks[13]

Chemicals are an integral part of modern society and represent a major industry in the U.S. economy. Used properly, most of these substances contribute positively to the quality of life. Yet exposure to chemicals can pose significant risks to society. Unfortunately, some of the health risks of chemical exposure, particularly long-term and permanent effects, were not known until *after* these substances had been introduced into commerce and become widely used.[14] Responding to the problem, Congress enacted the Toxic Substances Control Act (TSCA) in 1976. One of the act's primary objectives is to identify and control chemical substances that present a risk to health or the environment *before* they are introduced into commerce. By confronting the environmental and health risks of chemicals at the premanufacture stage, the government has an opportunity to prevent pollution rather than having to correct problems after the fact. TSCA also provides a way to monitor the risks

---

[12]Associated Press (September 21, 1993). For a discussion of other incentives to reduce pesticide use, see Williams (May/June 1992).

[13]Much of the following discussion is drawn from U.S. EPA, Office of Toxic Substances (June 1987), pp. 2–8 and U.S. EPA (August 1988), pp. 112–27.

[14]An important example is the chemical group polychlorinated biphenyls (PCBs), substances formerly used as insulators in electrical transformers because of their resistance to heat and electrical charges and as lubricants and dye carriers in paints, inks, and dyes. The toxicity of PCBs was not known until after these substances had leaked out into the environment and began to accumulate in the tissues of animals and fish, thereby entering the food chain. The discovery led to a 1976 ban on their manufacture, processing, distribution, and use in the United States, except in completely enclosed electrical equipment (U.S. EPA, August 1988, p. 120).

TSCA inventory
A database of all chemicals commercially produced or processed in the U.S.

of chemicals already on the market and to take action as needed. Since so little was known about most of the chemical substances in use, Congress also authorized the compilation of an inventory of all chemicals commercially produced or processed in the United States between 1975 and 1979. Using data collected from manufacturers and importers, the government published the first **TSCA inventory** in 1979, which contained information on more than 62,000 chemicals.

TSCA gives the EPA authority to gather information on chemical risks from producers, to require testing on existing chemicals as needed, and to review most newly introduced chemicals before they are manufactured and made available for use on a broad scale. Depending on its findings, the EPA takes appropriate action. The regulatory response can range from requiring warning information during production and distribution to banning the chemical's manufacture. Risk controls may be imposed at any stage in the chemical's life cycle, including its manufacture, processing, distribution in commerce, usage, and disposal.

To avoid the inefficiency and potential inconsistency of dual controls, TSCA acknowledges and accounts for the mandates of other laws dealing with toxic substances and the agencies that implement them. Some of these are listed in Table 18.2. Under the law, the EPA is to coordinate its control activities with those of other agencies such as the Food and Drug Administration (FDA), the U.S. Department of Agriculture (USDA), and the Occupational Safety and Health Administration (OSHA). As a chemical risk is discovered, the EPA must consider whether other agencies have investigated that risk, and if so, it must determine if existing laws adequately address the problem. In fact, the EPA must use other laws it administers to reduce risk, such as the Clean Water Act, the Clean Air Act, and RCRA, *before* implementing TSCA's provisions. Finally, eight product categories are explicitly exempted from TSCA, most of which are regulated under other laws.[15]

new chemical
Any substance not listed in the TSCA inventory of existing chemicals.

pre-manufacture notice (PMN)
Official notification made to the EPA by a chemical producer about its intent to produce or import a new chemical.

Controlling the Introduction of New Chemicals

Unlike the nation's pesticide law, TSCA does *not* use a registration procedure to control toxic chemical use. Instead, it requires manufacturers to notify the government at least 90 days before they intend to produce or import any **new chemical**—one that is not listed in the national inventory of existing chemicals. The notification is made to the EPA via a **premanufacture notice (PMN),** which provides information about the chemical's characteristics, the expected exposure to workers, its intended use, and the health and ecological effects. Upon receipt of the PMN, the EPA has a 90-day review period to evaluate the risks and respond. If the risks are too high or, in the absence of full information, are *expected* to be too high, the EPA may restrict usage of

---

[15]The eight product groups are tobacco, nuclear material, firearms and ammunition, food, food additives, drugs, cosmetics, and pesticides.

TABLE 18.2   **Selected Laws Governing the Control of Substances Exempted under TSCA**

Legislation	Agency	Substance/Control
Atomic Energy Act	Nuclear Regulatory Commission	Nuclear waste disposal, nuclear energy production
Federal Insecticide, Fungicide and Rodenticide Act	Environmental Protection Agency	Pesticides
Federal Food, Drug, and Cosmetic Act	Food and Drug Administration	Foods, food additives, drug additives, cosmetics
Safe Drinking Water Act	Environmental Protection Agency	Controls contaminants in drinking water supplies
Occupational Safety and Health Act	Occupational Safety and Health Administration	Controls hazards found in the workplace
Clean Air Act	Environmental Protection Agency	Controls the emissions of hazardous air pollutants
Clean Water Act	Environmental Protection Agency	Controls the discharge of hazardous pollutants into surface waters
Hazardous Materials Transportation Act	Department of Transportation	Regulates the transport of hazardous materials
Marine Protection, Research, and Sanctuaries Act	Environmental Protection Agency	Regulates waste disposal at sea
Resource Conservation and Recovery Act	Environmental Protection Agency	Regulates hazardous waste generation, storage, transport, treatment, and disposal
Comprehensive Environmental Response, Compensation, and Liability Act	Environmental Protection Agency	Provides for cleanup of inactive and abandoned hazardous waste sites
Surface Mining Control and Reclamation Act	Department of the Interior	Regulates environmental aspects of mining and reclamation

Source: U.S. Environmental Protection Agency, Office of Solid Waste, *Solving the Hazardous Waste Problem: EPA's RCRA Program* (Washington, D.C., November 1986).

the chemical permanently or, if more data is needed for a complete risk analysis, temporarily. The determination of unreasonable risk is based upon test results of exposure effects such as cancer or birth defects.[16]

Over 18,000 PMN's have been submitted to the EPA since 1979. Of this total, the EPA has restricted or prohibited the production or use of more than

---

[16]U.S. EPA, Office of Pollution Prevention (October 1991), p. 142; U.S. EPA, Office of Toxic Substances (June 1987), pp. 3–4. TSCA, Sec.4.(b)(2)(A).

500 chemicals pending further information. Over 350 additional chemicals have been controlled through voluntary agreements with producers, and almost 1,000 have been withdrawn or suspended from the review process by manufacturers in response to EPA concerns. In the aggregate, over 10 percent of the chemicals submitted for review since 1979 have been suspended, restricted, or withdrawn from production or use.[17]

Controlling Existing Chemicals in Use

Other provisions of TSCA deal with evaluating the risks of over 65,000 chemicals *already* on the market. The law requires manufacturers to notify the EPA if any chemical is found to present a substantial risk to human health or the environment. When this occurs, the EPA's Office of Toxic Substances evaluates the information and takes action, ranging from labeling requirements to outright bans. Between 1980 and 1991, about 5,000 of these notifications were received by the EPA. In more than 550 instances, producers have altered their processes to reduce the release of the substances, and the use of the chemical was temporarily or permanently halted. One of the more recent and significant instances of such an action is the three-stage phaseout of asbestos—a harmful substance that will be completely banned from manufacture, processing, and distribution by August 25, 1997.[18]

Analysis of TSCA

Risk-Benefit Analysis under TSCA

TSCA's statutory objectives are to obtain data on chemical risks and to regulate chemicals posing an "unreasonable risk" to human health or the environment. Interestingly, "unreasonable risk" is not explicitly defined in the law. However, a House of Representatives report sheds some light on what is implied, stating that the determination of "unreasonable risk" involves the following:[19]

> . . . balancing the probability that harm will occur and the magnitude and severity of that harm against the effect of proposed regulatory action on the availability to society of the benefits of the substance or mixture.

Notice how this determination supports the use of risk-benefit analysis in the approval process—just as is the case for pesticides. Like FIFRA, this act empowers the EPA to ban or restrict the use of toxic chemicals that do not pass

[17]U.S. EPA, Office of Pollution Prevention (October 1991), p. 142.

[18]U.S. EPA (August 1988), p. 114; *Federal Register* 54:29460–29513 (July 12, 1989), as cited in U.S. EPA, Office of Pollution Prevention (October, 1991), p. 143.

[19]Dominguez (1977), Section 5, p. 5.9

the risk-benefit test. Such actions should effectively encourage the substitution of alternative, less dangerous substances, which in turn mitigates the toxicity of the hazardous waste stream.

A major difference between TSCA and FIFRA is the process used for review of new substances. While FIFRA calls for extensive test data as part of a complex registration process, TSCA requires only a 90-day advance notice of intent to produce a new chemical. Testing is done only upon formal request by the EPA. It has been argued that this regulatory difference properly reflects the relative magnitude of risks between toxic substances and pesticides. Pesticides generally pose a greater risk, since they are biologically active. Hence, the more stringent controls and higher costs of introducing a new pesticide into commerce may be justified by the inherently greater risk potential.[20]

Bias against New Chemical Introductions[21]

A common observation about TSCA's effectiveness is that the EPA has been slow to develop data on *existing* chemicals despite the evidence that such information is critical. Ironically, much of the delay seems to be caused by how TSCA is written, imposing command-and-control procedures that are extremely time-intensive and possibly superfluous. For example, the EPA literally must write a new regulation each time it wishes to initiate testing on a chemical substance. Another contributing factor is the agency's current use of a single chemical review process rather than one aimed at a group of similar substances. Overall, the analysis of *existing* chemicals is highly complex and bogged down with time-intensive procedures—markedly different than the relatively straightforward rules in place for reviewing *new* substances. The result? Not only do these regulations delay the development of an important database, they also create a bias against the introduction of new chemicals. The government is much more efficient in its testing of new substances than it is for those already on the market. Consequently, chemical producers wishing to avoid such procedures and the associated costs can continue to sell existing and possibly more dangerous substances. Hence, certain of TSCA's rulings appear to generate the perverse outcome of deterring the development of new, safer chemicals.

A New Policy Direction[22]

Recognizing the weaknesses in certain of TSCA's provisions, the United States is in the process of revising the TSCA program. Although TSCA's premanufacture rulings for new chemicals have been effective in encouraging

---

[20]Shapiro (1990), pp. 213–14.

[21]This section is drawn from Shapiro (1990), pp. 223–24, 232–36.

[22]This discussion is drawn from U.S. EPA (December 1990b), as cited in U.S. EPA Office of Pollution Prevention (October, 1991), p. 145.

**Product
Stewardship
Rulemaking**
A proposal that
would require
chemical producers to
share risk
information with
their customers and
to conduct hazard
evaluations on
substances in use.

substitution of safer chemicals for toxic ones, there has been less success in fostering the same activity for existing chemicals. Among the proposals being considered is a **Product Stewardship Rulemaking.** If effected, the ruling would require chemical producers to share risk information with their customers and to conduct hazard evaluations on the substances their customers use. Notice that manufacturers would be held more accountable for the risks associated with their products and required to initiate a formal risk communication with buyers. The anticipated outcome is that manufacturers will be encouraged to find less toxic substitute products when human or ecological exposure is significant.

**multimedia,
multichemical
approaches**
Proposed regulatory
procedures that
would replace single
chemical regulatory
actions.

Proposals such as these are part of an overall plan to revitalize the TSCA program and replace single chemical procedures with **multimedia, multichemical approaches.** This change should lessen the procedural difficulties that now hinder the agency's review of existing chemicals. If successful, the bias against new chemical introductions should be reduced or eliminated, and the nation's inventory of chemicals in use can be more efficiently maintained.

An Economic Analysis of U.S. Solid Waste and Toxics Policy

National policy on toxic chemicals is inexorably linked to controls on solid waste. As we have observed, FIFRA and TSCA attempt to control the production and use of potentially harmful substances *before* they are released into the environment. If such initiatives are successful, there is less risk when these materials enter the waste stream. Given the connection, it is appropriate to evaluate the allocation of resources to both approaches and determine if the allocation makes sense from a risk management perspective. While there are many factors to consider, the major issues can be addressed by examining the evidence on the costs and benefits of these policy efforts.

Cost Analysis of U.S. Solid Waste and Toxic Control Policies[23]

On the cost side of the issue, much attention has been drawn to the enormous expenditures associated with implementing RCRA and Superfund. Given the magnitude and complexity of the problems addressed by these laws, high costs are not surprising. The issue is whether or not the costs are justified by the benefits accruing to society. As we suggested in Chapter 16, the benefit-based approach of both of these laws coupled with the lack of market incentives suggests that the high costs of implementing these laws may not be defensible on economic grounds. To accommodate a broader objective, we now use a

---

[23]The following discussion is drawn mainly from U.S. EPA, Office of Policy, Planning, and Evaluation (December 1990).

TABLE 18.3   **Pollution Control Costs for U.S. Solid Waste and Chemicals Programs** ($1986 millions)

Program	1972	1980	1987	1995†	2000†
RCRA total	$8,436	$13,612	$18,409	$32,468	$38,055
Nonhazardous solid waste	8,436	13,612	16,683	20,338	22,302
Hazardous solid waste	*	*	1,725	9,210	12,062
Underground storage tanks	*	*	1	2,920	3,691
CERCLA (Superfund)	*	*	683	4,690	8,093
Solid waste total	$8,436	$13,162	$19,092	$37,158	$46,148
TSCA	*	429	365	1,119	1,234
FIFRA	92	461	453	1,353	1,658
Chemicals total	$ 92	$ 889	$ 818	$ 2,472	$ 2,892

Notes:
*The program was not in existence.
†Projected costs.

Source: U.S. Environmental Protection Agency, Office of Policy, Planning, and Evaluation. *Environmental Investments: The Cost of a Clean Environment: A Summary* (Washington, D.C., December 1990), Table 3-4, p. 3-4; Table 3-5, p. 3-5.

different perspective and evaluate these costs *relative* to those associated with TSCA and FIFRA. Ultimately, we want to determine if the comparison makes sense in terms of the social benefits each set of laws is expected to achieve.

Direct costs associated with U.S solid waste and toxic control policy for selected years are presented in Table 18.3.[24] The annualized dollar values represent costs incurred by *all* economic sectors—the private sector, the EPA, other federal agencies, and state and local governments. All dollar values are expressed in millions of 1986 dollars.[25] Notice that there are two major cost categories for solid wastes, those associated with RCRA and those dealing with CERCLA or Superfund. The data for RCRA are further delineated by specific sets of provisions, that is, those for nonhazardous solid waste, those for hazardous waste, and the rulings for underground storage tanks. Cost data on chemical control policy are separated into those associated with toxic substances under TSCA and those for pesticides governed under FIFRA.

Solid Waste Control Costs.   Over the period shown in Table 18.3, the aggregate cost data on solid waste controls exhibit a strong positive trend, rising

---

[24]The ideal cost measure would be one that captures both the explicit and implicit costs to society. Since implicit costs are not available, we use the second-best approach of examining explicit or direct costs, recognizing that the magnitude likely undervalues the true social costs.

[25]These pollution control costs are estimates based on full implementation of federal regulations, using survey data on historical expenditures for years up to 1987 and *ex ante* estimates of forthcoming regulations not in place as of 1987.

from approximately $8.4 billion in 1972 to $19.1 billion in 1987—an increase of 126 percent for the 15-year period. Based on projections, this trend is expected to continue at least until the year 2000. For the most part, this general rise in costs reflects the strengthening of the U.S. policy position since the mid-1970s, particularly for hazardous wastes. Consider, for example, the high costs of implementing the "cradle-to-grave" approach mandated by RCRA—a financial commitment that was increased by the rulings of the 1984 Amendments. By 1987, national costs of controlling hazardous wastes had grown to $1.7 billion, and the projections indicate continued growth. These costs are forecasted to be $9.2 billion by 1995—an increase of over 400 percent from the 1987 level, and they are predicted to rise to $12.1 billion by the turn of the century. A similar trend is shown for the costs of regulating underground storage tanks. Notice that expenditures were $1 million in 1987 but are projected to reach nearly $3.7 billion by the year 2000.

Control costs are also on the rise for nonhazardous waste, though the trend is much more gradual. Federal laws on nonhazardous wastes have been in effect for a longer period of time and have undergone fewer revisions than those governing hazardous wastes. Furthermore, although these costs consistently represent the largest allocation of funding for any solid waste program, the great majority of them are incurred by local governments and private entities with only a small proportion directly linked to federal laws.

Superfund costs pale in comparison to those associated with RCRA, but the growth rate is higher than for any other solid waste program. Looking back at Table 18.3, notice that costs to fully implement the Superfund program in the year 2000 are expected to reach $8 billion—nearly 12 times the expenditure in 1987. In relative terms, the proportion of total solid waste control costs allocated to Superfund is expected to rise steadily from 3.6 percent in 1987 to a projected 17.5 percent in 2000. There is, however, considerable debate about the accuracy of Superfund cost projections.

Although the EPA's cost estimates for the Superfund program are based on many factors, none of these is certain. One of the key elements affecting the projections is the number of sites to be remediated. The Office of Technology Assessment (OTA) argues that as many as 10,000 sites will be placed on the National Priorities List (NPL)—much higher than the EPA's estimate of 2,000. Based on this projection, the OTA reports that it may take 50 years to clean up the 10,000 sites, with aggregate costs reaching as much as $100 billion.[26] Another uncertain data point is the expected cost of cleaning up each site. Such per unit estimates are averages that do not capture the variability across thousands of sites throughout the nation. If the EPA's estimate of $25 million per remedial action is used and if the OTA's projection of 10,000 NPL sites is accurate, aggregate costs could be as high as $250 billion.[27] Finally,

---

[26]U.S. Congress, Office of Technology Assessment (OTA) (1985), p. 3.

[27]There are many estimates that do not support the EPA's findings. For a summary of some of these projections, consult U.S. Congress, OTA (1985), Table 3-1, p. 62.

there is a common assertion that most Superfund cost projections are under-valued because they typically do not include litigation costs, which are expected to be significant.

Chemical Control Costs.   Referring again to Table 18.3, notice that aggregate control costs for both FIFRA and TSCA are much smaller than those incurred for solid wastes. However, they do exhibit a strong growth pattern. Total expenditures show a dramatic increase from $92 million in 1972 to nearly nine times that level, or $818 million, by 1987. Projected costs are expected to rise, though the growth rate should moderate somewhat.

On a less aggregated level, the growth rate of costs is fairly consistent for the two national programs under TSCA and FIFRA. Control expenditures under TSCA are directly related to the increasing number of premanufacture notices (PMNs) received each year. Since 1982, these have averaged over 1,000 per year—much higher than the number submitted in the 1970s and early 1980s. Projections indicate that this increase in new chemical introductions will continue. National controls on pesticides have a much longer history, dating back to 1947. Rising costs to implement FIFRA reflect increasingly tougher laws on registration, reregistration, and safety requirements mandated through recent revisions. The EPA anticipates that private costs will continue to rise as monies are allocated to research and development, cancellations and suspensions of pesticides, and compliance with more stringent farmworker safety and pesticide applicator requirements.

In sum, the costs of U.S. policy on solid waste and toxic substances are significant and rising over time. It is also true that the rate of increase is higher than for any other major environmental program. Based on EPA estimates, total expenditures for solid waste grew by nearly 67 percent from 1985 to 1990 and for chemicals by about 104 percent in the same period. These are much higher than the comparable growth rates for air and water control costs at 19 percent and 28 percent respectively. These observations may mean that standard-setting and the selection of policy instruments to execute solid waste and toxics control have missed the mark—at least from an efficiency perspective. Indeed this assessment has been suggested by some. However, such an assertion is unwarranted without considering whether these relatively high costs are justified by comparable levels of social benefits.

Benefits of U.S. Solid Waste and Toxic Substance Control Policies

As the government launches initiatives to control solid wastes and toxic substances, society's risk of exposure to these hazards should be reduced and the accompanying adverse effects should decline. In theory, the associated benefits can be assessed by measuring and monetizing the reduction in damages to human health and the ecology. Unfortunately, however, no comprehensive benefit analysis has been undertaken for the major U.S. programs on solid wastes and toxics. Even *specific* benefit measures are lacking. According to a recent article, of the tens of thousands of chemicals registered with the EPA, health studies have been conducted on only about 10,000, and of these, only about 1,000 have been studied for acute effects.[28] There is an even greater void in formal assessments of ecological benefits. These have particular relevance to Superfund, given its emphasis on compensation for damages to natural resources.[29] Why has so significant an issue escaped the rigors of formal analysis?

Part of the explanation is that national policy on solid waste and toxics is not as well established as air and water quality controls. The United States got a late start in initiating these policies, and there were long delays in implementation once the rulings were in place.[30] Beyond the timing issues, it is also true that certain of the expected benefits of these initiatives are difficult if not impossible to identify. Consider, for example, the manifest program under RCRA. An important expected benefit is the reduction in damages due to a lower incidence of illegal hazardous waste disposal. But it is not possible to measure a decrease in the number of illegal disposals when such activity is not observable. Even those data points that *are* observable are difficult to measure given the sheer magnitude of the relevant variables. There are nearly 36,000 identified CERCLIS sites, tens of thousands of registered chemicals, over 25,000 pesticide products in use, 5 to 6 million underground storage tanks, 500 hazardous waste land disposal facilities, and 16,000 municipal landfills.[31] These statistics help to explain the uncertainty in even defining the extent of the problem, much less assessing the progress achieved by policy.

Using Comparative Risk Analysis to Assess Benefits.   In the absence of quantitative benefit measures, **comparative risk analysis** can be used to gain some insight about expected social benefits. By examining how the risks of exposure to various environmental hazards compare with one another, we can make inferences about the *relative* benefits that accrue to society from regulating these hazards. These qualitative inferences can shed some light on whether or not the associated control costs are justified, assuming that risk-based priorities guide the nation's policy agenda. In this context, the objective is to compare the benefits of solid waste policies and those of chemical control policies to alternative mandates by analyzing the risks these regulations attempt to mitigate. Two EPA studies of risk ranking have been conducted in

comparative risk analysis
A decision rule that evaluates relative risk, also referred to as risk-risk analysis.

---

[28]Stranahan (February/March 1990).

[29]For more specific information on the nature of ecological risks, see U.S. EPA, Region 5 (May 1991).

[30]Recall that although FIFRA was enacted in 1947, it did not address environmental issues until its revision in 1972.

[31]Williams (May/June 1992); U.S. EPA (August 1988), pp. 52–53.

TABLE 18.4   **Risk Rankings for Selected Environmental Problems**

	Expert Risk Ranking				
Problem	*Cancer Risk**	*Noncancer Health Risk*	*Ecological Effects*	*Welfare Effects*	*Public Risk Ranking*
Active hazardous waste site	2	Low	Low	Medium	High
Inactive hazardous waste site	2	Low	Medium	Medium	High
Nonhazardous waste site: municipal	3	Medium	Medium	Medium	Not ranked
Nonhazardous waste site: industrial	2	Medium	Medium	Low	Not ranked
Accidental releases of toxics	4	High	Medium	Low	High
Releases from storage tanks	3	Low	Low	Low	Not ranked
Pesticide residues	1	High	High	Minor	Moderate
Other pesticide risks	2	Medium	High	Medium	Moderate
New toxic chemicals	2	Not ranked	Not ranked	Minor	Not ranked
Consumer product exposure	1	High	Not ranked	Minor	Low
Worker chemical exposure	1	High	Not ranked	Minor	Moderate

*Cancer rankings are on a scale of 1 through 5, with rank 1 being the highest relative risk and rank 5 being a "not assessed" or "no risk" rank.

Source: U.S. Environmental Protection Agency, Office of Policy Analysis, Office of Policy, Planning and Evaluation, *Unfinished Business: A Comparative Assessment of Environmental Problems* (Washington, D.C., February 1987).

the past several years. The findings of the first investigation, *Unfinished Business: A Comparative Assessment of Environmental Problems,* will be used to support the following analysis.[32]

EPA's Risk-Ranking Study.   To conduct the comparative risk study, a task force designated by the EPA defined the universe of environmental issues as a set of 31 problems. For each of these, the team of experts assessed four types of risks: (1) cancer risks; (2) noncancer risks; (3) ecological effects; and (4) welfare effects. The objective was to determine the *relative* risk of each

---

[32]U.S. EPA, Office of Policy Analysis, Office of Policy, Planning and Evaluation (February 1987). The conclusions of a follow-up study are reported in U.S. EPA, Science Advisory Board (September 1990).

TABLE 18.5   General Observations and Recommendations by the EPA Task Force on Relative Environmental Risks

---

1. No environmental problems were ranked consistently "high" or "low" across all four risk types.
2. The project has developed a useful tool to help set priorities.
3. Risks and EPA's current program priorities do not always match. In part, these differences seem to be explainable by public opinion on the seriousness of different environmental problems.

   - Areas of high risk/low EPA effort:
     Radon, indoor air pollution, stratospheric ozone depletion, global warming, accidental releases of toxics, consumer and worker exposure to chemicals, nonpoint sources of water pollution, and "other" pesticide risks.
   - Areas of medium or low risk/high EPA effort:
     Active (RCRA) and inactive (Superfund) hazardous waste sites, releases from storage tanks, and municipal nonhazardous waste.

4. Statutory authorities do not match neatly with risks.
5. National rankings do not necessarily reflect local situations—local analyses are needed.
6. Some chemicals show up as major concerns in multiple problem areas, notably lead, chromium, formaldehyde, solvents, and some pesticides.
7. More research is needed in several areas. The general weakness of exposure data is a special problem because exposure is such an important determinant of risk. In addition, specific data on the different types of risks and environmental problems are often lacking.
8. EPA should now study other areas important to setting priorities.

Source: U.S. Environmental Protection Agency, Office of Policy Analysis, Office of Policy, Planning and Evaluation, *Unfinished Business: A Comparative Assessment of Environmental Problems* (Washington, D.C., February 1987), pp. 94–100.

---

problem within each category. The risk-ranking process was based upon available quantitative risk data, subsequent interpretation, and expert judgment. Ultimately, the task force established a priority ranking of environmental problems that could be used to guide national policy. Findings were also compared to an ordinal ranking of the public's perception of environmental risks based upon a survey conducted by the Roper Organization. Both the expert ranking and the public's ranking for selected environmental problems are presented in Table 18.4. The overall observations and recommendations of the analysis are given in Table 18.5.

As the risk rankings in Table 18.4 indicate, it appears that the federal government's environmental priorities do not align consistently with the expert risk ranking—an observation that seems to be explained in part by how the general public perceives environmental risk. This observation is described more fully in the list of recommendations given in Table 18.5, specifically item 3. Notice how the task force identifies environmental hazards of high risk where EPA's control efforts are low and hazards of low or medium risk where the comparable effort is high. Every hazard in this latter category is a solid waste issue—active (RCRA) and inactive (Superfund) hazardous waste sites, releases from storage tanks, and municipal nonhazardous waste. According to this observation, the large amount of resources allocated to solid waste control does not appear to be justified by relative risk analysis. Now, examine the list of environmental hazards in the "high risk/low EPA effort category." Notice that there are several chemical exposure hazards identified in this category— consumer and worker exposure to chemicals, accidental releases of toxics, and "other" pesticide risks. (This latter category includes runoff, leaching, and air deposition associated with the use of pesticides and agricultural chemicals.) The same logic applies to this observation except in the opposite direction. Based on relative risk analysis, it appears that too few resources are being used to control pesticides and other chemicals.

Evaluating the Evidence

If we consider the results of the environmental risk analysis along with the national cost data discussed above, we can make three important observations about U.S. policy on solid waste and toxic chemicals:

1. There is reason to believe that economic resources are being misallocated across environmental risks.
2. National policy appears to be motivated at least in part by public perception of risk.
3. Inadequate data and uncertainty limit the policy analysis.

Each of these observations is discussed briefly below.

Misallocation of Resources.   Given an overall policy objective to reduce environmental risk, the benefits of regulation are appropriately measured by the risk reduction achieved. Based on benefit-cost analysis, resources should be allocated to balance the incremental benefits, or the reduction in risk, with the incremental costs of achieving them. Yet, the results of the risk-ranking study suggest that the high costs of implementing RCRA and Superfund are not justified by the expected risk reduction, which is low relative to other environmental hazards. Put another way, the comparative risk analysis suggests that resources may be being *overallocated* to solid waste pollution control.[33] Of course, if too many resources are being allocated to solid waste

---

[33]There is an important caveat here. As the task force indicates in their final observations, the "low risk/high EPA effort" areas may be indicating that the risks are low *because* of the intensified national effort. If so, some continuance of control efforts may be needed to maintain reduced risk. The issue hinges on whether the marginal benefit of further controls is justified by the marginal costs. In any case, the findings call for further investigation of how national resources are being allocated across competing needs.

problems, then it must be the case that too few are being used to satisfy other needs. It may be that the misallocation is *between* government and the private sector, meaning that all public policies are overfunded. Indeed, this is a common criticism. However, such a broad assertion is difficult to verify at best. What we can consider is how the allocation of resources *among* environmental public policies might be improved, based on the existing distribution between private and public uses.

Reexamine the list of high risk/low EPA effort problems identified by the task force in Table 18.5. Of particular relevance to the present investigation are the chemical-related hazards included in this list. The implication is that government should intensify its efforts under TSCA and FIFRA where there is greater opportunity for risk reduction. In fact, of the chemical-related problems in the high risk/low EPA effort category, worker exposure to chemicals is tied for first in the cancer risk ranking and ranked as "relatively high" in the noncancer health risk category.[34] Assuming the risk rankings are accurate, society would gain by transferring some resources away from those hazards where the risks are relatively low and reallocating them toward problems where the risks are higher. In theory, this transfer process should continue until the marginal benefit of reducing risk is the same across all environmental hazards in accordance with the equi-marginal principle of optimality.[35]

Although the evidence is far from complete, it seems reasonable to argue that the current standards specified by RCRA and Superfund may have erred on the side of being too stringent and that the controls under TSCA and FIFRA may be too lax. Hence, the costs of achieving these statutory standards likely cannot be justified on economic grounds.

Public Perception and Policy-Making.   Since it appears that allocative efficiency is not governing national priorities on the environment, we ought to consider what might be influencing these decisions. Referring back to Table 18.4, notice that there are major differences between the risk ranking of experts and that of the general public. Furthermore, the intensity of EPA efforts to

---

[34]Although not shown in Table 18.4, one of the more striking examples presented in the study is exposure to radon for which the cancer risk is tied for first among all defined problems. Estimates of annual cancer incidence associated with radon exposure are stated as 5,000 to 20,000. Yet there is no federal regulation controlling this risk. The EPA spends about $100 million per year to reduce the risk of cancer due to radon exposure, whereas some $6 billion are spent annually on hazardous waste cleanup. For more information on this and other possible misallocations, see Main (May 20, 1991).

[35]Notice that such a reallocation is based on relative rankings confined to regulated environmental problems. Hence, the result would optimize the environmental risk reduction possible from government efforts based on a *given* distribution of resources. A general solution could be determined only from a benefit-cost analysis across *all* competing uses and across all economic sectors. Were this empirically possible, one might determine that government uses too many resources for all of its programs as is commonly suggested.

combat environmental problems is more consistent with public *perception* of risk than it is with *actual* environmental risk. In fact, this assertion was one of the major conclusions of the EPA report as Table 18.5 indicates.

Consider, for example, the experts' risk ranking of active hazardous waste sites. The experts classify the associated cancer risk in category 2 of 5, adding that fewer than 100 cases of cancer per year should result nationwide.[36] They also give the problem a low ranking for noncancer risks and for ecological effects. Yet national efforts to control these sites through RCRA are high, and so too is the public perception of the associated risks. A similar argument applies to the mismatch of expert risk ranking for inactive hazardous waste sites relative to the intensity of national effort and the associated costs to control them. Yet again, the public perceives the associated risks as high.

Limitations of the Risk-Ranking Study.   There are important and in some cases disturbing findings associated with the EPA's landmark risk analysis. However, it is critical to understand not only what the study accomplishes but also what its limitations are. As the task force points out in its report, risk assessment data are not complete, and methods for assessing noncancer and ecological risks are not well defined. There is a need for further research to advance scientific knowledge about environmental hazards and the implications of short- and long-term exposure. In the interim, given the limited data and the scientific uncertainty, evaluations about U.S. policy on solid waste and toxics cannot be made without reservation.

Another qualification of the risk-ranking analysis is that some intangible aspects of risk were not considered. For example, the study did not account for the extent to which certain risks are voluntary, nor did it consider any risks to the existence value of natural resources. Furthermore, the task force acknowledges that its findings were not adjusted for environmental equity. In fact, one of the concluding observations is that national risk rankings are not always indicative of local conditions, and that these must be considered in setting environmental priorities at nonfederal levels of government.[37]

Some environmental problems affect certain geographical regions or specific segments of the population more than others. Hence, analyses based on overall or national risks tend to obscure the true implications of these hazards. A case in point is the risk of exposure to hazardous waste facilities—an instance of environmental inequity discussed in Application 18.3.

Even accepting the study's limitations, the risk-ranking analysis strongly suggests the need for further investigation of how the federal government sets priorities for environmental policy initiatives. In the context of solid waste

[36]U.S. EPA, Office of Policy Analysis, Office of Policy, Planning and Evaluation (February 1987), p. 73.
[37]U.S. EPA, Office of Policy Analysis, Office of Policy, Planning and Evaluation (February 1987), p. 7-97.

Application 18.3

Hazardous Waste Sites: Are the Risks Disproportionate?

Unlike the effects of acid rain that can be felt by people living hundreds of miles away from the polluting source, the risks of exposure to hazardous waste tend to be localized. For example, the health effects of groundwater contamination caused by a mismanaged waste site are confined to nearby residents. On that basis alone, we know that these environmental risks are not evenly distributed across the nation. But we need to look beyond this simple observation. The operative issue is to determine if these higher-risk communities are dominated by any racial, ethnic, or income groups. If so, policy officials have to consider how to address the environmental inequity.

Recently, the EPA formed the Environmental Equity Workgroup to study the evidence on whether certain socioeconomic groups face a disproportionate degree of environmental risk. Motivating this effort is the notion that risk-based priorities should guide the direction of U.S. environmental policy. Simply put, society can gain more from environmental policy initiatives if resources are allocated to high-risk regions of the country and high-risk population groups.

As part of its two-year long mission, the EPA's workgroup investigated available information on the characteristics of populations living near existing and abandoned hazardous waste facilities. Among other findings, the EPA workgroup discovered that there is a lack of good data on environmental health effects sorted on the basis of socioeconomic factors like race and income. Nonetheless, it did find that minorities and low-income groups appear to have a greater exposure to certain environmental threats, one of which is hazardous waste sites. Why are these groups more strongly represented in areas where these potentially dangerous sites are located? The reasons are complex, but among the determinants are land use decisions, historical residence patterns, and politics.

In its 1992 report, the EPA workgroup referenced a 1983 study conducted by the U.S. General Accounting Office (GAO), which focused on the socioeconomic characteristics of communities near four hazardous waste landfills. The GAO's findings are shown in the following table.

Landfill Company	Population		Median Family Income ($)		Population below Poverty Level		
	Total	% Black	All Races	Black	Total	%	% Black
Chemical Waste Management (Ala.)	626	90%	$11,198	$10,752	265	42%	100%
SCA Services (S.C.)	849	38	16,371	6,781	260	31	100
Industrial Chemical Co. (S.C.)	728	52	18,996	12,941	188	26	92
Warren County PCB Landfill (N.C.)	804	66	10,367	9,285	256	32	90

Source: U.S. GAO, (1983).

Notice from these statistics that three out of four of the landfills cited are located in communities where more than 50 percent of the population is black. At Chemical Waste Management in Alabama, blacks represent 90 percent of the local population. The income data are also important, indicating a fairly large proportion of the local population living below the poverty level—most of whom are black. In fact, for two of the sites, 100 percent of the families living in poverty are black.

A more recent study was conducted in 1987 by the United Church of Christ to investigate these same issues on a national scale. The results showed that minorities are more likely to live in communities where hazardous waste facilities are located. Specifically, minorities account for over 37 percent of the population in communities where one of the five largest hazardous waste landfills is located or where there is more than one treatment, storage, or disposal facility. This research did not find as strong an association for socioeconomic status as the GAO analysis discovered.

The EPA's work on environmental equity suggests that further research is needed to understand the extent of disproportionate environmental risk. In the interim, policy-makers must be cognizant of the potential equity implications of their decisions. Based on available information, this awareness is particularly important in devising policy for environmental hazards with localized risks, such as hazardous waste sites. In these instances, the decision-making process must go beyond economic and technological considerations and be sensitive to the welfare of local communities.

Sources: U.S. Environmental Protection Agency, Office of Policy, Planning, and Evaluation, *Environmental Equity: Reducing Risks for All Communities* (Washington D.C., June 1992); U.S. General Accounting Office (GAO), *Siting of Hazardous Waste Landfills and Their Correlation with Racial and Economic Status of Surrounding Communities* (Washington, D.C., 1983); United Church of Christ Commission for Racial Justice (UCC), *Toxic Wastes and Race in the United States: A National Report on the Racial and Socio-Economic Characteristics of Communities with Hazardous Waste Sites* (UCC, 1987).

and toxics, it appears that the costs incurred by society to develop and implement comprehensive legislation like RCRA and Superfund relative to those associated with FIFRA and TSCA are not justified by comparative risk analysis. Further research is needed, particularly in benefit assessment, to support and expand upon this hypothesis.

Conclusions

Recognizing the potential risks of chemical exposure and the enormous costs of remediation efforts, the U.S. government has developed legislation aimed at controlling hazardous substances *before* they become a part of the waste stream. Although many legislative acts contribute to this effort, two of the more significant are the Federal Insecticide, Fungicide, and Rodenticide Act (FIFRA) and the Toxic Substances Control Act (TSCA). Both of these major laws are designed to prevent the production and use of substances posing an unacceptable risk to society and to monitor the risks of those that have been introduced to the marketplace.

Although many pesticides and toxic substances are associated with known health and ecological effects, both can and do contribute to society's well-being. Hence, it is appropriate that decision-making under FIFRA and TSCA be guided by risk-benefit analysis. There are, however, practical problems that have hindered the realization of what this strategy can achieve. For example, registration decisions for new pesticides are based on risk data submitted by manufacturers, but benefits are *assumed* to justify those risks based on the registrant's willingness to pay the registration fee. There are similar flaws in the implementation of TSCA's rulings, particularly those applicable to chemicals already on the market.

New proposals are under consideration to streamline the implementation of both laws and to integrate more incentives that will encourage the production and use of safer substitutes. The direction is one that fosters pollution prevention to displace some of the reliance on treatment and cleanup. Such a shift in emphasis is supported by comparative risk analysis, particularly in light of the costs to support RCRA and Superfund relative to FIFRA and TSCA. According to this preventive approach, society has to be made to rethink how market decisions ultimately affect the size and toxicity of the waste stream. Firms must adjust how their products are designed, manufactured, and packaged, and households need to modify consumption and consider the external costs of their market decisions. Pollution prevention is an important theme in the ongoing development of environmental policy—one of several issues discussed in our concluding chapter.

Summary

- Congress enacted the Federal Insecticide, Fungicide, and Rodenticide Act (FIFRA) in 1947. The EPA assumed responsibility for FIFRA in 1970, and in 1972 Congress passed amendments that shifted the focus of the law to health and environmental protection. Amendments passed in 1988 were aimed at improving registration and reregistration procedures and authorized a fee system to help pay for the reregistration process.

- A major objective of FIFRA is to register all pesticides *before* they are distributed or sold. Registration is subject to EPA approval based upon a risk-benefit analysis. At the time of registration, the EPA must set tolerances on the amount of a pesticide that may remain as a residue on food without causing an unacceptable health risk.

- A five-phase approach has been developed to accomplish reregistration, which involves the listing of all pesticide active ingredients needing to be reevaluated, requests for updated information from registrants, and a summary and evaluation by the EPA.

- The dominant factor in pesticide registration decisions is a risk evaluation based on data submitted by manufacturers. If risks are found to be negligible, the EPA assumes that benefits exist based upon the manufacturer's willingness to absorb the registration costs.

- Scientists question the EPA's methods of assessing pesticide risks. Some argue that the risks are underestimated, while others claim that findings from animal bioassays overstate the potential harm to humans. There is also concern about the effect of more stringent pesticide controls on agricultural productivity.

- The Clinton administration has announced plans to develop a new pesticide program. The goal is to promote Integrated Pest Management (IPM), which would foster selective use of pesticides and greater reliance on natural deterrents.

- In 1976, Congress enacted the Toxic Substances Control Act (TSCA). One of the Act's primary objectives is to control chemicals that present a risk to health or the environment *before* they are introduced into commerce. TSCA also provides for the monitoring and regulation of chemicals already on the market.

- TSCA requires chemical producers to notify the government at least 90 days before they intend to produce or import any new chemical, using a premanufacture notice (PMN). The EPA has a 90-day review period to evaluate the risks and respond. If the risks are too high, the EPA may restrict usage of the chemical.

- For existing chemicals, TSCA requires manufacturers to notify the EPA if any chemical is found to present a substantial risk to human health or the environment. The EPA takes whatever action is appropriate, which can range from labeling requirements to outright bans.

- The EPA has been slow to develop data on *existing* chemicals. A contributing factor is the use of a single chemical review process rather than one aimed at a group of similar substances. Such delays create a bias against the introduction of new chemicals.

- The United States is planning to revise the TSCA program. Among the proposals is a Product Stewardship Rulemaking, which would require chemical producers to share risk information with their customers and to conduct hazard evaluations on the substances customers use. This proposal is part of a plan to replace single chemical procedures with multimedia, multichemical approaches.

- Aggregate cost data on solid waste controls exhibit a strong positive trend between 1972 and 1987, which reflects the strengthening of U.S. policy since the mid-1970s. Aggregate control costs for FIFRA and TSCA are much smaller, but they have increased dramatically over the same period.

- According to an EPA risk-ranking study, federal resources might be *overallocated* to solid waste control and *underallocated* to the regulation of toxic substances and pesticide use. These findings imply that the social costs of RCRA and Superfund relative to those of FIFRA and TSCA may not be justified by comparative risk analysis.

Key Concepts

pesticide registration	new chemical
risk-benefit analysis	premanufacture notice (PMN)
tolerances	Product Stewardship Rulemaking
pesticide reregistration	multimedia, multichemical approaches
Integrated Pest Management (IPM)	comparative risk analysis
TSCA inventory	

APPENDIX

A REFERENCE TO ACRONYMS IN TOXIC SUBSTANCES POLICY CONTROL

Environmental Science Acronyms

DDT	Dichloro-diphenyl-trichloroethane
EDB	Ethylene dibromide
PCBs	Polychlorinated biphenyls

Environmental Policy Acronyms

CERCLA	Comprehensive Environmental Response, Compensation, and Liability Act
CERCLIS	Comprehensive Environmental Response, Compensation, and Liability Information System
FDA	Food and Drug Administration
FFDCA	Federal Food, Drug, and Cosmetic Act
FIFRA	Federal Insecticide, Fungicide, and Rodenticide Act
IPM	Integrated Pest Management
NAS	National Academy of Sciences
NPL	National Priorities List
OSHA	Occupational Safety and Health Administration
PMN	Premanufacture notice
RCRA	Resource Conservation and Recovery Act
TSCA	Toxic Substances Control Act

Review Questions

1. *a.* Critically compare and contrast the policy approaches of TSCA and FIFRA.
   b. In your view, which of these is more effective in preventing pollution? Explain.

2. Suggest two market-based instruments that would support Clinton's proposed plan for reduced pesticide use. Explain.

3. Reconsider the proposal for Product Stewardship Rulemaking under TSCA. Explain how natural market incentives might encourage compliance with such a ruling. Are there any motivations that operate in the opposite direction? Explain.

4. In 1976, the United States banned the manufacture of PCBs. Propose an alternative policy that would effectively reduce society's exposure to these cancer-causing substances. Support your proposal by discussing two of its strong points. Realistically, why might opponents argue against your idea?

5. *a.* If you were to plan an empirical study of the benefits of RCRA and
   Superfund, how would you categorize the primary social benefits?

   b. How, if at all, would your answer differ if you were to do the same type of
   study for FIFRA and TSCA? Explain.

6. Critically evaluate the EPA's risk-ranking study. Cite one major
   accomplishment of this analysis and one major failure. Support your answer
   from a policy perspective.

Additional Readings

Ely, Clausen. "The Delaney Clause: Point/Counterpoint: An Obscure EPA Policy Is
    to Blame." *EPA Journal* 19, no. 1 (January/February/March 1993), pp. 44–45.

Gutfeld, Rose. "Pesticide Use Would Be Cut Under U.S. Plan." *The Wall Street
    Journal,* June 28, 1993.

Hamilton, James T. "Testing for Environmental Racism: Prejudice, Profits, Political
    Power?" *Journal of Policy Analysis and Management* 14, no. 1, 1995,
    pp. 107–32.

Kong, Dolores. "Pesticide Debate About to Resume." *Boston Globe,* September 6,
    1993.

Macauley, Molly K.; Michael D. Bowes; and Karen L. Palmer. *Using Economic
    Incentives to Regulate Toxic Substances.* Washington, D.C.: Resources for the
    Future, 1992.

Mendeloff, John M. *The Dilemma of Toxic Substance Regulation.* Cambridge,
    Mass.: MIT Press, 1988.

Meyerhoff, Al. "The Delaney Clause: Point/Counterpoint: Let's Reform a Failed
    Food Safety Regime." *EPA Journal* 19, no. 1 (January/February/March 1993),
    pp. 42–43.

U.S. Congress. Office of Technology Assessment (OTA). *Green Products by
    Design: Choices for a Cleaner Environment.* Washington, D.C.: U.S.
    Government Printing Office, October 1992.

Weber, Peter. "A Place for Pesticides?" *World Watch,* May/June 1992, pp. 18–25.

VII

ENVIRONMENTAL MANAGEMENT IN TRANSITION

As society learned about environmental damage and the associated risks, it recognized that economic advance and industrialization were largely responsible for the pollution problems it confronted. Such a realization seemed to suggest an unacceptable trade-off between competing social objectives—economic prosperity and environmental quality. Economic growth is not a goal that many consider to be optional, nor are advances such as air travel, electricity, computer technology, and telecommunications. Nonetheless, most saw the need for policy initiatives that would improve environmental quality and reduce the risk of exposure to hazards like urban smog, polluted rivers and streams, and abandoned hazardous waste sites.

The thrust of the policy response was to use "end-of-pipe" controls on the pollutants released into the environment. Although this approach has yielded some measure of progress, public officials and policy analysts have been concerned about the enormous costs, the unattained policy goals, and the conflict between economic growth and environmental protection. Over time, many revisions have been drafted and numerous new programs launched. Incentives displaced some command-and-control instruments, integrated programs replaced some pollutant- and media-specific initiatives, and prevention has superseded treatment as a waste management option. Taken together, these trends speak to a transition in policy development toward broader, more long-term solutions to environmental damage. The aim is to reconcile the goals of environmental quality and economic prosperity.

In retrospect, it is easy to be critical of what has at times been a painstakingly slow policy development process. But in truth, some of the accomplishments were a direct result of learning—sometimes the hard way from mistakes and failures. Believing that experience is perhaps the best teacher, we have reason to be optimistic about the direction of environmental policy both nationally and internationally. The wisdom of that experience coupled with scientific advances and technological innovation can bring about significant change. Perhaps more importantly, environmental objectives have broadened to consider the future along with the present and to accommodate global interests along with national and local needs. Such is the fundamental premise of sustainable development—a goal to integrate economic prosperity with environmental preservation as a legacy to future generations.

In this final chapter, we examine the strategic approach now evolving in the United States and elsewhere to meet the objective of sustainable development. Although there is much that has yet to be defined, several themes are beginning to emerge. Among them are efforts to advance environmental literacy, a redefinition of policy toward prevention, and the development of cooperative initiatives between the public and private sectors and among nations. Mindful of what has been accomplished and what remains to be done, we explore these themes that characterize what many view as an important transition in environmental management.

STRATEGIC PLANNING FOR SUSTAINABLE DEVELOPMENT

Direct regulation of economic activity has characterized much of the evolution of U.S. environmental policy. While this command-and-control approach has contained the problem, most recognize that the nation's reliance on ''end-of-pipe'' controls does not adequately address the long-term implications of environmental damage. Furthermore, this approach does not accommodate the broader objective of sustainable development—achieving environmental quality *and* economic prosperity.

The comprehensive goal of sustainable development calls for fundamental changes in how society makes market decisions—both in production and consumption. The challenge is to achieve economic prosperity but alter market activity so that the earth's natural resources are protected. Effecting changes of this magnitude calls for a much different policy approach than one that relies on rules and limits—control instruments that often run counter to the polluter's market incentive. If society is going to sustain a long-term commitment to preserving the earth, there has to be a motivation to do so beyond the avoidance of penalties for regulatory noncompliance.

Logically, the motivation should be consistent with economic incentives. The premise is that economic growth and environmental quality can be reinforcing rather than competing objectives. Perceptions must be changed to recognize that resource conservation and pollution abatement can enhance private as well as social interests. Communication must be improved to share information about technologies, inputs, and processes that can protect the environment without diminishing profitability. If successful, cooperation should displace what is sometimes an adversarial position between the public and private sectors of society, and there should be less reliance on costly monitoring and enforcement procedures.

Such a change in direction and attitude calls for a long-term strategic plan that involves all sectors of society. Several broad-based efforts are under way in the United States and elsewhere to begin the implementation. Among these are initiatives to promote pollution prevention and thus avoid unnecessary and costly abatement and remediation. At the same time, environmental literacy is being advanced—to educate society about the effects of environmental damage and to encourage responsible decision-making. Environmental technologies are being developed and an infrastructure established to share these advances throughout the global community. As these and other efforts are taking root, cooperative arrangements are forming both between the public and private sectors and among nations that are consistent with the long-term goal of sustainable development.

In this concluding chapter, we explore this transitional phase in environmental policy—both its objectives and its strategic implementation. To understand the motivation of sustainable development, we revisit the materials balance model introduced originally in Chapter 1. Recall that this model illustrates the link between economic activity and the natural environment, which is critical to the achievement of sustainable development. We then study several important trends that indicate how U.S. environmental policy is being redirected to consider this broader objective. In this part of our analysis, we focus on pollution prevention strategies, international cooperative arrangements, domestic partnerships, and information and technology transfer.

Sustainable Development

environmental quality
A reduction in anthropogenic contaminant to a level that is ''acceptable'' to society.

Over the last several decades of environmental policy development, the clear focus has been to achieve **environmental quality** by reducing anthropogenic pollution to a level that is ''acceptable'' to society. Policy-makers have struggled with the tough issue of ''how clean is clean'' and the challenge of devising cost-effective instruments to achieve whatever quality level has been set. Through revisions, political debate, and a growing social consciousness, there has been some progress and a number of shifts in policy development. Yet there also has been an increasing awareness of the need for change more fundamental than periodic revisions of legislative provisions—a redefinition of environmental policy objectives. A consensus is forming that both public and private decision-making should be driven by a broader goal that is global in scope and dynamic in perspective. One such goal is **sustainable development**— managing the earth's resources such that their long-term quality and abundance is assured for future generations. To analyze why this transition represents a significant change in environmental policy development, we reintroduce the **materials balance model,** which we studied initially in Chapter 1.

sustainable development
The management of the earth's resources such that their long-term quality and abundance is assured for future generations.

Revisiting the Materials Balance Model

Figure 19.1 reproduces the **materials balance model** that exemplifies the dynamic relationship between economic activity and nature. Recall that this relationship is defined by the flow of resources from nature to an economic

FIGURE 19.1

Revisiting the materials balance model: the implications for sustainable development

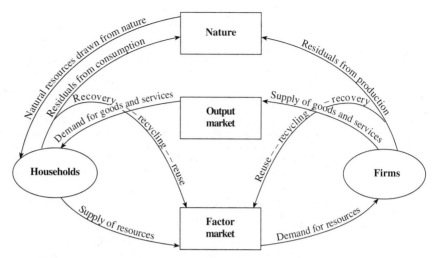

The materials balance model exemplifies the dynamic relationship between economic activity and nature. Resources flow from nature to an economic system, and by-products or residuals from economic activity represent the return flow back to the environment. Conventional environmental policy uses "end-of-pipe" instruments aimed at controlling the amount of polluting residuals released to the environment. These policies can improve environmental quality in the short run, but they do not adequately address the long-run consequences—the potential for intertemporal trade-offs between one generation and the next. In the long run, society must find ways to reconcile economic growth and environmental quality, which is the underlying premise of sustainable development.

Source: Adapted from Allen V. Kneese, Robert U. Ayres, and Ralph C. D'Arge, *Economics and the Environment: A Materials Balance Approach* (Washington, D.C.: Resources for the Future, 1970).

materials balance model
A depiction of the dynamic relationship between economic decision-making and the natural environment.

system and the return flow of residuals from economic activity back to the environment. Throughout our study of environmental economics, we have focused on the flow of residuals and the potential damages associated with their release to nature. Of primary interest has been an analysis of policy aimed at achieving environmental quality by controlling the size and toxicity of this flow. At this point, we use the materials balance model to explain how these initiatives are short term and hence inadequate to accommodate the broader aim of sustainable development.

A Short-Term Policy Approach

As we have discussed throughout the text, the conventional approach of environmental policy is the use of "end-of-pipe" command-and-control instruments to improve **environmental quality.** Relying primarily on performance- or technology-based standards, the aim has been to control the amount of polluting residuals released to the environment *after* they are generated. Implicit in this approach is a perception that the flow of materials through the economy is a linear one, as illustrated in Figure 19.2. As the graphic shows,

FIGURE 19.2

*The conventional
linear perspective of
materials flow*

The aim of performance- or technology-based standards is to control the amount of polluting
residuals released to the environment. Implicit in this approach is a perception that the flow of
materials through the economy is *linear,* as illustrated above. As the graphic shows, this view
assumes that materials run in *one* direction, entering an economic system as inputs and
leaving as wastes or residuals. Hence, the policy focus is on abating contaminating residuals
at the end of the flow.

Source: U.S. Congress, Office of Technology Assessment (OTA), *Green Products by Design: Choices for a
Cleaner Environment* (Washington, D.C.: U.S. Government Printing Office, October 1992) as cited in John
Gibbons, ''Moving Beyond the 'Tech Fix,' '' *EPA Journal* 18, no. 4 (September/October 1992), p. 31.

this view assumes that materials run in *one* direction, entering an economic
system as inputs and leaving as wastes or residuals. Hence, policy has focused
on abating contaminating residuals at the end of the flow. For example, U.S.
clean air policy attempts to control harmful residuals released into the atmosphere, officially termed criteria and hazardous air pollutants. Similarly, national clean water initiatives seek to control toxic, conventional, and
nonconventional pollutants released as effluents into waterways. And solid
waste policy focuses on managing the hazardous and nonhazardous waste
stream, including its final disposal back to nature. Although these policies can
improve environmental quality in the short run, they do not adequately address
the long-run consequences. To explain why, consider the dynamics of the
materials balance model in the context of policy initiatives.

First, nature's capacity to convert matter and energy is limited. Although
residuals can be converted to other forms that can flow back into productive
use, this process is not without bound. Hence, policy decisions affecting resource use and environmental damage have implications for future generations. Government programs to promote recovery and reuse of residuals shown
by the inner flows in Figure 19.1 have helped to delay their release but not
eliminate them. Second, end-of-pipe controls rely mainly on treatment of polluting residuals *after* they are created. Such methods draw resources away
from other productive activities—resources that ultimately are added to the
residual flow. Third, command-and-control initiatives generally operate at
cross purposes with private market incentives and the broader social goal of
economic growth. This observation points to the potential for intertemporal
trade-offs between one generation and the next. The pursuit of economic development today can so harm the natural environment as to leave future
generations less able to continue that progress. On the other hand, restricting
the pursuit of economic gains to protect the environment deprives today's
society as well as future generations of a higher standard of living.

What all of this suggests is that environmental policy must consider the long run. The materials balance model reminds us that nature and the circular flow of economic activity are inexorably linked, and this linkage is a dynamic one. Just as it is foolhardy to pursue economic growth without regard for the environmental implications over time, so too is it irrational to pursue environmental objectives that ignore the future economic consequences. An example of the potential conflict is discussed in Application 19.1, which focuses on the controversy surrounding government subsidies to support the timber industry.

Application 19.1

The Potential Conflict between Economic Gain and Environmental Quality: Below-Cost Timber Sales and the Implications for Recycled Materials

In the United States, industries dealing with the extraction and refining of natural resources, such as timber, minerals, and oil, have enjoyed the benefits of government subsidies for some time. The original intent of these tax preferences was to assure the survival of these major industries, particularly during economic slowdowns. In so doing, these subsidies also protect local and regional economies dependent on these markets by assuring employment and income stability in what are typically rural communities. While well intended from a market perspective, these programs have come under scrutiny because their economic objectives appear to compete with the nation's environmental goals.

One federal subsidy that has been the subject of recent public debate and media attention is the below-cost timber sale program. Administered by the U.S. Forest Service, this program grants companies the right to cut timber on federal lands at reduced costs. Environmentalists believe that this federal program has encouraged the practice of clear-cutting, causing severe soil erosion and threatening ecosystems and the already tenuous future of endangered species. Characterized as the controversy over the plight of the northern spotted owl, the much-publicized debate actually has much broader concerns. Among these is the allegation that federal subsidies foster the use of virgin resources, effectively discouraging the use of recycled materials.

Beyond the environmental implications, the timber subsidy program also has been questioned on economic grounds. In its sale of public timber, the Forest Service is not obligated to recover the federal government's cost of cultivating and marketing the valuable timber. Consequently, although its enormous assets would give it a top-five position in the *Fortune* 500, its pricing policies would classify it as bankrupt in the private sector. In practice, the sale of publicly owned timber is subsidized according to one of three methods: (1) charging a sale price based on the industry's ability to pay versus the timber's market value; (2) assigning a price based solely on the government's cost; or (3) using public funds to finance access roads for harvesting.

Responding to strong arguments on a number of fronts, the Clinton administration suggested the possibility of reducing or even eliminating the timber subsidy program. But the eventual outcome of such a proposal is not entirely predictable. In fact, the EPA has identified several possible scenarios, each of which would have very different impacts on the economy and on national recycling objectives. First, the timber industry might be able to maintain current production levels by reducing

Application 19.1 (concluded)

other operating costs to counter the effect of the subsidy reduction. As a result, there would be no effect on alternative markets or on the nation's recycling efforts. Second, it could encourage more efficient use of existing supplies and an overall reduction in lumber consumption. Third, the cost effect could precipitate a market shift away from domestic suppliers toward lower-cost foreign producers. Finally, there may be a substitution effect toward other domestic products, including recycled lumber materials.

While no one can forecast the future of the timber subsidy or the related market implications, most observers argue that such programs are in need of reform. Tax preferences such as these, however well intended, create market distortions. In this case, the subsidies embedded in the below-cost timber sales undervalue our nation's forests, setting up an artificial signal to use virgin materials over recycled substitutes. This distortion has serious implications. Overharvesting of national forests jeopardizes the long-term supply of timber, threatens the future of biological species, and endangers the overall quality of the environment.

Sources: Timothy E. Wirth and John Heinz, *Project 88—Round II Incentives for Action: Designing Market-Based Environmental Strategies* (Washington, D.C.: May 1991), pp. 77–86; Randal O'Toole, *Reforming the Forest Service* (Washington, D.C.: Island Press, 1988); U.S. Congress, Office of Technology Assessment (OTA), *Facing America's Trash: What Next for Municipal Solid Waste?* (Washington, D.C.: U.S. Government Printing Office, 1989), Chapter 5; U.S. Environmental Protection Agency, Office of Policy, Planning, and Evaluation, *Economic Incentives: Options for Environmental Protection* (Washington, D.C., March 1991), pp. 5-33–5-39; Michael Kranish, "Clinton Treads into Forests Dispute," *Boston Globe,* April 3, 1993.

Moving toward the Long Run: Sustainable Development

Sustainable development is based on the premise that economic growth and environmental quality must be reconciled. Statistical estimates on worldwide population and income growth help to explain why this is important. First, according to a recent article, per capita income levels have to grow by at least 2 percent per year to reduce world poverty and close the gap between the rich and poor. Second, world population is growing at about 1.7 percent each year, a rate that is expected to decline only very slowly. Both of these statistics indicate that economic growth has to be achieved. Hence, to avoid further pollution and natural resource depletion, the associated environmental impact per unit of income must decline at a rate between 3.5 and 4 percent per year.[1] We can generalize the relevant relationship at a point in time as follows:[2]

$$\text{Environmental impact} = \text{Income per capita} \times \text{Environmental impact per unit of income} \times \text{Population}$$

Developing countries face more urgent conditions, struggling to advance economically to accommodate a rapidly rising population and at the same time

---

[1]Nitze (April–June 1993).

[2]This relationship is just an identity, which is more apparent when the equation is rewritten using ratios:

$$\text{Environmental impact} = \frac{\text{Income}}{\text{Population}} \times \frac{\text{Environmental impact}}{\text{Income}} \times \text{Population}$$

FIGURE 19.3

Moving toward a closed system of materials flow

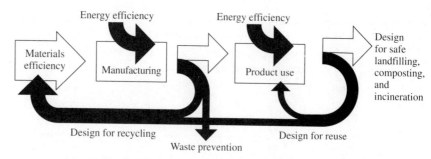

This model of the materials flow suggests a more comprehensive approach to environmental protection than controlling residuals *after* they have been generated. Instead, this perspective illustrates how economic activity can be altered *throughout* the cycle of production and consumption to reduce the associated environmental impact. Product design, manufacturing processes, and energy use can be modified so that materials flow through more of a closed system.

Source: U.S. Congress, Office of Technology Assessment (OTA), *Green Products by Design: Choices for a Cleaner Environment* (Washington, D.C.: U.S. Government Printing Office, October 1992) as cited in John Gibbons, "Moving Beyond the 'Tech Fix,' " *EPA Journal* 18, no. 4 (September/October 1992), p. 31.

confronted with the environmental contamination that these pursuits have exacerbated. For example, recent projections estimate an annual population growth through 2025 of 4.7 percent for Nigeria, 2.8 percent for Bangladesh, and 1.8 percent for India and Mexico.[3] Higher population necessarily increases the demand for goods and services. If an economy's productive capacity cannot accommodate the population growth, shortages arise and resources are misused in an attempt to compensate for the imbalance.[4]

In the context of the materials balance model, we know that population growth and economic development increase the flow of resources into market activity and the return flow of residuals back to nature. These changes can adversely affect the well-being of future generations if present decision-making is not mindful of the long run. Part of the answer is to recognize that the flow of materials through an economy need not be linear. Instead, product design, manufacturing processes, and energy use can be modified so that materials flow through more of a closed system, as shown in Figure 19.3. Notice that this model suggests a much broader approach to environmental protection than controlling residuals *after* they have been generated. This alternative perspective illustrates how economic activity can be altered *throughout* the cycle of production and consumption to achieve a reduction in the associated

---

[3]United Nations Population Division (1993) and International Labour Office (1993) as cited in World Resources Institute (1994b), Table 16.1, pp. 268–69.

[4]For a classic article illuminating the environmental implications of population growth, see Hardin (1968).

industrial ecosystem
A closed system of manufacturing whereby the wastes of one process are reused as the inputs for another.

environmental impact. A potential outcome of such a strategy is the formation of **industrial ecosystems** whereby residuals from one process are reused as inputs for another.[5] Application 19.2 discusses this concept and reports on several applications of its use in the United States and Denmark.

Application 19.2

Industrial Ecosystems: When a Bad Becomes a Good

All over the world, senior management is taking a second look at the traditional manufacturing process. Conceptually, every such process comprises a series of complex tasks that use energy, capital, and labor to convert raw materials into a variety of goods and services. A natural outcome of this productive activity is the generation of waste materials that must be discarded. While seemingly innocuous, it is precisely this generation and disposal of production wastes that has become a national concern and, as a consequence, the focus of a new manufacturing concept called the **industrial ecosystem.**

This strategic approach to industrial manufacturing arises from the premise that the conventional input-output process can be perceived as a closed system such that the residuals generated from one production process are used as raw inputs for another. This link between processes might occur within a single firm or among several different entities. Overall, the concept is in keeping with the broader concept of sustainable development, which promotes the achievement of both economic growth and environmental preservation. As such, it is directed toward two major objectives. The first is to employ energy and raw materials optimally to assure that each productive input achieves maximum efficiency. The second is to facilitate the reduction of waste material by minimizing the generation of nonreusable wastes that occur as part of the manufacturing function.

Some U.S. firms have already begun to alter their processes so that their wastes can be recycled for use either internally or by other companies. For example, one of ARCO's oil refinery facilities has saved about $2 million per year by selling some of what were formerly hazardous wastes to chemical companies, cement makers, and acid manufacturers. Applying the same general strategy, Dow Chemical has found a way to recover hydrochloric acid, which is then reused internally or sold to other entities. The result is a significant reduction in the release of acid wastes to the environment *and* a $20 million return to Dow. Du Pont, the largest chemical manufacturer in the world, found a thriving market for some of its nylon production wastes in the pharmaceuticals and coatings industries. So successful was this interindustry relationship that Du Pont began to manufacture these materials to meet what eventually became excess demand for the new "product."

Obviously, the shift toward "closing the loop" in manufacturing calls for coordination between the industrial participants. To illustrate, consider the experience of a group of five entities cooperating within a closed manufacturing system in Denmark. Specifically, the five participants include the city of Kalundborg, a refinery, a power plant, an enzyme plant, and a wallboard manufacturer. Just as the concept suggests, the participants are linking their manufacturing processes together to save resources, energy, and the environment. Three waste by-products are produced by the coal-fired electrical power plant: surplus steam, fly ash, and surplus heat. In a conventional manufacturing environment, these

---

[5]Frosch and Gallopoulos (1989).

---

wastes would simply be disposed of. For example, the steam would be condensed and dumped into a nearby waterway. However, as a result of establishing a "closed-loop" manufacturing environment, the surplus steam is sold to two of the other participants, the local enzyme plant and the oil refinery, for use in their respective manufacturing processes. This arrangement helps to conserve water supplies, which are pumped from a lake seven miles away. Similarly, the surplus heat is sold by the utility to the city of Kalundborg for its heating needs. The fly ash associated with the utility's pollution control equipment is actually a composition of limestone. This is sold to a wallboard manufacturer, which uses it in place of imported gypsum.

Of course, there are reciprocal arrangements as well. For example, the refinery sells two of its by-products to the utility. One is treated wastewater that the utility uses in its cooling process. The other is desulfurized gas, which the utility uses as fuel. In so doing, it is able to reduce its coal usage by some 30,000 tons per year, which in turn cuts down its sulfur dioxide emissions considerably. As the Kalundborg arrangement has evolved and met with

apparent success, other mutually beneficial arrangements are beginning to develop outside of the original five participants. Local farmers near Kalundborg are now using the wastes from the enzyme plant and from a nearby fishery as crop fertilizer, and the fishery is using some of the surplus heat generated by the utility.

Ultimately, innovative systems such as these help in the effort to achieve sustainable development. Arguably, this is a mutually beneficial concept to all participants that also offers important benefits to society as a whole. Of course, its implementation on a broad scale will necessitate a great deal of coordination, careful planning, and a fair amount of adjustment to existing corporate standards and practices. However, the environmental gains and the potential profits suggest that the rewards could be well worth the effort.

Source: Robert A. Frosch and Nicholas E. Gallopoulos, "Strategies for Manufacturing," *Scientific American* 261, no. 3 (September 1989), pp. 144–52; Emily T. Smith and David Woodruff, "The Next Trick For Business: Taking a Cue From Nature," *Business Week*, May 11, 1992, pp. 74–75; Stephan Schmidheiny, *Changing Course: A Global Business Perspective on Development and the Environment* (Cambridge, Mass.: The MIT Press, 1992), p. 105.

Sustainable development is an ambitious pursuit. Fundamental to its achievement are changes in how market activity is undertaken within the circular flow and in how environmental policy is drafted. The key is to modify behavior so that economic growth and environmental protection become reinforcing rather than competing goals. Although the needed changes will take time to orchestrate, several initiatives being developed in the United States and elsewhere are moving public and private efforts in this direction. One of these is the promotion of strategies to *prevent* rather than *control* pollution.

Pollution Prevention

There is an old adage that says, "An ounce of prevention is worth a pound of cure." This time-honored advice is now being used to help achieve sustainable development. Recent U.S. policy initiatives have begun to emphasize preventive measures that eliminate the release of contaminating residuals and hence

pollution prevention
Practices that reduce
or eliminate the
creation of
contaminating
residuals at the
source.

avoid having to deal with the associated adverse effects after the fact. According to a recent EPA directive, **pollution prevention** refers to:

the use of materials, processes, or practices that reduce or eliminate the creation of pollutants or wastes at the source. [This] includes practices that reduce the use of hazardous materials, energy, water or other resources, and practices that protect natural resources through conservation or more efficient use.[6]

Based on this definition, pollution prevention promotes a shift from ''end-of-pipe'' controls to ''front-end reduction'' strategies. Effectively, this implies that residual generation is a strategic variable and not simply a given to be dealt with after the fact. In the context of the materials balance model, preventive strategies change how economic activity is undertaken so that less contaminating residuals are released to nature.

Strong support for pollution prevention is offered by Barry Commoner, a scientist and director of the Center for Biology of Natural Systems at Queens College. He writes:

The impact of a pollutant on the environment can be remedied in two general ways: either the activity that generates the pollutant is changed to eliminate it; or, without altering the activity, a control device is added that traps or destroys the pollutant before it enters the environment. . . . The few real improvements have been achieved not by adding controls or concealing pollutants but by simply eliminating them. . . . This suggests an addition to the informal environmental laws: If you don't put something into the environment, it isn't there.[7]

Commoner supports his argument with references to such preventive policy initiatives as the elimination of leaded gasoline in the United States and the ban on DDT effected in 1972. Beyond these specific cases, the larger issue is to determine whether pollution prevention can and should be practiced on a broader scale.

Moving toward Pollution Prevention: U.S. Laws and Directives

Beginning with the National Environmental Policy Act of 1969 (NEPA), the federal government has attempted to integrate prevention into U.S. environmental legislation. One of the purposes of NEPA is ''to promote efforts which will prevent or eliminate damage to the environment and the biosphere.''

To formalize pollution prevention as an integral part of U.S. policy, Congress passed the Pollution Prevention Act of 1990. Its provisions outline the *priorities* for national environmental policy as follows:

---

[6]U.S. EPA (May 13, 1990) as cited in U.S. EPA, Office of Pollution Prevention (October 1991), p. 4.

[7]Commoner (1992), pp. 42–43.

TABLE 19.1   Key Provisions of the Pollution Prevention Act of 1990

The major provisions of the Pollution Prevention Act of 1990 call for the EPA to provide for the following:

- The creation of a new office within the EPA to establish and implement a national source reduction strategy to include:

  The definition of standard methods of measuring source reduction;

  The coordination of source reduction activities throughout EPA offices;

  The facilitation of source reduction methods to be used by business;

  The establishment of an advisory panel to assimilate and disseminate data;

  The initiation of a training program for EPA staff on source reduction opportunities;

  The development of improved methods to facilitate public access to data collected under environmental statutes;

  The creation of an annual award program to recognize firms operating innovative or outstanding source reduction programs.

- The institution of a matching grants program for states that establish pollution prevention programs for the private business sector.

- The creation of a database containing source reduction information established through a source reduction clearinghouse.

- The requirement of a toxic chemical source reduction and recycling report from all sources filing an annual toxic release inventory form under the provisions of SARA.

Source: Pollution Prevention Act of 1990, Sec.6604; 6605; 6606; 6607.

The Congress hereby declares it to be the national policy of the United States that pollution should be prevented or reduced at the source whenever feasible; pollution that cannot be prevented should be recycled in an environmentally safe manner, whenever feasible; pollution that cannot be prevented or recycled should be treated in an environmentally safe manner whenever feasible; and disposal or other release into the environment should be employed only as a last resort and should be conducted in an environmentally safe manner.[8]

Notice that the act ranks pollution prevention as the primary objective with management of residuals as a secondary objective to be achieved through recycling, treatment, and disposal—in that order. Beyond this prioritizing of national initiatives, the act also gives specific directives to guide the promotion of pollution prevention activities in the private and public sectors. Some of its key mandates are given in Table 19.1. Notice the emphasis on developing source reduction strategies and the use of incentives through awards and grants to help promote such practices in the business community.

In August 1994, President Clinton signed an executive order furthering the nation's commitment to pollution prevention. The thrust of this directive

---

[8]Pollution Prevention Act of 1990, Sec.6602(b).

is for all federal facilities to achieve a reduction of toxic emissions by 1999 and to require a reporting to the public of any releases made by these entities. The President explained the intent of this mandate as follows:

> With this Executive Order the federal facilities will set the example for the rest of the country and become the leader in applying pollution prevention to daily operations, purchasing decisions and policies.[9]

Strategies to Implement Pollution Prevention

source reduction
Any practice that lessens the amount of a hazardous substance that is released into the environment.

toxic chemical use substitution
The practice of using less harmful chemicals in place of more hazardous substances.

source segregation
A procedure that keeps hazardous waste from coming in contact with nonhazardous waste.

raw materials substitution
The practice of using productive inputs that generate little or no hazardous waste.

changes in manufacturing processes
The use of alternative production methods to generate less hazardous by-products.

While pollution prevention promotes the reduction of residuals or wastes generated by all segments of society, its emphasis has been on the industrial sector—the major source of hazardous pollution. In fact, two major preventive objectives for industry are: (1) **source reduction;** and (2) **toxic chemical use substitution. Source reduction** refers to any practice that lessens the amount of a hazardous substance or contaminant that either enters the waste stream or is otherwise released into the environment *before* recycling, treatment, or disposal.[10] **Toxic chemical use substitution** refers to the practice of using alternative, less harmful chemicals in place of more hazardous substances.[11]

These objectives are supported by several U.S. policy initiatives. For example, source reduction is explicitly listed as the first priority in the EPA's integrated waste management system that guides states' solid waste programs. The Federal Insecticide, Fungicide, and Rodenticide Act (FIFRA) promotes toxic chemical use substitution by empowering the EPA to cancel or restrict the use of any pesticide found to pose an unreasonable risk. In so doing, markets for less harmful pesticides should be created. Similar rulings are given in the Toxic Substances Control Act (TSCA) for nonpesticide chemicals.

A number of techniques have been proposed to help industry achieve the objectives of source reduction and toxic chemical use substitution. Among these are **source segregation, raw materials substitution, changes in manufacturing processes,** and **product substitution.**[12] The first of these, **source segregation** refers to any process that keeps hazardous waste from coming in contact with nonhazardous waste. This relatively simple and inexpensive method is widely used by many industries. By keeping the two types of waste materials separate, the accumulation of hazardous waste is not needlessly increased by contaminated nonhazardous waste. These efforts help generators lower their costs of managing wastes and enhance social benefits by reducing the risk of exposure.

Two other methods, **raw materials substitution** and **changes in manufacturing processes,** also hold promise for helping to prevent pollution. Both

---

[9]U.S. EPA, Office of Communications, Education, and Public Affairs (August 16, 1993).
[10]Pollution Prevention Act of 1990, Sec.6603(5)(A).
[11]U.S. EPA, Office of Pollution Prevention (October 1991), p. 7.
[12]This discussion is drawn from U.S. EPA, Office of Solid Waste (November 1986), p. 19.

product substitution
The selection of environmentally safe commodities in place of potentially polluting products.

can be used by industry during the production phase of its operations. By using inputs that generate little or no hazardous waste, the size of the residual flow can be dramatically reduced. Likewise, alternative manufacturing processes can be sought or existing ones altered to generate less hazardous by-products. Finally, **product substitution,** an adjustment made *after* the production phase, refers to the selection of environmentally safe commodities over their potentially polluting substitutes.

The Corporate Experience[13]

As environmental regulations strengthened during the 1970s, U.S. corporations realized that increasingly stringent controls would likely follow. Recognizing the trend, some forward-thinking firms decided it would be advantageous to respond in a progressive manner rather than to simply comply with the new mandates. One of the first U.S. companies to adopt this approach was 3M Corporation, launching its "Pollution Prevention Pays Program" in 1975. Through this "3Ps Program" as it is known, the corporate giant designed an employee-based plan aimed at finding ways to reduce the company's pollution while maintaining or improving financial performance. The majority of 3M's prevention strategies are based upon technological improvements, such as product reformulation, process modification, recycling, equipment redesign, and waste recovery for resale.

According to corporate officials, the payoffs of 3M's pollution prevention program have been substantial. First, the company has achieved significant reductions in the pollutants it releases into the environment. A recent corporate estimate reports that the program has been responsible for a worldwide reduction in annual releases of about 450,000 tons. In fact, since the program's inception in 1975 up through 1989, 3M claims that its innovative program has cut its pollution per unit of production in half. Secondly, the firm asserts that the technological changes it has introduced yielded a financial savings of over $400 million in the first year of the project's operations. Capitalizing on this success, 3M launched a companion program in 1988 called 3P+. Aimed specifically at reducing hydrocarbon emissions, the 3P+ plan calls for a $150 million capital investment that should yield results to surpass the statutory clean air requirements set by both federal and state governments. Thus far, corporate savings from its collective preventive initiatives total $710 million.

Following the lead of 3M and other corporate leaders in environmentalism, many other companies have implemented their own pollution prevention programs. By way of example, consider the summary of selected corporate plans given in Table 19.2 along with their objectives and recent

---

[13]Much of the following is drawn from U.S. EPA, Office of Pollution Prevention (October 1991), Chapter 3; Bringer (1988); and Kelly (November 7, 1994).

TABLE 19.2   Corporate Programs Aimed at Pollution Prevention

Company	Scope	Goals	Accomplishments
Chevron Save Money and Reduce Toxics Program (SMART) 1987	SMART adopts EPA's hierarchy, focusing on industrial source reduction, toxic chemical use substitution, and recycling for hazardous and nonhazardous solid wastes.	Reduce hazardous waste generation by 65% by 1992 and recycle the remainder; find nontoxic alternatives to toxic materials and processes; devise safer operating procedures to reduce accidental releases; ensure that pollution reductions in one area do not transfer pollution to another.	From 1987 to 1990, Chevron reduced hazardous waste by 60% and saved over $10 million in disposal costs.
Dow Waste Reduction Always Pays (WRAP) 1986	Industrial source reduction and on-site recycling.	Increase management support for waste reduction activities, establish a recognition and reward system for individual plants, compile waste reduction data; decrease SARA 313 air emissions by 50% by 1995 compared to 1988. Decrease toxic air emissions by 71% by December 1992.	SARA 313 overall releases are down from 12,252 tons in 1987 to 9,659 tons in 1989, off-site transfers are down by 15%. Air emissions have decreased by 54% from 1984.
General Electric Pollution, Waste and Emissions Reduction Program (POWER) 1989	Program encompasses all waste streams (e.g. hazardous, nonhazardous, packaging, and ultimate disposal of product) and adopts EPA's hierarchy, which places source reduction first.	Prevent or minimize "the generation or release of waste and pollutants, to the extent technically and economically feasible, throughout the life cycle of the product, including design, production, packaging, and ultimate fate in the environment."	GE Appliances' Louisville plant has reduced its production of hazardous wastewater treatment sludge by 95%. Other GE plants have experienced similar declines in hazardous wastes and air emissions.
Polaroid Toxic Use and Waste Reduction (TUWR) 1987	Industrial source reduction and toxic chemical use substitution are priorities followed by recycling and reuse.	Reduce toxic use at the source and waste per unit of production by 10% per year in each of the 5 years ending in 1993 and emphasize increased recycling of waste materials within the company.	Using 1988 as the base year, the company reported an 11% reduction in toxic use and waste in 1989.

Source: U.S. Environmental Protection Agency, Office of Pollution Prevention, *Pollution Prevention 1991: Progress on Reducing Industrial Pollutants* (Washington, D.C., October 1991), Table 3–2, pp. 45–49.

accomplishments. As these examples suggest, many firms seem to have recognized that pollution prevention is not only beneficial to the environment, but good for business as well.[14]

Economic Analysis of Pollution Prevention

Polluters must determine when preventive approaches should be employed, to what extent, and through which strategy. Economic criteria and their associated decision rules are just as applicable to guiding the use of preventive strategies as they are to any other environmental policy instrument. Whether or not a firm adopts pollution prevention as part of its business strategy will depend to a large extent on its cost relative to other options such as the use of treatment or abatement technologies. The goal is to select the least-cost option to achieve cost-effectiveness and enhance profit. Similarly, if the firm determines that pollution prevention *is* a cost-effective option, it then must select among the available strategies to implement it using the cost-effectiveness criterion as a guide. If, for example, the firm can access nontoxic raw materials more cheaply than converting its production processes, it will pursue that strategy.

Given the importance of relative costs in this decision-making process, government can help promote pollution prevention through various means. For example, it can encourage the development of inexpensive nontoxic chemical substitutes and cost-effective production changes perhaps through grants or subsidies. It might also develop ways to enhance the communication of effective pollution prevention strategies to industry. Look back at Table 19.1 to see how the Pollution Prevention Act calls for the EPA to perform some of these tasks. By the end of fiscal year 1993, over $25 million in grant monies were awarded to states for developing pollution prevention programs. Also important is for government to assist firms in making accurate cost assessments about pollution prevention strategies. This is precisely the motivation of the Environmental Accounting and Capital Budgeting Project under the EPA's Design for the Environment (DfE) Program. The project is a cooperative effort among government, business, and academia aimed at improving managerial accounting and capital budgeting practices to more fully incorporate environmental considerations. In so doing, the DfE project expects that more businesses will recognize the advantages of using preventive technologies and processes.[15]

Finally, benefit-cost analysis can help determine the extent to which a given preventive strategy should be employed. Qualitatively, we can identify

---

[14]Likewise, the public sector is taking action to integrate pollution prevention strategies in its activities. Of particular significance are the initiatives being undertaken by the Department of Defense and the Department of Energy, both of which are discussed in U.S. EPA, Office of Pollution Prevention (October 1991), Chapter 5.

[15]King and Schaeffer (July–September 1993); U.S. EPA, Office of Pollution Prevention and Toxics (October 1993).

some of the associated benefits to the firm as abatement cost savings, the avoidance of regulatory penalties for noncompliance, and the gain in revenues associated with presenting an environmentally responsible image to consumers. On the cost side, the firm has to assess the search costs in identifying available options, the administrative costs in analyzing these options, engineering design expenses, and the expenditures to implement the strategy such as retooling or capital investment. To achieve the efficient level at which a pollutant is eliminated, the decision rule is the same as in other contexts. The firm should find the point where the marginal cost of doing so is exactly offset by the marginal benefit.[16]

International Cooperative Arrangements

Sustainable development is intended to be a global objective, the benefits of which should accrue to all segments of society and to all nations. Because of its intent and its pervasive implications, it calls for a collaborative effort from all stakeholders. In this part of the chapter, we explore representative examples of international treaties and other types of cooperative agreements. Some we have discussed in other contexts, others are introduced for the first time. What they share is a joining together of national interests to promote some aspect of the dual goals of sustainable development.

United Nations Conference on Environment and Development (UNCED)[17]

More commonly called the Rio Summit, the U.N. Conference on Environment and Development was a 12-day worldwide forum held in Rio de Janeiro, Brazil, in 1992. Thousands of delegates from over 170 nations attended the event to discuss issues and concerns dealing with sustainable development. Three major documents were produced from the Summit: *Agenda 21*, the *Rio Declaration*, and the *Statement of Forest Principles*. A brief description of each follows.

Agenda 21.   This 40-chapter document is a voluntary action plan outlining the course for worldwide progress toward sustainable development. Table 19.3 summarizes its four primary sections collectively intended to guide decision-making into the 21st century. Major issues covered within the 900 pages of *Agenda 21* include: financing for developing countries; conservation and sustainable development for forests; prevention and minimization of hazardous

---

[16]For a recent economic analysis of pollution prevention and the hierarchy given in the Pollution Prevention Act of 1990, see Helfand (1994).

[17]The following discussion is drawn from Reilly (September/October 1992); Sessions (April–June 1993a), p. 12; and Parson, Haas, and Levy (October 1992).

TABLE 19.3   A Summary of the Rio Summit's *Agenda 21*

Section 1: "Social and Economic Dimensions"
Includes recommended actions on sustainable development cooperation, poverty, consumption, demographics, health, human settlements, and integration of the environment and development in decision-making.

Section 2: "Conservation and Management of Resources for Development"
Includes chapters on atmospheric protection, land resources, deforestation, desertification and drought, mountains, agriculture, biological diversity, biotechnology, oceans, freshwater resources, toxic chemicals, hazardous wastes, solid wastes, and radioactive wastes.

Section 3: "Strengthening the Role of Major Groups"
Includes ways to increase the participation in sustainable development efforts of major social groups: women, youth, indigenous peoples, nongovernmental organizations, local authorities, trade unions, business and industry, scientific and technological communities, and farmers.

Section 4: "Means of Implementation"
Comprises chapters on financial resources; technology transfer, cooperation, and capacity building; science; education; public awareness and training; institutional arrangements; legal instruments and mechanisms; and information collection, analysis, and dissemination.

Source: Kathy Sessions, "What's in Agenda 21?" *EPA Journal* 19, no. 2 (April–June 1993b), p. 14.

and solid wastes; reforms of international institutions to facilitate environmental protection; strategies to address ocean pollution and the protection of marine life; international cooperation for technological advance; and risk assessment and management of toxic chemicals. Perhaps the most important achievement of the Rio Summit, *Agenda 21* is the result of two and one-half years of negotiations to reach an international consensus on environmental issues.

Rio Declaration.   This document outlines 27 principles to act as guidelines for achieving global environmental quality and economic development. For example, Principle 4 requires that environmental protection be an integral part of development, and Principle 8 calls for a reduction in "unsustainable patterns of production and consumption."[18] Reportedly, the declaration is a compromise from what was originally anticipated. The preparatory meetings were intense, often immersed in seeking a balance among the views of developing and industrialized countries. So fragile was this agreement that it was adopted at Rio without further negotiation for fear that further discussion would jeopardize what was left of the intended Earth Charter.

---

[18]Interestingly, Principle 16 refers to the "polluter-pays principle" and the use of market instruments.

Statement of Forest Principles.   This document addresses forest management, calling for international cooperation on such issues as technical and financial aid, trade relations, and scientific advance. Included are 17 nonbinding principles for a global consensus on the sustainable development of all types of forests. Although the statement represents *some* progress, it is viewed as a second-best outcome to the anticipated, legally binding convention on forest management and conservation. The United States had proposed such a convention two years prior to the summit, but the proposal met with resistance from forest-owning, developing countries. Negotiations stalled because these nations are concerned about how such a convention might lead to an ''internationalization'' of their forest resources and threaten their sovereignty.

International Agreements to Control Transboundary Pollution

Some pollution problems are transboundary, such as acidic deposition, ozone depletion, global warming, and some surface water pollution. Hence, contamination in one nation can travel beyond its borders—a type of international externality. In these cases, formal treaties must be negotiated and agreed to by all affected countries. Within these agreements are often rulings specifically aimed at the distinct problems of developing nations and the need for financial and technical support from their wealthier and more advanced counterparts.

Montreal Protocol and Amendments.   Originally signed by 24 countries in September of 1987, the Montreal Protocol on Substances that Deplete the Ozone Layer is an important example of international cooperation aimed at environmental protection. Strengthened by the 1990 London Amendments and the 1992 Copenhagen Conference, this treaty is aimed at phasing out CFCs and other ozone-depleting substances. More than 90 countries have ratified the protocol to date, accounting for 96 percent of the world's usage of CFCs and 85 percent of the world population.[19] Recognizing the special problems of developing nations and at the same time the importance of gaining their support, industrialized countries set up a $160 million Interim Multilateral Fund to assist them in transitioning toward CFC-substitute technologies. They also were given a 10-year grace period to meet the targets of the agreement. An important accomplishment was the addition of China to the group of signatories in 1991. Its high rate of growth and enormous population mean that its commitment to the protocol is critical. Predictions indicate that China's production of CFCs at 117,000 metric tons in 1991 will more than double by the year 2000 if demand goes unchecked.[20]

---

[19]Dumanoski (November 26, 1992).

[20]National Environmental Protection Agency (March 1993) as cited in World Resources Institute (1994b), p. 78.

U.N. Framework Convention on Climate Change.   Adopted by more than 150 nations, including the United States, this convention established a baseline for a global, cooperative response to climate change. In March 1994, the treaty became legally binding following its ratification by the requisite number of 50 countries in 1993. Among the first 10 nations to ratify the agreement was China. It will need strong support from other nations to contain its rising consumption of coal and associated CO_2 emissions, predicted to triple over the next 35 years. A key provision and one that continues to be debated is a commitment by each signatory to implement a national strategy to limit greenhouse gas (GHG) emissions. Each strategy is to support the common objective of reducing emissions to their 1990 levels by the year 2000.[21] This provision was the focus of debate at a 1995 meeting of the U.N. Climate Conference in Berlin.

Some participants at the Berlin conference continued to support the commitment, while others argued it is inadequate. Further debate centered around the establishment of specific timetables and emissions targets. Major CO_2 generators like Japan and the United States were pressured to make stronger pledges to the climate control treaty, but lobbyists from these countries are concerned about what such commitments might mean to international competitiveness and domestic jobs. The conference produced little more than an agreement to conduct further negotiations called the Berlin Mandate. Over the next two years international representatives will negotiate to draft policy and to establish deadlines and emissions targets.[22]

London Dumping Convention (LDC).   Ocean dumping of certain wastes, including radioactive wastes, is prohibited by the Convention on the Prevention of Marine Pollution by Dumping of Waste and Other Matter, commonly referred to as the London Dumping Convention (LDC). Originally decreed in November 1972, the LDC now has been ratified by 70 nations, including the United States.[23] In fact, all nations that have recently engaged in ocean dumping of radioactive wastes are contracting parties to the LDC. A discussion of some of the recent initiatives brought before the convention is the subject of Application 19.3.

U.S.-Canada Air Quality Agreement.   In March 1991, an agreement was finalized between the United States and Canada to combat the problem of acid rain and visibility impairment. The agreement calls for each country to commit to national emissions caps on sulfur dioxide (SO_2) and nitrogen oxides (NO_x). The bilateral provisions also include directives to establish a forum for

---

[21]Council on Environmental Quality (January 1993), pp. 142–43; World Resources Institute (1994b), p. 202; Chandler, Makarov, and Dadi (September 1990), p. 125, as cited in World Resources Institute (1994b), p. 78.

[22]Reuters (April 8, 1995).

[23]For more detail on the origin and content of the LDC, see National Advisory Committee on Oceans and Atmosphere (April 1984).

Application 19.3

The London Dumping Convention (LDC): An International Agreement on Ocean Dumping Rules

Signed over 20 years ago, the London Dumping Convention (LDC) is an international agreement to control the practice of dumping wastes at sea. It is the only such convention to which the United States is a signatory nation. As of 1992, the LDC has been accepted by 70 nations, among them the major industrialized countries that generate most of the wastes being dumped into the sea. The LDC controls ocean dumping through various means. It bans the ocean disposal of so-called "black-listed" substances like mercury and cadmium. The disposal of "grey-listed" or less damaging substances is controlled through special permits, and the dumping of any other substances is managed through a general permitting system.

One of the convention's most significant achievements was a ban on the disposal of high-level nuclear waste in ocean waters. Another was a 10-year voluntary moratorium on the disposal of low-level nuclear waste, which was agreed to by the signatories in 1983. At the LDC's 1990 annual meeting, a consensus was reached to phase out ocean dumping of all industrial wastes by December 31, 1995. The phaseout is to be achieved without transferring the damage to some other environmental media. Each member nation is to be responsible for enforcing this resolution and for prosecuting any of its ships found to be in violation. At this same session, the delegates proposed that an international agreement be drafted to control land-based ocean pollution. This action is in direct response to the fact that more than 80 percent of ocean pollution is generated on land.

More recently, 44 of the 70 LDC signatories gathered at the 1992 meeting. The most significant decision to come out of this assembly was an agreement to update the rules of the convention in 1994. There are three major issues that the member nations must consider for revision: the disposal of low-level radioactive waste; the dumping of

industrial waste; and the incineration of toxic liquid waste. Several countries, namely Denmark, Norway, and Iceland, submitted their collective proposal to ban all of these activities on a permanent basis. In November 1993, 37 of the signatories *did* vote to permanently ban the ocean disposal of low-level radioactive wastes. Although there were no votes against, five nations abstained—Belgium and four nuclear powers, China, France, Russia, and the U.K. Of greatest concern was Russia's abstention, since this nation had just one month prior dumped over 237,000 gallons of low-level radioactive waste in the Sea of Japan. Russian authorities have stated that they need international aid to help them build proper waste storage facilities on land.

There is little question that the LDC must address some difficult decisions in the months and years ahead. While the convention is concerned with ocean pollution, the member nations *do* use the ocean to dispose of a significant amount of waste materials. In fact, according to LDC data, during the 1976 to 1982 period the members used the sea to dispose of some 300 to 400 millions tons of waste on average per year. Hence, as these nations restrict or eliminate waste disposal at sea, they must develop alternatives that will allow the advance of industrial activity without simply transferring the environmental damage from the earth's oceans to some place on land.

Sources: U.S. Congress, Office of Technology Assessment (OTA), *Wastes in Marine Environments* (Washington, D.C.: U.S. Government Printing Office, 1987), pp. 73, 149; Associated Press, "Industrial Nations Ban Dumping Waste at Sea," *Boston Globe,* November 3, 1990; Associated Press, "44 Nations Agree to Update Rules on Ocean Dumping," *Boston Globe,* November 14, 1992; Edith M. Lederer, "Ban on Atomic Dumping at Sea Voted; 4 Nuclear Powers Abstain," *Boston Globe,* November 13, 1993; Associated Press, "Russia to Continue Dumping Nuclear Waste at Sea," *Boston Globe,* October 19, 1993b.

addressing other transboundary air quality issues. Among these are rulings for each nation to undertake research to improve understanding of their common air pollution problems and stipulations to facilitate a regular flow of information about monitoring, effects of air pollutants, and control methodologies. The U.S. commitment to these concerns is confirmed by the 1990 Clean Air Act Amendments, which refer specifically to Canada's acid rain program. The statutes call for regular reporting to Congress on the SO_2 and NO_x emissions of all Canadian provinces participating in Canada's control program.

International Trade Agreements and Environmental Protection

International trade negotiations have always been the subject of political and economic debate. Although there are known economic advantages to trade, exchange between nations is nonetheless a complex undertaking. Trade negotiations are rarely if ever totally distinct from political objectives and national defense issues. The gains from trade can easily become clouded by protectionist attitudes fueled by differences in product safety regulations, labor laws, and nationalism. Recently, international trade discussions have triggered controversy of another sort—the potential conflict between the associated economic gains and a decline in environmental quality.

A common concern about foreign trade is that lenient labor laws and relatively low wage rates in less developed nations can adversely affect employment in more advanced countries. Similar apprehensions have arisen about differences in environmental regulations between trading partners. Production costs are lower in countries with lenient environmental standards, which can give producers there an unfair advantage relative to competitors in nations with more stringent controls. Another source of controversy is the quality of imports produced in nations with lax regulations on toxic chemical use, fuel efficiency, and coal consumption.

On the opposite side of the coin, trade advocates argue that the economic gains from trade will help poorer nations afford the costly cleanup of what is in many cases severe environmental pollution. In the case of transboundary pollution, the benefits from this response may accrue to bordering countries or those located downstream along a common river. These arguments are consistent with the premise of sustainable development—that economic prosperity, in this context enhanced through trade, can bring about improvements in environmental quality.

These and other issues were part of the lengthy and often contentious negotiations associated with the North American Free Trade Agreement (NAFTA) and the latest round of the General Agreement on Tariffs and Trade (GATT).

North American Free Trade Agreement (NAFTA).[24]   Following a difficult series of negotiations, many of which centered on environmental issues,

---

[24]Drawn from Council on Environmental Quality (January 1993), pp. 52–53.

NAFTA was reached by the United States, Mexico, and Canada in 1992 and approved by Congress in 1993. Among its provisions are the following, which are aimed at economic advance and environmental quality:

- Explicit language that asserts the signatories' commitment to sustainable development.
- Agreement among the three nations to implement NAFTA in accordance with the aim of environmental protection and not to lower health, safety, or environmental standards to attract investment.
- Consensus to aim for congruence of each country's respective environmental regulations while preserving each nation's right to select a level of environmental quality that it deems appropriate.
- Agreement that NAFTA dispute settlement panels will solicit environmental experts for advice on factual issues as needed.

Consistent with NAFTA, the United States and Mexico also implemented a 1992–1994 Integrated Environmental Plan for the border region. The 2,000-mile border has been a source of concern because of the concentration of the now infamous *maquiladora* factories positioned there for access to American markets. Effluent releases into the Rio Grande River and air emissions far exceed U.S. standards. The plan, supported by $208 million from Congress and $160 million from the Mexican government, was aimed at improving water quality, monitoring air pollution, tracking hazardous waste, developing enforcement cooperation, and promoting pollution prevention.

General Agreement on Tariffs and Trade (GATT).[25]   Originally executed in 1947, GATT is a major international treaty on foreign trade. Its avowed purpose is to reduce tariffs and other trade barriers. The 107 signatories, mostly developing countries, meet periodically for discussions called rounds, the latest being the Uruguay Round. This round began in 1986 and was signed in December 1993. The associated negotiations, much like those preceding the signing of NAFTA, had to consider environmental protection issues. However, most environmentalists say that the long-awaited agreement did not respond adequately to their concerns.

Green opposition to GATT was stronger than it had been to NAFTA. Reportedly, the intense debate was fueled by a 1991 GATT panel ruling that the United States could not block imports of tuna from Mexico harvested under conditions yielding an unacceptable, incidental kill rate of dolphins.[26] However, the arguments that ultimately pitted open-traders against environmentalists during the GATT round run broader and deeper than this single incident. Fundamentally, environmentalists are wary of any agreement that

---

[25]Drawn from Council on Environmental Quality (January 1993), pp. 52–53; Davis (January 10, 1994); Noah (December 16, 1993); Cough (April–June 1993); and *The Economist* (February 27, 1993), pp. 25–28.

[26]According to GATT provisions, import restrictions may be allowed to protect biological life only in the importing country, not the exporting nation.

promotes economic growth and hence increases the potential for ecological damage. Furthermore, they are concerned about how GATT rulings that deter trade restrictions run counter to environmental aims. A few examples will illustrate. A nation cannot use countervailing duties on imports from a country whose environmental regulations are lower, and therefore less costly to producers, than its own. An import cannot be restricted based solely on the exporter's use of a pollution-generating input or production method. Relatively high environmental standards in one country can be viewed as restrictions on free trade. In fact, in 1994 U.S. fuel-efficiency standards came under the review of a GATT panel to determine if they posed an unfair disadvantage on European-made cars. Reportedly, the standards could be overturned if the panel determines that an alternative instrument like higher fuel taxes could achieve the same objective with less of a restraint on free trade.

According to the Uruguay Draft, countries are required to use the least trade-restrictive measures to achieve environmental goals, and in most cases international standards should be employed rather than national ones. Economically, the concern is that such a universal set of guidelines may become a ceiling instead of a floor. Nations might recognize the incentive to keep standards and enforcement relatively low as a way to keep compliance costs down and attract foreign investment. Notice this is not unlike the incentive problems arising in state governments responsible for setting environmental standards in the United States. In any case, once this pattern emerges, other countries may follow suit to maintain export competitiveness.

On the opposite side of the debate are those less developed nations that view the stringent environmental standards in the United States and elsewhere as ''green'' protectionism and the unilateral use of trade restrictions as a form of ''eco-imperialism.'' During the negotiations, the United States had pushed for a permanent committee that would consider any environmentally motivated revisions in trade rules, but its proposal was blocked by India, Brazil, and other developing countries. Responding to congressional concerns that GATT could frustrate U.S. environmental legislation, the United States is continuing to promote the formation of an international Committee on Trade and the Environment.

Domestic Partnerships

Although the perspective is global, initiatives promoting sustainable development have to begin within national borders. Just as is the case for international agreements, domestic initiatives also require cooperation, but of a different sort. In many industrialized countries, collaborative arrangements are being developed between government and industry, between environmental groups and businesses, and among private firms and industries.

Sustainable development and related objectives like pollution prevention call for significant change in how firms make decisions, engineer their production, and design and market their products. If businesses perceive these changes as counter to their own self-interest, they will be met with resistance at best. To foster a positive evolution in thinking and business planning, governments are attempting to work with industry and environmental groups to share information, to foster needed technological development, and to find solutions that satisfy both environmental and business objectives. As these efforts have taken hold, cooperative arrangements have begun to form—some within the private sector, and others the result of government-sponsored partnership programs.

Government-Sponsored Partnerships

Green Lights Program
A plan that fosters partnerships between the business sector and the EPA aimed at improving energy efficiency.

Energy Star Program
A product-labeling plan encouraging manufacturers to develop energy-saving products.

33/50 Program
A program that encourages firms emitting one or more of 17 priority pollutants to voluntarily reduce releases of those substances.

In the United States, national efforts to achieve sustainable development are being implemented in part through the launching of voluntary partnership programs between the EPA and private industry. One of these is the **Green Lights Program** launched in 1991. The plan encourages private firms to commit to using energy-efficient lighting, but only if it improves or maintains lighting quality *and* if the conversion is profitable.[27] Another is a product-labeling plan called the **Energy Star Program.** Introduced in 1992, this plan urges manufacturers to develop personal computers that "power-down" or "sleep" when not in use. An "Energy Star" logo is then used to communicate to prospective buyers both the potential cost savings and the reduction in polluting emissions from lower and more efficient energy use. Among the program's participants are IBM, Apple Computer, and Digital Equipment. The EPA projects that the plan will yield a 50 percent reduction in energy use with no added costs. The program has recently been expanded to laser printers with commitments from manufacturers collectively responsible for 80 percent of U.S. sales. This plan is expected to yield an annual reduction of 6 billion kilowatt-hours of electricity, which translates to a measurable reduction in power plant emissions and a $450 million savings on utility bills.[28]

Another government-sponsored pollution prevention strategy is the **33/50 Program,** which uses the Toxics Release Inventory (TRI) database.[29] Administered by the EPA's Office of Toxic Substances, the 33/50 strategy is a noncompulsory program calling upon those firms emitting one or more of 17 priority pollutants to voluntarily reduce their releases of those substances. Using 1988 as a baseline, the goal is to achieve a 33 percent reduction nationwide by 1992 and a 50 percent reduction by 1995. Detail on this cooperative program is given in Application 19.4.

---

[27]For more detail, refer to Application 12.2, "The EPA's Green Lights Program" in Chapter 12.

[28]U.S. EPA, Office of Air and Radiation (October 1992), pp. 8–9; *EPA Journal* (April–June 1993), p. 7.

[29]Recall that the TRI database is authorized under the reporting requirements of Title III of the 1986 Superfund Amendments.

Application 19.4

A Government-Corporate Partnership: The 33/50 Program

Every member of society has much to gain from preventing pollution. Health and ecological improvements are important benefits that arise from any reduction in the release of polluting residuals into the environment. At the industry level, there also are financial gains from participating in this process. In fact, firms can realize a competitive advantage by integrating pollution prevention measures into their business plans. Through source reduction and toxic chemical use substitution, companies can significantly reduce their waste disposal expenses, avoid the high costs of regulatory compliance, and eliminate the risk of liability associated

with improper waste treatment or disposal. Beyond these direct financial benefits, businesses can also achieve intangible gains, such as improved public relations and stronger alliances with their employees.

Recognizing these natural incentives for firms to practice pollution prevention, the EPA initiated its 33/50 Program, a plan calling for the voluntary reduction of the release and off-site transfer of 17 highly toxic pollutants. These 17 targeted chemicals and their 1988 and 1990 release levels are shown in the graph below.

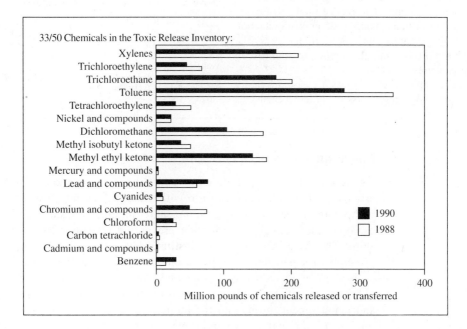

Source: U.S. Environmental Protection Agency, Office of Toxic Substances, Washington, D.C., 1992, cited in the Council on Environmental Quality, *Environmental Quality, 23rd Annual Report* (Washington, D.C.: U.S. Government Printing Office, January 1993), p. 180.

Application 19.4 (concluded)

Launched in 1991, the EPA's program is so named for its objective—a 33 percent reduction in national releases of the 17 chemicals by 1992 and a 50 percent reduction by 1995, using 1988 levels as a baseline. These pollutants were selected on the basis of three criteria cited by the EPA: (1) they are associated with environmental and health effects; (2) they are high-volume industrial chemicals; and (3) they potentially can be reduced through pollution prevention measures.

To initiate the program, the EPA invited nearly 6,000 companies to participate. While the agency had hoped for widespread participation, only 937 companies had committed to the plan by October 1992. However, included among the participants are over half of the largest releasers of the 17 target chemicals. Collectively, the 937 participating firms voluntarily committed to reduce their releases by nearly 350 million pounds—a 25 percent reduction below the 1988 baseline. By October 1994, the number of firms committed to the program rose to approximately 1,250.

Based on the 1992 Toxics Release Inventory data, releases and transfers of the 17 target chemicals declined by 40 percent between the baseline year of 1988 and 1992. This reduction exceeds the 33/50 program's interim goal by over 100 million pounds. According to the EPA, reductions such as these would take far longer under a command-and-control scheme and would likely be delayed by the lengthy legislative process. Another advantage is that the voluntary nature of the program allows participating firms the flexibility to choose the most cost-effective means to achieve their objectives. The agency believes that the 33/50 Program and other plans that *encourage* rather than *mandate* change hold great promise for the future.

Source: U.S. Environmental Protection Agency, Office of Prevention, Pesticides, and Toxic Substances, *The 33/50 Program: Forging an Alliance for Pollution Prevention* (Washington, D.C., August 1992); Council on Environmental Quality, *Environmental Quality, 23rd Annual Report* (Washington, D.C.: U.S. Government Printing Office, January 1993), pp. 179–80; U.S. Environmental Protection Agency, Office of Communications, Education, and Public Affairs, *Securing our Legacy, An EPA Progress Report 1989–1991* (Washington, D.C., April 1992), p. 22; U.S. Environmental Protection Agency, Office of Pollution Prevention and Toxics, *33/50 Program Company Profiles: Reduction Highlights* (Washington, D.C., October 1994).

Cooperative Arrangements within Industry

As the advantages of pollution prevention have become known, cooperative arrangements have begun to form within the private business sector—some without any intervention by government. A number of trade associations, for example, have developed pollution prevention programs for their memberships. The American Petroleum Institute devised a set of 11 environmental principles for petroleum facilities, one of which specifically sets a goal for each member to reduce emissions and waste generation. The institute also publishes reports to communicate information on trends in waste generation and management throughout the industry and to update members on waste minimization practices. A similar plan has been devised for the chemical industry, a major contributor to environmental pollution. This one, called the "Responsible Care Program," was developed by the Chemical Manufacturers Association and is the subject of Application 19.5.[30]

---

[30]U.S. EPA, Office of Pollution Prevention (October 1991), pp. 40–41.

Application 19.5

An Industry's Response to Pollution Prevention: The Chemical Manufacturers Association's "Responsible Care Program"

As a major contributor to the nation's hazardous waste stream, the chemical industry recently developed a pollution prevention program that signals the industry's commitment to a cleaner environment. In 1988, the industry's trade alliance, Chemical Manufacturers Association (CMA), launched its Responsible Care Program as a comprehensive chemical management plan to be adopted by its entire membership. Following the lead of the Canadian Chemical Producers Association, which established its plan in 1985, the U.S. program ushered in a series of principles to guide its members in reducing both waste generation and dangerous releases into the environment. The objectives are simple but powerful—to protect the health and safety of the workforce and to protect the environment from contamination.

Implementation of the comprehensive program is guided by a Code of Management Practices, which also includes a Waste and Release Reduction Code. The 10 guiding principles of CMA's Responsible Care Program are listed in the table below.

Britain's counterpart to the CMA, the Chemical Industries Association, also joined the ranks of trade associations working to prevent pollution. Their Responsible Care Program came on line in March 1989—the first such plan in Europe. Not surprisingly, the U.K. program is based upon a set of principles not unlike the CMA's list of 10.

The direct consequence of programs like CMA's is difficult to distinguish from the effects of tougher laws and various government-sponsored programs. Nonetheless, this industrywide commitment rooted in worker participation and communication with the general public is bound to complement regulatory efforts.

Sources: U.S. Environmental Protection Agency, Office of Pollution Prevention, *Pollution Prevention 1991: Progress on Reducing Industrial Pollutants* (Washington, D.C., October 1991), pp. 40–41; Chemical Manufacturers Association, *Improving Performance in the Chemical Industry* (September 1990), pp. 9–15; Peter Simmons and Brian Wynne, "Responsible Care: Trust, Credibility, and Environmental Management," in Kurt Fischer and Johan Schot, eds., *Environmental Strategies for Industry: International Perspectives on Research Needs and Policy Implications* (Washington, D.C.: Island Press, 1993), pp. 207–26.

CMA's Responsible Care Program Guidelines

1. Establish a strong and ongoing commitment by senior management to the reduction of wastes and releases to the environment.
2. Establish a quantitative inventory of each plant's waste generation and releases.
3. Evaluate the potential impacts of waste releases on workers and the general public.
4. Inform and obtain feedback from workers and the public about the facility's inventory and its potential environmental impact.
5. After accounting for both the potential environmental impacts and the community's feedback, establish priorities, goals, and plans for waste and release reduction.
6. Continue to work toward the reduction of wastes and releases through the following hierarchy: (i) source reduction; (ii) recycle/reuse; and (iii) treatment.
7. Monitor the progress of waste reduction and releases at each facility by updating the waste inventory at least once each year.
8. Maintain good communication with employees and the general public on progress, new information, and future plans.
9. Incorporate waste and release reduction objectives in the design of new or modified facilities, processes, or products.
10. Maintain a program that promotes and supports the waste and release reduction activities by others.

Source: Chemical Manufacturers Association (CMA), *Improving Performance in the Chemical Industry* (September 1990), pp. 9–15, as cited in U.S. Environmental Protection Agency, Office of Pollution Prevention (October 1991), pp. 40–41.

Other partnerships are forming among firms from *different* industries. One example is a recent merger of sorts that promotes recycling in the business community. Called the "Buy Recycled Business Alliance," the group was initiated in 1992 by the National Recycling Coalition with some financial backing from the EPA. The group comprises independent firms dedicated to buying goods produced from recycled materials. Currently, some 35 firms and trade associations are members, including major corporations like Anheuser-Busch, American Airlines, McDonald's Corp., AT&T, and The Coca-Cola Co. The founding members formalized the coalition by signing a charter. They also surveyed their current levels of recycled purchases, which summed to a substantial $3 billion, to use as a baseline from which to monitor progress. The alliance's two-year goal is to sign up 5,000 firms to join them in their efforts.[31]

Other collaborative efforts are the result of corporations joining forces with environmental groups. In 1990, McDonald's formed a Waste Reduction Task Force with the environmental group Environmental Defense Fund—a coalition successful enough to win it a Presidential Environment and Conservation Challenge Award for Partnership one year later. Among the results achieved by the task force were a 42-step action plan, the formulation of a corporate environmental policy, and the integration of waste reduction efforts throughout McDonald's organization. Already, the fast-food giant has replaced its chlorine-bleached paper products with brown, unbleached paper. It is recycling corrugated boxes, which account for over 33 percent of an average restaurant's trash, and it is asking suppliers to use boxes containing 35 percent recycled material. McDonald's is also testing and experimenting with a variety of reusable or recyclable packages, lids, and storage containers. In its "McRecycle USA" program, it purchases more than $125 million in recycled products each year for restaurant operations, renovation, and construction in addition to $80 million per year for recycled packaging, tray liners, napkins, and the like. It has also integrated waste reduction into its purchasing decisions along with cost, functionality, and availability. As of 1993, the average McDonald's in the United States has reduced its packaging by over 650 pounds, which adds up to nearly 3,000 tons of waste elimination from its 9,000 restaurants across America.[32]

Education and Technology Transfer

technology transfer
The advancement and application of technologies and strategies on a global scale.

Critical to consistent progress toward sustainable development is **technology transfer,** the advancement and application of technologies and management strategies across economic sectors throughout the world. Environmental

---

[31]U.S. EPA, Office of Solid Waste and Emergency Response (Winter/Spring 1993), pp. 1, 12.
[32]U.S. EPA, Office of Solid Waste and Emergency Response (Spring 1992), pp. 1, 3; U.S. EPA, Office of Solid Waste and Emergency Response (October 1993), p. 13.

dark green technologies
Technologies dealing directly with the remediation of pollution.

light green technologies
Technologies that benefit the environment indirectly.

environmental literacy
An awareness of the risks of pollution and natural resource depletion.

technologies cover a broad range of products and services. Included are the so-called **"dark green technologies"** such as those dealing with the control, abatement, monitoring, and remediation of pollution. In addition, there are more indirect but nonetheless important advances dubbed **"light green technologies."** These refer to strategies or production changes that benefit the environment even though that is not their primary intent. An example is the use of electronic mail in place of hard-copy memos, a change that reduces waste generation.[33] All of these advances and innovations are important to achieving economic growth while preserving and protecting the natural environment.

Effecting technology transfer relies on a number of interdependent factors—among them, research, physical capital investment, communication, financial resources, and perhaps most importantly education. It is critical that society be made aware of environmental risks and the importance of responding to those risks. The aim is to attain **environmental literacy** throughout all economic sectors and across all regions of the world. Without this awareness in place, society will not understand the need for change, will tend not to support it, and may be unwilling to participate in the process.

Environmental Literacy

In 1962, Rachel Carson's *Silent Spring* warned the world about the potential hazards of chemical use. In the early 1970s, a report of Ralph Nader's assessment of U.S. water quality awakened society to the deterioration of America's rivers and streams.[34] These and other such accounts sent shock waves through communities everywhere. For many years, most people had no idea of the extent of environmental degradation nor any sense of how rapidly the problem was advancing. As a result, society unwittingly continued to contribute to the problem. Learning from our mistakes, we now understand that **environmental literacy,** achieved through communication and education, is part of an effective strategy to protect the earth's resources.

On a global scale, efforts by the United Nations Educational, Scientific, and Cultural Organization (UNESCO) led to a 1977 intergovernmental conference on environmental education held in the former Soviet Union.[35] The international conference called for:

education directed towards the solution of practical environmental problems through an interdisciplinary approach and the active and responsible involvement of each individual and of the community.

The promotion of environmental education across the globe has grown over time and was an important theme at the recent Earth Summit in Rio.

---

[33]*EPA Journal* 20, nos. 3 and 4 (Fall 1994), p. 8.

[34]Zwick and Benstock (1971), as cited in Adler, Landman, and Cameron (1993), pp. 5–6.

[35]United Nations Environment Program/UNESCO (1987) as cited in Council on Environmental Quality (1992), pp. 384–85.

TABLE 19.4   Goals for Environmental Education in the United States

Established:	In 1992 by the U.S. EPA Office of Environmental Education
Purpose:	To help federal agencies achieve the excellence-in-education goals of the America 2000 strategy.
Goals:	1. To establish and expand communications and advisory networks with experts in environmental fields.
	2. To develop partnerships and collaborative ventures between federal agencies and various segments of the private sector to increase effectiveness and to optimize resource use.
	3. To increase the number of educators actively involved in the integration of environmental education into curricula.
	4. To encourage and support environmental education at the local level.
	5. To promote environmental careers and encourage participation in environmental degree programs.
	6. To provide educators and the general public with better access to appropriate and relevant materials in environmental education.
	7. To educate the general public to make better and more informed decisions about the environment.
	8. To extend efforts in environmental education beyond national and political boundaries.

Source: Council on Environmental Quality, *Environmental Quality, 23rd Annual Report* (Washington, D.C.: U.S. Government Printing Office, January 1993), pp. 59–70.

Agenda 21 specifically references the importance of education, public awareness, and training in helping to implement the global agenda.[36]

In the United States, the first National Environmental Education Act was passed by Congress in 1970. This legislation sponsored a small domestic grant program and authorized funding for research and curriculum development. In 1989, President Bush along with state governors launched the nation's America 2000 Strategy—a comprehensive plan to accomplish excellence-in-education goals by the year 2000. To facilitate the implementation of this national strategy, the newly created Office of Environmental Education in the EPA set specific goals for environmental education, shown in Table 19.4. Another landmark was the U.S. enactment of the second National Environmental Education Act in November 1990. Broader in scope than its predecessor, this act targets a more comprehensive student audience and calls for international cooperation as well as collaboration between government and the private sector. Programs are also under way within the EPA and other major agencies, such as the Department of Agriculture, the Department of Commerce, and the Smithsonian Institution. Private sector efforts also are contributing to environmental literacy. Some of these are taking place within

---

[36]Parson, Haas, and Levy (October 1992).

educational institutions, while others are being launched by private industry.[37] Examples of the business sector's role in this effort are given in Table 19.5.

Information and Technology Transfer

As a world economic leader, the United States has an important responsibility to promote environmental **technology transfer** both domestically and internationally. Globally, the environmental technology market is estimated to be between $200 billion and $300 billion per year and expanding at an annual rate of between 5 and 10 percent. Although the federal government supports about half of the active research undertaken in the nation, most of it is actually performed by private industry.[38]

To promote private-public research endeavors, Congress enacted the Federal Technology Transfer Act of 1986. This act supports **cooperative research and development agreements (CRADAs)** between private industry and the public sector. As of 1992, 1,100 CRADAs had been launched, many in environmental protection. A recent and highly innovative environmental CRADA is one formed in 1994 with Monsanto, General Electric, Du Pont and the EPA. This project is developing a new soil remediation process and has been dubbed the "Lasagna CRADA" because of its use of electrical current to move contamination through *layers* of soil. Another environmental CRADA teams up the U.S. Department of Agriculture and the EPA with a consortium of 32 pesticide producers to develop a new model for assessing pesticide risks.[39]

Transferring new technologies to developing nations is being effected in part through the **United States Environmental Training Institute (USETI).** Founded in 1991, the institute is a nonprofit entity that trains participants from developing countries at U.S. businesses and institutions to facilitate the transfer of cleaner technologies. Over 25 comprehensive, short-term courses were developed in 1994, nine of which were located overseas. Topics include environmental risk management, pollution prevention, bioremediation, and pollution control techniques. This cooperative effort of private industry and seven federal agencies has hosted participants from such nations as Thailand, Morocco, the Philippines, Mexico, Hong Kong, Taiwan, and India. Contributing further to this effort is an **Environmental and Energy Efficient Technology Transfer Clearinghouse** supported by the Department of Energy, the EPA, and the U.S. Agency for International Development (USAID). Its aim is to communicate information on pollution control, renewable energy, and

---

[37]Council on Environmental Quality (1992), Chapter 9; Council on Environmental Quality (January 1993), pp. 59–70.

[38]Council on Environmental Quality (January 1993), p. 205.

[39]Preuss (Fall 1994), Japikse (Fall 1994), Council on Environmental Quality (January 1993), pp. 205–06.

TABLE 19.5   Selected Business Efforts in Environmental Education

Industry/Company	Activity
Forest industry	International efforts in environmental education have been underwritten by the industry since 1973 through the design and implementation of what it calls Project Learning Tree.
Edison Electric Institute	The institute sponsors various programs in environmental education and provides funding for the annual conference of the North American Association for Environmental Education.
Chevron	Chevron has supported various efforts in curriculum development at the University of California at Berkeley. Included is a science curriculum on chemicals and a family science curriculum for minorities and women.
Times Mirror Magazines	In a collaborative effort, Times Mirror is donating a percentage of its advertising revenues to environmental education programs.
General Motors Corporation	General Motors entered into a cooperative arrangement with the U.S. EPA to produce a video and teacher's guide in environmental education, which was distributed to over 72,000 elementary schools.* The educational video package was later translated into various languages for subsequent distribution worldwide.
Phillips Petroleum Company	Through a $25,000 grant provided by Phillips Petroleum, a videotape about wildlife habitat entitled, ''A Home for Pearl'' was produced by the U.S. Fish and Wildlife Service. The video was transmitted via satellite to public television stations in 47 states by the Southern Educational Communications Association and to U.S. embassies all over the world by the U.S. Information Agency.

*As cited in General Motors Corporation, ''I Need the Earth and the Earth Needs Me,'' press release, Detroit, Mich.: April 13, 1990.

Source: Council on Environmental Quality, *United Nations Conference on Environment and Development: United States of America National Report* (Washington, D.C.: 1992, Chapter 9, pp. 394–95; Council on Environmental Quality, *Environmental Quality, 23rd Annual Report* (Washington, D.C.: U.S. Government Printing Office, January 1993), p. 63.

energy efficient technologies. Pilot programs have been launched in Mexico City and Vienna.[40]

To signify an ongoing commitment to technology transfer, President Clinton launched the **Environmental Technology Initiative (ETI)** in his 1993 State of the Union Address to the nation. The aim of this initiative is to

---

[40]Council on Environmental Quality (January 1993), pp. 187–88, 210–11; *EPA Journal* 20, nos. 3 and 4 (Fall 1994), p. 12.

promote research and development of environmental technologies both by the government and the private sector and to enhance U.S. exports of these newly developed goods and services. These efforts are to be advanced by the EPA in cooperation with such federal agencies as the Department of Commerce, Department of Labor, the Small Business Administration and the Export-Import Bank.[41] The primary international element of the President's initiative is an EPA-sponsored, environmental technology diffusion program called **U.S. Technology for International Environmental Solutions (U.S. TIES).** Initiated in 1994, this project brings together the supply and demand sides of environmental technology in an effort to engage private sector participation in global environmental goals. It does this by designing country-specific projects that help developing countries find solutions to their environmental problems by introducing them to available U.S. technologies. In so doing, market suppliers of environmental technologies learn more about the needs of the foreign sector, and prospective demanders are facilitated in their search for needed services. Among the initial U.S. TIES projects are demonstrations of drinking water treatment systems in Mexico and air pollution control technologies in Russia.[42]

Conclusions

Although many argue that the realization was long overdue, society is beginning to recognize the importance of achieving a balance between economic growth and the preservation of natural resources. Based on current trends, world population is estimated to increase by more than 3 billion by 2025 with 90 percent of the increase expected to occur in Africa, Asia, and Latin America—regions already struggling with poverty and inadequate food supplies.[43] Attempts to increase production to provide for this growth will place inordinate stress on the ecology and the earth's stock of resources.

Acknowledging and understanding the relevant issues is an important first step, but the real challenge is in establishing appropriate goals and in taking responsible action to achieve them. Critical to meeting this challenge is a true understanding of the interdependence between economic activity and nature. Understanding this connection is a precondition for effective policy development and informed decision-making, both of which are essential elements of the environmental planning process. If sustainable development is to be achieved, there must be a cooperative and educated effort from industry, private citizens, and public officials at all levels of government.

---

[41]*EPA Journal* 20, nos. 3 and 4 (Fall 1994), p. 8.

[42]Koehler and Lingle (Fall 1994).

[43]Stutz (March/April 1993); United Nations Population Division (1991) and International Labour Office (ILO) (1986), as cited in World Resources Institute (1992a), pp. 245–47.

Over the last decade or so, the United States and many other nations have made measurable progress in moving closer to what have become universal environmental objectives. But there is much more to be done. Aggregate statistics disguise those regions where environmental pollution is particularly severe. There are entire nations in Asia, Africa, and South and Central America that face extremely poor air quality, contaminated drinking water, and serious degradation of their land resources.

The need for setting a global environmental agenda and implementing it is more than apparent. Identifying an appropriate course of action is not easy, and it takes time. This collective effort calls for cooperation from every market sector and from every nation, a process that is now under way. As this important transition evolves, society must move forward to restore what can be repaired, to launch initiatives to prevent further degradation, and to educate people everywhere about the importance and fragility of the natural environment. This commitment was advanced at the 1992 Earth Summit in Rio and is articulated in the preamble of *Agenda 21:*

> Humanity stands at a defining moment in history. We are confronted with a perpetuation of disparities between and within nations, a worsening of poverty, hunger, ill health, and illiteracy, and the continuing deterioration of the ecosystems on which we depend for our well-being. However, integration of environment and development concerns and greater attention to them will lead to the fulfillment of basic needs, improved living standards for all, better protected and managed ecosystems and a safer, more prosperous future.

Summary

- A consensus is forming that both public and private decision-making should be driven by a broader goal that is global and dynamic in perspective. One such goal is sustainable development—managing the earth's resources such that their long-term quality and abundance is assured for future generations.
- Implicit in the conventional use of "end-of-pipe" command-and-control instruments is a perception that the flow of materials through the economy is a linear one, running in *one* direction. Hence, U.S. policy has focused on abating contaminating residuals at the end of the flow. Although this can improve environmental quality in the short run, it does not adequately address the long-run consequences.
- Sustainable development is based on the premise that economic growth and environmental quality must be reconciled. Part of the answer is to recognize that the flow of materials need not be linear. Instead, product design, manufacturing processes, and energy use can be modified so that materials flow through more of a closed system.

- Pollution prevention refers to practices that reduce or eliminate the creation of pollutants or wastes at the source. In the context of the materials balance model, preventive strategies change how economic activity is undertaken so that less contaminating residuals are released to nature.

- To formalize pollution prevention as an integral part of U.S. policy, Congress passed the Pollution Prevention Act of 1990. In August 1994, President Clinton signed an executive order furthering the nation's commitment to pollution prevention.

- Two major preventive objectives for industry are source reduction and toxic chemical use substitution. Among the techniques proposed to help industry achieve these objectives are source segregation, raw materials substitution, changes in manufacturing processes, and product substitution. Economic criteria and their associated decision rules are applicable to guiding the firm's use of preventive strategies.

- Thousands of delegates from over 170 nations attended the Rio Summit in 1992 to discuss issues dealing with the objective of sustainable development. Three major documents were produced from the Summit: *Agenda 21,* the *Rio Declaration,* and the *Statement of Forest Principles.*

- When pollution problems are transboundary, the preservation of environmental resources can become an international concern that may require a formal treaty among affected nations. Examples include the Montreal Protocol, the U.N. Framework Convention on Climate Change, the London Dumping Convention (LDC), and the U.S.-Canada Air Quality Agreement.

- Recently, international trade discussions triggered concerns about the potential conflict between the associated economic gains and a decline in environmental quality. These issues affected negotiations for the North American Free Trade Agreement (NAFTA) and the latest round of the General Agreement on Tariffs and Trade (GATT).

- Governments are attempting to work with industry and environmental groups to share information, to foster technological development, and to find solutions that satisfy both environmental and business objectives.

- In the United States, the national strategy to achieve sustainable development is being implemented in part through voluntary partnership programs between the EPA and private industry. Examples include the Green Lights Program, the Energy Star Program, and the 33/50 Program.

- Cooperative arrangements have begun to form within the private business sector. A number of trade associations have developed pollution prevention programs for their memberships.

- Environmental literacy, achieved through communication and education, is part of an effective strategy to preserve and protect the earth's resources.

- Critical to consistent progress toward sustainable development is technology transfer, the advancement and application of technologies and management strategies across economic sectors throughout the world.

Key Concepts

environmental quality
sustainable development
materials balance model
industrial ecosystem
pollution prevention
source reduction
toxic chemical use substitution
source segregation
raw material substitution
changes in manufacturing processes
product substitution
Green Lights Program
Energy Star Program
33/50 Program

technology transfer
dark green technologies
light green technologies
environmental literacy
cooperative research and development
    agreements (CRADAs)
U.S. Environmental Training Institute
    (USETI)
Environmental and Energy Efficient
    Technology Transfer Clearinghouse
Environmental Technology Initiative
    (ETI)
U.S. Technology for International
    Environmental Solutions (U.S. TIES)

Review Questions

1. Critically discuss the following statement: "Without a well-enforced command-and-control regulatory structure, society will not take the necessary steps toward a sustainable future."

2. Environmental technology is argued to be an important element in society's effort to achieve sustainable development.
    a. Choose a specific market-based instrument that likely would encourage the advance of "dark green technologies" *and* improve U.S. exports of these goods and services. Explain using economic analytical tools.
    b. Now propose a different market-based instrument that would foster the use of more "light green technologies" domestically and internationally.

3. a. Identify the economic incentives that motivate private firms to engage in pollution prevention activities.
    b. How might the government devise policy initiatives to exploit these natural incentives?

4. As of 1995, it appears that most industrialized countries will not achieve the GHG targets agreed to at the Rio Summit of 1992. What are the primary obstacles to implementing a successful international treaty on global warming? Based on the discussions at the 1995 meeting of the U.N. Climate Conference in Berlin, formulate a proposal that might improve the results of this convention.

5. a. Critically evaluate the provision in GATT that requires that the least trade-restrictive measures be used to achieve environmental goals. Include in your answer both the environmental and economic implications.
    b. Support or refute the use of international environmental standards among trading partners.

6. In your view, does NAFTA support or hinder the achievement of sustainable development? Explain.

7. Reconsider the discussion in the text about the "Buy Recycled Business Alliance" formed in 1992. Qualitatively analyze the benefits and costs of participation in this alliance by firms such as Anheuser-Busch, American Airlines, and The Coca-Cola Co.

8. Explain the economics of how U.S. TIES attempts to bring together the supply and demand sides of environmental technology. In your view, how effective is this program likely to be for the United States? For developing nations? Explain.

Additional Readings

Bylinsky, Gene. "Manufacturing for Reuse." *Fortune,* February 6, 1995, pp. 102–12.

Carnegie Commission on Science, Technology, and Government. *Environmental Research and Development: Strengthening the Federal Infrastructure.* New York: The Carnegie Commission, December 1992.

Choucri, Nazli, ed. *Global Accord: Environmental Challenges and International Responses.* Cambridge, Mass.: The MIT Press, 1993.

Commoner, Barry. "Economic Growth and Environmental Quality: How To Have Both." *Social Policy,* Summer 1985, pp. 18–26.

Daly, Herman E. "The Perils of Free Trade." *Scientific American,* November 1993, pp. 50–57.

Flynn, Julia; Zachary Schiller; John Carey; and Ruth Coxeter. "Novo Nordisk's Mean Green Machine." *Business Week,* November 14, 1994.

Goldberg, Cheryl J. "Green Machines." *Entrepreneur,* January 1994, pp. 34–37.

Gutfeld, Rose. "Keeping It Green: In a Free-Trade Pact, Is the Environment the Big Loser?" *The Wall Street Journal,* September 24, 1992.

Jaffe, Adam B.; Steven R. Peterson; Paul R. Portney; and Robert N. Stavins. "Environmental Regulation and the Competitiveness of U.S. Manufacturing: What Does the Evidence Tell Us?" *Journal of Economic Literature* 33 (March 1995), pp. 132–63.

Kempton, Willett, and Paul P. Craig. "European Perspective on Global Climate Change." *Environment* 35, no. 3 (April 1993), pp. 16–20, 41–45.

Oldenburg, Kirsten U., and Joel S. Hirschhorn. "Waste Reduction: A New Strategy to Avoid Pollution." *Environment* 29, no. 2 (March 1987), pp. 16–20, 39–45.

O'Riordan, Timothy; William C. Clark; Robert W. Kates; and Alan McGowan. "The Legacy of Earth Day: Reflections at a Turning Point." *Environment* 57, no. 3 (April 1995), pp. 6–15, 37–42.

Solow, Robert M. ''Sustainability: An Economist's Perspective.'' In Robert Dorfman and Nancy S. Dorfman, eds. *Economics of the Environment: Selected Readings.* New York: W. W. Norton & Company, 1993.

Taylor, Jerry. ''Policy Analysis: NAFTA's Green Accords: Sound and Fury Signifying Little.'' Cato Institute, November 17, 1993.

U.S. Environmental Protection Agency, Office of the Administrator. *The Greening of World Trade.* Washington, D.C., February 1993.

REFERENCES

AAA World. "CFC-Free A/C." *AAA World.* March/April 1993, p. 23.

Abdalla, Charles. "Measuring Economic Losses from Ground Water Contamination: An Investigation of Household Avoidance Cost." *Water Resources Bulletin* 26, no. 3 (June 1990), pp. 451–63.

Ackerman, Frank. "Taxing the Trash Away." *Environment,* June 1992, pp. 2–5, 43.

Ackerman, B., and W. Hassler. *Clean Coal/Dirty Air.* New Haven, Ct.: Yale University Press, 1981.

Adams, Walter, and James W. Brock. "The Automobile Industry." In Walter Adams, ed. *The Structure of American Industry.* New York: Macmillan Publishing Company, 1990.

Adler, Jerry, and Mary Hager. "How Much Is a Species Worth?" *National Wildlife,* April/May 1992, pp. 4–14.

Adler, Robert W. "Revitalizing the Clean Water Act." *Environment* 35, no. 9 (November 1993), pp. 4–5, 40.

Adler, Robert W.; Jessica C. Landman; and Diane M. Cameron. *The Clean Water Act: 20 Years Later.* Washington, D.C.: Island Press, 1993.

Aeppel, Timothy. "Green Groups Enter a Dry Season as Movement Matures." *The Wall Street Journal,* October 21, 1994, pp. B1, B4.

Alexander, Michael. "The Challenge of Markets: The Supply of Recyclables Is Larger than the Demand." *EPA Journal,* July/August 1992, pp. 29–33.

Allen, Frederick, and Gregg Sekscienski. "Greening at the Grassroots: What Polls Say about American's Environmental Commitment." *EPA Journal* 18(4), September/October 1992, pp. 52–53.

Allen, Scott. "Boston Harbor's Waters Have Started to Heal: Cleanup Helping to Shed 'Dirtiest' Label." *Boston Globe,* September 6, 1992, p. 1.

Allen, Scott. "Polluting Power Plants to Pay Price." *Boston Globe,* November 12, 1992, p. 29.

Allen, Scott. "State Touts Give-and-Take on Clean Air." *Boston Globe,* January 8, 1993, p. 1.

Allen, Scott. "Rights to Pollute Given Up." *Boston Globe,* March 20, 1993.

Allen, Scott. "Mass. Firms May Now Trade Clean Air Credits." *Boston Globe,* September 29, 1993, p. 26.

Alliance for Responsible CFC Policy. *Montreal Protocol: A Briefing Book.* Rosslyn, Va.: Alliance for Responsible CFC Policy, December 1986.

Anderson, Frederick R. "Natural Resource Damages, Superfund, and the Courts." *Environmental Affairs,* 1989, pp. 405–57.

Anderson, James E. *Public Policy-Making: Decisions and Their Implementation.* New York: Praeger, 1975.

Anderson, James E.; David W. Brady; and Charles Bullock, III. *Public Policy and Politics in America.* North Scituate, Mass.: Duxbury Press, 1978.

Andrews, Richard N. L. "Economics and Environmental Decisions, Past and Present." In V. Kerry Smith, ed. *Environmental Policy under Reagan's Executive Order: The Role of Benefit-Cost Analysis.* Chapel Hill, N.C.: The University of North Carolina Press, 1984, pp. 43–85.

Associated Press. "Industrial Nations Ban Dumping Waste at Sea." *Boston Globe,* November 3, 1990, p. 7.

Associated Press. "Japanese Environmentalist Says Gas Too Cheap in U.S." *Brockton Enterprise,* February 2, 1992.

Associated Press. "44 Nations Agree to Update Rules on Ocean Dumping." *Boston Globe,* November 14, 1992, p. 61.

Associated Press. "EPA: Fish Aren't Safe to Eat from 46 Waterways." *Brockton Enterprise,* November 20, 1992.

Associated Press. "Updating Previous Big Spills." *Boston Globe,* January 6, 1993, p. 6.

Associated Press. "Quietly, EPA Drops Some Tobacco Research." *Boston Globe.* January 7, 1993, p. 3.

Associated Press. "EPA Warns of Exposure to Smoke." *Boston Globe.* July 23, 1993, p. 9.

Associated Press. "German Recycling Is Too Successful." *Brockton Enterprise,* July 27, 1993.

Associated Press. "White House to Seek Reduced Use of Pesticides." *Boston Globe,* September 21, 1993, p. 7.

Associated Press. "Voluntary Effort Pressed by Clinton on Clean Air." *Boston Globe,* October 19, 1993a, p. 12.

Associated Press. "Russia to Continue Dumping Nuclear Waste at Sea." *Boston Globe,* October 19, 1993b, p. 2.

Associated Press. "EPA Clipping Lawn Mower Pollution." *The Enterprise,* May 5, 1994, p. 3.

Associated Press. "Study: Dioxin Health Threat Much Worse Than Suspected." *Brockton Enterprise,* September 12, 1994.

The Association of State and Interstate Water Pollution Control Administrators in cooperation with the U.S. Environmental Protection Agency. *America's Clean*

Water: The States' Evaluation of Progress, 1972–1982. Washington, D.C.: 1984.

Atkinson, Scott E., and Donald H. Lewis. "A Cost-Effectiveness Analysis of Alternative Air Quality Control Strategies." *Journal of Environmental Economics and Management* 1 (1974), pp. 237–50.

Bailey, Jeff. "Curbside Recycling Programs Divert Little Trash from Dumps, Study Finds." *The Wall Street Journal,* October 4, 1994, p. A2.

Baker, Stephen. "Mexico's Motorists Meet the Smog Patrol." *Business Week.* June 25, 1990, p. 100.

Bartik, Timothy. "Evaluating the Benefits of Non-marginal Reductions in Pollution Using Information on Defensive Expenditures." *Journal of Environmental Economics* 15, 1988, pp. 111–27.

Baumol, W.J., and W.E. Oates. *The Theory of Environmental Policy.* Englewood Cliffs, N.J.: Prentice Hall, Inc. 1975.

Beamish, Rita. "Clinton Emissions Plan Is Mainly Voluntary." *Brockton Enterprise,* October 18, 1993.

Beckerman, Wilfred. "Global Warming: A Sceptical Economic Assessment." In Dieter Helm, ed. *Economic Policy Towards the Environment.* Cambridge, Mass.: Blackwell Publishers, 1990.

Bhargava, Sunita Wadekar, ed. "Growing Clean Air Down on the Algae Farm." *Business Week,* February 24, 1992, p. 72.

Biers, Dan. "China Creates Environmental Nightmare in Industrial Rush." *The Brockton Enterprise,* June 16, 1994.

Blinder, Alan S. "How to Cut Pollution and the Deficit at the Same Time." *Business Week,* August 24, 1987, p. 10.

Blinder, Alan S. "Two Cheers for Bush's Plan to Clean Up the Clean Air Act." *Business Week,* July 10, 1989, p. 14.

Block, Debbie Galante. "CD Jewel Box Only, or Alternatives Too?" *Tape-Disc Business,* June 1993, p. 12.

Blomquist, Glenn C. "Value of Life Saving: Implications of Consumption Activity." *Journal of Political Economy* 87, no. 3 (June 1979), pp. 540–58.

Bowker, James, and John R. Stoll. "Use of Dichotomous Choice Nonmarket Methods to Value the Whooping Crane Resource." *American Journal of Agricultural Economics* 70, no. 2 (May 1988), pp. 372–81.

Boyle, Kevin J., and Richard C. Bishop. "Valuing Wildlife in Benefit-Cost Analyses: A Case Study Involving Endangered Species." *Water Resources Research* 23, no. 5 (1987), pp. 615–16.

Brajer, Victor, and Jane V. Hall. "Recent Evidence on the Distribution of Air Pollution Effects." *Contemporary Policy Issues,* April 1992, pp. 63–71.

Bratton, D., and G.L. Rutledge. "Pollution Abatement and Control Expenditures, 1985–1988." *Survey of Current Business* 70 (1990), pp. 32–38.

Bringer, Robert P. "Pollution Prevention Plus." *Pollution Engineering* XX, no. 10 (October 1988), pp. 84–89.

Brookshire, D.S., and T.D. Crocker. "The Advantages of Contingent Valuation Methods for Benefit Cost Analysis." *Public Choice* 36 (1981), pp. 235–52.

Brookshire, D.; B. Ives; and W. Schulze. "The Valuation of Aesthetic Preferences." *Journal of Environmental Economics and Management* 3 (December 1976), pp. 325–46.

Brown, Gardner M. Jr., and Ralph W. Johnson. "Pollution Control by Effluent Charges: It Works in the Federal Republic of Germany, Why Not in the U.S." *Natural Resources Journal* 24 (October 1984), pp. 929–66.

Browner, Carol M. "The Administration's Proposals." *EPA Journal* 20, no. 1–2 (Summer 1994), pp. 6–9.

Burtraw, Dallas, and Paul Portney. "Environmental Policy in the U.S." In Dieter Helm, ed. *Economic Policy towards the Environment.* Cambridge, Mass.: Blackwell Publishers, 1991.

Butler, John C. III.; Mark W. Schneider; George R. Hall; and Michael E. Burton. "Allocating Superfund Costs: Cleaning Up the Controversy." *Environmental Law Reporter,* March 1993, pp. 10133–44.

Cahan, Vicky. "Waste Not, Want Not? Not Necessarily." *Business Week,* July 17, 1989, p. 116–17.

Cairncross, Frances. "How Europe's Companies Reposition to Recycle." *Harvard Business Review,* March-April, 1992, pp. 34–45.

Campbell, John. "The Ecology Alchemists." *Federal Reserve Bank of Boston Regional Review,* Winter 1994, pp. 13–18.

The Canadian Institute of Chartered Accountants. *Environmental Auditing and the Role of the Accounting Profession.* Toronto, Ontario: The Canadian Institute of Chartered Accountants, 1992.

Carson, Rachel. *Silent Spring.* Boston, Mass.: Houghton Mifflin Company, 1962.

Carson, Richard T., and Robert Cameron Mitchell. "The Value of Clean Water: The Public's Willingness to Pay for Boatable, Fishable, and Swimmable Quality Water." Discussion Paper 88–13. La Jolla, Calif.: University of California at San Diego, 1988.

Carson, Richard T., and Robert Cameron Mitchell. "The Value of Clean Water: The Public's Willingness to Pay for Boatable, Fishable, and Swimmable Water." *Water Resources Research* 29, no. 7 (July 1993), pp. 2245–54.

Chandler, William; Alexei Makarov; and Shou Dadi. "Energy for the Soviet Union, Eastern Europe, and China." *Scientific American,* September 1990.

Chase, Marilyn. "Scientists Term Food-Pesticide Cancer Risk Overrated." *The Wall Street Journal,* October 9, 1992, p. B1.

Chemical Manufacturers Association (CMA). *Improving Performance in the Chemical Industry.* September 1990.

Cirone, Patricia, and Matthew Coco. "The Lessons of Commencement Bay." *EPA Journal* 19, no. 1 (January/February/March 1993), pp. 33–34.

Clawson, Marion, and Jack L. Knetch. *Economics of Outdoor Recreation.* Washington, D.C.: Resources for the Future, 1966.

Cline, William R. "Global Warming: Estimating the Economic Benefits of Abatement." In Organisation for Economic Co-operation and Development. *Global Warming: The Benefits of Emission Abatement.* Paris: OECD, 1992.

Coalition for Environmentally Responsible Economies (CERES). "The Valdez Principles." USA, 1989.

Coase, Ronald H. "The Problem of Social Cost," *Journal of Law and Economics* 3 (October 1960), pp. 1–44.

Coase, Ronald H. "The Lighthouse in Economics." *Journal of Law and Economics,* October 1974.

Cogan, Douglas G. *Stones in a Glass House: CFCs and Ozone Depletion.* Washington, D.C.: Investor Responsibility Research Center, Inc., 1988.

Cohen, Brian A., and Erik D. Olson. *Victorian Water Treatment Enters the 21st Century.* March 1994.

Commoner, Barry. *Making Peace with the Planet.* New York: The New Press, 1992.

The Conservation Foundation. *State of the Environment: An Assessment at Mid-Decade.* Washington, D.C.: The Conservation Foundation, 1984.

Consumer Reports. " 'Greener' Cooling." *Consumer Reports.* March 1993, p. 133.

Cormier, William. "Smog Eats Mexico City's Monuments." *The Brockton Enterprise.* November 23, 1992.

Cough, Paul. "Trade-Environment Tensions: Options Exist for Reconciling Trade and Environment." *EPA Journal* 19, no. 2 (April-June 1993), pp. 28–30.

Council of Economic Advisers. "The Annual Report of the Council of Economic Advisers." *Economic Report of the President Transmitted to the Congress February 1982.* Washington, D.C.: U.S. Government Printing Office, 1982.

Council on Environmental Quality. *Environmental Quality—1976.* Washington, D.C.: U.S. Government Printing Office, 1976.

Council on Environmental Quality. *The Global 2000 Report to the President of the U.S.* New York: Pergamon Press, 1980a.

Council on Environmental Quality. *Environmental Quality—1980.* Washington, D.C.: U.S. Government Printing Office, 1980b.

Council on Environmental Quality. *Environmental Quality—1982.* Washington, D.C.: U.S. Government Printing Office, 1982.

Council on Environmental Quality. *Environmental Trends.* Washington, D.C.: U.S. Government Printing Office, 1989.

Council on Environmental Quality. *Environmental Quality, 22nd Annual Report.* Washington, D.C.: U.S. Government Printing Office, March 1992.

Council on Environmental Quality. *United Nations Conference on Environment and Development: United States of America National Report.* Washington, D.C., 1992.

Council on Environmental Quality. *Environmental Quality, 23rd Annual Report.* Washington, D.C.: U.S. Government Printing Office, January 1993.

Cox, Meg. "Music Firms Try Out 'Green' CD Boxes." *The Wall Street Journal,* July 25, 1991, p. B1.

Crandall, Robert W. "The Political Economy of Clean Air: Practical Constraints on White House Review." in V. Kerry Smith, ed. *Environmental Policy Under Reagan's Executive Order: The Role of Benefit-Cost Analysis.* Chapel Hill, N.C.: UNC Press, 1984.

Cropper, Maureen L., and Wallace E. Oates. "Environmental Economics: A Survey." *Journal of Economic Literature* 30 (June 1992), pp. 675–740.

Cummings, Ronald G.; David S. Brookshire; and William D. Schulze. *Valuing Environmental Goods: An Assessment of the Contingent Valuation Method.* Totowa, N.J.: Rowman and Allanheld, 1986.

Daly, Herman E. "The Economic Growth Debate: What Some Economists Have Learned But Many Have Not." In Anil Markandya and Julie Richardson, eds. *Environmental Economics: A Reader.* New York: St. Martin's Press, 1992.

Dardis, Rachel. "The Value of a Life: New Evidence from the Marketplace." *American Economic Review* 70, no. 5 (December 1980), pp. 1077–82.

Davis, Bob. "U.S. Is Hoping to Blend Environmental World Trade Issues at Morocco Meeting." *The Wall Street Journal,* January 10, 1994, p. A9.

Denison, Richard A., and John Ruston, eds. *Recycling and Incineration: Evaluating the Choices.* Washington, D.C.: Island Press, 1990.

Dickerson, Kenneth R. "At the Gasoline Pump." *EPA Journal* 17, no. 1 (January/February 1991), pp. 48–50.

Dolin, Eric Jay. "Boston Harbor's Murky Political Waters." *Environment* 34, no. 6 (July/August 1992), pp. 7–11, 26–33.

Dominguez, George, ed. *Guidebook: Toxic Substances Control Act.* Cleveland: CRC Press, Inc., 1977.

Doneski, D. "Cleaning Up Boston Harbor: Fact or Fiction?" *Boston College Environmental Affairs Law Review* 12 (Spring 1985), p. 567.

Drummet, Susan. "Molten Metals Vies for Mexican Cleanup Work." *Boston Globe,* January 18, 1994.

Dumanoski, Dianne. "Some See Profits; We See Obstacles." *Boston Globe,* November 5, 1990, p. 45.

Dumanoski, Dianne. "Nations Act to Speed Phaseout of Ozone-Depleting Chemicals." *Boston Globe,* November 26, 1992, p. 26.

Dumanoski, Dianne. "Activists Cite Trade Rules as a Force Shaping Nature." *Boston Globe,* July 1, 1993, p. 13.

Dunlap, Riley E., and Angela G. Mertig. "The Evolution of the U.S. Environmental Movement from 1970 to 1990: An Overview." In Riley E. Dunlap and Angela G. Mertig, eds. *American Environmentalism: The U.S. Environmental Movement, 1970–1990,* Washington, D.C.: Taylor and Francis New York, Inc., 1992.

Dzurik, Andrew A. *Water Resources Planning.* Savage, Md.: Rowman & Littlefield Publishers, Inc., 1990.

The Economist. "The Greening of Protectionism." February 27, 1993, pp. 25–28.

Eheart, Wayland; E. Downey Brill, Jr.; and Randolph M. Lyon. "Transferable Discharge Permits for Control of BOD: An Overview." In Erhard F. Joeres and Martin H. David, eds. *Buying a Better Environment: Cost-Effective Regulation through Permit Trading.* Madison, Wis.: University of Wisconsin Press, 1983.

Elmore, T.; J. Jaksch; D. Downing; M. Podar; B. Morrison; B. Zander; and S. Sessions. *Trading between Point and Nonpoint Sources: A Cost-Effective Method for Improving Greater Quality. The Case of Dillon Reservoir.* Washington, D.C.: U.S. EPA, 1984.

EPA Journal. " 'Cash for Clunkers' to Cut Pollution." *EPA Journal* 18, no. 2 (May/June 1992), p. 2.

EPA Journal. "State Your Claim." *EPA Journal* 18, no. 3 (July/August 1992), p. 10.

EPA Journal. "Two Faces of Risk." *EPA Journal* 19, no. 1 (January/February/March 1993), p. 19.

EPA Journal. "Some Statutory Mandates on Risk." *EPA Journal* 19, no. 1 (January/February/March 1993), p. 15.

EPA Journal. "A Step Toward Ecological Risk Guidelines." *EPA Journal* 19, no. 1 (January/February/March 1993), p. 33.

EPA Journal. "EPA 'Energy Star' Expands to Computer Printers." *EPA Journal* 19, no. 2 (April-June 1993), p. 7.

EPA Journal. "Safe Drinking Water Act Reform." *EPA Journal* 20, no. 1–2 (Summer 1994), p. 9.

EPA Journal. "President Clinton's Clean Water Initiative." *EPA Journal* 20, no. 1–2 (Summer 1994), p. 7.

EPA Journal. "What is Environmental Technology?" *EPA Journal* 20, no. 3–4 (Fall 1994), p. 8.

EPA Journal. "U.S. Environmental Training Institute." *EPA Journal* 20, no. 3–4 (Fall 1994), p. 12.

Epstein, Samuel S., M.D.; Lester O. Brown; and Carl Pope. *Hazardous Waste in America.* San Francisco: Sierra Club Books, 1982.

Farman, J.C.; B.G. Gardiner; and J.D. Shanklin. "Large Losses of Total Ozone in Antarctica Reveal Seasonal ClO_x/NO_x Interaction." *Nature* 315 (1985), pp. 207–10.

Fisher, Ann; Dan Violette; and Lauraine Chestnut. "The Value of Reducing Risks of Death: A Note on New Evidence." *Journal of Policy Analysis and Management* 8, no. 1 (1989), pp. 88–100.

Food and Drug Administration. "Food and Drug Administration Pesticide Program Residues in Foods." *J. Assoc. Off. Anal. Chem.,* vols. 71–74, (1988, 1989, 1990, 1991).

Fortuna, Richard C., and David J. Lennett. *Hazardous Waste Regulation: The New Era.* New York: McGraw Hill Book Company, 1987.

Freeman, A. Myrick III. "A Survey of the Techniques for Measuring the Benefits of Water Quality Improvement." In Henry M. Peskin and Eugene P. Seskin, eds. *Cost Benefit Analysis and Water Pollution Policy.* Washington, D.C.: The Urban Institute, 1975, pp. 67–104.

Freeman, A. Myrick III. "Air and Water Pollution Policy." In Paul R. Portney, ed. *Current Issues in U.S. Environmental Policy.* Baltimore, Md.: The Johns Hopkins University Press for Resources for the Future, 1978, pp. 12–67.

Freeman, A. Myrick III. "Hedonic Prices, Property Values and Measuring Environmental Benefits: A Survey of the Issues," *Scandinavian Journal of Economics* 81 (1979), pp. 154–73.

Freeman, A. Myrick, III. *The Benefits of Air and Water Pollution Control: A Review and Synthesis of Recent Estimates.* A Report Prepared for the Council on Environmental Quality, December 1979.

Freeman, A. Myrick, III. *Air and Water Pollution Control: A Benefit-Cost Assessment.* New York: John Wiley & Sons, 1982.

Freeman, A. Myrick III. ''Water Pollution Policy.'' In Paul R. Portney, ed. *Public Policies for Environmental Protection.* Washington, D.C.: Resources for the Future, 1990, pp. 97–149.

Frosch, Robert A., and Nicholas E. Gallopoulos. ''Strategies for Manufacturing.'' *Scientific American* 261, no. 3 (September 1989), pp. 144–52.

General Motors Corporation. ''I Need the Earth and the Earth Needs Me.'' Press release, Detroit, April 13, 1990.

Gianessi, Leonard P., and Henry M. Peskin. ''The Distribution of the Cost of Federal Water Pollution Control Policy.'' *Land Economics* 56, no. 1 (February 1980), pp. 85–102.

Gibbons, John. ''Moving Beyond the 'Tech Fix.' '' *EPA Journal* 18, no. 4 (September/October 1992), pp. 29–31.

Gibbs, Lois Marie. *The Love Canal: My Story.* Albany: State University of New York Press, 1982.

Glenn, J. ''Louisiana Environmental Scoring System/Property Tax Exemptions.'' In U.S. Environmental Protection Agency. *Innovative Regulatory Strategies Workshop: Market-Based Incentives and Other Innovations for Air Pollution Control.* Sponsored by Air Quality Management Division, Office of Air and Radiation, and Regulatory Innovations Staff, Office of Policy, Planning, and Evaluation. Washington, D.C., January 15–17, 1992.

Goddard, Haynes C. ''Integrated Solid Waste Management: Incentives for Reduced Waste Generation, Increased Recycling and Extension of Landfill Life.'' Paper presented at the BioCycle National Conference, Minneapolis, Minn., May 14, 1990.

Goddard, Walter E. *Just-in-Time: Surviving by Breaking Tradition.* Essex Junction, Vt.: Oliver Wight Limited Publications, 1986.

Goldberg, Dan. ''The Magic of Volume Reduction.'' *Waste Age.* February 1990, pp. 98–104.

Gosselin, Peter G. ''Environmental Ruling Blocks Free Trade Pact.'' *Boston Globe.* July 1, 1993, p. 1.

Griffin, Melanie L. ''The Legacy of Love Canal.'' *Sierra,* January/February 1988, pp. 26–28.

Gross, Neil. ''The Green Giant? It May Be Japan.'' *Business Week.* February 24, 1992, p. 74.

Gruenspecht, Howard K. ''Differentiated Regulation: The Case of Auto Emissions Standards.'' *American Economic Review* 72, no. 2 (May 1982), pp. 328–31.

Gutfeld, Rose. ''Environmental Group Doesn't Always Lick'em; It Can Join'em and Succeed.'' *The Wall Street Journal,* August 20, 1992.

Haas, Peter M.; Marc A. Levy; and Edward A. Parson. ''Appraising the Earth Summit: How Should We Judge UNCED's Success?'' *Environment* 34, no. 8 (October 1992), pp. 6–11, 26–33.

Hahn, Robert W. "An Evaluation of Options for Reducing Hazardous Waste." *Harvard Environmental Law Review,* 1988, pp. 201–230.

Hahn, Robert W. "Economic Prescriptions for Environmental Problems: How the Patient Followed the Doctor's Orders." *Journal of Economic Perspectives* 3, no. 2 (Spring 1989), pp. 95–114.

Hahn, Robert W., and Gordon L. Hester. "Marketable Permits: Lessons for Theory and Practice." *Ecology Law Quarterly* 16 (1989), pp. 361–406.

Hahn, Robert W., and Roger Noll. "Designing a Market for Tradable Emissions Permits." In Wesley Magat, ed. *Reform of Environmental Regulation.* Cambridge, Mass.: Ballinger Publishing Company, 1982.

Haigh, John A.; David Harrison, Jr.; and Albert L. Nichols. "Benefit-Cost Analysis of Environmental Regulation: Case Studies of Hazardous Air Pollutants." *Harvard Environmental Law Review* 8, no. 2 (1984), pp. 395–434.

Hall, John, and Ciannat Howett. "Albemarle-Pamlico: Case Study in Pollutant Trading." *EPA Journal* 20, no. 1–2 (Summer 1994), pp. 27–29.

Halvorsen, Robert, and Michael G. Ruby. *Benefit-Cost Analysis of Air-Pollution Control.* Lexington, Mass.: D.C. Heath and Company, 1981.

Hamilton, Joan O'C., and Geoffrey Smith. "Making Clean Energy Sweeter to Utilities." *Business Week,* July 15, 1991.

Hardin, Garrett. "The Tragedy of the Commons." *Science* 162 (1968), pp. 1243–48.

Harrington, Winston; Alan J. Krupnick; and Henry M. Peskin. "Policies for Nonpoint-Source Water Pollution Control." *Journal of Soil and Water Conservation,* January-February 1985, pp. 27–32.

Harrison, D., Jr., and D. Rubinfeld. "Hedonic Housing Prices and the Demand for Clean Air." *Journal of Environmental Economics and Management* 5 (March 1978), pp. 81–102.

Haveman, Robert H., and Burton A. Weisbrod. "The Concepts of Benefits in Cost-Benefit Analysis: With Emphasis on Water Pollution Control Activities." In Henry M. Peskin and Eugene P. Seskin, eds. *Cost Benefit Analysis and Water Pollution Policy,* Washington, D.C.: The Urban Institute, 1975.

Hazilla, Michael, and Raymond J. Kopp. "Social Cost of Environmental Quality Regulations: A General Equilibrium Analysis." *Journal of Political Economy,* 98, no. 4 (1990), pp. 853–73.

Heath, Jenifer. "Moynihan Bill Sets Goals." *Water Environment and Technology,* July 1993, pp. 28–30.

Heath, Ralph C. "Ground Water." In David H. Speidel, Lon C. Ruedisili, and Allen F. Agnew, eds. *Perspectives on Water: Uses and Abuses.* New York: Oxford University Press, 1988.

Hebert, H. Josef. "EPA Says Air is Improving; Cool Weather Plays Key Role." *Boston Globe.* October 20, 1992, p. 14.

Helfand, Gloria E. " Pollution Prevention As Public Policy: An Assessment." *Contemporary Economic Policy* 12 (October 1994), pp. 104–13.

Heritage, John, ed. *EPA Journal* 18, no. 1 (March/April 1992).

Herzog, Henry W. "Economic Efficiency and Equity in Water Quality Control: Effluent Taxes and Information Requirements." *Journal of Environmental Economics and Management* 2 (1976), pp. 170–84.

Hof, Robert D. "The Tiniest Toxic Avengers." *Business Week,* June 4, 1990, pp. 96, 98.

Holtermann, S.E. "Externalities and Public Goods." *Economica* 39 (February 1972).

Hong, Peter. "John Henry: A Power Broker for Cleaner Power." *Business Week,* July 20, 1992.

Hong, Peter, and Michele Galen. "The Toxic Mess Called Superfund." *Business Week,* May 11, 1992, pp. 32–34.

Houghton, J.T.; G.J. Jenkins; and J.J. Ephraums, eds. *Climate Change: The IPCC Scientific Assessment.* Report Prepared for the Intergovernmental Panel on Climate Change by Working Group I. Cambridge, England: Cambridge University Press, 1990.

Howe, Charles W. "An Evaluation of U.S. Air and Water Policies." *Environment* 33, no. 7 (September 1991), pp. 10–15, 34–36.

Humphrey, Hubert H. III., and LeRoy C. Paddock. "The Federal and State Roles in Environmental Enforcement: A Proposal for a More Effective and More Efficient Relationship." *Harvard Environmental Law Review,* 1990, pp. 7–44.

ICF Resources International. *Economic, Environmental, and Coal Market Impacts of SO_2 Emissions Trading under Alternative Acid Rain Control Proposals.* Report prepared for the Regulatory Innovations Staff, Office of Policy, Planning and Evaluation, U.S. Environmental Protection Agency, 1989.

International Labour Office (ILO), unpublished data. Geneva, Switzerland: ILO, 1986.

International Labour Office (ILO), unpublished data. Geneva, Switzerland: ILO, 1993.

Japikse, Catharina. "Lasagna in the Making." *EPA Journal* 20, no. 3–4 (Fall 1994), p. 27.

Jenkins, Robin. *The Economics of Solid Waste Reduction: The Impact of User Fees.* Brookfield, Vt.: Edward Elgar Publishing Company, 1993.

Johansson, Per-Olov. "Valuing Environmental Damage." In Dieter Helm, ed. *Economic Policy Towards the Environment.* Cambridge, Mass.: Blackwell Publishers, 1991, pp. 111–36.

Johnson, Edwin L. "A Study in the Economics of Water Quality Management." *Water Resources Research* 3 (1967).

Jondrow, James, and Robert A. Levy. "The Displacement of Local Spending for Pollution Control by Federal Construction Grants." *American Economic Review* 74, no. 2 (1984), pp. 174–78.

Kamrin, Michael A. *Toxicology.* Chelsea, Mich.: Lewis Publishers, Inc., 1988.

Kelly, Kevin. "It Really Can Pay to Clean Up Your Act." *Business Week,* November 7, 1994, p. 141.

Kemp, David D. *Global Environmental Issues: A Climatological Approach.* New York: Routledge, 1990.

Kenworthy, Tom. "Puerto Rico Oil Spill Tests Law Passed after Valdez." *Boston Globe,* January 10, 1994.

Kharbanda, O.P., and E.A. Stallworthy. *Waste Management: Towards a Sustainable Society.* New York: Auburn House, 1990.

Kimm, Victor J. "The Delaney Clause Dilemma." *EPA Journal* 19, no. 1 (January/February/March 1993), pp. 39–41.

King, David J., and Eric Schaeffer. "EPA's Flagship Programs." *EPA Journal* 19, no. 3 (July-September 1993), pp. 26–30.

Kinsman, Art. "Fueling the Future." *AAA World,* April 1992.

Kirchhoff, Sue. "FDA Proposes Bottled Water Measure Up to Tap Standards." *Boston Globe.* January 1, 1993.

Kirkpatrick, David. "Environmentalism: The New Crusade." *Fortune,* February 12, 1990, pp. 44–52.

Kneese, Allen V.; Robert U. Ayres; and Ralph C. D'Arge. *Economics and the Environment: A Materials Balance Approach.* Washington, D.C.: Resources for the Future, 1970.

Knepper, Mike. "Recycling: Investment in the Future." *BMW Magazine,* January 1993, pp. 66–69.

Knopman, Debra S., and Richard A. Smith. 'Legislative Status of the U.S. Clean Water Act,' in "20 Years of the Clean Water Act," *Environment* 35, no. 1 (January/February 1993), p. 18.

Koehler, Jamison, and Stephen Lingle. "U.S. TIES: Diffusing Technologies Abroad." *EPA Journal* 20, no. 3–4 (Fall 1994), pp. 32–33.

Kohlhase, Janet E. "The Impact of Toxic Waste Sites on Housing Values." *Journal of Urban Economics* 30 (1991), pp. 1–26.

Kopp, Raymond J., and Alan J. Krupnick. "Agricultural Policy and the Benefits of Ozone Control." *American Journal of Agricultural Economics* 69, no. 5 (December 1987), pp. 956–62.

Kranish, Michael. "Energy Tax Plan Changes Sought." *Boston Globe,* February 19, 1993, pp. 57–58.

Kranish, Michael. "Clinton Treads into Forests Dispute." *Boston Globe,* April 3, 1993, p. 3.

Krimsky, Sheldon, and Dominic Golding. "Factoring Risk into Environmental Decision Making." In Richard A. Chechile and Susan Carlisle. *Environmental Decision Making: A Multidisciplinary Perspective.* New York: Van Nostrand Reinhold, 1991.

Krupnick, Alan. "Costs of Alternative Policies for the Control of Nitrogen Dioxide in Baltimore." *Journal of Environmental Economics and Management* 13, 1986, pp. 189–97.

Krutilla, John, V. "Conservation Reconsidered." *American Economic Review* 57 (1967), pp. 777–86.

Kuhn, Thomas S. *Structure of Scientific Revolutions.* Chicago: University of Chicago Press, 1970.

Lancaster, Kelvin J. "A New Approach to Consumer Theory." *Journal of Political Economy* 78 (1966), pp. 311–29.

Landy, Marc K.; Marc J. Roberts; and Stephen R. Thomas. *The Environmental Protection Agency: Asking the Wrong Questions.* New York: Oxford University Press, 1990.

Lareau, Thomas J. "The Economics of Alternative Fuel Use: Substituting Methanol for Gasoline." *Contemporary Policy Issues* 8 (October 1990), pp. 138–52.

Larson, Charles D. "Historical Development of the National Primary Drinking Water Regulations." In Edward J. Calabrese, Charles E. Gilbert, and Harris Pastides, eds. *Safe Drinking Water Act: Amendments, Regulations and Standards.* Chelsea, Mich.: Lewis Publishers, Inc., 1989, pp. 3–15.

Lashof, D., and D. Tirpak, eds. *Policy Options for Stabilizing Global Climate, Draft Report to Congress.* Washington, D.C.: U.S. EPA, Office of Policy, Planning, and Evaluation, February 1989.

Lave, Lester B., ed. *Quantitative Risk Assessment in Regulation,* Washington, D.C.: The Brookings Institution, 1982a.

Lave, Lester B. "Methods of Risk Assessment." In Lester B. Lave ed. *Quantitative Risk Assessment in Regulation,* Washington, D.C.: The Brookings Institution, 1982b, pp. 23–54.

Lawrence, Jennifer. "Mobil." *Advertising Age,* January 29, 1991, p. 12.

Lederer, Edith M. "Ban on Atomic Dumping at Sea Voted; 4 Nuclear Powers Abstain." *Boston Globe,* November 13, 1993.

Lee, David. "Ozone Loss: Modern Tools for a Modern Problem." *EPA Journal* 18, no. 2 (May/June), 1992, pp. 16–18.

Letson, David. "Point/Nonpoint Source Pollution Reduction Trading: An Interpretive Survey." *Natural Resources Journal,* 32, no. 2 (Spring 1992), pp. 219–32.

Light, Alfred R. "A Defense Counsel's Perspective on Superfund." *Environmental Law Reporter* 15, no. 7 (July 1985), pp. 10203–07.

Lippmann, Morton, and Richard B. Schlesinger. *Chemical Contamination in the Human Environment.* New York: Oxford University Press, 1979.

Liroff, Richard A. *Reforming Air Pollution Regulation: The Toil and Trouble of EPA's Bubble.* Washington, D.C.: The Conservation Foundation, 1986.

Luttner, Mark. "President Clinton's Clean Water Act Initiative: Costs and Benefits." *EPA Journal* 20, no. 1–2 (Summer 1994), pp. 30–31.

Lyklema, J., and T.E.A. van Hylckama. "Water Something Peculiar." In David H. Speidel, Lon C. Ruedisili, and Allen F. Agnew, eds. *Perspectives on Water: Uses and Abuses.* New York: Oxford University Press, 1988.

Main, Jeremy. "The Big Cleanup Gets it Wrong." *Fortune,* May 20, 1991, pp. 95–96, 100–101.

Malik, Arun S.; David Letson; and Stephen R. Crutchfield. "Point/Nonpoint Source Trading of Pollution Abatement: Choosing the Right Trading Ratio." *American Journal of Agricultural Economics* 75 (November 1993), pp. 959–67.

Maloney, Michael T., and Bruce Yandle. "Estimation of the Cost of Air Pollution Control Regulation." *Journal of Environmental Economics and Management* 11, 1984, pp. 244–63.

Mandel, Michael J. ''The Right to Pollute Shouldn't Be For Sale.'' *Business Week.* May 22, 1989, p. 158G.

Manly, Lorne. ''It Doesn't Pay to Go Green When Consumers are Seeing Red.'' *Adweek,* March 23, 1992, pp. 32–33.

Marchant, Gary E., and Dawn P. Danzeisen. '' 'Acceptable' Risk for Hazardous Air Pollutants.'' *Harvard Environmental Law Review* 13, no. 2 (1989), pp. 535–58.

Marley, Michael. ''Germany Eyes Recycling Law.'' *American Metal Market,* April 2, 1993, p. 9.

Marshall, Alfred. *Principles of Economics.* 1st ed., 1890; 8th ed., London: Macmillan, 1930.

Marshall, Jonathan. ''How Ecology Is Tied to Mexico Trade Pact.'' *San Francisco Chronicle,* February 25, 1992, p. A8.

Mathtech Inc. *Benefit and Net Benefit Analysis of Alternative National Ambient Air Quality Standards for Particulate Matter, Volume I.* Prepared for U.S. Environmental Protection Agency, Economic Analysis Branch, Office of Air Quality Planning and Standards. Research Triangle Park, N.C.: U.S. EPA, March 1983.

Mazmanian, Daniel, and David Morell. *Beyond Superfailure: America's Toxics Policy for the 1990s.* Boulder, Colo.: Westview Press, 1992.

McCarthy, James E. ''Packaging Waste: How the United States Compares to Other Countries.'' *Reusable News,* Winter/Spring 1993, p. 3.

McCarthy, James, and Mark Reisch. *Hazardous Waste Fact Book.* Environment and Natural Resources Policy Division, Congressional Research Service, 87–56 ENR, June 30, 1987.

McDermott, H. ''Federal Drinking Water Standards—Past, Present, and Future.'' *Water Well Journal* 27, no. 12 (1973), pp. 29–35.

McGartland, Albert M. ''Marketable Permit Systems for Air Pollution Control: An Empirical Study.'' Unpublished Ph.D. dissertation, University of Maryland, 1984.

Metz, Robert. ''N.M. Firm Is Ready to Roll into the Tire Recycling Industry.'' *Boston Globe,* December 28, 1993, p. 34.

Miller, Krystal. ''Big 3 to Cooperate on Efforts to Meet Clean-Air Rules.'' *The Wall Street Journal,* June 9, 1992, p. B9.

Miller, William. ''Oil Spill Threatens North Sea Wildlife.'' *Boston Globe,* January 6, 1993.

Mills, Edwin S. *The Economics of Environmental Quality.* New York: W.W. Norton & Company, Inc. 1978.

Mitchell, Robert Cameron, and Richard T. Carson. *Using Surveys to Value Public Goods: The Contingent Valuation Method.* Washington, D.C.: Resources for the Future, 1989.

Mitchell, Robert Cameron; Angela G. Mertig; and Riley E. Dunlap. ''Twenty Years of Environmental Mobilization: Trends Among National Environmental Organizations.'' In Riley E. Dunlap and Angela G. Mertig, eds. *American Environmentalism: The U.S. Environmental Movement, 1970–1990.* Philadelphia, Pa.: Taylor and Francis New York, Inc., 1992.

Monaghan, Peter. "Taking on the Tail Pipe—and the EPA." *The Chronicle of Higher Education,* March 10, 1993, p. A5.

Moore, Michael J., and W. Kip Viscusi. "Doubling the Estimated Value of Life: Results Using New Occupational Fatality Data." *Journal of Policy Analysis and Management* 7, no. 3 (Spring 1988), pp. 476–90.

Moynihan, Daniel Patrick. "A Legislative Proposal: Why Not Enact a Law that Would Help Us Set Up Sensible Priorities." *EPA Journal,* January/February/March, 1993, pp. 46–47.

Mullen, John K., and Fredric C. Menz. "The Effect of Acidification Damages on the Economic Value of the Adirondack Fishery to New York Anglers." *American Journal of Agricultural Economics* 67, no. 1 (February 1985), pp. 112–19.

National Academy of Sciences. *Risk Assessment in the Federal Government: Managing the Process.* Washington, D.C.: U.S. Government Printing Office, 1983.

National Academy of Sciences and National Academy of Engineering. *Air Quality and Automobile Emission Control,* vol. 4, *The Costs and Benefits of Automobile Emission Control.* Washington, D.C.: U.S. Government Printing Office, 1974.

National Acid Precipitation Assessment Program. *1990 Integrated Assessment Report.* Washington, D.C.: NAPAP Office of the Director, November 1991.

National Advisory Committee on Oceans and Atmosphere. *Nuclear Waste Management and the Use of the Sea.* Washington, D.C.: U.S. Government Printing Office, April 1984.

National Commission on Air Quality. *To Breathe Clean Air.* Washington, D.C.: U.S. Government Printing Office, March 1981.

National Commission on Water Quality. *Report to the Congress.* Washington, D.C.: U.S. Government Printing Office, March 1976.

National Environmental Protection Agency. "China Country Program for the Phaseout of Ozone-Depleting Substances under the Montreal Protocol." Report submitted to the Ninth Meeting of the Executive Committee of the Multilateral Fund of the Montreal Protocol, Montreal, March 1993.

National Research Council. *Carbon Dioxide and Climate: A Scientific Assessment.* Washington, D.C.: National Academy Press, 1979.

National Research Council. *Current Issues in Atmospheric Change.* Washington, D.C.: National Academy Press, 1987.

National Research Council, Committee on Passive Smoking, Board on Environmental Studies and Toxicology. *Environmental Tobacco Smoke: Measuring Exposures and Assessing Health Effects.* Washington, D.C.: National Academy Press, 1986.

National Solid Waste Management Association (NSWMA). *Recycling in the States: Mid-Year Update 1990.* Washington, D.C.: NSWMA, October 1990.

Nazario, Sonia L. "EPA under Fire for Pesticide Standards." *The Wall Street Journal,* February 17, 1989, p. B1.

Nelson, Jon. *Airports and Property Values: A Survey of Recent Evidence.* University Park, Pa.: Pennsylvania State University Press, 1979.

Newcomb, Peter. " 'Ban the Box'." *Forbes,* May 13, 1991, p. 70.

Nitze, William A. ''Stopping the Waste: Technology Itself Is Not the Problem.''
  EPA Journal 19, no. 2 (April-June 1993), pp. 31–33.

Noah, Timothy. ''EPA Declares 'Passive' Smoke a Human Carcinogen.'' *The Wall
  Street Journal,* January 6, 1993, p. B1.

Noah, Timothy. ''EPA Finds Unsafe Lead Levels in Water.'' *The Wall Street
  Journal,* May 12, 1993, p. B6.

Noah, Timothy. ''Environmental Groups Say Deal Poses Threats.'' *The Wall Street
  Journal,* December 16, 1993, p. A10.

Nordhaus, William. ''A Perspective on Costs and Benefits.'' *EPA Journal,* March/
  April 1990, pp. 44–45.

Nussbaum, Bruce, and John Templeman. ''Built to Last—Until It's Time to Take It
  Apart.'' *Business Week,* September 17, 1990, p. 102.

Oates, Wallace E.; Paul R. Portney; and Albert M. McGartland. ''The Net Benefits
  of Incentive-Based Regulation: A Case Study of Environmental Standard-
  Setting.'' *American Economic Review* 75, 1989, pp. 1223–42.

Ohnuma, Keiko. ''Missed Manners.'' *Sierra,* March/April 1990, pp. 24–26.

O'Neil, William B. ''Pollution Permits and Markets for Water Quality.'' Ph.D.
  dissertation, University of Wisconsin-Madison, 1980.

O'Neil, William B.; Martin H. David; Christina Moore; and Erhard F. Joeres.
  ''Transferable Discharge Permits and Economic Efficiency: The Fox River.''
  Journal of Environmental Economics and Management 10, no. 4 (December
  1983), pp. 346–55.

Opschoor, J.B., and Has B. Vos. *Economic Instruments for Environmental
  Protection.* Paris: Organisation for Economic Cooperation and Development,
  1989.

Organisation for Economic Cooperation and Development (OECD). *Economic
  Instruments for Environmental Protection.* Paris: OECD, 1989a.

Organisation for Economic Cooperation and Development (OECD). *OECD
  Environmental Data Compendium 1989.* Paris: OECD, 1989b.

Organisation for Economic Cooperation and Development (OECD). ''Recent
  Developments in the Use of Economic Instruments for Environmental
  Protection in OECD Countries.'' OECD Environment Monographs 41, Paris:
  OECD, February 1991.

Organisation for Economic Cooperation and Development (OECD). *Global
  Warming: The Benefits of Emission Abatement.* Paris: OECD, 1992.

O'Toole, Randal. *Reforming the Forest Service.* Washington, D.C.: Island Press, 1988.

Palmer, A.R.; W.E. Mooz; T.H. Quinn; and K.A. Wolf. ''Economic Implications of
  Regulating Chlorofluorocarbon Emissions from Nonaerosol Applications.''
  Report #R-2524-EPA, prepared by the Rand Corporation for the U.S. EPA,
  June 1980.

Park, Richard A.; Manjit S. Trehan; Paul W. Mausel; and Robert C. Howe. ''The
  Effects of Sea Level Rise on U.S. Coastal Wetlands.'' Contributing project to
  U.S. Environmental Protection Agency, Office of Policy, Planning, and
  Evaluation, Office of Research and Development, *The Potential Effects of
  Global Climate Change on the United States.* Washington, D.C., December
  1989.

Parrish, Michael. "GM Signs on to Environmental Code of Conduct." *Los Angeles Times,* February 4, 1994.

Parson, Edward A.; Peter M. Haas; and Marc A. Levy. "A Summary of the Major Documents Signed at the Earth Summit and the Global Forum." *Environment* 34, no. 8 (October 1992), pp. 12–15, 34–36.

Patton, Dorothy E. "The ABCs of Risk Assessment: Some Basic Principles Can Help People Understand Why Controversies Occur." *EPA Journal* 19, no. 1 (January/February/ March 1993), pp. 10–15.

Perl, Lewis, and Frederick C. Dunbar. "Cost Effectiveness and Cost-Benefit Analysis of Air Quality Regulations." *American Economic Review 72,* no. 2 (May 1982), pp. 208–13.

Phifer, Russell W., and William R. McTigue, Jr. *Handbook of Hazardous Waste Management.* Chelsea, Mi.: Lewis Publishers, Inc., 1988.

Pigou, A.C. *The Economics of Welfare.* 4th ed., London: 1952.

Porter, Richard C. "Michigan's Experience with Mandatory Deposits on Beverage Containers." *Land Economics* 59 (1983), pp. 177–94.

Portney, Paul R. "Air Pollution Policy." In Paul R. Portney, ed. *Public Policies for Environmental Protection.* Washington, D.C.: Resources for the Future, 1990a, pp. 27–96.

Portney, Paul R. "Economics and the Clean Air Act." *Journal of Economic Perspectives* 4, no. 4 (Fall 1990b), pp. 173–81.

Preuss, Peter W. "EPA's CRADA Agreements: Sharing Expertise with Industry." *EPA Journal* 20, nos. 3–4 (Fall 1994), pp. 28–29.

Preuss, Peter W., and William H. Farland. "A Flagship Risk Assessment: EPA Reassesses Dioxin in an Open Forum." *EPA Journal* 19, no. 1 (January/February/March 1993), pp. 24–26.

Protzman, Ferdinand. "Germany's Push to Expand the Scope of Recycling." *New York Times,* July 4, 1992.

Pryde, Lucy T. *Environmental Chemistry: An Introduction.* Menlo Park, Ca.: Cummings Publishing Company, 1973.

Puga, Ana. "Envirotech Goes Global." *Boston Globe,* June 6, 1993, p. 78.

Putnam, Hayes, and Bartlett, Inc. "Economic Implications of Potential Chlorofluorocarbons Restrictions: Final Report." December 2, 1987.

Quirk, James, and Katsuki Terasawa. "Choosing a Government Discount Rate: An Alternative Approach." *Journal of Environmental Economics and Management* 20 (1991), pp. 16–28.

Radin, Charles A. "With China's 'Miracle,' Pollution Surges." *Boston Globe,* January 2, 1995, pp. 47, 50.

Ramanathan, V. "The Greenhouse Theory of Climate Change: A Test by an Inadvertent Global Experiment." *Science* 240 (1988), pp. 293–99.

Ramanathan, V.; R.D. Cess; E.F. Harrison; P. Minnis; B.R. Barkstrom; E. Ahmad; and D. Hartmann. "Cloud-Radioactive Forcing and Climate: Results from the Earth Radiation Budget Experiment." *Science* 243 (1989), pp. 57–63.

Ramphal, Shridath. "Beyond Mere Survival." *EPA Journal* 19, no. 2 (April-June 1993), pp. 10–14.

Raven, Peter H.; Linda R. Berg; and George B. Johnson. *Environment.* New York: Saunders College Publishing, Harcourt Brace Jovanovich College Publishers, 1993.

Reese, Craig E. "State Taxation of Hazardous Materials." *Oil and Gas Tax Quarterly* 33 (1985), pp. 502–26.

Regan, Mary Beth; Joseph Weber; Chris Roush; and Kevin Kelly. "Toxic Turnabout? A Deal on Superfund May Finally Be At Hand." *Business Week,* April 25, 1994, pp. 30–31.

Reilly, William K. "The Road from Rio." *EPA Journal* 18, no. 4 (September/October 1992), pp. 11–13.

Repetto, Robert. "Accounting for Environmental Assets." *Scientific American,* June 1992, pp. 94–100.

Repetto, Robert. "Earth in the Balance Sheet: Incorporating Natural Resources in National Income Accounts." *Environment* 34, no. 7 (September 1992), pp. 12–20, 43–45.

Research Triangle Institute. *Benefit-Cost Assessment Handbook for Water Programs, Volume 1,* prepared for the EPA, Economic Analysis Division, April 1993.

Resource Integration Systems, Ltd., and Waste Matters Consulting, Portland, Oregon. *Decisionmaker's Guide to Recycling Plastics.* Prepared for The Oregon Department of Environmental Quality Solid Waste Reduction and Recycling Section and U.S. Environmental Protection Agency, Region X, Solid Waste Program. December 1990.

Reuters. "Environmentalist Predicts Marked Change in U.S. Policy." *Boston Globe,* December 7, 1992.

Reuters. "New Emissions Plan Sought." *Boston Globe,* April 8, 1995, p. 2.

Roach, Fred; Charles Kolstad; Allen V. Kneese; Richard Tovin; and Michael Williams. "Alternative Air Quality Policy Options in the Four Corners Region." *Southwest Review* 1, no. 2 (1981), pp. 44–45.

Rose-Ackerman, Susan. "Effluent Charges: A Critique." *Canadian Journal of Economics* 6, no. 4 (November 1973), pp. 512–528.

Rose-Ackerman, Susan. "Market Models for Water Pollution Control: Their Strengths and Weaknesses." *Public Policy* 25, no. 3 (Summer 1977), pp. 383–406.

Rosen, Harvey S. *Public Finance.* Burr Ridge, Il.: Richard D. Irwin, 1995.

Rosenberg, Ronald. "Taking a (Really) Hot Bath." *Boston Globe,* July 7, 1993.

Ross, Karl. "Some Foul Air in Puerto Rico." *Boston Globe.* January 7, 1993.

Rowe, Robert D.; Ralph C. d'Arge; and David S. Brookshire. "An Experiment on Economic Value of Visibility." *Journal of Environmental Economics and Management* 7, no. 1 (March 1980), pp. 1–9.

Rowe, Robert D.; Michael G. Shelby; Joshua B. Epel; and Ari Michelsen. "Using Oxygenated Fuels to Mitigate Carbon Monoxide Air Pollution: The Case of Denver." *Contemporary Policy Issues* 8 (January 1990), pp. 39–53.

Ruff, Larry. "The Economic Common Sense of Pollution." *The Public Interest* 19 (Spring 1970), pp. 69–85.

Russell, Clifford, S. "What Can We Get From Effluent Charges?" *Policy Analysis* 5, no. 2 (Spring 1979), pp. 155–80.

Rutledge, G.L., and M.L. Leonard. "Pollution Abatement and Control Expenditures, 1972–90." *Survey of Current Business.* Washington, D.C.: Department of Commerce, Bureau of Economic Analysis, June 1992.

Samuelson, Paul A. "The Pure Theory of Public Expenditure." *Review of Economics and Statistics* 36 (1954), pp. 387–89.

Samuelson, Paul A. "Diagrammatic Exposition of a Theory of Public Expenditure." *Review of Economics and Statistics* 37 (1955), pp. 350–56.

Samuelson, Paul A. "Aspects of Public Expenditure Theory." *Review of Economics and Statistics* 40 (1958), pp. 332–38.

Sassone, Peter G., and William A. Schaffer. *Cost-Benefit Analysis: A Handbook.* New York: Academic Press, 1978.

Scheuplein, Robert. "Uncertainty and the 'Flavors' of Risk." *EPA Journal* 19, no. 1 (January/February/March 1993), pp. 16–17.

Schlesinger, Jacob M. "In Japan, Environment Means an Opportunity for New Technologies." *The Wall Street Journal,* November 5, 1990, p. A1.

Schmidheiny, Stephan. *Changing Course: A Global Business Perspective on Development and the Environment.* Cambridge, Mass.: The MIT Press, 1992.

Schmidt, William E. "Aground, Tanker Spills Oil on Shetland." *The New York Times,* January 6, 1993, p. A3.

Schrage, Michael. "In Tokyo, 'Just-in-Time' Deliveries in Need of Administrative Guidance." *Boston Globe,* March 22, 1992.

Schulze, William D., and David S. Brookshire. "The Economic Benefits of Preserving Visibility in the National Parklands of the Southwest." *Natural Resources Journal* 23, no. 1 (January 1983), pp. 763–72.

Seattle Solid Waste Utility. *Seattle Solid Waste Utility Rate Sheet and Customer Reply Card.* Seattle, Wash., 1988.

Seskin, Eugene P. "Automobile Air Pollution Policy." In Paul R. Portney, ed. *Current Issues in U.S. Environmental Policy.* Baltimore: The Johns Hopkins University Press, 1978, pp. 68–104.

Sessions, Kathy. "Products of the Earth Summit." *EPA Journal* 19, no. 2 (April-June 1993a), p. 12.

Sessions, Kathy. "What's In Agenda 21?" *EPA Journal* 19, no. 2 (April-June 1993b), p. 14.

Shalal-Esa, Andrea. "Tobacco Industry Sues EPA Over Secondhand Smoke Report." *Boston Globe,* June 23, 1993, p. 41.

Shapiro, Michael. "Toxic Substances Policy." In Paul R. Portney, ed. *Public Policies for Environmental Protection.* Washington, D.C.: Resources for the Future, 1990, pp. 195–241.

Shea, Cynthia Pollock. "Getting Serious in Germany." *EPA Journal* 18, no. 3 (July/August 1992), pp. 50–52.

Simmons, Peter, and Brian Wynne. "Responsible Care: Trust, Credibility, and Environmental Management." In Kurt Fischer and Johan Schot, eds. *Environmental Strategies for Industry: International Perspectives on Research*

Needs and Policy Implications, Washington D.C.: Island Press, 1993, pp. 207–26.

Sims, William A. *Economics of Sewer Effluent Charges.* Ph.D. Thesis in Political Economy, University of Toronto, 1977.

Smith, Adam. *An Inquiry into the Nature and Causes of the Wealth of Nations.* New York: Random House, 1937 (originally published in 1776).

Smith, Emily T. "Developments to Watch: Aerosol Cans That Run On Compressed-Air Power." *Business Week,* June 12, 1989, p. 63.

Smith, Emily T.; Vicki Cahan; Naomi Freundlich; James E. Ellis; and Joseph Weber. "The Greening of Corporate America: 'Sometimes You Find That the Public Has Spoken and You Get On With It.' " *Business Week,* April 23, 1990, pp. 96–103.

Smith, Emily T., and David Woodruff. "The Next Trick For Business: Taking a Cue From Nature." *Business Week,* May 11, 1992, pp. 74–75.

Smith, V. Kerry, and William H. Desvousges. "The Generalized Travel Cost Model and Water Quality Benefits: A Reconsideration." *Southern Economic Journal* 52 (October 1985), pp. 371–81.

Smith, V. Kerry, and William H. Desvousges. *Measuring Water Quality Benefits.* Norwell, Mass: Kluwer-Nijhoff, 1986.

Smith, V. Kerry; William H. Desvousges; and Matthew P. McGivney. "Estimating Water Quality Benefits: An Econometric Analysis." *Southern Economic Journal,* October 1983, pp. 422–37.

Smith, V. Kerry, and John V. Krutilla, eds. *Explorations in Natural Resource Economics.* Baltimore: John Hopkins Press, 1982.

Smith, Velma. "Disaster in Milwaukee." *EPA Journal* 20, no. 1–2 (Summer 1994), pp. 16–18.

Snyder, Adam. "The Color of Money." *SuperBrands,* 1992, pp. 30–31.

Spofford, Walter O., Jr. "Efficiency Properties of Alternative Source Control Policies for Meeting Ambient Air Quality Standards: An Empirical Application to the Lower Delaware Valley." Unpublished Resources for the Future discussion paper D-118, February 1984.

Spurlock, Stan R., and Ivery D. Clifton. "Efficiency and Equity Aspects of Nonpoint Source Pollution Controls." *Southern Journal of Agricultural Economics,* December 1982, pp. 123–29.

Stern, Arthur C. "History of Air Pollution Legislation in the United States." *Journal of the Air Pollution Control Association* 32, no. 1 (January 1982), pp. 44–61.

Stiglitz, Joseph E. *Economics of the Public Sector.* New York: W.W. Norton & Company, 1988.

Stranahan, Susan Q. "It's Enough to Make You Sick." *National Wildlife.* February/March 1990, pp. 8–15.

Stutz, Bruce. "The Landscape of Hunger." *Audubon* 95, no. 2 (March/April 1993), pp. 54–63.

Tanner, James. "Carbon Tax to Limit Use of Fossil Fuels Becomes Embroiled in Global Politics." *The Wall Street Journal,* June 9, 1992, p. A2.

Taylor, Jeffrey. "Auction of Rights To Pollute Fetches About $21 Million." *The Wall Street Journal,* March 31, 1992, p. A6.

Taylor, Jeffrey. "CBOT Plan for Pollution-Rights Market Is Encountering Plenty of Competition." *The Wall Street Journal,* August 24, 1993, pp. C1, C6.

Taylor, Jeffrey, and Rose Gutfeld, "CBOT Selected to Run Auction for Polluters." *The Wall Street Journal,* September 25, 1992, p. C1.

Taylor, Jeffrey, and Dave Kansas. "Environmentalists Vie for Right to Pollute." *The Wall Street Journal,* March 26, 1992, p. C1.

Thaler, Richard, and Sherwin Rosen. "The Value of Life Savings." In Nester Terleckyj, ed. *Household Production and Consumption.* New York: Columbia University Press, 1976.

Tietenberg, T.H. *Emissions Trading: An Exercise in Reforming Pollution Policy.* Washington, D.C.: Resources for the Future, 1985.

Tregarthen, Timothy. "Garbage by the Bag: Perkasie Acts on Solid Waste." *The Margin,* September/October 1989, p. 17.

Tresch, Richard W. *Public Finance: A Normative Theory.* Plano, Tx.: Business Publications, 1981.

Tuxen, Linda. "EPA's IRIS Data Base: Accessing the Science." *EPA Journal* 19, no. 1 (January/February/March 1993), pp. 22–23.

United Church of Christ Commission for Racial Justice (UCC). *Toxic Wastes and Race in the United States: A National Report on the Racial and Socio-Economic Characteristics of Communities with Hazardous Waste Sites.* UCC, 1987.

United Nations. *Water Development and Management Volumes 1–4, Proceedings of the United Nations Water Conference,* March 1977, Mar del Plata, Argentina. Oxford, England: Pergamon Press for the United Nations, 1978.

United Nations Environment Program/UNESCO, Congress on Environmental Education and Training. *International Strategy.* Moscow: 1987.

United Nations Population Division. *World Population Prospects 1990.* New York: United Nations, 1991.

United Nations Population Division. *Interpolated National Populations (The 1992 Revision),* on diskette. New York: United Nations, 1993.

U.S. Congress, Congressional Budget Office (CBO) from Office of Technology Assessment, Statement of Joel S. Hirschhorn for the Hearing Record, Senate Committee on Environment and Public Works, 98:2 (September 10, 1984).

U.S. Congress, Congressional Budget Office (CBO). *Efficient Investments in Wastewater Treatment Plants.* Washington, D.C.: U.S. Government Printing Office, 1985a.

U.S. Congress, Congressional Budget Office (CBO). *Hazardous Waste Management: Recent Changes and Policy Alternatives.* Washington, D.C.: U.S. Government Printing Office, 1985b.

U.S. Congress, Congressional Budget Office (CBO). *Curbing Acid Rain: Cost, Budget, and Coal-Market Effects.* Washington, D.C.: U.S. Government Printing Office, June 1986.

U.S. Congress, Congressional Budget Office (CBO). *Financing Municipal Water Supply Systems.* Washington, D.C.: U.S. Government Printing Office, May 1987.

U.S. Congress, Congressional Research Service. *History of the Water Pollution Control Act Amendments of 1972.* ser. 1, 93rd Congress, 1st session (1972), 137.

U.S. Congress, Office of Technology Assessment (OTA). *Technologies and Management Strategies for Hazardous Waste Control.* Washington, D.C.: U.S. Government Printing Office, 1983.

U.S. Congress, Office of Technology Assessment (OTA). *Protecting the Nation's Groundwater From Contamination.* Vol. I., Washington, D.C.: U.S. Government Printing Office, October 1984.

U.S. Congress, Office of Technology Assessment (OTA). *Superfund Strategy.* Washington, D.C.: U.S. Government Printing Office, 1985.

U.S. Congress, Office of Technology Assessment (OTA). *Wastes in Marine Environments.* Washington, D.C.: U.S. Government Printing Office, 1987.

U.S. Congress, Office of Technology Assessment (OTA). ''Water Supply: The Hydrologic Cycle.'' In David H. Speidel, Lon C. Ruedisili, and Allen F. Agnew, eds. *Perspectives on Water: Uses and Abuses.* New York: Oxford University Press, 1988.

U.S. Congress, Office of Technology Assessment (OTA). *Facing America's Trash: What Next for Municipal Solid Waste?* Washington, D.C.: U.S. Government Printing Office, 1989.

U.S. Congress, Office of Technology Assessment (OTA). *Green Products by Design: Choices for a Cleaner Environment.* Washington, D.C.: U.S. Government Printing Office, October 1992.

U.S. Department of Commerce, Bureau of the Census. *Government Finances.* various issues.

U.S. Department of Commerce, Bureau of the Census. *Statistical Abstract of the United States.* Washington, D.C., 1990.

U.S. Department of Commerce, Bureau of Economic Analysis. *Pollution Abatement Costs and Expenditures, Current Industrial Reports,* MA-200 (annual). Washington, D.C.: Department of Commerce.

U.S. Department of Commerce, National Oceanic and Atmospheric Administration (NOAA), National Ocean Survey, Ocean Assessments Division, Strategic Assessment Branch. *Trends in Harvest-Limited Shellfish Areas.* Rockville, Md.: Data taken from National Estuarine Inventory database.

U.S. Department of Energy (DOE). *Saving Energy by Managing Urban Heat Islands: Something We Can Do About the Weather.* Washington, D.C., 1991.

U.S. Department of the Interior, U.S. Fish and Wildlife Service. *Endangered Species Technical Bulletin* 15(11), Washington, D.C., December 1990.

U.S. Environmental Protection Agency (EPA). *Review of the Municipal Wastewater Treatment Works Program.* Washington, D.C., November 1974.

U.S. Environmental Protection Agency. *Economic Report—Alternative Methods of Financing Wastewater Treatment.* Washington, D.C., 1975.

U.S. Environmental Protection Agency. *The Risk-Cost Analysis Model: Phase III Report.* Washington, D.C., March 1, 1984.

U.S. Environmental Protection Agency. *Final Report: The Cost of Clean Air and Water.* Washington, D.C., 1984a.

U.S. Environmental Protection Agency. *Non-Point Source Pollution in the U.S., Report to Congress.* Washington, D.C., 1984b.

U.S. Environmental Protection Agency. *Site Discovery Methods.* EPA Contract 68-01-6888, Washington, D.C., March 1987.

U.S. Environmental Protection Agency. *The New Superfund: What It Is, How It Works.* Washington, D.C., August 1987.

U.S. Environmental Protection Agency. *Environmental Progress and Challenges: EPA's Update.* Washington, D.C., August 1988.

U.S. Environmental Protection Agency. *Comparing Risks and Setting Environmental Priorities.* Washington, D.C., August 1989.

U.S. Environmental Protection Agency. *Environmental Protection Agency Pollution Prevention Directive* (draft). Washington, D.C., May 13, 1990.

U.S. Environmental Protection Agency. *Charging Households for Waste Collection and Disposal: The Effects of Weight or Volume-Based Pricing on Solid Waste Management.* Final Report #EPA/53-SW-90–047, Washington, D.C., September 1990.

U.S. Environmental Protection Agency. *Meeting the Environmental Challenge: EPA's Review of Progress and New Directions in Environmental Protection.* Washington, D.C., December 1990a.

U.S. Environmental Protection Agency. *Toxic Substances 4-Year Strategy 1993–1996.* Washington, D.C., December 1990b.

U.S. Environmental Protection Agency. *Superfund NPL Characterization Project: National Results.* Washington, D.C., 1991.

U.S. Environmental Protection Agency. *Bottled Water Fact Sheet.* Washington, D.C., March 1991.

U.S. Environmental Protection Agency. "1994 EPA SO_2 Allowance Auction." Washington, D.C., 1994a.

U.S. Environmental Protection Agency. "1994 EPA Allowance Auction Results." Washington, D.C., 1994b.

U.S. Environmental Protection Agency, Environmental Criteria and Assessment Office. *IRIS Data Base,* Research Triangle Park, N.C., 1993.

U.S. Environmental Protection Agency, Information Access Branch, Information Management and Services Division. *Access EPA.* Washington, D.C., 1991.

U.S. Environmental Protection Agency, Office of Air and Radiation. *The Clean Air Act Amendments of 1990: Summary Materials.* Washington, D.C., November 15, 1990.

U.S. Environmental Protection Agency, Office of Air and Radiation. *Clean Air Act Amendments of 1990: Detailed Summary of Titles.* Washington, D.C., November 30, 1990.

U.S. Environmental Protection Agency, Office of Air and Radiation. *Green Lights Program: The First Year.* Washington, D.C., February 1992.

U.S. Environmental Protection Agency, Office of Air and Radiation. *The Climate is Right for Action: Voluntary Programs to Reduce Greenhouse Gas Emissions.* Washington, D.C., October 1992.

U.S. Environmental Protection Agency, Office of Air Quality Planning and Standards. *National Air Pollutant Emission Estimates 1940–1990.* Research Triangle Park, N.C., November 1991.

U.S. Environmental Protection Agency, Office of Air Quality Planning and Standards. *National Air Quality and Emissions Trends Report, 1991.* Research Triangle Park, N.C., October 1992.

U.S. Environmental Protection Agency, Office of Air Quality Planning and Standards. *National Air Quality and Emissions Trends Report, 1992.* Research Triangle Park, N.C., October 1993.

U.S. Environmental Protection Agency, Office of Communications and Public Affairs. *Glossary of Environmental Terms and Acronym List.* Washington, D.C., December 1989.

U.S. Environmental Protection Agency, Office of Communications and Public Affairs. ''EPA Tightens Standards for Lead in Drinking Water.'' *Environmental News.* Washington, D.C., May 7, 1991.

U.S. Environmental Protection Agency, Office of Communications, Education, and Public Affairs. *Securing Our Legacy, An EPA Progress Report 1989–1991.* Washington, D.C., April 1992.

U.S. Environmental Protection Agency, Office of Communications, Education, and Public Affairs. *Terms of Environment, Glossary, Abbreviations and Acronyms.* Washington, D.C., September 1992.

U.S. Environmental Protection Agency, Office of Communications, Education, and Public Affairs. ''President Signs Pollution Prevention Executive Order.'' *EPA Activities Update,* August 16, 1993.

U.S. Environmental Protection Agency, Office of Communications, Education, and Public Affairs. ''Federal Actions Address Environmental Justice.'' *EPA Activities Update.* Washington, D.C., February 22, 1994a.

U.S. Environmental Protection Agency, Office of Communications, Education and Public Affairs. ''Major Changes Recommended in the Clean Water Act.'' *EPA Activities Update,* Washington, D.C., February 22, 1994b.

U.S. Environmental Protection Agency, Office of Communications, Education and Public Affairs. ''Clinton Administration Proposes New Superfund Law.'' *EPA Activities Update,* Washington, D.C., February 22, 1994c.

U.S. Environmental Protection Agency, Office of Communications, Education, and Public Affairs. ''EPA, Chicago Board of Trade Announce Results of Second Acid Rain Auction.'' *Environmental News,* Washington, D.C., March 29, 1994.

U.S. Environmental Protection Agency, Office of Communications, Education and Public Affairs. ''Administrator's Statement on Superfund Reform: October 5.'' *EPA Activities Update,* Washington, D.C., October 17, 1994.

U.S. Environmental Protection Agency, Office of Drinking Water. *Bottled Water: Helpful Facts and Information.* Washington, D.C., (undated).

U.S. Environmental Protection Agency, Office of Drinking Water. *Survey of Operating and Financial Characteristics of Community Water Systems,* prepared by Temple, Barker, and Sloan, Inc., October 1982.

U.S. Environmental Protection Agency, Office of Emergency and Remedial Response. *Superfund Progress—Aficionado's Version.* Washington, D.C., June 1992.

U.S. Environmental Protection Agency, Office of Ground Water and Drinking Water. *Fact Sheet: National Primary Drinking Water Regulations for Lead and Copper.* Washington, D.C., May 1991.

U.S. Environmental Protection Agency, Office of Mobile Sources. "Clean Fuels: An Overview." Fact Sheet OMS-6, Ann Arbor, Mich., January 1993a.

U.S. Environmental Protection Agency, Office of Mobile Sources. "Vehicle Fuels and the 1990 Clean Air Act." Fact Sheet OMS-13, Ann Arbor, Mi., January 1993b.

U.S. Environmental Protection Agency, Office of Pesticides and Toxic Substances. *Highlights of the 1988 Pesticide Law: The Federal Insecticide, Fungicide, and Rodenticide Act Amendments of 1988.* Washington, D.C., December 1988.

U.S. Environmental Protection Agency, Office of Pesticides and Toxic Substances. *Pesticides in Drinking-Water Wells.* Washington, D.C., September 1990.

U.S. Environmental Protection Agency, Office of Pesticides and Toxic Substances. *EPA's Pesticide Programs.* Washington, D.C., May 1991.

U.S. Environmental Protection Agency, Office of Pesticides and Toxic Substances. *For Your Information: Pesticide Reregistration.* Washington, D.C., June 1991.

U.S. Environmental Protection Agency, Office of Pesticides and Toxic Substances. *Pesticides and Ground-Water Strategy.* Washington, D.C., October 1991.

U.S. Environmental Protection Agency, Office of Planning and Management. *Incremental Cost Effectiveness of Selective EPA Regulations.* Washington, D.C., January 1981.

U.S. Environmental Protection Agency, Office of Policy Analysis. *Costs and Benefits of Reducing Lead in Gasoline, Final Regulatory Impact Analysis.* Report No. EPA-230-05-85-006, Washington, D.C., February 1985.

U.S. Environmental Protection Agency, Office of Policy Analysis, Office of Policy, Planning and Evaluation. *Unfinished Business: A Comparative Assessment of Environmental Problems.* Washington, D.C., February 1987.

U.S. Environmental Protection Agency, Office of Policy Analysis, Office of Policy, Planning, and Evaluation. *EPA's Use of Benefit-Cost Analysis, 1981–1986.* EPA Report #230-05-87-028, Washington, D.C., August 1987.

U.S. Environmental Protection Agency, Office of Policy, Planning, and Evaluation. *Environmental Investments: The Cost of a Clean Environment, A Summary.* Washington, D.C., December 1990.

U.S. Environmental Protection Agency, Office of Policy, Planning, and Evaluation. *Economic Incentives: Options for Environmental Protection.* Washington, D.C., March 1991.

U.S. Environmental Protection Agency, Office of Policy, Planning, and Evaluation. *Environmental Equity: Reducing Risk for All Communities.* Washington, D.C., June 1992.

U.S. Environmental Protection Agency, Office of Policy, Planning, and Evaluation. *State Implementation of Nonpoint Source Programs,* draft report. Washington, D.C., June 29, 1992.

U.S. Environmental Protection Agency, Office of Policy, Planning, and Evaluation. *The United States Experience with Economic Incentives to Control Environmental Pollution.* Washington, D.C., July 1992.

U.S. Environmental Protection Agency, Office of Policy, Planning, and Evaluation, Office of Research and Development. *The Potential Effects of Global Climate Change on the United States.* Washington, D.C., December 1989.

U.S. Environmental Protection Agency, Office of Pollution Prevention. *Pollution Prevention 1991: Progress on Reducing Industrial Pollutants.* Washington, D.C., October 1991.

U.S. Environmental Protection Agency, Office of Pollution Prevention and Toxics. *1991 Toxics Release Inventory.* Washington, D.C., May 1993.

U.S. Environmental Protection Agency, Office of Pollution Prevention and Toxics. *Design for the Environment: Environmental Accounting and Capital Budgeting Project Update #1.* Washington, D.C., October 1993.

U.S. Environmental Protection Agency, Office of Pollution Prevention and Toxics. *33/50 Program Company Profiles: Reduction Highlights.* Washington, D.C., October 1994.

U.S. Environmental Protection Agency, Office of Prevention, Pesticides, and Toxic Substances. *The 33/50 Program: Forging an Alliance for Pollution Prevention.* Washington, D.C., August 1992.

U.S. Environmental Protection Agency, Office of Solid Waste. *National Screening Survey of Hazardous Waste Treatment, Storage, Disposal, and Recycling Facilities.* Washington, D.C.

U.S. Environmental Protection Agency, Office of Solid Waste. *Solving the Hazardous Waste Problem: EPA's RCRA Program.* Washington, D.C., November 1986.

U.S. Environmental Protection Agency, Office of Solid Waste. *Recycling Works! State and Local Solutions to Solid Waste Management Problems,* Washington, D.C., January 1989.

U.S. Environmental Protection Agency, Office of Solid Waste and Emergency Response. *The New RCRA Fact Book.* Washington, D.C., October 1985.

U.S. Environmental Protection Agency, Office of Solid Waste and Emergency Response. *Decision-Makers Guide to Solid Waste Management.* Washington, D.C., November 1989.

U.S. Environmental Protection Agency, Office of Solid Waste and Emergency Response. *EPA's Report to Congress on Methods to Manage and Control Plastic Wastes.* Washington, D.C., February 1990.

U.S. Environmental Protection Agency, Office of Solid Waste and Emergency Response. *Unit Pricing: Providing an Incentive to Reduce Municipal Solid Waste.* Washington, D.C., February 1991.

U.S. Environmental Protection Agency, Office of Solid Waste and Emergency Response. "EPA's Role in Market Development." *Reusable News,* Washington, D.C., Fall 1991.

U.S. Environmental Protection Agency, Office of Solid Waste and Emergency Response. *Summary of Markets for Scrap Tires,* Washington, D.C., October 1991.

U.S. Environmental Protection Agency, Office of Solid Waste and Emergency Response. *Leaking Underground Storage Tanks and Health: Understanding Health Risks from Petroleum Contamination.* Washington, D.C., January 1992.

U.S. Environmental Protection Agency, Office of Solid Waste and Emergency Response. ''The Wisdom of Waste Reduction at McDonald's.'' *Reusable News,* Spring 1992, pp. 1, 3.

U.S. Environmental Protection Agency, Office of Solid Waste and Emergency Response. *Superfund Progress, Spring 1992.* Washington, D.C., May 1992.

U.S. Environmental Protection Agency, Office of Solid Waste and Emergency Response. *Characterization of Municipal Solid Waste in the United States: 1992 Update.* Washington, D.C., July 1992a.

U.S. Environmental Protection Agency, Office of Solid Waste and Emergency Response. *Environmental Fact Sheet,* ''Recycling Municipal Solid Waste: Facts and Figures.'' Washington, D.C., #EPA/530-SW-91-024, July 1992b.

U.S. Environmental Protection Agency, Office of Solid Waste and Emergency Response, ''FTC Announces Environmental Marketing Guidelines For Industry.'' *Reusable News,* Fall 1992.

U.S. Environmental Protection Agency, Office of Solid Waste and Emergency Response. ''Businesses Unite to Boost Demand for Recycled Products.'' *Reusable News,* Winter/Spring 1993, pp. 1, 12.

U.S. Environmental Protection Agency, Office of Solid Waste and Emergency Response. *WasteWise: EPA's Voluntary Program for Reducing Business Solid Waste.* Washington, D.C., October 1993.

U.S. Environmental Protection Agency, Office of Toxic Substances. *The Layman's Guide to the Toxic Substances Control Act.* Washington, D.C., June 1987.

U.S. Environmental Protection Agency, Office of Water. *Lead Contamination Control Act.* Washington, D.C., July 1988.

U.S. Environmental Protection Agency, Office of Water. *Marine and Estuarine Protection: Programs and Activities.* Washington, D.C., February 1989.

U.S. Environmental Protection Agency, Office of Water. *Fact Sheet: National Primary Drinking Water Standards.* Washington, D.C., August 1991.

U.S. Environmental Protection Agency, Office of Water. ''Is Your Drinking Water Safe?'' Washington, D.C., December 1991.

U.S. Environmental Protection Agency, Office of Water. *Managing Nonpoint Source Pollution.* Washington, D.C., January 1992.

U.S. Environmental Protection Agency, Office of Water. *National Water Quality Inventory: 1990 Report to Congress,* Washington, D.C., April 1992a.

U.S. Environmental Protection Agency, Office of Water. *Drinking Water Regulations and Health Advisories.* Washington, D.C., April 1992b.

U.S. Environmental Protection Agency, Office of Water. ''Phase V Rule: Fact Sheet.'' Washington, D.C., May 1992.

U.S. Environmental Protection Agency, Office of Water. *National Water Quality Inventory: 1992 Report to Congress.* Washington, D.C., March 1994.

U.S. Environmental Protection Agency, Office of Water, Office of Pesticides and Toxic Substances. *National Pesticide Survey: Update and Summary of Phase II Results.* Washington, D.C., Winter 1992.

U.S. Environmental Protection Agency, Office of Water Regulations and Standards. *Introduction to Water Quality Standards.* Washington, D.C., September 1988.

U.S. Environmental Protection Agency, Region 5. *A Risk Analysis of Twenty-Six Environmental Problems.* Washington, D.C., May 1991.

U.S. Environmental Protection Agency, Risk Assessment Forum. *Framework for Ecological Risk Assessment.* Washington, D.C., February 1992.

U.S. Environmental Protection Agency, Science Advisory Board. *Reducing Risk: Setting Priorities and Strategies for Environmental Protection.* Washington, D.C., September 1990.

U.S. Environmental Protection Agency, Stratospheric Protection Program, Office of Air and Radiation. *Regulatory Impact Analysis: Vols I–III.* Washington, D.C., December 1987.

U.S. Environmental Protection Agency, U.S. Department of Health and Human Services, and U.S. Public Health Service. *A Citizen's Guide to Radon: The Guide to Protecting Yourself and Your Family From Radon.* Washington, D.C., May 1992.

U.S. General Accounting Office (GAO). *Siting of Hazardous Waste Landfills and Their Correlation with Racial and Economic Status of Surrounding Communities.* Washington, D.C., 1983.

U.S. General Accounting Office (GAO). *Illegal Disposal of Hazardous Waste: Difficult to Detect or Deter.* Washington, D.C., February 22, 1985.

U.S. General Accounting Office (GAO). *SUPERFUND: Extent of Nation's Potential Hazardous Waste Problem Still Unknown.* Washington, D.C., December 1987.

U.S. General Accounting Office (GAO). *Water Pollution: More EPA Action Needed to Improve the Quality of Heavily Polluted Waters.* Washington, D.C., January 1989.

U.S. General Accounting Office (GAO). *Drinking Water: Compliance Problems Undermine EPA Program as New Challenges Emerge.* Washington, D.C., June 1990.

U.S. General Accounting Office (GAO). *Water Pollution: Greater EPA Leadership Needed to Reduce Nonpoint Source Pollution.* Washington, D.C., October 1990.

U.S. General Accounting Office (GAO). *Pesticides: EPA's Use of Benefit Assessment in Regulating Pesticides.* Washington, D.C., March 1991.

U.S. General Accounting Office (GAO). *Water Pollution: Stronger Efforts Needed by EPA to Control Toxic Water Pollution.* Washington, D.C., July 1991.

U.S. National Acid Precipitation Assessment Program. *1990 Integrated Assessment Report.* Washington, D.C.: The NAPAP Office of the Director, November 1991.

U.S. Office of Management and Budget. ''Discount Rates to Be Used in Evaluating Time-Distributed Costs and Benefits.'' Circular A-94 (revised), Washington, D.C., March 27, 1972.

U.S. Senate, Staff of the Subcommittee on Air and Water Pollution of the Committee on Public Works. *The Impact of Auto Emission Standards.* Washington, D.C.: U.S. Government Printing Office, October 1973.

U.S. Water News. "Utilities Getting the SDWA Bill." January 1991, p. 10.

Van Putten, Mark C., and Bradley D. Jackson. "The Dilution of the Clean Water Act." *Journal of Law Reform* 19, no. 4 (Summer 1986), pp. 863–901.

Vaughan, William J. "The Water Quality Ladder." In Robert Cameron Mitchell and Richard R. Carson. *An Experiment in Determining Willingness to Pay for National Water Quality Improvements,* Appendix II (draft report), Washington, D.C.: Resources for the Future, 1981.

Vaughan, William J., and Clifford S. Russell. "Valuing a Fishing Day: An Application of a Systematic Varying Parameter Model." *Land Economics* 58, no. 4 (November 1982), pp. 450–63.

Vaupel, James W. "Truth or Consequences: Some Roles for Scientists and Analysts in Environmental Decisionmaking." In Wesley A. Magat, ed. *Reform of Environmental Regulation.* Cambridge, Mass.: Ballinger Publishing Company, 1978, pp. 71–92.

Vogel, David. *National Styles of Regulation, Environmental Policy in Great Britain and the United States.* Ithaca, N.Y.: Cornell University Press, 1986.

Wald, Matthew L. "Sun Oil Takes Environmental Pledge." *New York Times,* February 11, 1993, p. D5.

Wartzman, Rick. "Administration Alters Proposal for Energy Tax." *The Wall Street Journal,* April 2, 1993, p. A2.

Wernette, D., and L. Nieves. "Minorities and Air Pollution: A Preliminary Geo-Demographic Analysis." Unpublished conference presentation, 1991.

Wernette, D.R., and L.A. Nieves. "Breathing Polluted Air." *EPA Journal* 18, no. 1 (March/April 1992), pp. 16–17.

West, Patrick C. "Invitation to Poison? Detroit Minorities and Toxic Fish Consumption From the Detroit River." In Bunyan Bryant and Paul Mohai, eds. *The Proceedings of the Michigan Conference on Race and the Incidence of Environmental Hazards,* 1992.

West, Patrick C. "Health Concerns for Fish-Eating Tribes? Government Assumptions Are Much Too Low." *EPA Journal* 18, no. 1 (March/April 1992), pp. 15–16.

White, Gilbert W. "Water Resource Adequacy: Illusion and Reality." In David H. Speidel, Lon C. Ruedisili, and Allen F. Agnew, eds. *Perspectives on Water: Uses and Abuses.* New York: Oxford University Press, 1988.

White, Lawrence J. *The Regulation of Air Pollutant Emissions from Motor Vehicles.* Washington, D.C.: American Enterprise Institute for Public Policy Research, 1982.

Whiteman, Lily. "Trades to Remember: The Lead Phasedown." *EPA Journal* 18, no. 2 (May/June 1992), pp. 38–39.

Williams, Marcia E. "Pesticides: The Potential for Change." *EPA Journal* 18, no. 2 (May/June 1992), pp. 15–16.

Wirth, Timothy E., and John Heinz. *Project 88—Round II Incentives for Action: Designing Market-Based Environmental Strategies.* Washington, D.C., May 1991.

Wittwer, S. "The Rising Level of Atmospheric Carbon Dioxide: An Agricultural Perspective." In J.H. McBeath, ed. *The Potential Effects of Carbon Dioxide-Induced Climatic Change in Alaska: Conference Proceedings.* Fairbanks, Alaska: School of Agriculture and Land Resources Management, University of Alaska, 1984.

Wolf, Sidney M. *Pollution Law Handbook: A Guide to Federal Environmental Laws.* New York: Quorom Books, 1988.

World Resources Institute. *World Resources 1992–93, A Guide to the Global Environment.* New York: Oxford University Press, 1992a.

World Resources Institute. *The 1992 Information Please Environmental Almanac.* Boston: Houghton Mifflin Company, 1992b.

World Resources Institute. *The 1993 Information Please Environmental Almanac.* Boston: Houghton Mifflin Company, 1993.

World Resources Institute. *The 1994 Information Please Environmental Almanac.* Boston: Houghton Mifflin Company, 1994a.

World Resources Institute. *World Resources 1994–1995, A Guide to the Global Environment.* New York: Oxford University Press, 1994b.

Yang, Dori Jones; William C. Symonds; and Lisa Driscoll. "Recycling Is Rewriting the Rules of Papermaking." *Business Week,* April 22, 1991, pp. 100H–101H.

Yess, N.J.; M.G. Houston; and E.L. Gunderson. "Food and Drug Administration Pesticide Monitoring of Foods: 1978–1982." *J. Assoc. Off. Anal. Chem.* vol. 74, pp. 265–72, 1991a.

Yess, N.J.; M.G. Houston; and E.L. Gunderson. "Food and Drug Administration Pesticide Monitoring of Foods: 1983–1986." *J. Assoc. Off. Anal. Chem.* vol. 74, pp. 273–80, 1991b.

York, Michael. "President Wins One On NAFTA; Court Reverses Order to Study Environment." *The Washington Post,* September 25, 1993, p. A1.

Younger, Joseph D. "Cleaner, 'Greener' Gasoline?" *AAA World,* November/December 1992.

Zwick, David, and March Benstock. *Water Wasteland.* New York: Bantam Books, 1971.

INDEX